Stone: Building stone, rock fill and armourstone in construction

Geological Society Special Publications
Series Editor
M. E. BARTON

It is recommended that reference to this book should be made in the following way:

SMITH, M. R. (ed.) 1999. *Stone: Building stone, rock fill and armourstone in constuction*. Geological Society, London, Engineering Geology Special Publications, **16**.

Geological Society Engineering Geology Special Publication No. 16

Stone: Building stone, rock fill and armourstone in construction

EDITED BY

M. R. Smith
Institute of Quarrying
7 Regent Street
Nottingham
NG1 5BY

1999
Published by
The Geological Society
London

THE GEOLOGICAL SOCIETY

The Society was founded in 1807 as The Geological Society of London and is the oldest geological society in the world. It received its Royal Charter in 1825 for the purpose of 'investigating the mineral structure of the Earth'. The Society is Britain's national society for geology with a membership of around 8500. It has countrywide coverage and approximately 1500 members reside overseas. The Society is responsible for all aspects of the geological sciences including professional matters. The Society has its own publishing house, which produces the Society's international journals, books and maps, and which acts as the European distributor for publications of the American Association of Petroleum Geologists, SEPM and the Geological Society of America.

Fellowship is open to those holding a recognized honours degree in geology or cognate subject and who have at least two years' relevant postgraduate experience, or who have not less than six years' relevant experience in geology or a cognate subject. A Fellow who has not less than five years' relevant postgraduate experience in the practice of geology may apply for validation and, subject to approval, may be able to use the designatory letters C Geol (Chartered Geologist).

Further information about the Society is available from the Membership Manager, The Geological Society, Burlington House, Piccadilly, London W1V 0JU, UK. The Society is a Registered Charity, No. 210161.

Published by The Geological Society from:
The Geological Society Publishing House
Unit 7, Brassmill Enterprise Centre
Brassmill Lane
Bath BA1 3JN
UK
(*Orders*: Tel. 01225 445046
Fax 01225 442836)

First published 1999

British Library Cataloguing in Publication Data
A catalogue record for this book is available from the British Library.

ISBN 1-86239-029-0
ISSN 0267-9914

Typeset by Aarontype Ltd, Unit 47, Easton Business Centre, Felix Road, Bristol BS5 0HE, UK.

Printed by The Alden Press, Osney Mead, Oxford, UK.

Distributors

USA
AAPG Bookstore
PO Box 979
Tulsa
OK 74101-0979
USA
(*Orders*: Tel. (918) 584-2555
Fax (918) 560-2652)

Australia
Australian Mineral Foundation
63 Conyngham Street
Glenside
South Australia 5065
Australia
(*Orders*: Tel. (08) 379-0444
Fax (08) 379-4634)

India
Affiliated East-West Press PVT Ltd
G-1/16 Ansari Road
New Delhi 110 002
India
(*Orders*: Tel. (11) 327-9113
Fax (11) 326-0538)

Japan
Kanda Book Trading Co.
Cityhouse Tama 204
Tsurumaki 1-3-10
Tama-Shi
Tokyo 0206-0034
Japan
(*Orders*: Tel. (0423) 57-7650
Fax (0423) 57-7651)

Cover photograph supplied by Steinindustrie Vetter GmbH.

Contents

Members of the Working Party

Dr Max E. Barton	University of Southampton 1995–1999
Mr Poul Beckmann	Ove Arup & Partners, London (retired) 1994–1999
Dr J. Andrew Charles	Building Research Establishment Ltd., Watford 1993–1999
Professor Peter G. Fookes	*Chairman* – Consultant, Winchester 1993–1999
Dr Colin D. Gribble	University of Glasgow 1993–1999
Mr Barry J. Hunt	STATS Consultancy, St Albans 1997–1999
Dr David P. Jefferson	Jefferson Consulting Ltd. Melton Mowbray 1993–1999
Mr Anthony L. Johnson	Rattee & Kett, Cambridge (now Stirling Stone Group plc, London) 1993–1999
Dr John Perry	TRL (now Mott MacDonald, Croydon) 1993–1999
Dr Alan B. Poole	University of London (Queen Mary & Westfield College) 1993–1999
Dr Ian Sims	*Secretary* – STATS Consultancy, St Albans 1993–1999
Mr Alan M. Smith	Bickerdike Allen Partners, London 1993–1996
Dr Mick R. Smith	*Editor* – University of London (Imperial College) 1993–1999
Dr Graham West[1]	Transport Research Laboratory, Crowthorne (retired) 1993–1999
Dr Tim J. S. Yates	Building Research Establishment Ltd., Watford 1993–1999

[1] Geological Society Engineering Group Representative.

Acknowledgements

The Working Party has been most grateful to receive considerable help from numerous individuals, organizations and companies who have contributed in various ways by providing advice, information and illustrations or by acting as reviewers and referees for particular chapters. We give thanks to all these people and organizations. In addition, those to whom particular appreciation is due include the following:

Mr David W. Anderson (Arup Façade Engineering), Ms Michelle Barkley (EPR Architects Ltd), Professor Brian Bluck (University of Glasgow), Mr John Brighton (Natural Stone Products Ltd), Mr Alan Bruce (John Fyfe Ltd), Mr Dennis Cole (ARC), Mr Mike Dickinson (Burlington Slate), Dr Malcolm Eddleston (Bechtel Water Technology), Dr William J. French (London University, QMW), Mr David Gregory (Realstone Ltd), Dr Carlota Grossi (STATS Consultancy), Mr Paul Johnson (Burlington Slate), Dr Jean-Paul Latham (London University, QMW), Dr Elizabeth Laycock (Sheffield Hallam University), Mr Julian Limentani (Marshall Sisson Architects), Mr John Lloyd (Wincilate Ltd), Dr George Matheson (TRL Scotland), Mr David Methven (Natural Stone Products Ltd), Mr Bruno Miglio (Ove Arup & Partners), Mr Geoff S. Pettifer (Freelance Geologist), Dr Andy Pickles (Hong Kong Airport Authority), Mr Geraint Roberts (Alfred McAlpine Slate Products Ltd), Dr Chris A. Rogers (Ontario Ministry of Transportation), Mr Robin W. Sanderson (Natural History Museum, retired), Herr Paulus Sinner (Rock Block Trading GmbH), Dr Bernard J. Smith (Queen's University, Belfast), Mr Ian Southgate (ARC), Mr Richard Thomas (Posford Duvivier), Mr J. Thompson (Hong Kong Airport Authority), Dr Geoffrey Walton (Geoffrey Walton Practice), Mr Garth Weston (Bath & Portland Stone Ltd), Mr Eifion Williams (Ffestiniog Slate Products Ltd), Dr M. Winter (TRL Scotland).

The very significant contribution made by companies whose staff were afforded the time and permission to accomplish the task of the Working Party cannot be overstated. In this respect, particular mention is made of the following:

Building Research Establishment Limited, Watford
Imperial College of Science, Technology & Medicine, University of London
Rattee & Kett, Cambridge (a division of John Mowlem & Co Plc)
Queen Mary & Westfield College, University of London
Sandberg, London
STATS Consultancy (a division of STATS Limited), St Albans
Transport Research Laboratory, Crowthorne
University of Glasgow
University of Southampton

Grateful appreciation is also recorded for the drafting and clerical assistance afforded to the Editor by Mr T. Allen and Mrs K. Clarke of the Department of Earth Resources Engineering, Imperial College, London University. The Editor also expresses his gratitude for the support of a lectureship at Imperial College by the sponsors of Quarry Engineering, namely:

ARC Limited
Aggregate Industries Plc (formerly Bardon Group & CAMAS Aggregates)
Blue Circle Industries Plc
Hepworth Minerals & Chemicals
ICI Explosives
Nordberg (UK) Limited
Pioneer Aggregates (UK) Limited
RJB Mining
Redland Aggregates Limited
RMC Aggregates (UK) Limited
Rugby Cement
Tarmac Quarry Products Limited
Tilcon Limited

Foreword 1

Stone is a natural product which has been vital to mankind's shelter and development from the earliest known times. Past generations have built vast temples and mausoleums out of stone (Egyptian and Mayan civilizations), while in Europe there are many examples of stone structures contemporary with these, including the regular standing stones (Callanish, Carnac, Stenness and Stonehenge) and large burial chambers (Maes Howe), settlements (Skara Brae) and individual buildings (Scottish Brochs). These were clearly places of some importance and are beautifully preserved to this day.

In more modern times, limestone in the Loire valley in France was quarried underground in riverside caves (rather than open cast, because it was softer in the moist condition) and which was used to build the chateaux for which the region is so famous, and only much later were the caves used for bottling and storing wine. In the UK, most of the prestigious buildings in London and the south have been constructed from Portland limestone while whole towns in Scotland (Grantown on Spey, Aberdeen) have come from vast granite quarries. Most of our pavement flagstones have been sourced from well bedded sandstones, our kerbstones and cobbled sheets have come from Devon or Scottish granites, while our roofs have been made watertight for centuries with slate, much of it from North Wales. Even today, whilst many of our buildings, bridges and other structures are made predominantly from concrete and steel, both make extensive use of natural store cladding.

It is an unfortunate fact that we have allowed our indigenous quarry industry to wither and most of the half million tonnes of natural stone used in the construction industry is imported. In terms of tonnage, probably the majority is used as armourstone in civil engineering works, for example for coastal protection, breakwaters, jetties, harbours, revetments, sea walls, dams, embankments, slope stabilization, river defences and reclamation.

This book provides a comprehensive and up-to-date presentation of all aspects of the use of stone and rock for engineering and building purposes and will, I am sure, establish itself as the definitive guide for civil and structural engineers, engineering geologists, field geologists and building restorers.

Roger Sainsbury FEng
President, Institution of Civil Engineers

Foreword 2

Here is a report which takes the reader all the way through an examination of stone – from definitions, to sources, to its differing properties, to extraction – adding the science to the art of the use of stone in building and engineering. Its strength is in bringing together every conceivable technical aspect of stone in one source. Its credibility is underlined by being a report of a working party of The Geological Society, which is both a learned society and a charter-giving body, and the wide range of experts who have contributed to the study.

Long gone are the days when an architect might specify local stone and might visit the quarry to inspect the seam; discuss particular properties of a given stone with the quarry owner; even watch it cut. Architects now use stone quarried from all over the world, cut by mechanical means, and procured by remote control. The time (and therefore money) pressures under which architects (and engineers) have to run projects has made the whole process of understanding the qualities and properties of the stone we specify, and its reliable procurement, more difficult than before. Since it was not the perceived job of the Working Party to tackle this question, we perhaps need now a companion study to consider how we get this process right.

Nevertheless, this very readable and competent report can help the architect who has a very clear view on the visual quality or colour of stone best suited for the project but needs more detailed knowledge of performance characteristics: equally the engineer who has clear requirements on, say, density and crushing capability but who also has to meet, say, a colour prerequisite. It is a rich mine of information about the qualities, performances and uses of stone, as well as *how* to use, restore and repair. Perhaps one day it can be available on CD-ROM so that the material can be interrogated quickly?

As an architect and a painter I was particularly pleased that the weathering quality was included in the appraisal of a material which contributes so much visual pleasure as well as structural strength to past, present and future built environments.

I would have been pleased had this report been available to me as a student and young architect, and I don't doubt that it will prove an invaluable work of reference in the proper understanding of stone and rock for construction purposes. I commend it.

David Rock
President, RIBA

Foreword 3

This book is the report of a special Working Party of the Engineering Group of the Geological Society consisting of geologists, civil engineers and architects. This was entirely fitting because the science of geology, and geologists, have for many years been much concerned with the practical use of rocks in building and construction. William Smith (1769–1839), who is regarded as 'the father of English geology' was himself a civil engineer and, amongst other things, was involved in the search for a suitable freestone with which to build the then new Houses of Parliament in 1838.

The need for strong, durable and attractive building stones continues. To give some idea of the size and importance of the present-day stone industry in Western Europe, Italy produces about 7.5 million tonnes of dimension stone per year, twice as much as the next biggest producer, Spain, while the United Kingdom produces 0.5 million tonnes. These figures would be much larger if armourstone and rock fill were to be included.

All this stone has to be geologically surveyed, prospected for, evaluated, excavated, processed, tested and selected before it can be used in buildings and other civil engineering works. And, once constructed, stone in buildings needs to be repaired, restored and cleaned. I am very glad that armourstone and rock fill were included by the Working Party as well as the more familiar uses of stone. It is the purpose of this report to give authoritative and up-to-date information and advice on all these aspects of the use of stone and rock in modern construction and restoration, and I therefore commend it to all those who have to work with these materials.

It is very heartening that my fellow Presidents of the Institution of Civil Engineers and the Royal Institute of British Architects have joined with me in introducing this report: it is a testimony to the importance of stone and rock to the professions of civil engineering and architecture, and to the success of the joint venture of the Working Party. I thank all the members of the Working Party for their efforts, and I am very proud that such a useful book is being published by the Geological Society.

Robin Cocks
President, The Geological Society

Preface

This book is one of a series of reports produced by the Engineering Group of the Geological Society through its Working Parties over the past thirty years on the application of geology to engineering. This particular book was conceived as a successor to the popular Working Party Report on Aggregates: Sand, Gravel and Crushed Rock Aggregates for Construction Purposes (Collis & Fox 1985, 1st edn, and Smith & Collis 1993, 2nd edn).

The Aggregates Report concentrated on the major uses in construction of granular materials produced from natural superficial deposits and bedrock covering particle size ranges from fine sand to around 100 mm. However, it was recognized by the Engineering Group that rock was being increasingly used in construction in a much coarser grading, especially as rock fill and as armourstone and in the resurgence of natural stone for cladding of buildings and for paving. Therefore, in 1993 it instigated a new Working Party on Stone for Construction Purposes and is, at the time of publishing this book, actively considering another book to make a trilogy on geological materials in construction. The third book would be devoted to the finer grades, silt and clay size material.

The definition of the word 'stone' in the broad sense, and the specific sense used in this book, is discussed in the opening paragraphs of Chapter 1. It is intended that the book's definition of 'stone' is appropriate for all the potential uses of this book by Architects, Builders, Engineers, Geologists and in the Winning and Processing Industries. The book is not only about dimension stone as modern usage relies heavily on undressed stone for fill and protection works and this aspect of the stone industry is now larger than that concerned with the traditional uses of building stone. It is, therefore, wide-ranging in its discussions on the various categories of stone and in the overlapping ground of investigation, winning and production.

Objectives of the Working Party

For several months after its instigation the initial direction and development of the Working Party on Stone was in the hands of a small steering committee composed of its Officers. At this time it was agreed that the scope of the Working Party should include rock fill and armourstone as well as dimension stone and the Report would be largely based on UK experience but would include overseas examples and aspects wherever possible. It was considered that the Working Party Report should be presented in the scientific style of a text book and would probably be published separately as a book rather than in the *Quarterly Journal of Engineering Geology*. The potential readership of the Report was considered to be wider than the Engineering Geology Group membership alone and a separate publication as a book would enhance availability to others in allied professions both nationally and internationally. Similar considerations had previously led to the separate publication of the Aggregates Working Party Report.

It was recognized that the intention to include rock fill and armourstone as well as the various types of dimension stone would complicate the Report structure, and there were both overlapping similarities and essential differences between these use categories.

The Members of the Working Party on Stone were drawn widely from experts in their fields to represent users of stone, the investigation, winning, production, architectural and engineering aspects of the industry and researchers. Corresponding members who kindly assisted with specialized items and reviewed chapters of the book were similarly chosen from the same broad spectrum of those associated with stone and rock in construction and the Working Party is indebted to these participants. Where applicable, the Working Party is also indebted to the employers of members and corresponding members for the generous donation of their invaluable time and logistical assistance.

In addition to the ongoing review of each chapter by the Working Party and written observations and suggestions by corresponding members, the book, in keeping with the practice of previous Working Parties, in an early draft stage was presented for open discussion on 16 April 1996 at Warwick University in a dedicated session of the Extractive Industry's Geology Conference. Copies of the draft were available beforehand and were used to inform the delegates in addition to verbal presentations made by all the Members of the Working Party. The following discussions at the Conference and written contributions have been incorporated where appropriate into the final revision of the book.

Each chapter of the book was initially drafted by one, two or three members of the Working Party and subsequently through many day-long meetings, edited and cross-checked by all members and commented upon by the corresponding members. In this way, every aspect of the book carries the collective authority of the whole Working Party. Appendices were handled in a similar way. An effort was made to make the book as comprehensive as possible and, despite being a Committee, to achieve as far as possible continuity of style, and to ensure a uniformity in the technical level and mode of presentation. it was decided to support the main text throughout with separate text boxes related to specialized or detailed topics so that the main flow of the text was not interrupted for the general reader by technical discourse on subjects which might not be of immediate interest.

The brunt of the early work, like that of the Aggregates Report, was borne by the Secretary to the Committee, Dr I. Sims and the later work by the Editor, Dr Mick Smith. To these members and their families, to Dr G. West, the Treasurer, and the other members of the Working Party and their families, I give my particular thanks. I hope you agree that it has been worthwhile and in the best tradition of the Engineering Group Working Party Reports.

P. G. Fookes, F.Eng
Chairman of the Working Party
Winchester, January 1997

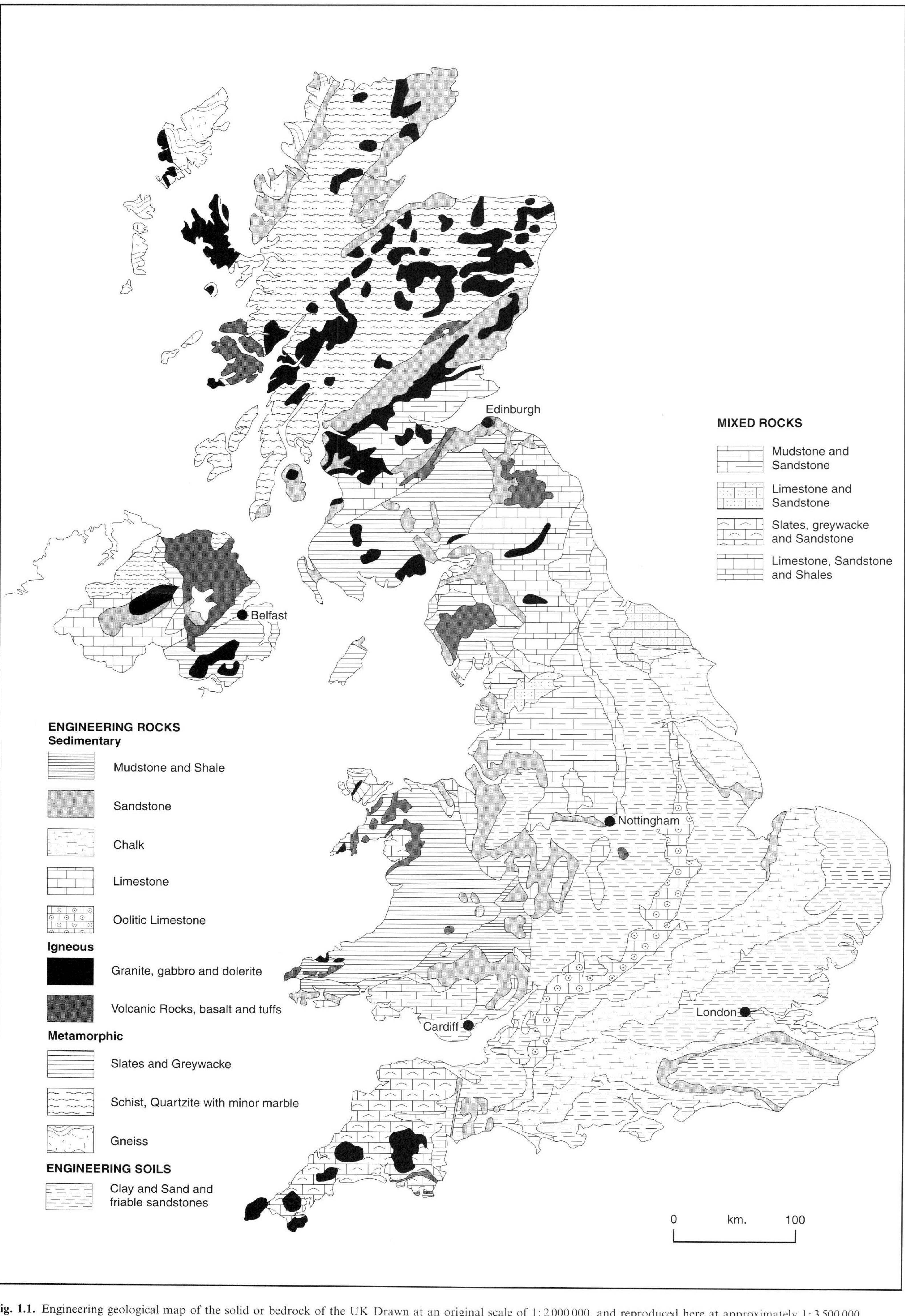

Fig. 1.1. Engineering geological map of the solid or bedrock of the UK Drawn at an original scale of 1:2 000 000, and reproduced here at approximately 1:3 500 000 (After Bickmore & Shaw, 1963; Map of Predominant Types of Rock) (from Dearman 1991).

1. Introduction

1.1. Stone

The word 'stone' has several meanings which, for understanding, have generally to be evaluated in their context and it is therefore necessary to highlight this and to define how 'stone' is used in this Book. The *Concise Oxford Dictionary* defines stone as 'Piece of rock of any shape usu. detached from earth's crust and of no great size, esp. a pebble, a cobble, or a single piece used or usable in building or road-making or a missile'; in *Chambers Dictionary of Science and Technology* stone is 'A jewel'; in the popular *Penguin Dictionary of Geology*, it is stated that 'the word 'stone' is admissible only in combinations such as limestone, sandstone, etc. or where it is used as the name for extracted material – building stone, road stone. It should not be used as a synonym for rock or pebble'.

In the *Penguin Dictionary of Civil Engineering*, stone is said to be synonymous with coarse aggregate which is defined as that material which stays on a sieve of 5 mm square opening when used in concrete, or on a sieve of 3 mm square opening when used in bituminous material. Aggregates are those stones, i.e. particles of rock which are brought together in a bound or unbound condition to form part of the whole of an engineering building structure. In civil engineering, normal use for aggregates is in concrete or roadstone (Smith & Collis 1993).

In this Book, 'stone' is *rock which is used, other than as concrete or roadstone aggregate, in the construction of buildings or structures made by man.* In order to give emphasis and clarity, the word 'stone' can be supplemented with further descriptive terms, for example dressed stone, dimension stone, gabion stone, armour stone, to illustrate the use to which it has been put or the method used to modify its characteristics to be suitable for the construction use.

Stone has been fashioned by man since Palaeolithic times. Ancient stone buildings demonstrate its durability and many buildings and structures owe their attractiveness to the stone selected for its colour, decorative and ornamental appearance, as well as its strength. No civilisation appears to pay much attention to the cost where its prestigious buildings are concerned. The Pyramids, Roman temples and baths and Norman castles are examples of symbols of prestige where no expense was spared to make a maximum impression on the general populace.

Britain is potentially well endowed with stone and a glance at Fig. 1.1 is sufficient to show that it has a variety of rock which it is difficult to match elsewhere in a similar small area. The local buildings reflect this wide variety of stone and Britain has a long tradition of building in stone. However, this book is not solely about British stone and, where appropriate because of differences in practice, circumstance or environment, the different uses and performance of stone overseas are discussed.

1.1.1. Production statistics

Table 1.1 shows recent production statistics for the principal minerals and rocks in the United Kingdom, including England, Wales and Scotland as separate totals, and the principal rock types extracted in UK which are given with further subdivisions by end use.

Statistical data on stone is notoriously difficult to correlate owing to changes in annual production, changes to classification of materials and end-uses, incomplete records and erroneous data. Nevertheless, Table 1.1 can be used to obtain an appreciation of the order of magnitude of production of rock types for construction and other uses.

As can be seen, in general England extracts by far the largest amount of rock and also, of that, building stone is a relatively small proportion of which the most is limestone. From the table, 'building stone' is approximately 2 million tonnes per annum. Rock used as aggregate is by far the largest use, particularly as roadstone, approximately 100 million tonnes per annum. 'Other constructional uses' presumably including general fill, rock fill and armour stone are, as can be seen, also considerably larger in amount than building stone.

Table 1.2 presents information for other countries and is based on 'quarry production' and may well contain data on aggregates as well as dimension stone.

Obtaining detailed information for many countries is difficult, if not impossible, and Table 1.2 has many omissions. It shows 'marble' (loosely interpreted as polishable limestones and true marbles), granite and all 'other stone', quarried for stone products. The pre-eminence of Italy as a stone producer stands out; by comparison with Italy and several other countries, Britain is not a large producer.

As an example of the problems of correlating statistics, it can be seen that the estimate for the UK in Table 1.2 (1.1 million) agrees only very approximately with Table 1.1 (1.86 million).

1.1.2. A future for building stone

The use of stone is currently rising for both local materials and imported materials. At present it seems that the growth in new stone for building is in granite and marble – possibly because these are generally higher value materials and have a greater range of textures and colours. In some areas there is also a growth in

Table 1.1. *Mineral production in Great Britain in 1991 excluding coal gypsum salt and potash (in '000 of tonnes)*

Mineral	*England*	*Wales*	*Scotland*	*Great Britain*
Sand and Gravel (a)				
Sand of which				
for: coating	3 517	–	–	4 654
other uses (excl. fill)	10 854	266	1 299	12 419
concreting sand	22 330	831	5 644	26 805
Gravel of which				
for: coating	356	–	135	490
concrete aggregate	19 843	321	2 824	22 988
other uses (excl. fill)	2 210	–	–	2 569
Sand gravel hoggin				
for: fill	12 308	221	8 025	15 554
Total	**71 417**	**1 836**	**12 226**	**85 479**
Limestone (b)				
for: building stone	1 407	22	–	1 430
coated roadstone	11 226	–	–	13 060
uncoated roadstone	31 691	7 918	214	39 823
railway ballast	9	–	–	291
concrete aggregate	9 089	–	–	11 665
other constructional uses	19 560	4 821	446	24 827
agricultural use	836	–	–	1 206
iron and steel	–	–	–	2 206
cement	–	–	–	8 903
glassmaking	231	–	–	231
asphalt fillers (c)	–	5	–	393
other fillers (c)	–	–	5	910
other uses	–	–	–	2 824
Total	**86 762**	**18 986**	**2 018**	**107 767**
Dolomite				
for: building stone	70	–	–	70
coated roadstone	–	–	–	–
uncoated roadstone	–	–	–	9 391
railway ballast	–	–	–	–
concrete aggregate	–	–	–	1 994
other constructional uses	2 897	–	–	3 435
agricultural use	–	–	–	2 096
other non-constructional uses	–	–	–	1 520
Total	**16 602**	–	–	**19 454**
Chalk				
for: cement	7 057	–	–	7 057
constructional use	1 036	–	–	1 036
agricultural use	547	–	–	547
fillers powders whitings	–	–	–	(330)
other uses	–	–	–	(920)
Total	**10 317**	–	–	**10 317**
Igneous rock				
for: building stone	22	11	94	127
coated roadstone	6 794	1 087	3 074	10 955
uncoated roadstone	7 407	992	8 236	16 635
railway ballast	1 711	248	361	2 320
concrete aggregate	1 270	168	1 513	2 951
other constructional uses	5 770	777	6 298	12 846
other uses	151	12	12	175
Total	**23 126**	**3 294**	**19 588**	**46 008**
Sandstone				
for: building stone	227	9	–	(130)
coated roadstone	1 502	447	424	2 373
uncoated roadstone	3 457	532	302	4 290
railway ballast	–	–	–	206
concrete aggregate	376	49	165	590
other constructional uses	4 143	431	605	5 179
other uses	–	–	–	–
Total	**9 907**	**1 466**	**1 555**	**12 928**
Common clay and shale				
for: bricks pipes and tiles	8 365	315	361	9 042
cement	–	50	–	2 626
lightweight aggregate	–	–	7	–
constructional use	909	72	–	–
other uses	–	–	–	–
Total	**11 916**	**436**	**686**	**13 038**
Fireclay				
for: bricks pipes and tiles	306	–	–	475
refractory use	–	–	–	(285)
other uses	–	–	–	(15)
Total	**657**	–	–	**867**
Special sands				
for: foundry use	–	–	–	1 556
of which naturally bonded	174	–	16	190
glass manufacture	–	–	–	1 692
other industrial uses	854	16	91	953
Total	**3 651**	**16**	**553**	**4 201**
Slate				
for: roofing and damp-proof courses	–	–	–	53
architectural and cladding uses	–	–	–	14
powder and granules	–	–	–	51
fill and other uses	–	–	–	242
Total	–	–	–	**360**

(a) Excluding marine-dredged.
(b) Including dolomite used for constructional uses.
(c) Asphalt filler includes as mine dust; other fillers include powders and whitings e.g. in animal feed polymers paint paper and pharmaceuticals.

Figures in brackets are for 1985 where 1991 data was unavailable.
Source: Central Statistical Office ('91) and Business Statistics office ('85).

Table 1.2. *Production of Dimension Stone in other Countries (tonnes)*

Country	*Marble*	*Granite*	*Other stone*	*Total*
Argentina	16 500	54 000	20 100	90 600
Australia	200	7 900	27 290	35 530
Austria	–	14 000	8 100	22 100
Belgium				364 000
Brazil				1 673 400
Bulgaria	47 400	–	85 300	132 700
Canada	240 500			240 500
China	678 000	1 867 000	–	2 545 000
France	634 000	384 200	nd/na	1 018 300
Germany	215 900	–	–	215 900
Japan	64 300	188 500	–	252 800
Greece	2 250 000	–	–	2 250 000
India	1 966 400	989 500	–	2 955 900
Indonesia	158 000	65 000	–	223 000
Italy	4 800 000	1 100 000	1 346 000	7 246 000
Korea	65 000	1 380 000	–	1 445 000
Mexico	712 000	–	–	712 000
Philippines	712 200	–	–	712 200
Portugal	962 000	182 000	–	1 114 000
Saudi Arabia	–	154 300	398 000	552 300
Spain	2 000 000	980 000	–	2 980 000
South Africa	17 200	574 800	26 400	618 400
Taiwan	280 000	–	–	280 000
Thailand	87 000	91 750	–	178 750
Turkey	65 000	–	–	65 000
United Kingdom				1 100 000
United States of America	29 000	615 000	375 000	1 019 000
Venezuela	24 150	43 700	3 600	71 450

(Data Source: Stone Statistics 1991–1995 Internazionale Marmi & Macchine Correra S.p.A. 1996).

traditionally used local stones where new constructions are restricted to materials that match existing building.

On a world scale the stone sector may be in danger of expanding too far and too rapidly. Any visit to an international stone exhibition reveals a bewildering array of materials from many countries, the latter including a large number classed as developing. The stone from newer areas is often very competitively priced and consequently often sells well – but it is also a novel material with little known about its performance. As a result there is often resistance from architects and specifiers who seem to prefer materials with which they are experienced or for which they can obtain test results in an understandable form. It is important that all countries are able to produce information to common standards – whether ISO or CEN – as this will help to promote the use of stone and create a feeling of confidence amongst architects, engineers and specifiers.

Worldwide, it seems that the natural stone production industry has an assured future with more stone being used in more innovative ways. This will include the use of stone in composite materials, for example 'stone veneer cladding'. It is also likely that the production industry will continue to undergo modernization and development changes and become drawn into debates on the environmental impact of quarries and processing plants. In the UK the extension and development of quarries is already subject to tight controls and, as many quarries are in areas that are designated as being of outstanding natural beauty, environmental constraints are likely to become more restrictive. It is possible that this could increase the volume of imports as other countries, particularly from those where the industry is still developing and expanding, may have less rigid controls on health and safety, and the environment.

1.1.2.1. Europe

In addition to the development of the worldwide market for stone there has been the development of standards for the single European Market. These standards contain mandatory and regulatory parts that at present cover specification and testing of stone for construction. It is hoped that there will also be guidance on the design and installation for the many uses of stone but these are unlikely to be ready for many years. The new standards seem to show a trend towards the use of performance standards and increasingly for the performance of preformed units rather than materials. Provided that the new standards are not too onerous then they should help to promote the use of stone in Europe.

1.2. Objectives of the Working Party

The objectives of the Working Party Report upon which this book is based were:

- To review the influence of the occurrence, mineral composition and geological history on the engineering properties of stone used in construction. No account would be taken of artificial stone.
- To consider stone essentially in terms of its intrinsic properties as a geological and engineering material, recognising that, depending on the circumstance, the engineering performance of the stone can be a function of the design as well as the local environment. However, detailed consideration of design was not seen as a role of the Report.
- To concentrate mainly on stone produced and used in the United Kingdom but to refer wherever possible to stone in other countries, particularly but not exclusively, where British specification, design and construction practices are, or are likely to be, followed.
- To review the different geological situations in which the sources of stone can occur, no attempt being made to quantify UK or other national resources

or to forecast trends in supply and demand. It would be beyond the scope of the publication to deal in any detail with the many commercial and environmental factors which influence the practical choice of stone.

- To take into account the increasing emphasis being placed on the planning of mineral extraction, quality assurance and control, and protection for the environment, while recognizing that the Report would not have the intention nor enough space to permit extended treatment of these subjects.
- To identify relevant Standards and other Specifications and Codes of Practice and, where appropriate, to summarize and discuss some of the currently accepted limits.
- To explore some of the problems commonly encountered in applying Specifications and Codes, for example, where limits for different properties might be incompatible with each other, or the Specification of Properties which would tend to be mutually exclusive for geological or other reasons, or Specifications which might not be appropriate to the available materials in the local environment. It would not be the intention to propose alteration or alternative specification so much as to assist the reader in the interpretation and implementation of selected portions of existing Standards and Codes of Practice, and in the development of Specifications where these are not readily available.
- To provide an authoritative, comprehensive and as up-to-date as possible presentation of all aspects of stone and rock in construction in one document.

To achieve the maximum possible breadth and balance of the Report, it was intended that advice and criticism be canvassed from a range of individual specialists, professional institutions, learned societies, industrial associations and research bodies.

As such, it must be made clear that the concepts and techniques described in the Report are drawn from a wide scientific spectrum in which geologists, chemists, other scientists, engineers, architects and other disciplines all collaborate with those involved in the investigation, extraction, processing, design, building and maintenance of structures using stone. As such, a report which links such diverse fields in a common theme will inevitably be considered by persons of widely differing vocational backgrounds. Consequently, basic material which is included in one section might be considered by an expert in that particular field to be oversimplified. However, it is thought that this approach is justified in order to serve a wide readership and hoped that any elementary facts might assume a new significance when presented in relation to the central theme.

It was further recognized that, although the objectives focused on specific areas within a wide field, difficulties would remain with Standards and Codes of Practice being under more or less constant revision throughout the world, especially in the European Union; and with the rapid progress of experience and research in the subject making it virtually impossible for a review to be up to date and wholly comprehensive in this respect.

1.3. The Working Party and the Report

The Working Party was drawn widely from experts in their fields to represent all principal aspects of the industry, together with users and researchers. Similarly, chapter reviewers (i.e. corresponding members) were also chosen from the same broad spectrum of those associated with stone. Individuals are listed after the Preface.

Having made the decision to include stone used in heavy civil engineering works in addition to that used in traditional building it was decided, after some deliberation, to structure the book in two parts: the first to deal with aspects common to stone, including geology, excavation, winning and processing, and the second to be specifically concerned in each chapter with the various uses of stone in construction.

The chapter on the *geology* is written, with difficulty, to be as palatable as possible for non-geologists, yet to give a sufficient level of expertise for geological readers to be useful for reference. Special text boxes of introductory geology have been included in this chapter for readers with no or little geological knowledge. Rock classification and composition, and rock structure, two important topics for the stone industry, especially in selection, winning and processing, are highlighted in this chapter. This chapter, in common with the others, is cross-referenced where appropriate to other chapters and has references and bibliography to lead readers, should they wish, to further information sources.

The *exploration* and *assessment* chapters are closely related and review the qualification and quantification of potential usable rock resources and their assessment for economic extraction. The following chapters on the principles and practices in the *extraction* and *processing* of stone were considered essential for the balance of the Book with emphasis being placed on the influence of geological conditions and the extraction methods employed and, where appropriate, the relationship of geology and extraction to further processing of the rock.

The specific chapters concerned with the uses of stone are essentially self-contained but make necessary cross-reference to the earlier background chapters. A very large amount of rock is used in construction as civil engineering fill, often for dams and highway and railway embankments. The *rock fill* chapter emphasises the changes which follow from the development of modern, heavy compaction plant, with rock properties of primary importance to the performance being explained and supported by case histories. *Armourstone*, i.e. rock used for coastal protection and harbour works, is reviewed and particular emphasis placed on the demand and selection criteria for suitable material, testing procedures peculiar to armour stone and case studies.

Although stone is historically used as masonry in buildings and civil engineering structures, its modern use tends to be somewhat restricted to masonry façades to frame buildings and various claddings. This change and its consequences are considered in the chapter on *natural stone for building and civil engineering*, with attention being paid to particular factors which need to be considered when using thinner stone slabs for cladding. Testing regimes for the various uses of stone are described. The last chapter, based largely on practical experience, concerns *stone repair and restoration*, including the explanation of the mechanisms by which stone deteriorates in service together with details on modern approaches to cleaning and remedial action.

The book includes three *appendices*. The first is a *glossary of terms* used in the various parts of the book and the second contains a compilation of *test methods* which are referred to in the main text. This has been included to give an outline of procedures which are not readily accessible in nationally standardized tests. The third is a compilation of the *physical and strength properties* of stones, together with some explanatory notes. It is most strongly emphasized by the Working Party that data in this appendix should only be used with considerable caution. We have no knowledge of the provenance or reliability of the data assembled for the Appendix. Rocks of identical or similar name and petrological description vary widely in their properties due to fabric and textural differences, state of weathering and/or alteration, small mineralogical differences, differences in induration, cementation, cohesion and grain boundary conditions, microfracturing, stress, together with method of working in the quarry, processing and subsequent history. Therefore, it must not be assumed that similar rocks from different locations will have similar properties: they may or may not. Instead, reliance should be placed on comprehensive sampling and testing and quality control of the individual rock sources.

Attention is drawn to the implications of the use of such terms as 'weathering' and 'weathered rock' throughout the text. Near-surface rock weathers in geological time by subaerial agencies. This weathering slowly changes the rock to a soil, or specifically a residual soil, and long before it reaches this condition the properties of the rock, even when slightly weathered, begin to change (Anon 1990). Many quarries in the UK and around the world work a slightly to moderately weathered rock and, even in an otherwise uniform rock, small changes in weathering, which occur throughout the weathering profile from the ground surface downwards, will bring about various changes in the properties of the rock. Therefore, the form and influence of the weathering on rock must be taken into consideration in its evaluation and use. Test properties reported are often those of fresh rock whereas delivered rock may be somewhat weathered and have different properties. Users and specifiers must be aware of this.

Weathering also occurs in stone when in place in its construction. Such weathering is commonly referred to by architects and engineers and the form and style of weathering, together with the rate of weathering, are important in buildings and other structures, particularly historic buildings. Such weathering occurs in engineering time and does not lead to the development of soil but does disfigure stone in use and hence is a most important topic. Rates and style of such weathering will depend on the original properties of the rock, its method of winning and processing and the environment in which it is placed.

Rock weathering in geological time is discussed mainly in the chapter on *geology* and stone weathering in engineering time is discussed mainly in the last two chapters on *stone in building and civil engineering use* and in *stone repair and restoration*. It is also mentioned in Appendix C.

References

ANON 1990, Tropical Residual Soils. Geological Society Engineering Group Working Party Report. *Quarterly Journal of Engineering Geology*, **23**, 1–101.

BICKMORE, D. P. & SHAW, M. A. 1963. *The Atlas of Britain and Northern Ireland*. Clarendon, Oxford.

COLLOCOTT, T. C. & DOBSON, A. B. (eds) 1975. *Chambers Dictionary of Science and Technology*, **2**, L-Z. Chambers, Edinburgh.

DEARMAN, W. R. 1991. *Engineering Geological Mapping*. Butterworth Heinemann, Oxford.

SYKES, J. B. (ed.) *The Concise Oxford Dictionary of Current English*, 6th Edition 1977, University Press, Oxford.

WHITTEN, D. G. A. & BROOKS, J. R. V. 1979. *The Penguin Dictionary of Geology*. Penguin, Harmondsworth.

SCOTT, J. S. 1991. *The Penguin Dictionary of Civil Engineering*, 4th Edition Penguin, London.

SMITH, M. R. & COLLIS, L. (eds) 1993. *Aggregates: Sand, Gravel and Crushed Rock Aggregates for Construction Purposes* (2nd edn). Geological Society, London, Engineering Geology Special Publication, **1**.

Stone Statistics 1991–1995. Internazionale Marmi & Macchine Correra S.p.A. 1996.

2. Geology

2.1. Introduction

The science of geology is the study of the Earth and particularly the study of the rocks and loose materials on the surface of the Earth. Geologists are interested in the origin, composition, structure and geological history of the Earth and, unless they are applied geologists, are not usually concerned with their practical use; geology is a science, not a technology. Architects, structural engineers and civil engineers, by contrast, are interested in rocks as construction materials and are not usually concerned about any of their other attributes.

One of the concerns of this book is to demonstrate that geology has a relevance to the study of rocks as construction materials and this chapter sets the geological scene for the book. Newcomers to geology are often put off by the jargon in the form of special names for rocks, minerals, fossils and geological periods and by what seems to be the lack of practical relevance of many aspects of the subject. One of the considerations in writing this chapter was to dispel this antipathy by providing comprehensible definitions of geological terms and including only those aspects of geology relevant to the use of rocks in construction.

Nevertheless, it is recognized that the chapter may be difficult to assimilate at first reading by the non-geologist and, because of this, boxed items are provided which, it is suggested, the non-geologist should read first. These provide simple explanations of several concepts of importance to the use of rock in construction, especially discontinuities, rock classification and rock hardness. This basic information should enable the reader to move on to the following chapters, returning to the main text of Chapter 2 as required. Civil engineers and structural engineers will find they are on more familiar ground in Appendix C, which deals with the physical and strength properties of stones and rocks used in construction.

Geology can be divided into a number of more specialised subjects as follows. *Petrology* deals with the study of rocks including their occurrence, field relationships, structure, origins and geological history as well as the study of the mineral constituents of rocks and rock texture. Included in this broad definition are the processes by which rocks are formed. *Igneous rocks* are formed by the crystallization of liquid rock material. Removal of existing material by erosion after weathering and transportation by rivers, wind, ice, and the eventual deposition of this eroded material produces *sedimentary rocks*. The recrystallization of existing rocks in response to a change in pressure or temperature or volatile content forms *metamorphic rocks*. *Stratigraphy* is concerned with the study and correlation of layered sedimentary rocks in time and space and *palaeontology* is the study of fossil plants (flora) and animals (fauna) in sedimentary rocks. *Structural geology* deals with the structures which affect rocks and includes both the large-scale events which led to mountain building as well as the small-scale internal structures seen in a hand specimen of a rock. *Mineralogy* is the study of the mineral constituents comprising rocks as well as rock texture which describes the inter-relationships of these minerals in rocks. *Physical geology* and *geomorphology* deal with the scientific study of land forms on the Earth's surface and the physical processes that have fashioned them.

There are many other branches of the subject of geology which are described in textbooks, most of which are readily available from libraries and bookshops, and need not be described here in detail. However, two branches of geology: *geophysics*, which is the science concerned with all aspects of physical properties of rocks and processes of the Earth and their interpretation, and *engineering geology*, the application of geological techniques for engineering purposes which includes site investigation, rock properties and uses of rock materials, do have applications to the subject matter of this book. The branches of the subject highlighted in italics above will be dealt with in more detail in this Chapter, but for a full and detailed understanding of the subject of geology the reader is referred to texts such as Press & Siever (1994); Windley (1984); Kennett (1982) and Tucker (1981).

2.2. Stratigraphy and historical geology

Stratigraphy examines rocks in time and space and deals with the various methods of correlation required to compare rocks from different localities. Correlation techniques may involve the use of fossils, rock units or intervals of time.

2.2.1. Stratigraphic unit

A stratigraphic unit is a body of rock forming a discrete and definable unit. Such units may be determined by their lithology, that is the types of sedimentary and other rocks making up a unit. Lavas are often included in such a unit. A sequence of these stratigraphic units may give rise to a stratigraphic column which represents the succession of rocks laid down during a specific interval of geological time. The phrase 'stratigraphic column' often refers to the entire sequence of strata deposited throughout all geological time. Simplified stratigraphic columns are frequently used to compare and contrast sequences of rocks of similar ages in a particular region

Rocks commonly used for natural building stones

A most important fact for a non-geologist to appreciate is that the 'stone industry' has used and continues to use names for rock types with much less precision than the geologist. In this respect the most important differences of usage by the stone industry are: 'granite' for any strong or hard igneous rock and some metamorphic rocks; 'marble' for any limestone that will polish and 'slate' for any rock that cleaves into thin slabs or roof tiles. Appendix C provides information on the correct geological name for some commercially available British stones.

In the past, the choice of which rocks to use as natural building stones was decided primarily on availability, ease of extraction and workability. Although local availability was undoubtedly the dominant factor, it should be noted that, where transport by water was possible, stones were often obtained from distant sources, for example Caen Stone, Portland Stone and Bath Stone. At that time, colour, attractive appearance and durability were secondary considerations but today, with relatively easy international transport, these have become primary considerations.

In the UK the most frequently quarried types of rock used as natural building stones are shown in the following table which gives the number of quarries for each type of rock reported in 1996, see also §2.10.

Sandstones	Limestones	Slates	Granites	Others
131	95	50	21	3

Sandstones

Sandstones are sedimentary rocks composed of grains of sand cemented together. In the most recent geological classification system they are described as 'arenites', from the Latin word meaning sand and, even more exactly, they belong to the group of *terrigenous siliciclastic* sediments being derived by erosion of the land (terrigenous) and composed of fragments (clastic) of rocks containing silica (siliceous), see §2.6.2.3 for more detail. The sand grains are commonly made of colourless quartz, which is the mineral form of silica, but the cement is often made of iron oxides which are red, orange, brown or yellow in colour and give sandstones their attractive colours. Many churches and public buildings are made of sandstone; for example the Anglican Cathedral in Liverpool.

Limestones

Limestones are sedimentary rocks composed of calcium carbonate, often the detrital remains of shells or skeletons of marine organisms but sometimes containing the organisms completely preserved as fossils. They are usually grey or white except for the oolitic limestones which are brown or yellow, see §2.6.2.4 for more detail of these carbonate rocks. Many buildings in London are made of one particular limestone – the Portland Stone – including St Paul's Cathedral.

Slates

True slates are metamorphic rocks composed originally of fine-grained particles (silt and clay) tightly compressed together and hardened. Intense pressure has caused the rock to become fissile so that it can be easily split into thin sheets, see §2.6.3. The colours of slates are various shades of dark grey, purple, blue, green or even red. Much of the urban housing of Victorian Britain is roofed in grey Welsh slate – well seen from above on a wet day.

Granites

True granites are igneous rocks largely composed of an interlocking mass of crystalline grains of three minerals ; quartz, feldspar and mica. The grains are easily visible to the naked eye and, being of different colours, give the rock an attractive speckled appearance, see §2.6.1. Other rocks described as 'granite' include basic igneous rocks, which do not contain quartz, such as basalt, dolerite and gabbro often called 'black granite' and the metamorphic rock, gneiss, see §2.7.2. Granites can be highly polished and are much in demand for the facings of prestigious buildings such as banks. Granite is also used in ordinary masonry construction, as for example in the city of Aberdeen.

so that, for example, a rock horizon yielding a sandstone of good quality for building may be correlated with horizons of similar age within the area should further deposits of this particular material be sought. Such correlations require detailed geological investigation of many local sedimentary rock successions before genuine correlations can be established. This technique employs stratigraphic cross sections where a vertical section, the stratigraphic column, usually with an exaggerated vertical scale, is drawn to show the thickness and relationships of the stratigraphic units across a particular horizontal distance. In these sections topographic scales may be ignored and the stratigraphic units and their boundaries are related to a geological time-scale. Figure 2.1 shows an example from the 'Economic Geology of the Fife Coalfields' (Francis *et al.* 1961) where vertical sections of the Upper Limestone Group across Fife are correlated.

2.2.2. Stratigraphic nomenclature

Stratigraphic and other related units are named according to established principles and practices. Formal naming of a stratigraphic unit occurs when a type section is chosen which then remains as the standard reference for that unit. The name given is usually binomial so that time and rock types comprising the unit are taken into account along with its geographical location. In the early days of geological mapping stratigraphic units such as Giffnock Sandstone or Charlestown Limestone represented lithostratigraphic units, that is, sequences of rocks based on their rock types, whereas modern terminology tends to subjugate rock types in favour of a larger unit which may encompass both time and rock type, e.g. Highland Border Group. Biostratigraphic units consist of the name of the characteristic fossil found in that unit plus the relevant unit term. In practice many well-known units, e.g. 'Coal Measures', were named long before the present terminologies were invented and these are usually preserved in their original form.

2.2.3. Geological time-scale

This is a two-fold scale that subdivides all time since the Earth was first formed into named units of abstract time and subdivides all the rocks formed over the same time into successions of rock formed during each particular interval of time. The branch of geology that deals with the age relations of rocks is known as chronostratigraphy. Advances in isotope geology and knowledge of the value of the half-lives of some radio-active isotopes make it possible to date selected rocks with a reasonable degree of accuracy. Thus, it has become possible to assign revised dates to geological boundaries. It is still not possible to produce a time-scale which satisfies all rocks everywhere but the chart, shown as Table 2.1, gives an outline geological time-scale employing current names and dates.

The terms most commonly used are geological time units, called geochronological units, which are based upon the rock record of the chronostratigraphic units described immediately above. Terms in use include eon (longest), era, period, epoch, age and chron (shortest). Chronostratigraphic terms such as system are in common use and this is equated with the term period; series correlates with epoch and stage with age. It is not possible to discuss details of UK stratigraphy here and the reader is referred to texts such as *The Phanerozoic Time-scale* (Harland *et al.* 1964) and *A Guide to Stratigraphic Procedure* (Holland 1978) for further study.

The relevance of stratigraphy

Sedimentary rocks are usually stratified and, in any sequence of strata, the layers at the bottom are older than those at the top, unless the sequence has been turned upside down by folding and/or faulting. Sedimentary rocks may also contain fossils, that is, the remains of organisms that lived at the time the sediment was accumulating, by which exposures or outcrops of the strata may be correctly identified, correlated, traced across country and mapped. Strata that were originally horizontal may now be tilted, folded, faulted and otherwise disturbed by later earth movements. The study of these matters is the branch of geology known as stratigraphy and the stratigraphic column lists the entire sequence of strata deposited in an area. See Fig. 2.1 for an example of a local stratigraphic column and Table 2.1 for a global column. For the purposes of this book, stratigraphy is important because it explains why certain rocks can be found in some places and not others. The geological map, which embodies all the geographical information on the strata in a region, is the starting point when looking for the location of a new quarry, as described in Chapter 3. The dip of a stratum (see §2.3 for explanation) will determine the direction in which it would be best to extend an existing quarry. Working down the dip will expose more of the rock, whilst working up the dip the rock will thin out when the outcrop is reached. At the risk of gross oversimplification, in UK the sedimentary strata are generally harder the older they are, but this is not always so elsewhere.

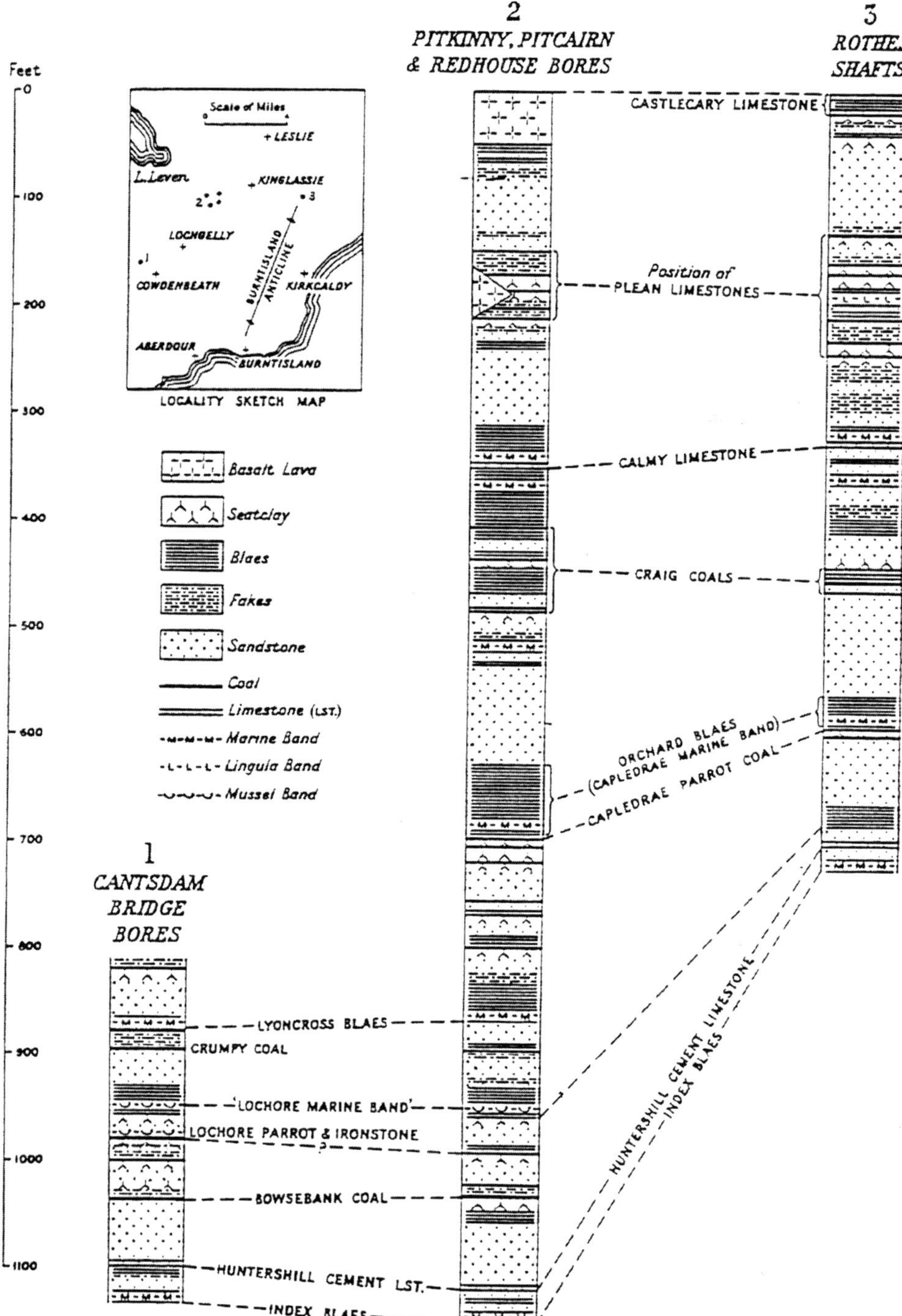

Fig. 2.1. Comparative vertical sections of the Upper Limestone Group (taken from Francis *et al.* 1961).

Table 2.1. *Geological time-scale*

Age (Ma BP)	*Geological age*			
	Epoch	*Period*	*Era*	*Eon*
	Holocene (Recent)	Quaternary	Cenozoic ('recent life')	Phanerozoic ('evident' life, i.e. many fossils)
0.01	Pleistocene			
1.6	Pliocene	Tertiary		
5.2	Miocene			
23	Oligocene			
35	Eocene			
56	Palaeocene			
65	(Numerous epochs recognizable throughout the world)	Cretaceous	Mesozoic ('middle life')	
146		Jurassic		
208		Triassic		
245		Permian	Palaeozoic ('ancient life')	
290		Carboniferous		
363		Devonian		
409		Silurian		
439		Ordovician		
510		Cambrian		
570		Precambrian	Proterozoic ('early life') Archaean	
4600			< Origin of the Earth	

2.3. Structural geology

Rocks can be found in different forms or structures the understanding of which is important to the exploration and extraction of rock for construction. This is certainly the case for sedimentary rocks and metamorphosed sediments.

Sedimentary rock strata are rarely horizontal and the individual rock beds or layers usually show some angle of inclination to the horizontal, called the angle of dip . There is a maximum value for the angle of dip in any dipping bed and this value represents the true angle of dip of a rock unit. The direction of this maximum angle of dip is recorded by engineers as, for example, 090°/45° which means that the rocks have a maximum dip of 45° to the east, which has a compass bearing of 90°. Note that the compass bearing, or azimuth, should always be given as a three-digit number so as not to confuse it with dip readings which are given as two-digit numbers. Geologists use a different notation and measure the direction of strike as well as the angle of dip. The angle of dip is the same as before but the direction of strike is the direction of a horizontal line on the dipping rock strata; the direction of strike is at an angle of exactly 90° to the maximum dip direction. Thus, the geologist would not only write the direction of strike and the angle of dip but also the direction of the dip. For example, using the previous figures, a geologist

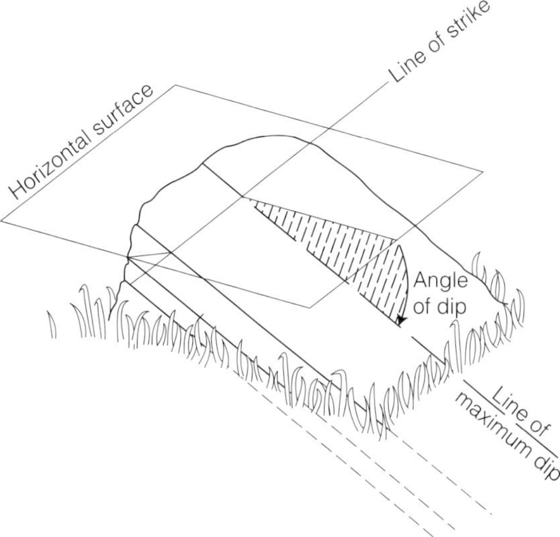

Fig. 2.2. Dip and strike measurement on a rock exposure.

would initially write 360°/45°, which gives the strike as north (360°) and the maximum dip as 45°. Strictly speaking, the strike is really a north-south line and the reading could have been written 180°/45°. However, as this does not indicate whether the strata are dipping to the east or west, writing the data as 360°/45°E removes all doubt, see also Fig. 2.2.

Rocks can also be folded, faulted, thrust over other rocks and split by natural discontinuities which may be faults, joints, unconformities, bedding planes, metamorphic foliation and so on.

2.3.1. Folds

A fold is a bend in rock strata or in any planar feature such as bedding or layering. The feature is deflected sideways or upwards and the amount and direction of dip is altered. Four principal forces acting in the Earth's crust, called regimes, are responsible for folding and these are:

- lateral compression
- differential vertical subsidence
- differential shearing and
- thrusting

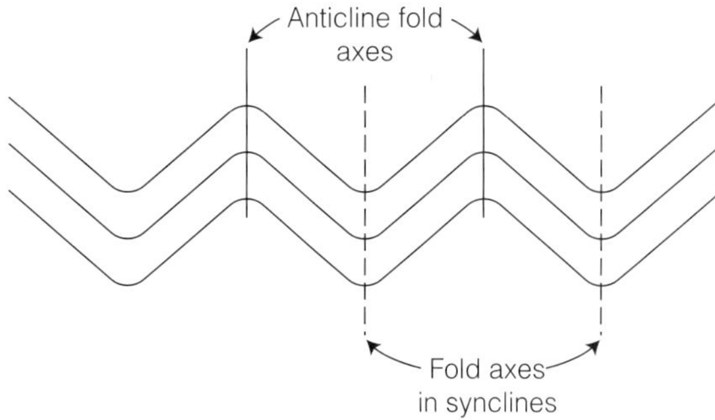

Fig. 2.3. Regular folds with fold axes.

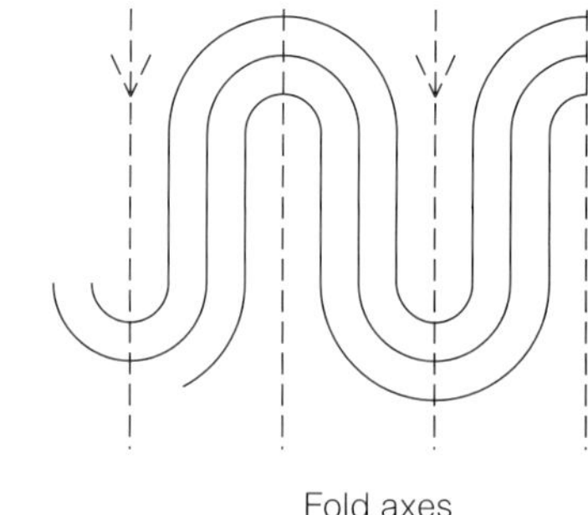

Fig. 2.4. Iosclinal folds.

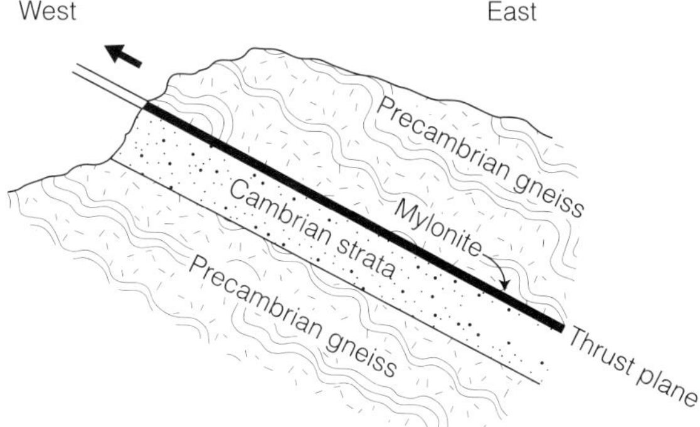

Fig. 2.5. Thrust fault. At Loch Glencoul basement Precambrian gneisses have been thrust westwards over younger Cambrian sediments.

Simple folds may be synclines in which a succession of sedimentary layers are folded into a V-type structure with the V opening upwards; or anticlines in which the V opening is downwards, see Fig. 2.3. The plane through the axis of a syncline or an anticline is called a fold axis. Various types of folds may arise from open folds to tight isoclinal folds, see Fig. 2.4. Folds may be vertical or inclined and it is often important to define the attitude of a fold correctly. A fold and thrust belt is a linear or arcuate zone in which compression has produced a combination of thrusts and folds, see Fig. 2.5.

2.3.2. Faults and thrusts

A fault is a roughly planar surface of fracture in a rock body caused by brittle failure along which observable relative displacement has occurred between adjacent

Discontinuities

All rock masses are naturally broken up, to a greater or less extent, by partings. These partings may be of different geological origins, e.g. bedding plane partings, joints, faults, fissures, cracks and cleavage planes. However, whatever their origin, all these breaks are referred to by engineering geologists as discontinuities. The discontinuities are in three dimensions and have the effect of dividing the rock mass up into discrete blocks, the size of which depends on the spacing of the discontinuities. If the discontinuities are widely spaced in all three dimensions the blocks will be large in size and, therefore, may be suitable for large masonry construction and armourstone. If the discontinuities are widely spaced in two dimensions but closely spaced in the third dimension, the blocks will be slab-like and may be suitable for paving or tiling. If the discontinuities are closely spaced in all three dimensions, the blocks will be small and the material may only be suitable for aggregate, rubble or rock fill. A scale for discontinuity spacing is given in Table 2.2. The orientation and spacing of discontinuities may have an important bearing on quarry layout and operation.

blocks. There are a number of possible faults that may occur and these are known as dip-slip , both normal and reverse, strike-slip and oblique-slip, all of which are shown diagrammatically in Fig. 2.6a, b, c & d. Strike-slip faults result from horizontal displacement, to the right or the left, in the direction of the strike. Thrusts are low angle, usually less than 45°, reverse faults with a significant movement in the direction of dip, dip-slip, so that the hanging wall overhangs the footwall. Thrust sets form complex structures, described as imbricate, which may together form a duplex zone. Single thrusts may show a staircase effect of ramps and flats. Figures 2.7a to 2.7d show these different structures.

2.3.3. Joints

Joints are planar discontinuities in a rock body caused by discrete brittle fracture along which there has been little or no movement parallel to the plane of fracture but slight movement at right angles to it. The orientation of a joint is measured in exactly the same way as the dip and strike of a sedimentary bed, see §2.3 above. Fractures may be caused by shrinkage due to cooling or desiccation or unloading by the removal of the weight of overlying rocks by erosion or tectonism, see §2.5.1. A group of parallel joints constitutes a joint set, see §4.2.3. Joint systems comprise two or more joint sets which are usually arranged systematically with respect to the axes of the principal stresses created by the regional deformation, see Fig. 2.8.

Discontinuity spacing is extremely important in the assessment of a particular rock mass to produce large natural blocks of rock for building purposes and it should be noted that rock exposures are needed to provide a full evaluation of the discontinuity pattern, i.e. frequency and orientation. Borehole cores provide essentially one-dimensional data on discontinuity spacing. A descriptive scheme for discontinuity spacing is given in BS 5930: 1981 and is reproduced here in Table 2.2.

Cooling joints, or shrinkage joints, such as those which give rise to columnar structures in lava flows are caused by differential volume changes in cooling and contracting magmas, see Fig. 2.26. Sheet-like joints and joint sets may be caused by the erosional unloading of overlying strata (unloading joints) and are common in granites and high grade gneisses. In granites and other igneous, plutonic rocks horizontal joints of this type are common and are of particular importance in the production of large equidimensional natural blocks and also in aiding the extraction of such blocks from a quarry, see §5.3.9.3. Cleavage in igneous rocks such as granite refers to planar surfaces along which the rock will preferentially split, and a fuller explanation is given in §2.6.1.3.

Joints and other discontinuities may be infilled with other substances such as clays which affect the engineering properties of the rock mass. Other infilling materials may also be important as they can facilitate the splitting of the intact rock along these planar surfaces; calcite infillings in slate, mentioned in §5.3.2.8 are good examples of this. Tight joints and microfractures may be opened naturally by the deposition of minerals in the joint aperture from salt solutions, a process that will further weaken the rock mass, see §2.4.1. The rock mass rating (RMR) scheme of Bieniawski considers joints of great importance in determining the quality of the rock mass and sets out a number of criteria for which joints should be examined in order to determine the geotechnical classification of the rock but the reader is referred to his book 'Engineering Rock Mass Classifications' (Bieniawaski 1989) and §5.3.2.4 for a fuller explanation.

Joints and other discontinuities will be discussed in detail later in the text with reference to specific rock types where their importance to the use of a particular rock type in construction will be given.

2.3.4. Bedding planes and unconformities

Bedding planes between sedimentary rock layers also constitute discontinuities affecting the rock mass, as

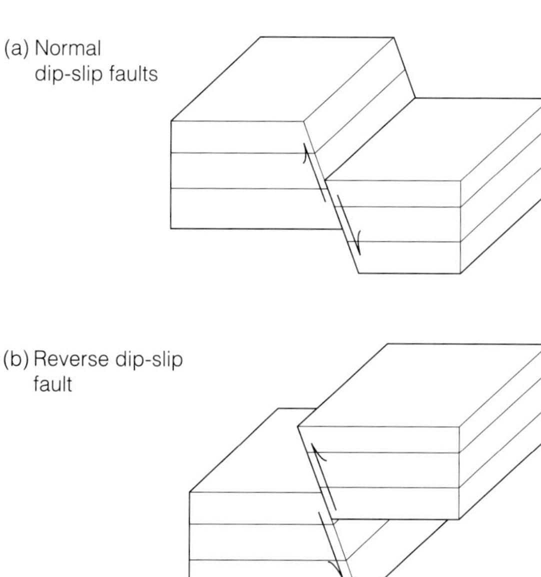

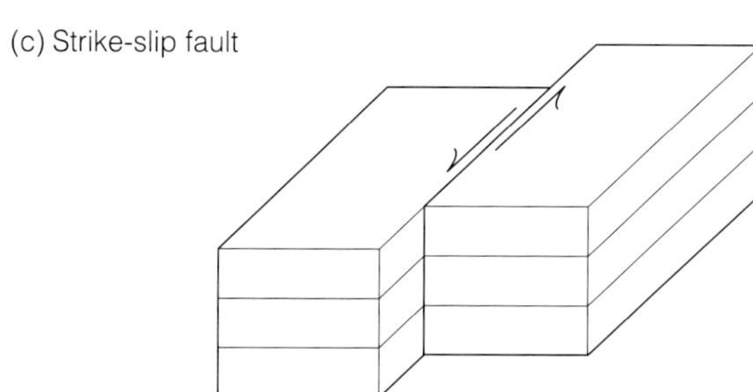

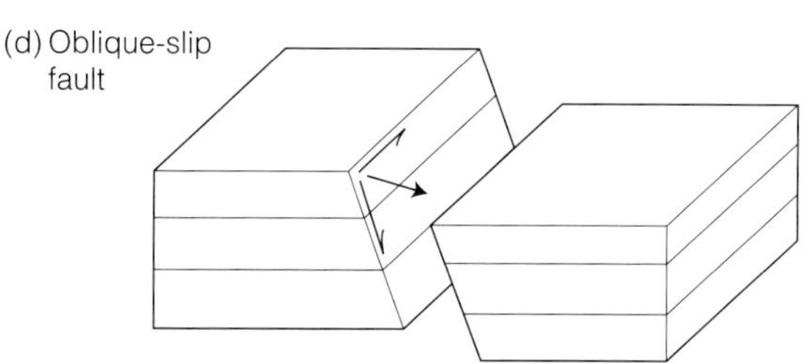

Fig. 2.6. Faults: (a) normal, dip-slip fault, (b) reverse dip-slip fault (c) strike-slip fault, (d) oblique-slip fault.

splitting may occur along them, see §2.8. Importantly, the thickness of the sedimentary layer or bed will determine the maximum thickness of the blocks that can be extracted from any sedimentary layer. Unconformities are also planar discontinuities and they occur when there is a time interval between one layer of rock strata being deposited and another being laid on top of it (Fig. 2.9). An unconformity may separate beds of different dip since the older layers may well have been tilted and, or, folded and then eroded before the new layer is deposited on top of them.

If a sediment containing a wide range of grain sizes is sorted vertically such that there is a continuous gradation from coarse particles at the bottom to fine grains at the top, the sediment is said to display graded bedding (Fig. 2.10). The sequences of graded beds can be used to determine the direction in which the sequence becomes younger. Sedimentary rocks will get younger in their geological age towards the fine material as the coarse material is laid down before the fines. The change in grain sizes across a block of sandstone that graded bedding produces will often enhance the appearance of the blockstone. An example is the Wallace Tower, near Stirling, which is built of coarse sandstone blocks exhibiting graded bedding.

Cross-bedding, or current bedding, is also found in sedimentary rocks and represents material either laid down in shallow water or deposited as dunes by the wind. In this structure, successive minor layers are deposited as sand grains settle in the very slow-moving deeper water at the downstream end of a sandbank or delta. Each minor layer is S-shaped and the complete layer grows downstream. Subsequent erosion of the sandbank by the stream removes the top of a complete layer, with the minor layers still curving tangentially towards the basal bedding plane, but truncated sharply at the top (Fig. 2.11). This can also be used as a 'way-up criterion' as the asymmetry of the structure allows the top to be recognized.

2.3.5. Metamorphic cleavage and foliation

Regional metamorphism of clay-rich rocks such as mudstones or shales gives rise to hardened, slightly coarser-grained rocks still containing clay minerals but possessing a preferred direction of fracturing roughly analagous to mineral cleavages. Metamorphic cleavage, or slaty cleavage, is the formation of a set of fractures along closely spaced parallel surfaces in a low grade metamorphic rock such as a slate caused by the alignment of various mineral and structural elements during metamorphism (Fig. 2.12 and §2.9). As the temperature rises during regional metamorphism, minerals such as muscovite and chlorite develop from the clay minerals within the slaty cleavage planes leading to the formation of a rock, termed a phyllite, possessing very shiny surfaces. If the temperature continues to rise and biotite appears, the original bedding planes disappear and the cleavage planes are replaced by bands or foliae of aligned minerals such as micas (Fig. 2.13). Metamorphic rocks such as schists frequently show foliation representing a continuous sub-planar rock fabric formed by the preferred orientation of minerals with a general platy shape, such as micas.

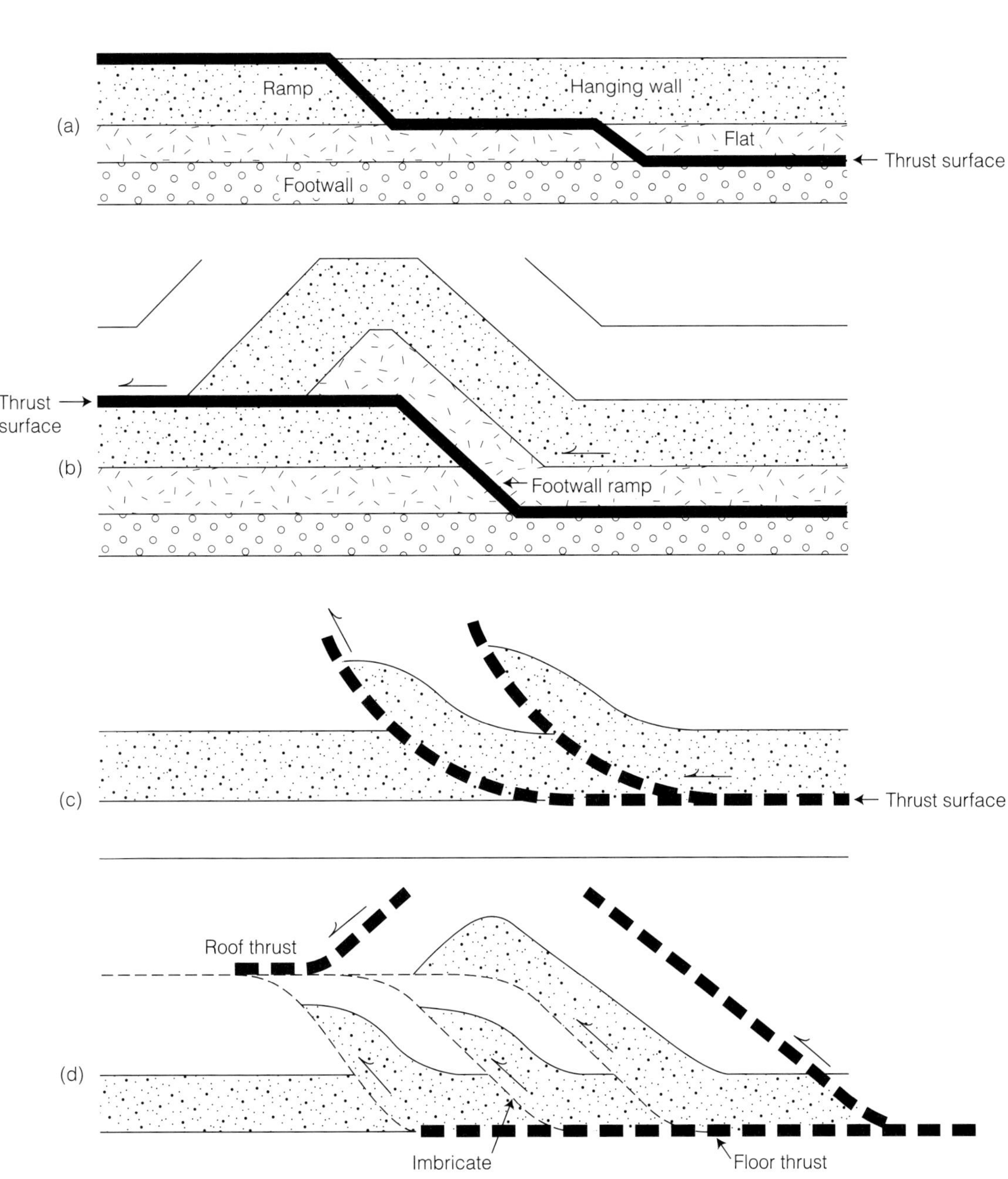

Fig. 2.7. Simple and complex structures created by faulting and thrusts, (a) shape of thrust surface-ramps and flats, hanging wall and footwall, (b) fold in hanging wall resulting from a ramp, (c) thrust sequences in footwall and (d) duplex structure: imbricate thrust slices are contained between a floor thrust and a roof thrust.

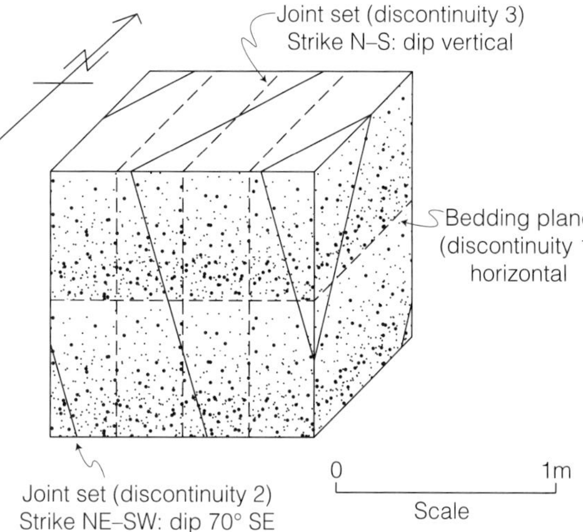

Fig. 2.8. Discontinuities in the rock mass.

Rock cleavages may be divided into two groups:

(1) continuous cleavage such as that found in slates (called slaty cleavage), or in schists or gneisses due to foliation
(2) spaced cleavages caused by the microfolding of a pre-existing fabric in the rock.

This second type of cleavage rarely acts as a planar joint and does not cause the rock to split along it.

2.4. Weathering

Weathering is the term employed to describe processes of degradation and alteration of minerals and rocks.

Table 2.2. *Descriptive scheme for discontinuity spacing in one dimension*

Term	*Spacing*
Very widely spaced	>2 m
Widely spaced	600 mm to 2 m
Medium spaced	200 mm to 600 mm
Closely spaced	60 mm to 200 mm
Very closely spaced	20 mm to 60 mm
Extremely closely spaced	<20 mm

There is a number of processes involved of which mechanical, chemical and biological action are the most important.

2.4.1. Mechanical weathering

Freezing of water confined in cracks or rock joints exerts a pressure of 14 MPa on the surrounding rock which forces it apart. As the process is repeated by alternate thawing and freezing, fragments are broken off the rock mass to form loose scree.

In desert areas the same mechanical effect may be produced by water containing some chemical compounds in solution penetrating into individual rocks and depositing these chemicals as salts in cracks within the rock. The pressure of the crystallization of these salts eventually causes the rock to split along these cracks and exfoliation results. Large diurnal temperature changes, although an important factor in allowing fluids to enter the rock, cannot themselves split the rock unless fluids are also present. Such temperature changes may, however, set up stresses in the rock which may assist exfoliation.

Mineral particles can be moved by wind, such as in a desert environment, and these will tend to abrade any

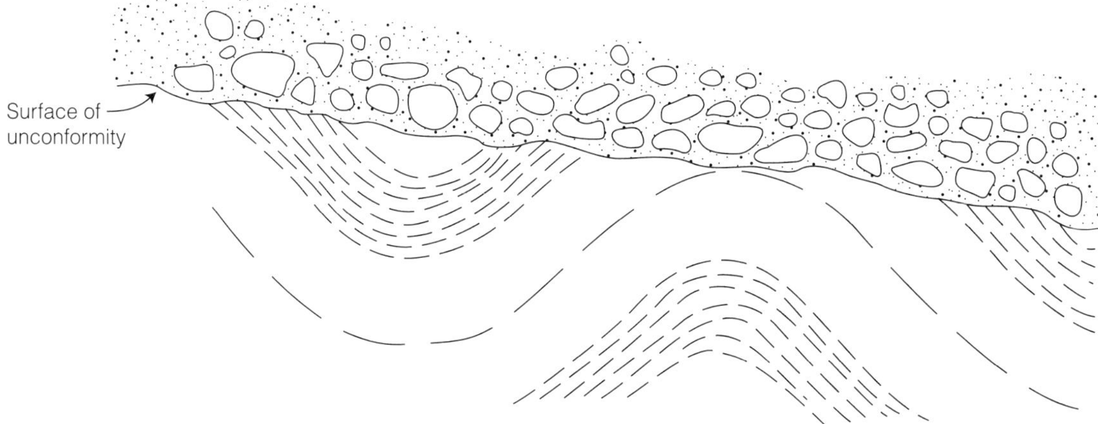

Fig. 2.9. Unconformity: conglomerate layer deposited on top of eroded folded strata.

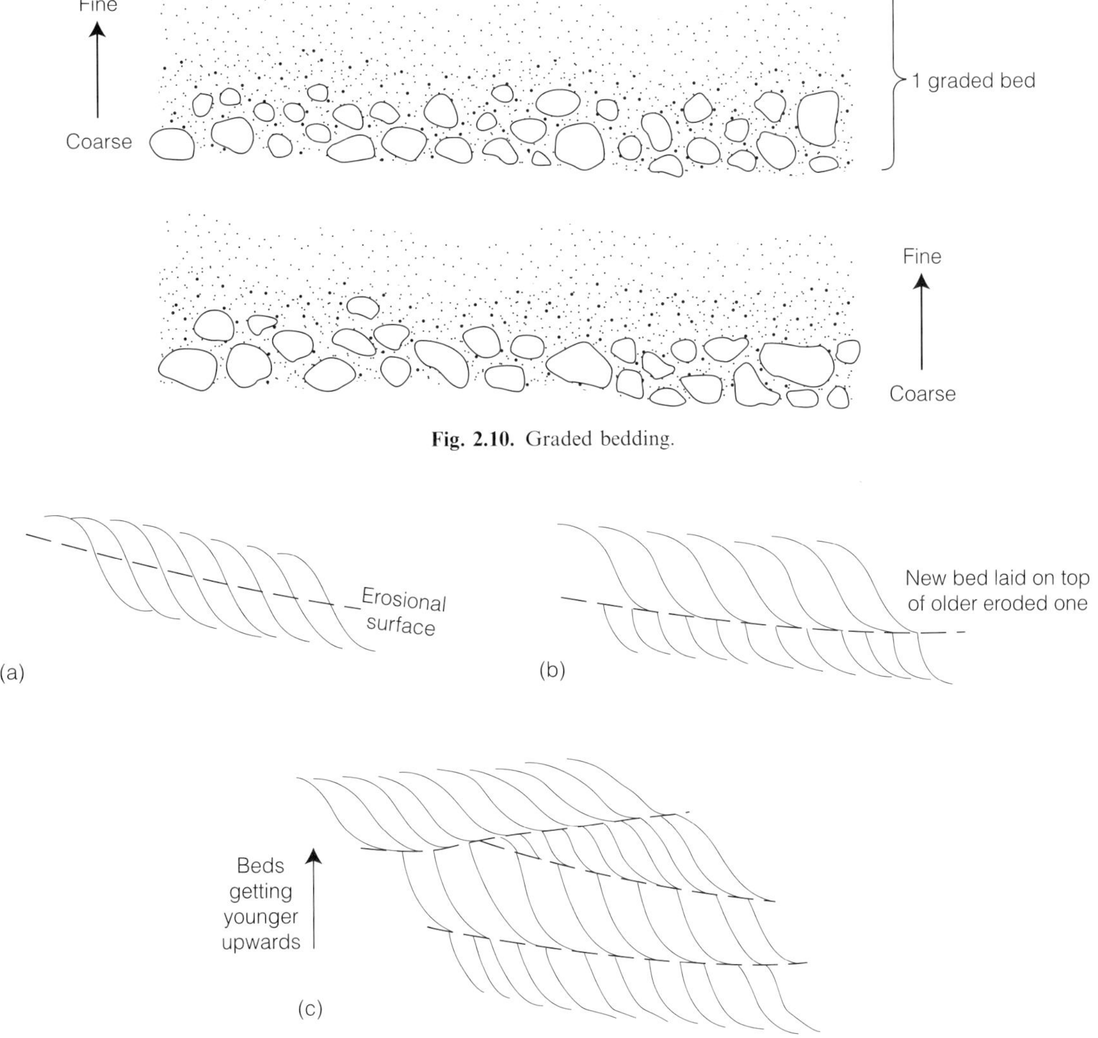

Fig. 2.10. Graded bedding.

Fig. 2.11. Current (or cross) bedding: (a) single bed (b) two beds (c) current or cross bedding displayed in sedimentary beds.

rock formations they encounter, leading to mechanical weathering of rocks. The pounding of waves against cliffs at the edge of the sea is another situation which will, in time, lead to the mechanical breakdown of the cliffs and a receding coastline.

2.4.2. Chemical weathering

Chemical reactions between the original minerals of the rock, surface water, oxygen of the atmosphere and organic acids at the Earth's surface produce new minerals which are stable under the new conditions; any soluble constituents produced are removed in solution. The main chemical reactions are described below.

Hydration is a reaction involving water and a rock mineral to produce a new stable mineral containing hydroxyl groups (OH) in its structure. Many minerals react in this way including feldspars, which produce the clay minerals by hydration reactions shown in Table 2.3, and olivine. Under normal conditions, the hydration of feldspar and olivine is very slow relative to historic time. However, in geological time, super-heated, hydrothermal fluids, which can be generated during the late

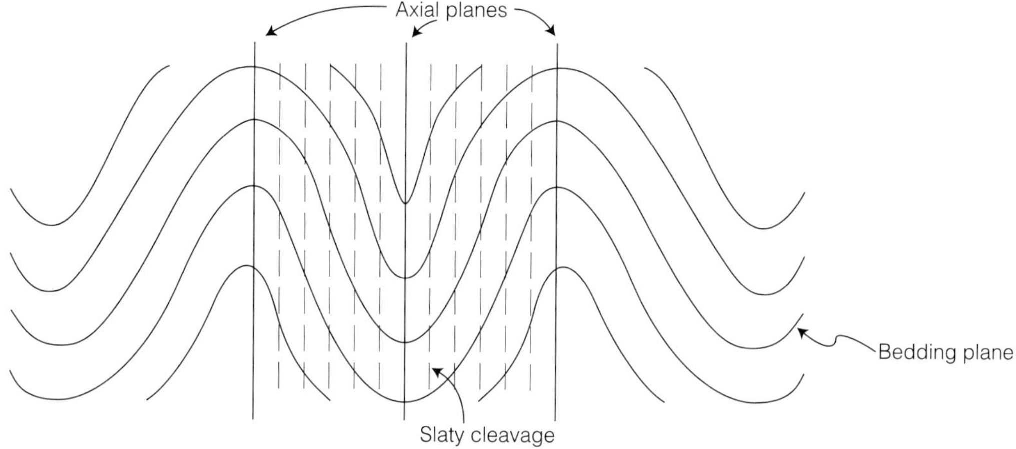

Fig. 2.12. Tightly folded, thin sedimentary strata. Slaty cleavages develop parallel to or sub-parallel to the axial planes of the folds. Note the high angle of intersection between cleavage and bedding planes which still exists even though the rock has suffered low grade metamorphism.

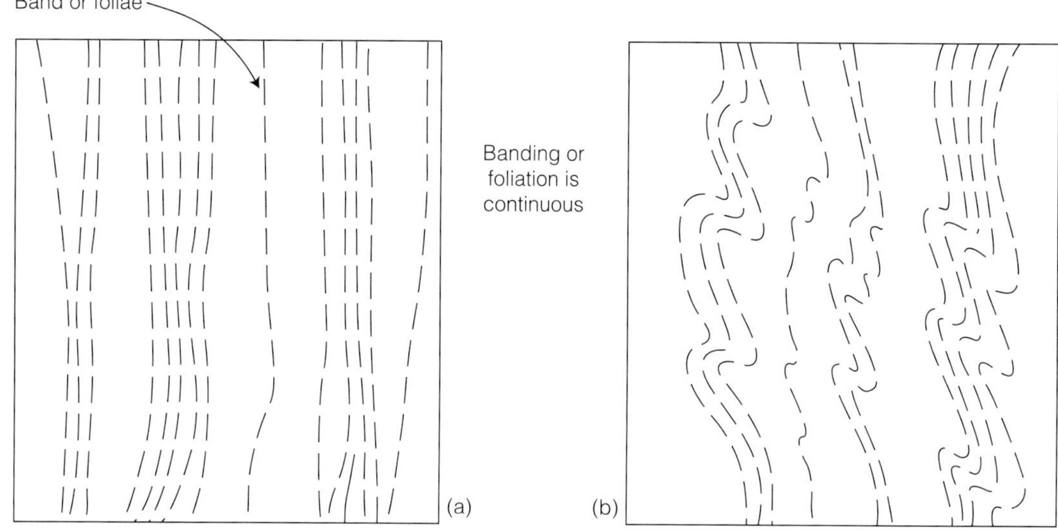

Fig. 2.13. Foliation of schists. The platy or tabular minerals are aligned in roughly parallel bands or folia which are more or less at right angles to the directed pressure. Foliation is continuous and may be simple (a) or show contortion (b). It is displayed by rocks subjected to medium grade regional metamorphism.

stages of cooling of molten rock, can cause pervasive and almost complete alteration or weathering of these primary minerals, producing kaolin and chlorite respectively which are described as secondary minerals. This alteration process is known as late-stage hydrothermal alteration.

Carbonation is a reaction in which atmospheric CO_2 combines with water to give carbonic acid, which then reacts with limestone to produce soluble calcium bicarbonate, which is carried away in solution. The recent concern in Europe about acid rain affecting forests is relevant to building stone decay since sulphur dioxide (SO_2) from coal-burning power stations combines with water and oxygen from the atmosphere to form sulphuric acid. An attempt to reduce the production of these harmful substances is being made by passing gases generated at power stations through a slurry of finely ground limestone sprayed into the gas, as for example

Weathering

Weathering is a word commonly used to describe the degradation of materials by climatic, atmospheric factors that have operated during the recent past or historic time. Weathering of this type is explained below.

However, weathering is also a name given by geologists to the general degradation and alteration of rock over much longer periods of geological time when climatic conditions and, indeed, even the composition of the atmosphere were different from those experienced today. Furthermore, geologists may also sometimes describe the alteration of minerals in a rock by hot, mineralized solutions produced by the cooling of molten rock as a type of weathering.

When rocks are exposed at the surface, the process of weathering begins. This applies both to rocks in the field and to stones in buildings or other structures. The agents of weathering are water, gases, wind, frost and temperature change. In the UK, water is probably the most important of these. As water falls through the atmosphere as rain it absorbs gases from the atmosphere, of which the most important is carbon dioxide. As a result, by the time it reaches the surface it is a mixture of dilute acids. This can be illustrated by the following reaction:

$$\underset{\text{Water}}{H_2O} + \underset{\text{Carbon dioxide}}{CO_2} \longrightarrow \underset{\text{Carbonic acid}}{H_2CO_3}$$

The situation is worse in industrialized and urbanized regions where there are gases, especially sulphur dioxide and oxides of nitrogen, produced by combustion of fossil fuels which give rise to the phenomenon of 'acid rain' (see §2.4.2). When the acidic rainwater seeps into a rock it commences dissolving any soluble rock minerals, at first along the grain boundaries. This weakens the rock and eventually can lead to its complete disintegration. Limestone is particularly susceptible to weathering in areas of industrial acid rain and the dissolution of the limestone masonry of buildings and churches in industrial cities is a major problem. The aspect of the masonry is important: stone exposed on the weathered side of a building often deteriorates more rapidly than stone on the sheltered side. These matters are discussed further in Chapter 10.

In quarries the depth of weathering is usually indicated by a colour change in the rock, typically dark grey unweathered rock at depth gradually giving way to red, brown or yellow weathered rock as the surface is approached. Weathering often takes place first along joints and bedding planes so that a block of rock may have a grey centre with a brown outer zone – so called 'blue hearted' stone – which is prized for the two colours of its appearance in masonry. In some tropical countries the depth of weathering may be so great that fresh unweathered rock may not be accessible at practicable quarrying depths. Table 2.4a summarizes the progressive changes from fresh rock to completely weathered rock as seen in typical quarry exposures in the UK.

Table 2.3. *Chemical weathering of feldspars to give various clay minerals. Alteration of feldspars is first initiated by hydrothermal alteration at an earlier stage*

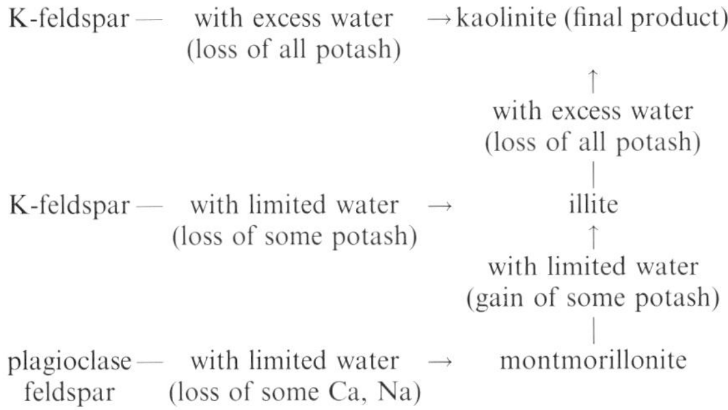

K-feldspar —	with excess water (loss of all potash)	→	kaolinite (final product)
			↑ with excess water (loss of all potash) |
K-feldspar —	with limited water (loss of some potash)	→	illite
			↑ with limited water (gain of some potash) |
plagioclase feldspar —	with limited water (loss of some Ca, Na)	→	montmorillonite

in flue gas desulphurization (FGD) at Drax power station, South Yorkshire. The sulphuric acid reacts with the carbonate to produce carbonic acid and gypsum ($CaSO_4$) which can be used for plaster walls in building. Such a scheme should dramatically reduce the harmful effects of acid rain on building stone.

In oxidation, oxygen combines with a rock mineral either with or without water present to produce new stable phases. For example, oxygen reacts with magnetite (Fe_3O_4, actually a double iron oxide, $FeO.Fe_2O_3$) to give hematite (Fe_2O_3):

$$4FeO.Fe_2O_3 + O_2 \longrightarrow 6Fe_2O_3.$$

However, if water is present then the reaction produces limonite ($FeO(OH)nH_2O$). Note that the oxidation of ferrous iron (Fe^{2+}) to give ferric iron (Fe^{3+}) involves a colour change from blue-green to red. Such a change is best seen in weathered zones, called' red boles', which are frequently found as capping layers on lava flows. The lavas are extruded with the iron present in the ferrous state, either in silicate minerals or in magnetite, a common iron accessory mineral in basalt lava flows. Weathering oxidizes any iron present so that the magnetite changes to hematite which is russet brown in colour. The Old Red Sandstones of Scotland owe their red colour to the main cementing material which is a thin covering of hematite on each grain of quartz or other mineral grain. Although this hematite cement is no more than a thin film it dominates the colour of the sandstone. Similar effects can be found in other sedimentary rocks including impure limestones, as long as a certain amount of iron is present in the oxidized state in the rock to act as a cementing agent.

Reduction takes place in environments deficient in oxygen, such as that within marine or lake muds at great depth, and elements occur in their reduced form. For example, ferric iron (red–brown–orange) is reduced to ferrous iron (green–blue–black); $Fe^{3+} \longrightarrow Fe^{2+}$. In such conditions, iron combines with any sulphur present to give iron sulphide, usually iron pyrites (FeS_2). As a result, pyrite is a common constituent of mudrocks, mudstones and shales. When these rocks are metamorphosed the iron sulphide, which is often in disseminated form in the rock, forms large, brass-yellow cubic crystals which are frequently found on the surfaces of slates used in roofing. Pyrite nodules can also be found in limestones, causing staining and surface degradation. The pyrite will be changed to dark grey-blue veins if the limestone is later metamorphosed to marble.

2.4.3. Biological weathering

Bacteria, fungi and algae are collectively described as micro-organisms, all of which may cause the weathering of rock and building stone. Bacteria can be either aerobic (needing oxygen for respiration) or anaerobic (not requiring oxygen) and are, thus, capable of living under virtually all conditions including within the rock itself. Aerobic bacteria may oxidize certain minerals, especially sulphides such as pyrite, causing degradation of the rock, colour changes and staining. Anaerobic bacteria commonly produce methane and carbon dioxide from organic matter or reduce minerals containing iron and sulphate so are less likely to be agents of weathering.

Algae are typically small single-celled plants that obtain energy from sunlight, not from oxidation of minerals or chemicals. Their presence on the surface of rock is unlikely to harm the rock except that they may create an environment suitable for other organisms, such as plants, by retaining moisture.

Fungi certainly secrete organic acids and enzymes which may attack the rock to release certain chemicals which are nutrients for the organism.

Lichens are combinations of fungi and algae and may contribute to weathering of rocks, perhaps by drawing chemicals from them, but their precise role in this is uncertain.

All the weathering processes outlined above may affect building stone. Many rocks are affected by hydration leading to the production of clays and clay-related minerals; limestones are affected by carbonation; igneous rocks and some iron-bearing sandstones (red-coloured ones for example) are affected by oxidation; and many building stones are affected by the action of micro-organisms both before and after cleaning. In this last biological process, modern analytical techniques are able to provide evidence of micro-organisms present and the reactions which have been involved.

2.4.4. Classification schemes

A scheme for grading rock weathering is described in BS 5930: 1981 (Fookes *et al.* 1971; Dearman 1974). In this scheme, a rock mass is divided into six grades or divisions denoted by Roman numerals depending upon its state of weathering. Table 2.4a gives this scheme and Fig. 2.14 shows weathering profiles of two different rock types, one a folded sedimentary or metamorphic rock and the other a weathered basic igneous rock mass such as a basalt or dolerite.

The thickness of such weathering profiles will depend upon the climate affecting the rock mass. For instance, a typical basic rock mass in Scotland possessed an entire profile of weathered rock, from grade I to grade VI, within a depth of less than 10m; whereas a similar profile through a weathered granite underlying part of the city of Singapore was more than 100m thick because of the severity of tropical weathering there.

According to BS 5930 the modern soil layer is split into an 'A' layer, or layer of leaching, and a 'B' layer, or layer of deposition, above the weathered layer 'C' which equates to grades II to VI, and the fresh bedrock layer 'D' or 'R' which equates to grade I (and possibly some grade II). In fact, it is almost impossible in practical terms to separate grade VI from the modern soil layer and, in some parts of the world, particularly desert areas, it is very difficult indeed to identify the layer or weathered grade with which you are dealing.

In the desert a typical weathered profile from surface into fresh rock may be only 2 m or so in depth but difficulties in recognition may occur. For example, in a weathered profile in central Libya, a strong limestone occurred below the surface soil, quite unlike any rocks supposedly underlying the area, which were weak, friable Tertiary limestones. A trench dug through the hard limestone revealed caverns beneath and very poor limestones

Table 2.4a. *Descriptive scheme for grading the degree of weathering of homogeneous rocks which are moderately strong or stronger*

Grade	*Term*	*Description*	*Thickness*
VI	Residual Soil	All rock material is converted to soil; the mass structure and material fabric are destroyed; there is a large change in volume but the soil has not been significantly transported	<2 m
V	Completely weathered	All rock material is decomposed and/or disintegrated to soil; the original mass structure is still intact. Material is considerably weakened and will slake in the presence of water	variable; can be several metres thick
IV	Highly weathered	More that 50% of the rock material is decomposed and/or disintegrated to a soil; fresh or discoloured rock is present either as a discontinuous framework or as corestones. Does not slake when dry sample is immersed in water	variable; often many tens of metres thick
III	Moderately weathered	Less than 50% of the rock material is decomposed and/or disintegrated to a soil; fresh or discoloured rock is present either as a continuous framework or as corestones. Pieces of rock cannot be broken by hand but rock is considerably weakened	2 m–6 m
II	Slightly weathered	Slight discoloration indicates weathering of rock material and discontinuity surfaces; all the rock material may be discoloured by weathering	up to 5 m but discoloration may extend down for many tens of metres
I	Fresh	no visible sign of rock material weathering; perhaps slight discoloration on major discontinuity faces	

Table 2.4b. *Classification of weathering for rock which was originally moderately weak or weaker, such as many sedimentary rocks: including porous sandstones, siltstones and argillaceous shales and mudstones*

Class	*Term*	*Description*
E	Residual or reworked	Matrix with random lithorelicts, occasionally altered, bedding destroyed. Classed as 'reworked' when foreign inclusions appear as a result of transportation
D	Destructured	Greatly weakened, mottled colouring, ordered lithorelicts in weakened and disordered matrix, bedding disturbed
C	Distinctly weathered	Much weaker, grey reduction colour, much closer fracture spacing
B	Partially weathered	Slightly reduced strength, brown oxidation, closer fracture spacing, weathering penetrating in from fractures
A	Unweathered	Fresh, with original strength, colour and fracture spacing

Table 2.4c. *Classification of weathering for heterogeneous masses*

Zone	*Proportion of weathering grades*	*Description*
6	100% IV to VI	May behave as soil (although residual soil is not necessarily 100% of zone 6). Any relict fabric may still be significant
5	<30% I to III >70% IV to VI	Weak grades (IV to VI) present will control behaviour. Corestones may be significant
4	30–50% I to III 70–50% IV to VI	Rock framework contributes to strength. Matrix or weathering products control stiffness and permeability
3	50–90% I to III 50–10% IV to VI	Rock framework still controls strength and stiffness. Matrix controls permeability
2	>90% I to III <10% IV to VI	Weak materials along discontinuities. Shear strength, stiffness and permeability affected
1	100% I to III	Behaves as rock. Apply rock mechanics principles to mass assessment and design

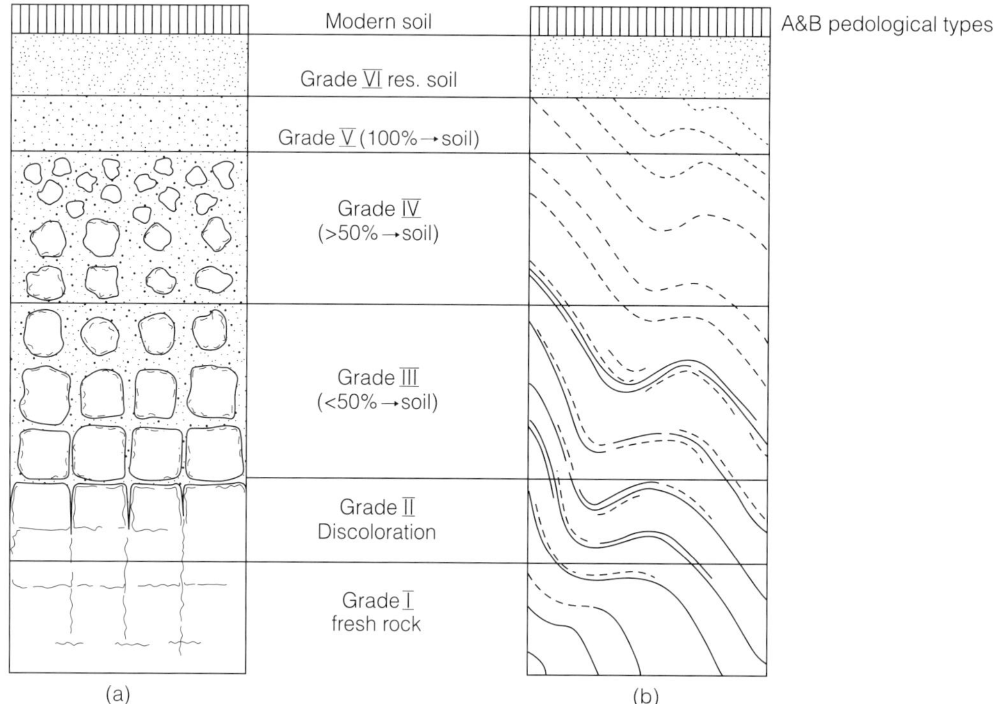

Fig. 2.14. Emerging grades of weathered rock. (a) Corestone development from original bedrock (basalt, dolerite) with corestones decreasing upwards until total decomposition occurs in grades V and VI. (b) Continuous framework with ghost structures appearing in the decomposed rock (a structured saprolite). Total decomposition to a massive saprolite occurs below the modern soil layer. Thicknesses of the engineering zones may vary with Zone II up to 5 m but discolouration may penetrate deep into the rock mass; Zone III up to 6 m or so; Zone IV can be tens of metres thick; Zone V up to 5 m and Zone VI is thin, usually <2 m and is difficult to distinquish from the modern soil.

below 2 m depth, with the fresh Tertiary material a further 1 m below this. The explanation was that, over time, desert rainfall had dissolved the carbonate from the A layer below the surface and deposited it further down in the B layer. The desert heat, however, brought the lower solutions back towards the surface by capillary action and the carbonate was then deposited near the surface as the water evaporated. In this particular situation it was impossible to separate layer A from layer B and from the weathered grades of rock.

Thus, weathering of the rock mass may produce a completely false impression of the geological situation but a knowledge of the mechanisms of weathering will usually allow an interpretation to be made which can explain what has happened.

A Geological Society Working Party considered the classification of weathered rock and its recommendations are given in the *Quarterly Journal of Engineering Geology* (Anon 1995). In summary, it is recommended that a description of the weathering in every rock mass is always made which should include comments on the degree, extent and nature of any weathering effects at material or mass scales. The rock mass can be subdivided into zones of like character and descriptions should include:

- changes in colour
- reductions in strength
- changes in fracture state
- presence, type and extent of any weathering products

If the rock is uniform and strong or moderately strong in the fresh state, having a compressive strength between 50 MPa and 200 MPa, then Table 2.4a, already described, is still relevant and will be the one to use to describe weathering in igneous or metamorphic rocks. If, however, the rock is moderately weak or less in a fresh state, that is, a compressive strength of less than 50 MPa, then Table 2.4b is required, where the six grades I to VI are replaced by five divisions or classes, labelled A to E. This classification is likely to be used for weak sedimentary rocks such as porous sandstones, siltstones, shales and mudstones, although many strong sedimentary rocks such as greywackes, arkoses and well-cemented sandstones and so on will still be described using Table 2.4a. The final classification table recommended by the Working Party (Anon 1995) is one for heterogeneous rocks in which six zones (1 to 6) are again used, see Table 2.4c, but, because of the heterogeneity of the rock, various zones used in Table 2.4a may occur together. Thus, zone 1 would contain weathered rock incorporating grades I II and III (from Table 2.3a). The possible inclusion of these new classifications into a revised version of BS 5930 is under consideration and may well be recommended. Since the study of rock weathering is an important factor in any rock mass being considered as a likely source of building stone, these new classifications have been presented in Chapter 2 although the ease of use of the new tables, particularly Table 2.4c, will only be determined through time.

In different climatic regions of the Earth, weathering is likely to have different effects on similar rock types. The severity and depth of weathering will vary as will the mechanisms involved. Weathering is almost nil in the Arctic, whereas it is severe in the tropics with tropical rainfall; less so in temperate zones, and much less so in desert regions. It is also very important to be able to assess rock for building stone purposes by carrying out a personal examination of the rock profile so that the weathering grades can be correctly assigned and an accurate rock section depicted. Since weathering seriously reduces rock strength and increases porosity and water absorption, the importance of this type of exercise cannot be too highly stated.

2.5. Geomorphology and physical geology

Geomorphology deals primarily with the topographical features of the Earth's surface. It is concerned with the classification, description and origin of land forms. The shape of land forms reflect both the nature of the rocks beneath the surface as well as the processes that take place on or close to the surface. Deep crustal processes may also play an important part in the formation of land forms.

2.5.1. Deep-seated Earth processes

The rigid outer shell of the Earth, the lithosphere, rests on top of the asthenosphere, and parts of this outer shell, called plates, move. The study of this movement is known as plate tectonics by geologists and popularly as 'continental drift'. The concept is that the surface of the Earth is composed of rigid, undeformable, thin plates of thickness less than 150 km, and that seven major plates cover most of the Earth's surface, although many smaller plates also exist. These plates of stable, ancient rocks are commonly the foundation of the major continents recognized today, hence the popular name for the concept. Where these ancient rocks have been exposed by uplift and erosion they are known as 'Shield Areas'. In addition, it must also be remembered that, singly or together, these plates may have formed other land masses or continents during the geological history of the Earth some of which have been given names such as Gondwana and Laurasia The plates are continually in motion both in relation to each other and to the axis of rotation of the Earth.

Plates are bounded by active ridges and trenches. Ridges, such as mid-ocean ridges, are the centres of divergence or of spreading apart of two plates where new crust is created; known as constructive plate margins. Mid-ocean ridges are rarely continuous but have a stepped appearance due to transform faults. These are types of strike-slip faults (Fig. 2.6), occurring at the boundary of the plates in which the direction of movement of the crustal blocks is reversed, or transformed, in comparison with strike-slip faults on land.

Physical geology

For many people, their introduction to geology is through physical geology which is the study of the relation between geology and the landscape. It is easy to see why this is so because the concept that the underlying geology influences the surface landforms is easy to understand. Moreover, in Great Britain there are many clear examples of landscapes associated with particular rocks (e.g. the chalk downland of southern England and the granite tors of Dartmoor). Two books developing this theme are classics of geological literature (Holmes 1947; Dudley Stamp 1962). The wide availability of air photographs has contributed greatly to the understanding of landforms and the ability to interpret them in terms of the underlying geological structure. Much of the UK has been subjected to glaciation in the recent geological past: in upland areas the ice has removed the superficial deposits and bedrock is close to the surface, whilst in lowland areas a mantle of glacial till, gravel and sand often obscures the underlying rock. The importance of physical geology to the subject of this book lies mainly in Chapter 3 where it is relevant to the exploration for rock for building stone and armourstone, and Chapter 7 where it is relevant to the location of borrow areas for obtaining rock fill.

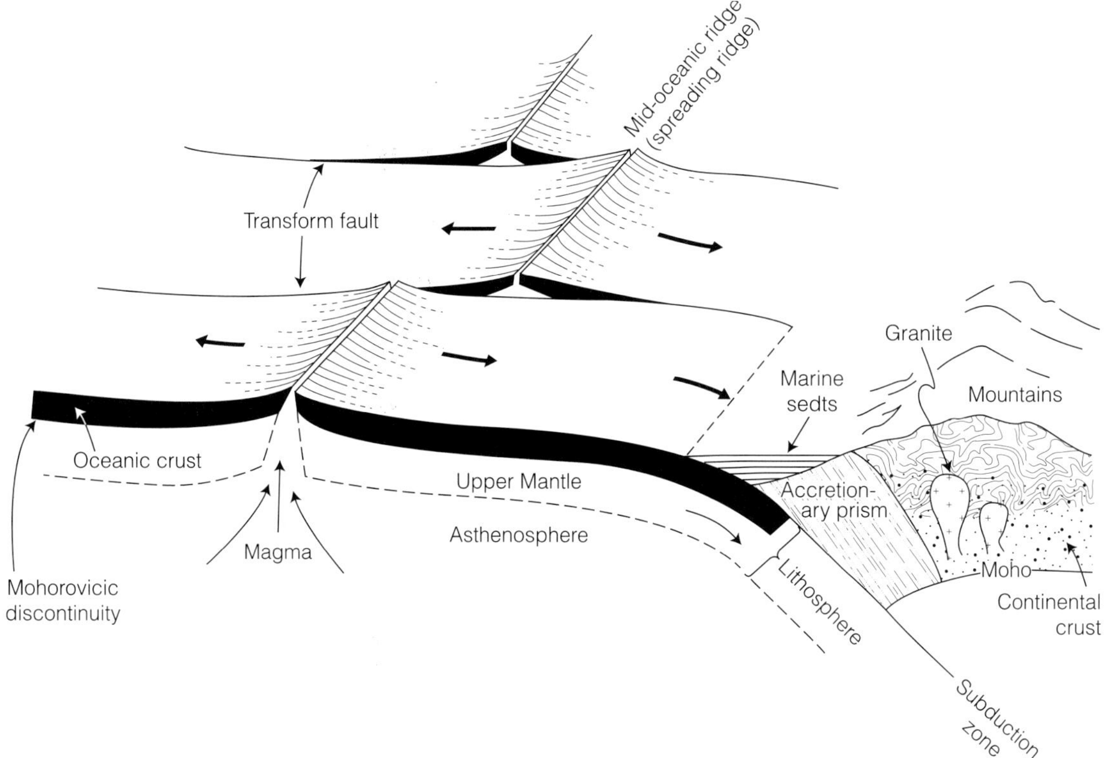

Fig. 2.15. Divergent plate boundary. Oceanic crust is being generated at the mid-ocean ridge and spreading away from it. At the continental margin a convergent plate boundary occurs and the oceanic crust and the upper mantle (which together comprise the lithosphere) move below the continental plate along a subduction zone. Marine sediments accumulate in the trench above the subduction zone and an accretionary prism of sediments forms there. Granitic melts are generated in the lower crust above the zone and rise into the deformed and metamorphosed sediments forming the mountain belt.

Where plates converge or collide, one plate is thrust under another and is consumed at depth along the contact boundary, which is called a subduction zone. Figure 2.15 shows these features. Earthquakes may mark the position of these subduction zones which have been shown to extend down to depths greater than 250 km. Trenches also form at these destructive plate margins and on the surface of the Earth above the collision island-arcs or mountain ranges, such as the Alps or the Himalayas, are formed (Fig. 2.15). The formation of mountains belts, particularly by compression from lateral forces, is termed an orogeny. There have been many orogenies in the evolution of the Earth's Crust each extending over many millions of years (Blyth & de Freitas 1984*a*).

2.5.2. Surface processes

The intricate shape of mountains is mostly the result of processes of erosion that remove material from the rocks composing the ranges. Erosive processes include weathering and soil formation and the transportation of material by rivers, wind and ice.

Rivers can transport huge volumes of sediments which may be deposited at the river mouth. There the material is deposited as a delta and the deltas of the Nile and the Mississippi are huge features within which the main rivers split up into many smaller braided channels as they flow through them.

In the desert regions fine material is transported by wind action. Such movement may be air-borne, with the sand in motion also acting as a severely abrasive weathering agent, as well as a continuous movement of sand slowly creeping across the land as dunes and barchans. The latter are crescent-shaped, mobile dunes in which the wind predominantly blows from one direction. Sand erodes from the windward side and accumulates on the steeper leeward side of the dune, which stands at an angle of about 32°. These barchans move at about 10 m to 20 m per year.

Glacial action has been very important in many regions, particularly northern Europe and the UK, in shaping the landscape. As well as these destructive processes shaping the landscape, there are constructive processes such as volcanic activity and land uplift that will build up the land, so that a particular land form is the result of the interplay between constructional and destructional processes acting upon the land at any one period of time. Some of the main landforms are described and illustrated below. An understanding of the role of geology in determining landforms may be useful in the exploration for construction materials.

2.5.3. Erosional landforms

Scarp and dip slope indicates the presence of a resistant layer or stratum in less durable rock, such as a bed of limestone in shale or a dolerite sill in sediments dipping at a low angle. The scarp occurs along the strike and its height depends upon the thickness of the resistant bed

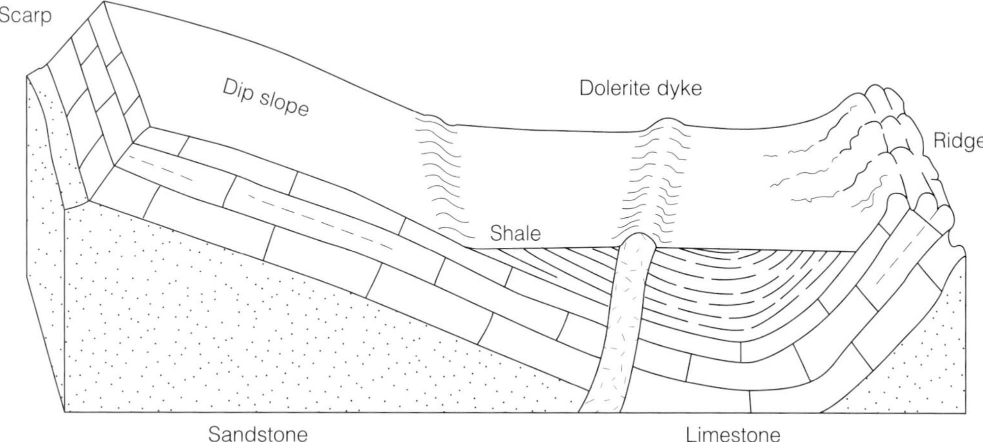

Fig. 2.16. Scarp and dip slope.

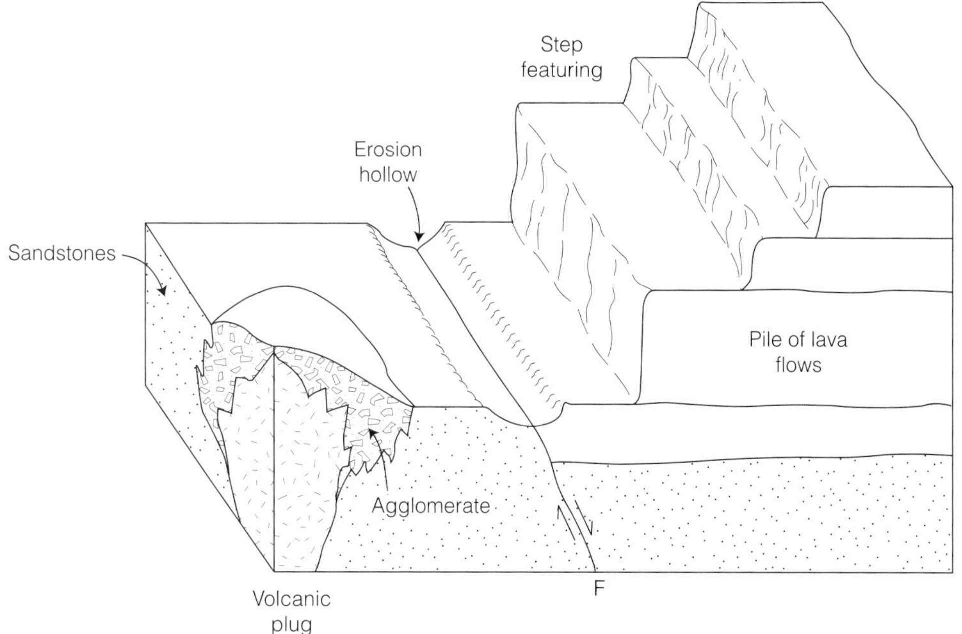

Fig. 2.17. Step featuring in lava flows, erosion hollow along the fault and a volcanic plug.

(Fig. 2.16). A ridge occurs where a resistant bed dips steeply and the dip slope is as steep as the scarp. In gently dipping strata a ridge may indicate a dolerite dyke, see hypabyssal igneous rocks, §2.6.1.1.

Step featuring occurs in areas underlain by lava flows. The top and bottom surface of a lava flow are often relatively weak owing to the concentration of gas bubbles, called vesicles, and weathering can further alter the weak top surfaces to soils as well as etching out the weaker zones within the underlying flows. This process gives rise to a stepped profile of successive scarps, each scarp corresponding to an individual lava flow (Fig. 2.17). The size of each step depends upon the thickness of each lava flow but is typically within the range 5 m to 25 m.

An erosion hollow represents a line of weakness which may be caused by erosion along a fault line, or erosion of a less resistant rock. This latter may be a weaker member of a rock succession if the line of weakness is parallel to the strike of the sedimentary rocks or a dyke if the line cross-cuts the other rock types. Figure 2.17 shows this feature and also a small, conical hill caused by the presence of an underlying volcanic plug.

Other small erosion hollows called swallow-holes or collapse structures found in ground underlain by limestone (Fig. 2.23), may be caused by leaching of the limestone by weathering processes. Indeed, in places streams may disappear down swallow-holes into underground caverns and river systems.

2.5.4. Depositional landforms

Weathering of rock to soil *in situ*, that is, with the material remaining in the same place, gives rise to residual soils, which are relatively rare in the UK. Most soils in the UK

Hard and soft rocks

Geologists speak loosely of hard and soft rocks. By hard rocks they mean rocks that require a hard blow from a geological hammer to break or which cannot be broken (e.g. limestone and granite). By soft rocks they mean loose material (e.g. sand and gravel) or rocks that can be easily broken by the geological hammer (e.g. chalk and clay). From this usage it can be seen that what is meant by 'hard' and 'soft' in this context is better described as 'strong' and 'weak'. The geological hammer is useful as a rough field guide but, to characterize the strength properties of rocks more precisely, rock strength tests are carried on specimens prepared in the laboratory. These tests are basically of three kinds: compressive strength, tensile strength and flexural strength. Details of the test procedure are given either in the text or in Appendix B and test results for different kinds of rock are given in Appendix C together with a scale of rock strength. Great Britain can be roughly divided into two regions by a line drawn from Portland Bill to the Flamborough Head: to the northwest of the line is a region of predominantly hard rocks and to the southeast is a region of predominantly soft rocks. In Great Britain hard rocks are generally more suitable than soft rocks for many of the uses of stone and rocks dealt with in this book. But in countries with drier, warmer climates having no frosts, soft rocks are often widely used as building stones because they can be quarried and shaped readily (Fig. 2.18). Some porous soft rocks get harder when they lose their 'quarry sap' on drying, an important consideration if the rock is to be shaped.

The reason why some rocks are hard (strong) and others are soft (weak) is mainly because the mineral grains that make up different rocks are held together with different degrees of bonding. Igneous rocks are nearly all hard because the mineral grains have crystallized in contact with each other, giving a very strong bond. Most metamorphic rocks are hard because the mineral grains have been fused together by heat or pressure (or both), again giving a very strong bond. Sedimentary rocks, by contrast, range from very hard to very soft depending on the strength of the grain bond. In sedimentary rocks of sand size (e.g. sandstone), the grains are held together by various natural cements: silica, iron oxides and calcium carbonate are three common ones. If the cement fills all the space between the mineral grains the rock will be difficult to break and regarded as hard but, if the grains are cemented only where they touch each other, the rock will crumble easily and be regarded as soft. In sedimentary rocks of silt and clay size (e.g. siltstones, mudstone) the hardness depends on the extent to which the sediments have been subject to pressure, thus compressing the grains into close contact to form a solid mass. The calcareous sedimentary rocks range from hard crystalline limestone through medium strength oolitic limestone to soft chalk and the hardness has different causes in each. Hard crystalline limestones are akin to igneous rocks with well bounded crystal boundaries, oolitic limestones are akin to sand-sized sedimentary rocks with cemented grains and chalk is somewhat like a silt-sized sedimentary rock in that it consists of fine-grained material composed of calcium carbonate compressed together. One of the effects of weathering is to weaken the bonding between mineral grains with the result that weathered rocks are not as hard (strong) as their unweathered parent rocks, see Appendix C.

are quite thin and usually overlie glacial deposits. In heavily glaciated terrains such as the northern parts of the UK, much of the local topography has been shaped by the movement of ice in the recent geological past, meaning less than 25 000 years ago. Material is removed and carried along by the ice eventually to be deposited in one of a number of glacial landforms.

Drumlins are low hills of till or boulder clay, a name given to heterogeneous deposits of clays, sands and rock debris carried by the ice sheet, streamlined by ice sheet as it moves along. Other similar deposits include kames and eskers, both of which contain appreciable amounts of sands and gravels. Morainic mounds occur as deposits from ice melt waters laid down close to the ice front. Figure 2.19 shows all of these glacial features. A crag and tail structure is formed when the moving ice sheet encounters a small hill, such as a volcanic plug. The side facing the direction of ice flow is eroded and a 'tail' of deposited material builds up on the other (lee) side (Fig. 2.20).

Fig. 2.18. Sawn masonry blocks of soft, cream coloured limestone, Mdina, Malta G.C.

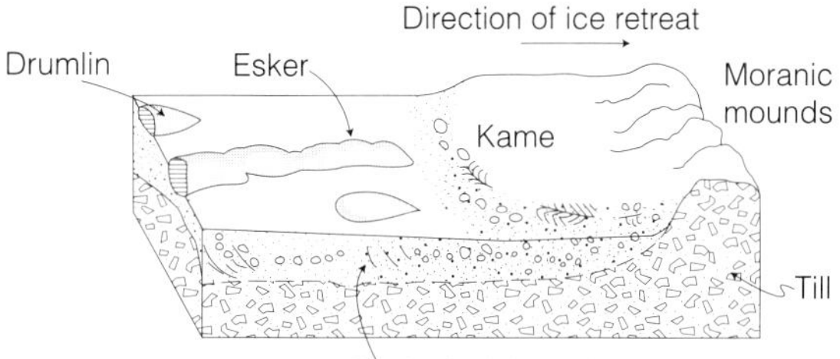

Fig. 2.19. Glacial features: drumlins, kame and esker left by glaciers. Sands and gravels worked by streams (fluvioglacial deposits) overly till dumped by a retreating glacier.

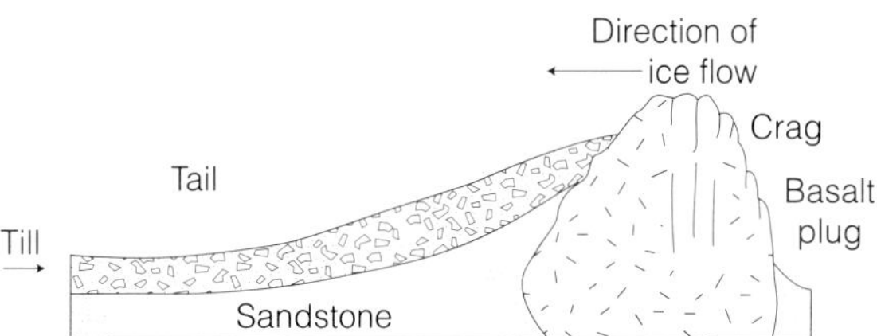

Fig. 2.20. Crag and tail structure.

Extensive parts of the World are covered by materials deposited by wind (aeolian) and others by rivers (alluvial) in the form of river terraces, levees and alluvial fans, each of which has been recognized in older rock formations. However, all the deposits described in this section are superficial deposits which can be easily eroded. Thus, the topography of every country exhibits landforms resulting from erosional and depositional processes acting together which have moulded the landscape into what is seen today.

2.6. The main rock divisions

There are three major divisions of rocks: igneous, sedimentary and metamorphic.

2.6.1. Igneous rocks

2.6.1.1. Grain size, texture and classification

Igneous rocks can be classified in a number of ways. The simplest method is based upon grain size in crystallized igneous rock which depends on the time which the magma took to cool. Three divisions of igneous rocks result from this type of classification: extrusive, hypabyssal and plutonic.

Extrusive igneous rocks result from the rapid cooling of magma that has been extruded onto the surface of the Earth by means either of conduits in volcanoes or elongate fissures. The rock is extruded as lava flows which cool giving a maximum grain size of less than 1 mm, which is termed fine-grained. Various other textures occur in volcanic rocks and these described below.

Rock classification and description

Geologists basically classify rocks according to their origin and their grain size. The primary classification is into igneous, sedimentary and metamorphic rocks. Igneous rocks have crystallized on cooling from molten material in the Earth's crust, sedimentary rocks have been formed from the debris produced by erosion of pre-existing rocks and metamorphic rocks have been formed by the action of heat or pressure, or both, on igneous and sedimentary rocks. Many rocks are formed from an agglomeration of mineral grains, and the secondary classification is one of grain size: coarse, medium and fine. Most rocks can be put into a table in which these two components denote the columns and rows as shown in the example below. Each box contains only one rock, solely in order to illustrate the principle.

	Igneous rocks	*Sedimentary rocks*	*Metamorphic rocks*
Coarse grained	Granite	Conglomerate	Gneiss
Medium grained	Dolerite	Sandstone	Schist
Fine grained	Basalt	Shale	Slate

Further refinements of classification are given in the main text. Rock descriptions sometimes also contain a word denoting the geological age of the rock. Thus, Hercynian granite, Triassic sandstone and Cambrian slate, for example, indicate the age of these rocks as well as their type. Sedimentary rocks are also designated by geological formation names (always written with initial capitals), often based on a type locality, such as Hythe Beds and Durness Limestone. Natural building stones have names that are nearly always based on the quarry or location of the stone (see Appendix C) but sometimes also include a colour designator such as Corrennie Pink and Hillend Black.

Porphyritic texture is displayed by rocks which have been subjected to several stages of cooling in the passage from the magma at depth until the surface is reached. Initially, at depth and at high temperatures, certain minerals, which are stable at these high temperatures and thereby called high-temperature minerals, crystallize from the magma as it starts to cool (see Appendix A). Note that it does not matter whether the composition of the magma is basic or acid since high-temperature minerals will crystallize from both types. These crystals of high-temperature minerals appear and continue to grow and attain a reasonable size, especially if the magma remains at nearly the same temperature for some time. Zoning of some of these crystals may occur. In, for example, plagioclase feldspars, slightly different feldspar compositions crystallize as cooling proceeds. A rounded crystal comprising concentric shells of mineral of differing composition is described as orbicular.

Thus, the situation may arise where a magma contains high-temperature minerals suspended in a liquid melt. These minerals may be of more than one type, depending on the way in which the magma cooled, i.e., whether it cooled in a series of 'steps' in temperature with different minerals appearing at each 'step'. Eventually the magma, which by this time is a crystal-liquid mush, is extruded onto the surface and cools to a rock with large crystals (phenocrysts) dispersed in a fine-grained matrix. Some porphyritic granites can create very attractive building stone, such as Shap granite (Fig. 9.28), and orbicular granites from Scandinavia (§2.7.1 and Fig. 2.21).

Amygdaloidal and vesicular texture occurs because the magma contains dissolved volatile components such as gases and water, which cannot evolve at the great pressure created by deep burial. On reaching the surface, the magma tries to degas itself because of the drop in pressure and gas bubbles, called vesicles, form in the liquid magma. However, the outer surface of the lava has cooled and the bubbles cannot escape, so remain trapped within the magma. These zones of bubbles occur at the top *and* bottom of the lava flow because of the way the outer surface moves over the ground and, when the lava cools, the rock is said to be vesicular. If late-stage hydrothermal activity allows the fluxing of solutions through the cooling magma, then the salts in solution may be deposited within these vesicles as amygdales, literally almond-shaped inclusions. On cooling completely, the magma is said to be amygdaloidal. Fig. 2.22 shows amygdaloidal and vesicular texture in a lava flow. This texture weakens volcanic rocks considerably and vesicular or amygdaloidal rocks are rarely used as building stones.

Hypabyssal igneous rocks occur as small intrusive bodies such as dykes, thin sheets of rock of thickness less than 10 m, which cut the existing strata at high angles and sills which are thicker sheets of rock of less than

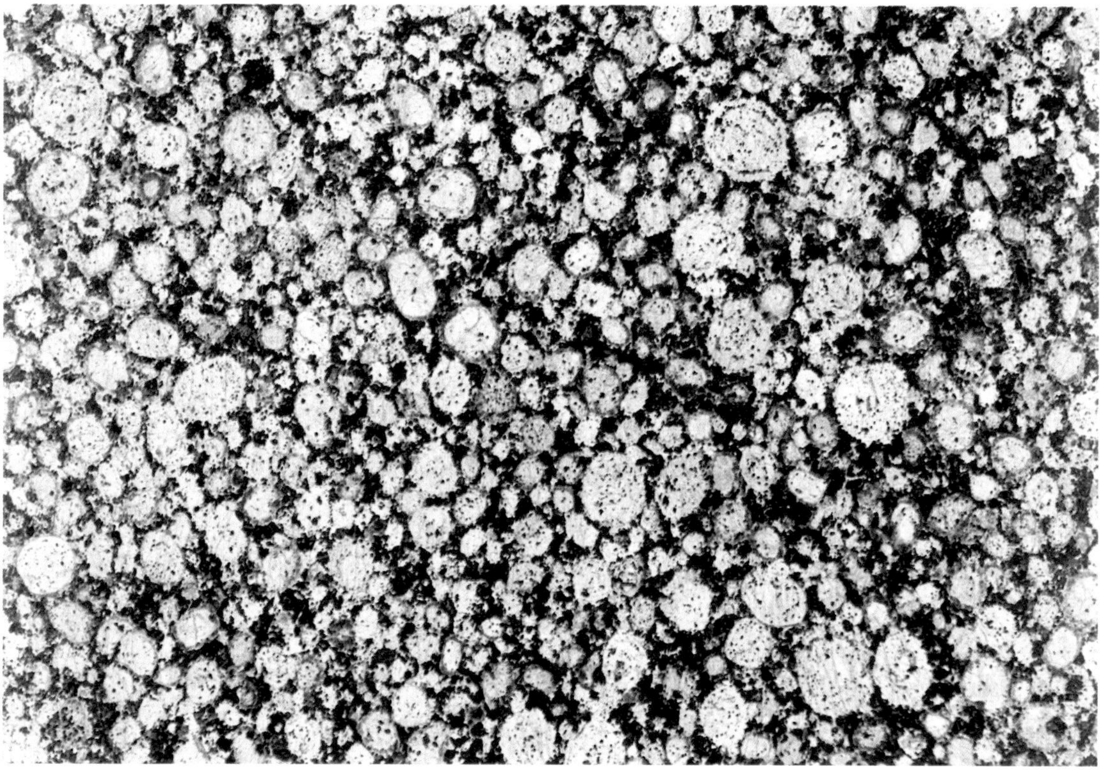

Fig. 2.21. Porphyritic (orbicular) texture of igneous rock.

Fig. 2.22. Amygdaloidal and vesicular texture of igneous rock.

50 m, which are concordant or sub-concordant to the bedding planes in the existing strata (Fig. 2.23). These rocks cool at a moderate rate at a high level in the crust, but not on the surface, and achieve grain sizes between 1 mm and 3 mm which are larger than those found in extrusive rocks. They are said to have medium grain size. Hypabyssal rocks may also be porphyritic and basic varieties invariably exhibit ophitic texture. In the basic magma, two minerals, plagioclase feldspar and a pyroxene (usually augite), crystallize together as the magma cools and the laths of feldspar are locked in place by large spongy crystals of pyroxene which crystallize around them. The resultant texture is termed ophitic and is characteristic of the rock type dolerite, or diabase as it is known in the USA. The mineral olivine may also appear in these rocks. Dolerite is not commonly used as building stone in the UK due to its black colour and the fact that it weathers to a dark brown colour due to oxidation of iron. Furthermore, it tends to occur in sills and dykes where the natural block shape is columnar, which makes it difficult to produce well-shaped blocks. However, doleries are used for kerbing and setts in Scotland and also for gravestones (see §2.7.2).

Plutonic igneous rocks are rocks which form from magma that takes a long time to cool. The magma is held deep within the crust and is well insulated by the overlying crustal strata. The result after cooling is a coarse-grained rock with crystal size greater than 3 mm. Granites are plutonic rocks which form in this way from the cooling of vast reservoirs of acid magma. Note that the 'black granites' of South Africa which are available as blockstones are not in fact granites but basic, igneous plutonic rocks. At late stages in the cooling history of such a magma, the magmatic liquid becomes rich in water and other volatiles. These lower the temperature of crystallization of the minerals forming at this stage and these watery fluids may be injected into cracks and fissures in the overlying strata. When they eventually crystallize in thin veins, called pegmatites, these veins contain exceptionally large crystals described as a pegmatite texture. The same fluids may also react with the crystallized mass of plutonic, igneous rock to cause hydrothermal alteration of some of the minerals, especially feldspars in granites and olivine in gabbros.

Both plutonic rocks and hypabyssal rocks can also develop a porphyritic texture, the only difference being that a porphyritic granite contains very large phenocrysts in a coarse-grained matrix.

It is worth mentioning that the grain sizes given are those commonly used in igneous rock textbooks, although the coarsest group boundary may be placed at 5 mm rather than 3 mm. An attempt to standardize all rock grain sizes by using the scheme for sediments and sedimentary rocks and adapting it for igneous (and metamorphic rocks) was given in table 9 of BS 5930: 1981, summarised here as Table 2.5. In this the extrusive/hypabyssal boundary is at 0.06 mm, equivalent to the siltstone/sandstone boundary, and the hypabyssal/plutonic boundary is at 2 mm, equivalent to the sandstone/conglomerate or sand/gravel boundary in sedimentary rocks and sediments. However, igneous petrologists have not been persuaded to use this scheme and have continued to use the one described in Table 2.6. Table 2.6, therefore, uses the scheme in common geological practice, as also does Table 2.14 (for metamorphic rocks). The grain sizes given in classification schemes in this Chapter were those given in *The Concise Oxford Dictionary of the Earth Sciences* (Allaby & Allaby 1990), a publication which post-dates BS 5930: 1981.

2.6.1.2. Composition and petrography

Igneous rocks can also be classified by their composition. If igneous rocks are analysed the amount of silica (SiO_2) present can be used to determine igneous rock

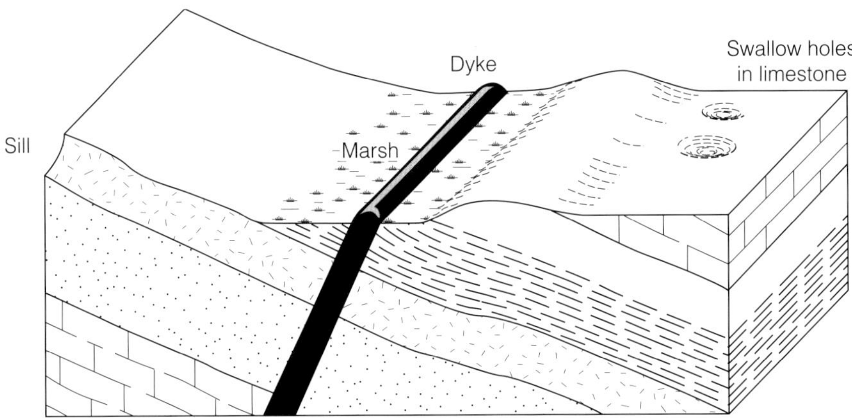

Fig. 2.23. Dyke, sill and swallow holes. Note marshy ground due to the impermeable shale underlying the surface.

Table 2.5. *Classification scheme for all rocks based on grain size and taken from tables 6 & 9 in BS 5930: 1981 (c = coarse; m = medium; and f = fine)*

<table>
<tr><th>Grain size</th><th>Sediments</th><th>Sedimentary rocks</th><th>Igneous rocks</th><th>Metamorphic rocks</th></tr>
<tr><td>>200 mm</td><td>Boulders</td><td rowspan="5">Rudaceous</td><td rowspan="5">Plutonic</td><td rowspan="5">High Grade</td></tr>
<tr><td>60–200</td><td>Cobbles</td></tr>
<tr><td>20–60</td><td>c</td></tr>
<tr><td>6–20</td><td>Gravels m</td></tr>
<tr><td>2–6</td><td>f</td></tr>
<tr><td>0.6–2</td><td>c</td><td rowspan="4">Arenaceous</td><td rowspan="3">Hypabyssal</td><td rowspan="3">Med Grade</td></tr>
<tr><td>0.2–0.6</td><td>Sands m</td></tr>
<tr><td>0.06–0.2</td><td>f</td></tr>
<tr><td>0.002–0.06</td><td>Silts</td><td rowspan="2">Extrusive
(glassy types)</td><td rowspan="2">Low Grade</td></tr>
<tr><td><0.002 mm</td><td>Clays</td><td>Argillaceous</td></tr>
</table>

categories. These categories are shown in Table 2.6, which classifies igneous rocks on their SiO_2 content and their petrography which includes their mineralogy, grain size and texture determined by the examination of hand specimens by eye and thin sections by microscope. The minerals found in the different categories can be seen in Fig. 2.24 which also gives the percentage of each mineral present. Table 2.6 lists the main rock types in the different categories for extrusive, hypabyssal and plutonic rock.

The igneous rock types given in Table 2.6 are of rocks rich in calcium (Ca) and alkalis (potassium (K) plus sodium (Na) oxides) and these are termed calc-alkaline igneous rocks. These are by far the most common igneous types occurring in the crust. However, other magma types exist, including alkaline magmas, so rich in alkalis that the alkali content exceeds that of calcium, which crystallize to give rocks rich in alkali feldspars such as the extrusive, alkali basalt, called trachyte, and its hypabyssal and plutonic equivalents, felsite and syenite, respectively. Magmas that are rich in alkalis and low in silica, described as undersaturated, crystallize to give rock types containing minerals known as feldspathoids such as nepheline and leucite. These may be basalt (extrusive) or phonolites (hypabyssal) or nepheline-syenites (plutonic). Other important rock types, which are difficult to place in the categories already discussed, include lava flows of any liquid composition extruded under water, lava flows under the sea and the lava extruded into the deep ocean at expanding plate margins, the abyssal tholeiites. The latter are found as masses resembling piles of pillows; the pillow lavas or spilites which are hydrothermally altered submarine tholeiitic basalts. Alkali basalts also occur, not on the sea floor, but on oceanic islands and guyots, small, flat-topped seamounts found at depths in excess of 1000 m below the ocean surface.

Table 2.6. *A classification scheme for the main igneous rock types based upon grain size and percentage of silica present*

	Main igneous rock groups		
	Extrusive	*Hypabyssal*	*Plutonic*
Grain Size	<1 mm	1–3 mm	>3 mm
	Main igneous rock types		
% SiO_2			
>65 Acidic	Dacites Rhyolites Obsidian	Quartz & Orthoclase Porphyries	Granites Granodiorites Aplites
55–65 Intermediate	Andesites Pitchstones	Feldspar & Hornblende Porphyries	Diorites Tonalites
45–55 Basic	Basalts	Dolerites Diabases	Gabbros Norites Troctolites
<45 Ultrabasic	Komatiites (ultrabasic lavas)	some rare ultrabasic types	Picrites Peridotites Dunites Serpentinites Pyroxenites

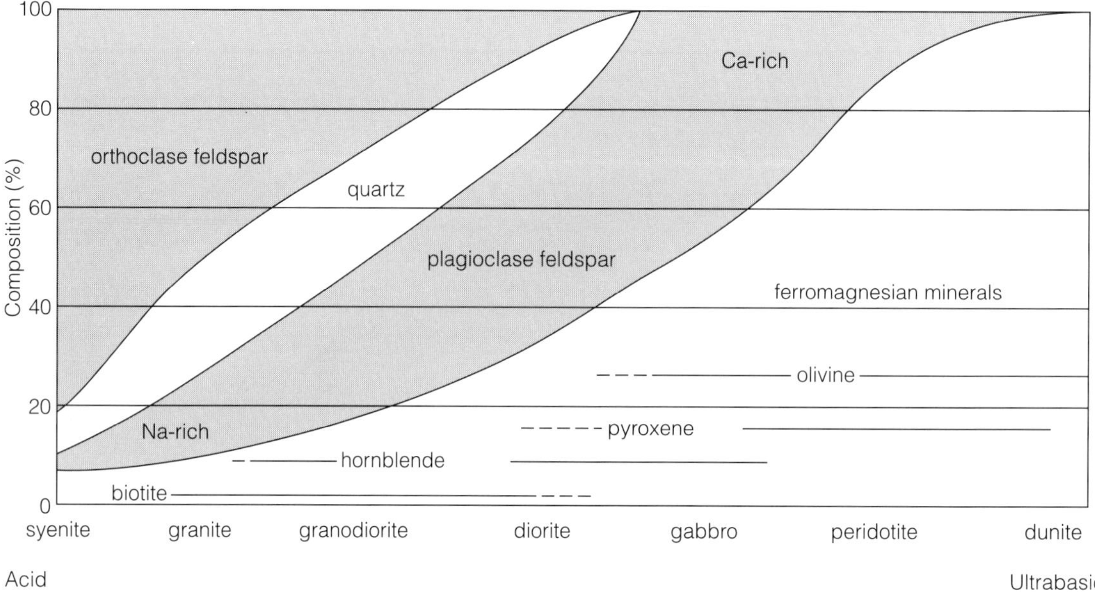

Fig. 2.24. Igneous rock classification based upon the proportions of each mineral present.

2.6.1.3. Fabric

As well as grain size and the other textural types described earlier, igneous rocks may also possess a fabric that may affect their engineering properties. Such a fabric may be a simple alignment of minerals forming a lineation in the rock such as might appear near the edges of a large granite intrusion where crystals align themselves parallel to the contact edge of the intrusion, or in a porphyritic lava flow where the high temperature, early-formed crystals often align themselves parallel to the upper surface of the lava. Banding may also occur, particularly in basic plutonic rocks where crystallization of minerals in the magma has been accompanied by mineral fractionation in the magma chamber. In this process the minerals appear from the magma in order of their temperature of crystallization. For example, olivine and basic plagioclase feldspars preceed augite and the minerals appear as bands of varying thicknesses in the basic rocks, such bands of mineral varying in composition as the magma cools. This particular feature is common in the major Tertiary basic igneous complexes such as those that occur in the Cuillins of Skye and Rum. This feature can also be seen in the huge basic igneous intrusions such as the Bushveld in South Africa, the Stillwater in the US and the basic igneous intrusions of northeast Scotland. The mineral banding may be accompanied by deposition of some important metallic minerals, such as ores of chromium and nickel and, in places, platinum and other precious metals.

In some lava flows, the minerals align themselves in an orientation parallel to the direction of flow of the magma, i.e. parallel to the top and bottom of the moving lava. This fabric is called flow-banding and is a common feature in trachyte lavas as well as many normal basalts and andesites. Some lavas are extruded onto the surface so quickly that they crystallize without any crystals forming glassy lava flows, where the liquid magma has solidified as rock glass known as obsidian. Some of these glassy lavas may exhibit flow banding with bands of differing colour representing slight variations in chemistry as is common in rhyolite lava flows (Fig. 2.25). In the past masons used the reed and hem of rocks such as granite to facilitate the working of these and other similar rocks. These terms referred to planes parallel to which the rock will easily split. The 'reed' was the direction of easiest cleavage and the 'hem' the direction of second easiest cleavage which was always at right angles to the reed. These were sometimes called first-way (reed) and second-way (hem) and the two directions were together referred to as the rift or grain of the rock. At right angles to both these directions the rock is difficult to split, producing an uneven surface, and this direction was referred to as the hard-way, tough-way or head. The reed and hem often coincided with jointing directions but this was not a general rule as a joint direction could coincide with the hard-way. These directions were also used in the Scottish Midland valley dolerites which were widely used throughout Scotland for kerbing.

The presence of reed and hem have been related to mineral orientation in the rock, microcracking at a microscopic scale or smaller, alignment of fluid cavities

Fig. 2.25. Flow banding in rhyolite lava.

in quartz crystals or to a superimposition of crustal stresses acting on the intrusion immediately after consolidation.

Microscopic fissuring, particularly in feldspars, may occur in many granites and other plutonic rocks and this was considered to be a factor in determining their suitability or otherwise as building stones.

2.6.1.4. Igneous rock forms

Extrusive rocks are poured onto the surface as lava flows where a large number of flows may constitute a feature (a pile of lavas) showing step features, see §2.5.3. Lavas usually possess several vertical joint sets which, together with occasional poorly defined horizontal or sub-horizontal joints, produce a natural block shape of elongate polygonal columns of rock, for example the Giant's Causeway (Fig. 2.26). Lavas may be emitted by a volcano which usually comprises a conical hill with a crater at the top representing the intersection of the magma conduit with the surface. At the end of a volcanic episode the conduit often fills with magma which congeals there. Since the volcano usually consists of both lava flows and pyroclastic material (ash, dust, lava bombs) which has been thrown out during eruptions it is usually not particularly resistant to erosion and the volcanic hill may vanish in a relatively short period of time leaving the congealed magma in the conduit, the volcanic plug, as the only manifestation of the extinct volcano. In Scotland and other countries these volcanic plugs are often glaciated with the glacier stripping away the material surrounding the plug as it passes by. This removed material is then dumped as a sort of tail on the other side of the plug to form a feature called a 'crag and tail' structure. Edinburgh Castle is built on such a feature (Fig. 2.20).

Hypabyssal rocks occur as dykes and sills described earlier in this section (Fig. 2.23) and variations in these forms may appear, such as cone sheets (thin, conically shaped dykes intruded into conical fractures above the magma reservoir), and ring dykes (thick vertical cylindrical sheets of magma again occurring above a magma reservoir and caused by subsidence of overlying blocks of country rock into the reservoir). These forms are rare but are frequently found in centres of igneous activity of Tertiary age in the Inner Hebrides (Fig. 2.27).

Plutonic rocks may show a number of forms, some small and some very large. Small bodies include laccoliths which are small, mushroom-shaped intrusions

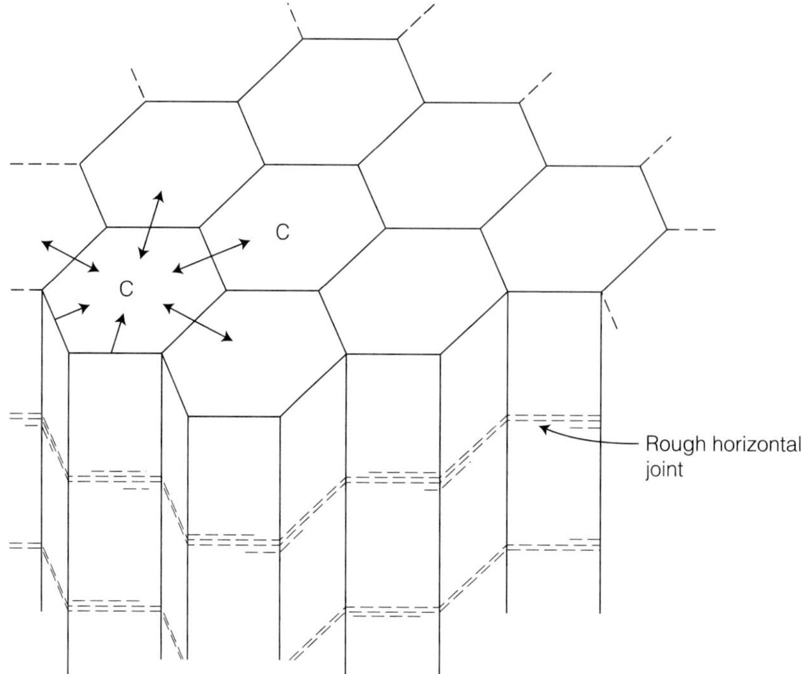

Fig. 2.26. Upper surface of sill (plug or rare lava flow) with cooling centres (c) where the temperature is lower than elsewhere on the surface. Solidification started at these centres and further cooling and contraction have produced a polygonal system of cooling (tensional) joints lying midway between adjacent centres. These joints also grow downwards into the magma as it cools producing a three-dimensional columnar structure, see Giants Causeway and Fingal's Cave.

about 1 km in diameter such as can be seen in the hills called laws in East Lothian, Scotland (Fig. 2.28). Bosses and stocks are small intrusive bodies associated with larger intrusions such as batholiths. Batholiths are huge bodies of acid magma which have crystallized deep within the Earth's crust, eventually to be exposed by prolonged erosion or tectonic forces as granite intrusions (Fig. 2.29). These are coarse-grained, very homogeneous rocks, often with signs of mineral alignment along the margins of the intrusion. The presence of two vertical widely spaced joint sets and a horizontal joint plane in granites produces very large natural blocks, relics of which may remain after weathering as tor structures on hills underlain by granite. For the reasons given above, batholiths are important sources of building stone.

Large, basic, plutonic intrusions usually occur as thick sheets of basic magma which have fractionated into a layered structure as the magma cools producing huge sequences of banded rocks, often with alternate bands of feldspar-rich and feldspar-poor material. These can be seen in northeast Scotland, the Bushveld in South Africa, and elsewhere (Fig. 2.30). The basic rocks, gabbros and anorthosites found in these sequences are coarse-grained and probably contain joints similar to granites, although some joints are parallel to the banding. Basic rocks weather more rapidly than acid rocks since many of their minerals (olivine, pyroxenes, amphiboles) are subject to hydrothermal alteration at a

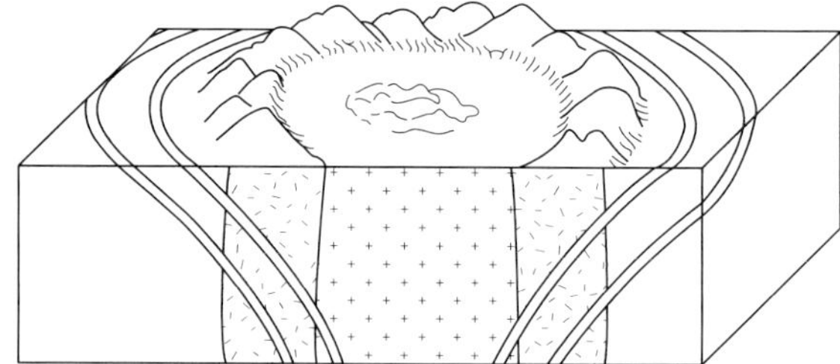

Fig. 2.27. Cone sheets and ring dykes. Cone sheets focus at depth in the magma chamber. The rise of magma into the upper crust produces cracking-the conical cracks are filled by cone sheets; vertical cracks which are ring shaped allow magma to rise up along them in thick vertical ring shaped sheets of magma. Cone sheets are usually thin-often <5 m thick, whereas ring dykes can be up to 1 km thick.

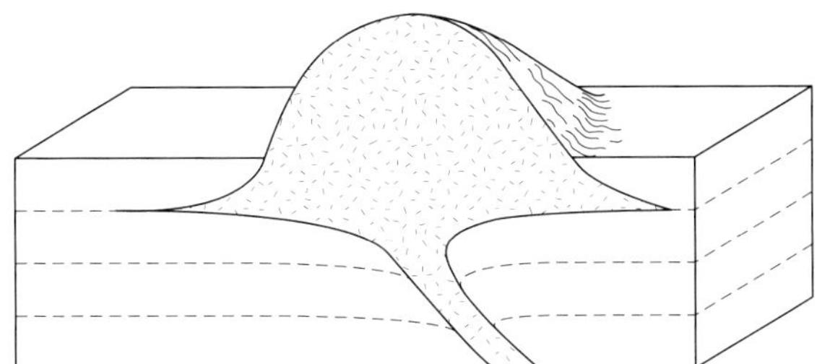

Fig. 2.28. Laccolith, a mushroom-shaped igneous intrusion, emplaced into horizontal strata.

late stage of the solidification of the magma and later chemical weathering. In northeast Scotland these basic intrusions form low, rolling hills, unlike the granite batholiths which form most of the higher Scottish Grampian Mountains.

2.6.1.5. Occurrence of igneous rocks

The continental crust, as opposed to the oceanic crust, consists of rocks formed at various times throughout the history of the earth. It consists of very old shield areas, containing igneous and metamorphic rocks; younger platform areas, containing sedimentary rocks and metamorphosed sedimentary rocks overlying the shield areas; and younger fold mountain belts, called mobile belts, of variable age.

Of the six groupings below, most building stone is obtained from calc-alkaline plutonic rocks (second group) which includes granites and related rock types. Some ornamental stone may be obtained from the first group where tuffaceous rocks are used, see §2.7.2, and some acid extrusive rock types, but their use is limited because of their dark colour and difficulty in obtaining large natural blocks. Very little stone is obtained from the other groups although some material may be used if it is available locally. Witness to this is the use of kentallenite, which belongs to the last group, in Scotland because the village of Kentallen is built on this small intrusion and gives its name to the rock.

The main associations of igneous rocks are briefly described below.

Calc-alkaline volcanic rocks include arc volcanoes with extrusive rocks such as basalt, andesite, dacite and rhyolite occurring and also pyroclastic deposits, material ejected during volcanic eruptions, and flow deposits of pyroclastic material called ignimbrites.

Calc-alkaline plutonic rocks are mainly found in continental settings with granitic and granodioritic batholiths, and minor diorites and gabbros. The most common occurrence is along continental margins above subduction zones, see §2.5.1.

Continental, tholeiitic, basaltic rocks and ultramafic rocks. A tholeiite is a basalt exhibiting a particular texture. In continental regions plateau basalts or flood basalts (basalt to rhyolite in composition) occur, with gabbros and ultrabasic (ultramafic) rocks – anorthosites, dunites etc. – being produced in much the same tectonic settings. The layered, differentiated intrusions of different sizes, ranging from huge sheets to small sills, are included in this group.

Oceanic, tholeiitic, basaltic to ultramafic rocks. Tholeiitic basaltic magmas occur both in oceanic and continental settings as island arc basalts, abyssal tholeiites

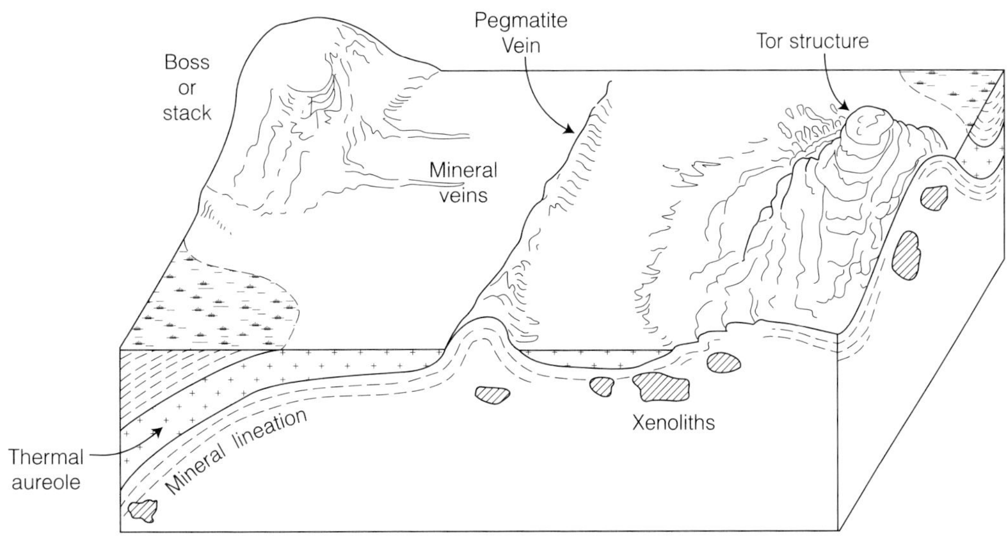

Fig. 2.29. Granite batholith consisting of acid magma, with surface and contact features.

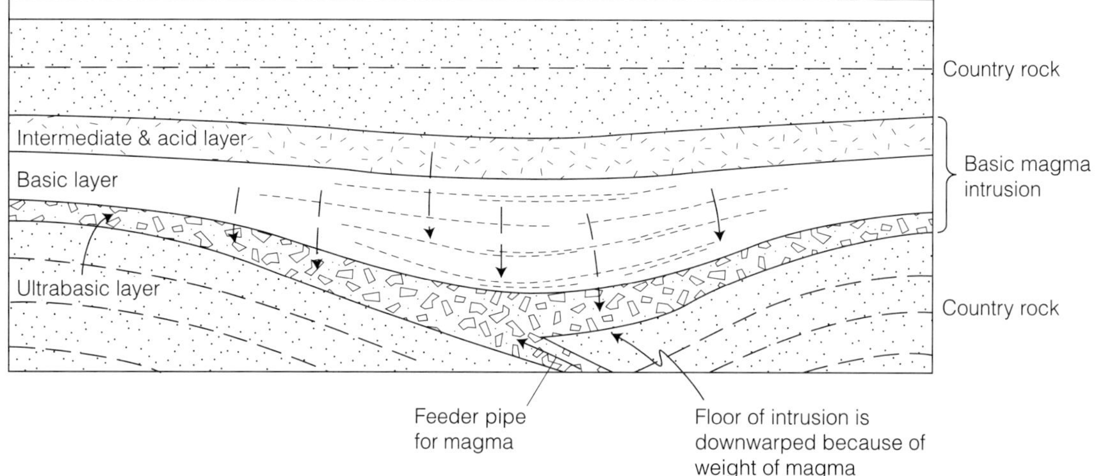

Fig. 2.30. A large basic igneous intrusion or lopolith. In this the high temperature minerals crystallize first from the magma and, because they are denser than the liquid magma, sink to the bottom. Layers build up with an ultrabasic layer at the base and then a thick basic layer above (which may contain internal mineral banding) and finally more acidic (late stage) material at the top. Lopoliths can be very large-the Bushveldt in South Africa is 5 km thick and hundreds of kilometres across.

and flood basalts. There are two types of associations connected with this group:

(1) intraplate volcanoes that are distant from plate boundaries and may appear as islands;
(2) volcanic rocks at mid-ocean ridges and in marginal or back-arc basins behind island arcs.

Rocks which occur include subalkaline tholeiites (basic rocks containing only just sufficient silica to satisfy the alkalis) and tholeiitic basalts. Oceanic lithosphere assemblages, called ophiolites, are found in an oceanic setting, either a mid-ocean rift or a dilating back-arc basin. An idealized section through a typical ophiolite sequence is shown in Table 2.7.

Oceanic alkaline rocks are associated with magmatic activity within the plate, well away from plate boundaries. Rocks exposed on volcanic islands may range from tholeiitic to highly alkaline and from ultrabasic to felsic. Typical rocks include alkali olivine basalts, feldspathoid-bearing basalts and subordinate trachyte and phonolites.

Continental alkaline rocks are found associated with areas of continental rifting. As well as alkaline lava flows, the magmatism occasionally produces rocks such as carbonatite. This is the only igneous rock composed largely of carbonates of calcium, magnesium and sodium with subordinate feldspar, pyroxene and olivine. It is associated with fenite, a metasomatic rock produced by sodium metasomatism of the contact rocks into which the carbonatite was intruded, and nephelinite, a sodium-rich, undersaturated basic rock found, for example, in the volcanic cone into which the carbonatite was intruded. Rocks rich in potassium such as kimberlites occur as small, carrot -shaped intrusions, called diatremes, in the ancient crust and contain diamonds. They derive from well below the Earth's crust in the upper Mantle.

2.6.2. Sedimentary rocks

2.6.2.1. Origin, composition and classification

The main modes of origin of sedimentary rocks are shown in Table 2.8. The classification of sedimentary rocks employs reference to both the mode of origin and the composition as shown in Table 2.9. Only the main mode of origin is given in Table 2.9 because, in many cases, several mechanisms may be involved during the formation of the sediment. This is particularly true for the carbonate rocks. Of the groups of sedimentary rocks

Table 2.7. *Idealized section through an ophiolite*

Ophiolite Unit	*Thickness*
Sediment	variable, thin
Pillow lavas	0.3–5.0 km
Sheeted dolerite dykes	0.1–4.0 km
Gabbroic rocks	0.5–2.3 km
Ultramafic rocks	0.5–2.0 km
Metamorphosed, ultramafic rocks	variable thickness

Table 2.8. *Main modes of origin of sedimentary rocks*

Term	*Typical modes of origin*
Detrital	Deposition by wind (aeolian) or rivers (fluviatile), lakes (lacustrine) or sea (marine) of debris derived by erosion of existing rocks
Chemical and Biochemical	Precipitation from solution (e.g. evaporites from salt lakes)
Biological	Remains of plants or animals (fossils) or biological secretions
Volcaniclastic	Volcanic ash or dust, deposits from gaseous emanations or volcanic mudflows

listed, the first group, the terrigenous siliciclastic sediments, accounts for approximately 75% of the total volume of sediments in the earth's crust, with the carbonate rocks making up a substantial proportion of the rest (Ronov 1983). This section will concentrate on those rock groups which are of proven utility for construction purposes. Space is available only for reference to the more salient aspects: for a fuller treatment the reader should refer to major texts such as those by Boggs (1992), Greensmith (1989), Pettijohn (1975), Pettijohn *et al.* (1987) and Tucker (1991).

2.6.2.2. Diagenesis

Before considering each group in turn, it is necessary to recognize the stages of evolution through which a sediment progresses from being a recent deposit to an indurated sedimentary rock (Fig. 2.31). There is a primary stage of formation or deposition and a secondary stage of diagenesis which involves compaction, changes to the fabric and alteration of minerals, solution or recrystallization under pressure of minerals at inter-particle contacts and the possible introduction of cements. In general the deeper the burial, the greater the temperature and the more reactive the percolating fluids, the more extensive the diagenetic changes. At great depths these will grade into mild metamorphism and eventually the production of a metamorphic rock. With subsequent uplift and erosion, diagenetically altered sediments will be subject to different physical and chemical conditions which lead to further mineralogical and textural changes: a stage which can be referred to as epi-diagenesis. This stage grades into and includes weathering but the latter term is best thought of as a separate stage experienced when the rock is in a near surface environment as discussed in §2.4.

The diagenetic processes are of the utmost importance since their actions will have produced the induration which turns loose sediment into rock. It is reasonable to state, therefore, that these processes will have as much significance for the characteristics and subsequent utility of sedimentary rock as its original mode of origin or initial particulate state. For a full treatment of diagenesis reference should be made to the texts written by Chilingarian & Wolf (1988), Larsen & Chilingarian (1979, 1983) and Parker & Sellwood (1983).

2.6.2.3. Terrigenous, siliciclastic sediments

These rocks are classified according to their component grain sizes but unfortunately there are several different grain size schemes in general use (see Table 2.10 for definition). The most relevant scheme is that universally used by soil and rock engineers and known, after its originating institution, as the M.I.T. (Massachusets Institute of Technology) scale and adopted by the I.S.S.M.F.E. (International Society for Soil Mechanics & Foundation Engineering) and British Standard 5930, and shown in Table 2.10.

The range of grain sizes within a sediment is most conveniently shown as a grain size distribution chart, see

Table 2.9. *Main sedimentary rock groups. Note that the adjective 'terrigenous' (i.e. derived from erosion of the land surface) used for the first rock group is required to distinguish these from the volcaniclastic rock group which also consist mainly of silicates in 'clastic' (i.e. particulate) form*

Main mode of origin	*Dominant chemical constituent(s)*	*Rock group name*	*Examples*
Detrital	Silica + Silicates	Terrigenous Siliciclastic rocks	Conglomerate, sandstone, mudstone, shale
Chemical & biochemical	Carbonates	Carbonate rocks	Limestones, chalk
	Chlorides & sulphates	Evaporites	Rock salt, gypsum
	Various forms of silica	Siliceous rocks	Chert, flint
	Ferruginous minerals	Ironstones and iron-rich rocks	Sedimentary ironstones
	Phosphates	Phosphorites	Phosphorites
Biological	Carbon & organic residues	Carbonaceous rocks	Coal, sapropelites
Deposits from volcanic sources	Silicates	Volcaniclastic rocks	Agglomerates, tuffites, ignimbrites

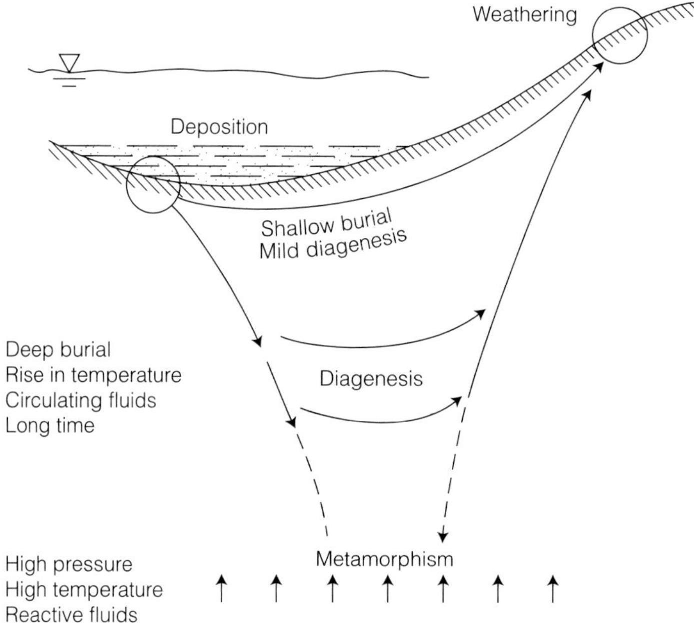

Fig. 2.31. Diagram of the stages of evolution of sedimentary rocks.

Fig. 2.32. The spread of grain sizes is known as the sorting: a geologically *well sorted* rock tends to a single grain size and conversely a geologically *poorly sorted* rock has a wide spread of grain sizes. From an engineering viewpoint, a wide spread of sizes confers mechanical stability and is thought of as being well graded This is an example of the often confusing differences in terminology between geologists and engineers.

Where the spread of grain sizes crosses class boundaries, the convention is to place the dominant constituent as the noun and the minor constituent as an adjective as in, say, a silty sand where sand is the dominant constituent. There are, of course, cases where the dominant constituent may be determinable from laboratory measurements only and may even vary within a single rock exposure: in such cases the descriptive names should indicate the uncertainty rather than try to be too precise.

The detrital grains will be derived from the breakdown of pre-existing rocks. Where these are sedimentary, the grains are in the process of being recycled and an individual grain may be recycled many times in the course of geological history. The minerals of the detrital grains will tend to be those which are sufficiently stable chemically to survive weathering, erosion, transport and deposition. Pre-eminent amongst these will be quartz, the dominant constituent of most arenaceous rocks, and certain kinds of clay minerals, the dominant constituents of mudrocks. However, it should be noted that when

Table 2.10. *Grain size classification according to the M.I.T. or I.S.S.M.F.E. scheme*

Grain diam (mm)	*Category*	*Term*	*Indurated equivalent*	*Adjectival term*
>2.0	—	Gravel	Conglomerate	Rudaceous
0.60–2.00	Coarse			
0.20–0.60	Medium	Sand	Sandstone	
0.06–0.20	Fine			
				Arenaceous
0.020–0.060	Coarse			
0.006–0.020	Medium	Silt	Siltstone	
0.002–0.006	Fine			
<0.002	—	Clay	Mud-Rock	Argillaceous

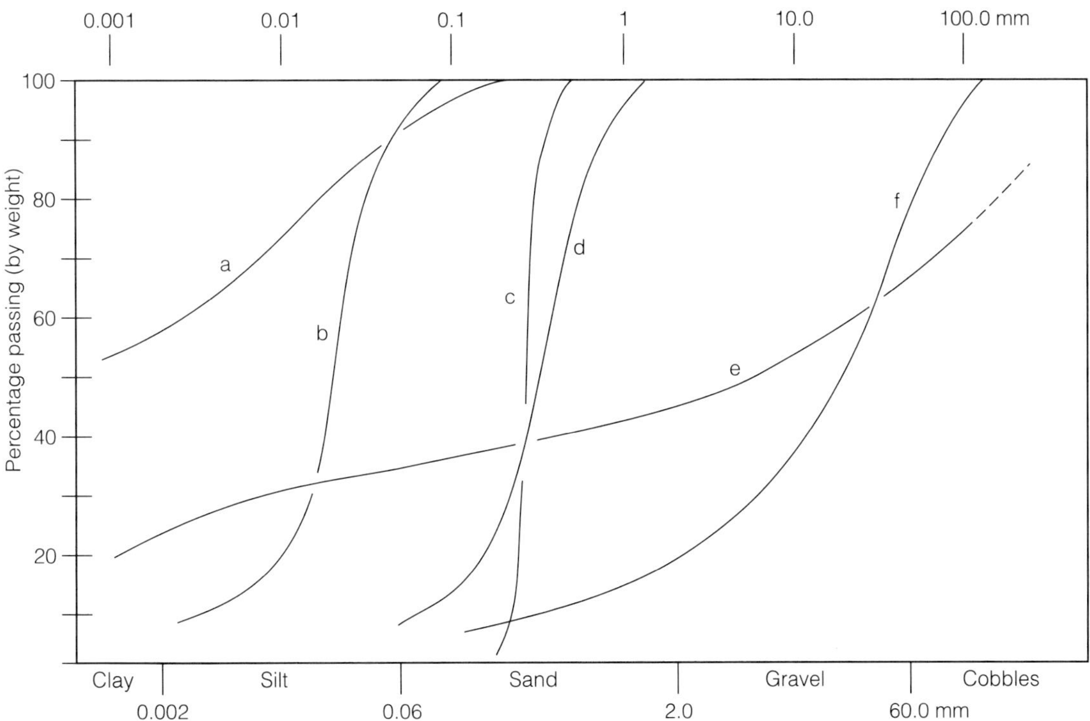

Fig. 2.32. Particle size distribution curves for sedimentary materials. (a) clay (b) loess (c) dune sand (d) estuarine sand (e) till or boulder clay (f) alluvial fan. In geological terms b, c and d are well sorted but a e and f are poorly sorted.

finely ground, quartz crystals can become clay-sized and that very tightly bound aggregates of clay crystals will be recorded as silt or even as sand size particles. Less resistant, but still fairly common in sediments, are felspars and micas but the common rock forming minerals of igneous rocks such as pyroxenes, hornblende and olivine rarely survive the processes of sedimentation unless erosion and deposition take place very rapidly. Where such minerals are present, alteration has often taken place in-situ within the sedimentary rock, a fate which can occur to the felspars and micas, leading to weakening of the fabric or microstructure of the rock.

Some of the accessory minerals, that is those present in small amounts, in igneous, metamorphic and older sedimentary rocks can be very stable in a sedimentary environment and, hence, are preserved as minor constituents, often known as the heavy minerals in comparison to the lighter quartz. Common amongst these are zircon, tourmaline, rutile, apatite, epidote, staurolite and garnet. As well as single crystals, the detrital grains can include rock fragments (lithoclasts) or material of biological origin (bioclasts).

Siltstones, sandstones and conglomerates. These are the coarser or 'granular' end of the grain size spectrum shown in Table 2.10 and originate as deposits of individual grains. Measures of the tightness of packing of granular materials can be made with reference to either the porosity or dry density. See Appendix C for definitions. The terms 'loose', 'medium' or 'dense' are applied according to the degree of compaction achieved in the laboratory. The initial porosity of water-laid sands is generally in the range of loose to medium. Packing can be tighter for wind-blown sands where impacting occurs on the surface of deposition. An accumulating thickness of overlying sediment will cause compaction with the porosity decreasing to below the lowest value achievable in the laboratory owing to the effects of creep at the interparticle contacts. For a poorly sorted detrital rock, tighter packings can be produced if the fines are able to fit into the macro-pores created by the skeleton of the coarser particles. There is, however, a limit to the porosity reduction achievable by the overburden pressure alone.

Significant reductions in porosity will occur if pressure solution takes place at grain contacts. Under high contact pressures, preferential solution of the grain material will occur in the vicinity of the contacts. This material may then either be precipitated further out in the pore space, where it forms a crystalline overgrowth, or else removed from the sedimentary (grain-pore) system in solution. The processes of compaction and pressure solution result in a gradual transformation of grain contacts (Fig. 2.33). Initially a high percentage of these will be tangential contacts but with time these will tend to decrease with a concomitant increase in straight and concavo-convex contacts. Pressure solution will eventually produce sutured contacts though substantial numbers of these only occur during metamorphism.

The reduction in porosity and change in grain contacts increase grain interlocking. This feature is a significant contributor to the strength of a rock: a well interlocked grain fabric without any other source of cohesion can produce quite a strong rock. Further increases in strength are produced by the introduction of cements during diagenesis. The principal cementing agents are shown in Table 2.11.

Clay mineral intergrowths are common in granular materials even with a low grade of diagenesis and tend to produce a weak bonding action. Silica introduced into predominantly quartzose sediments will tend to form quartz overgrowths and contribute to interlocking rather than a true binding cement. However, when most of the pore space is filled in this way, an extremely strong rock can be produced. Thus, the well known Permian age Penrith Sandstone, where the quartz overgrowths produce a very attractive texture viewed microscopically, although hard, is said not to be very durable (Clifton-Taylor 1972). This can be contrasted with the extremely

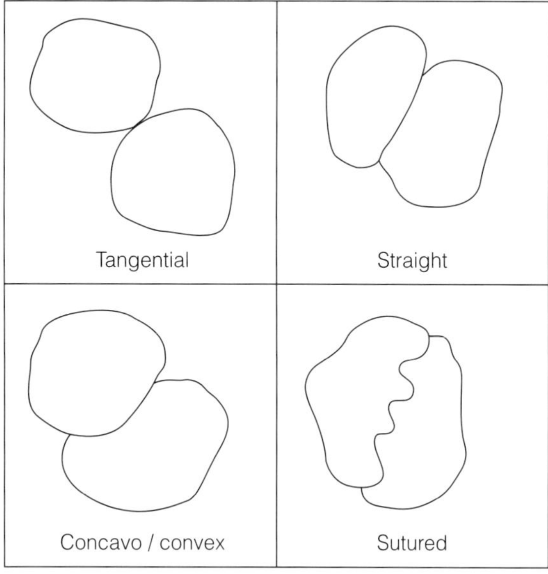

Fig. 2.33. Types of interparticulate contact.

Table 2.11. *Cementing agents common in siliciclastic rocks*

Cementing agent	*Descriptive term*
Clay Minerals	Argillaceous
Silica, SiO_2	Siliceous
Calcite, $CaCO_3$	Calcareous
Dolomite, $CaMg(CO_3)_2$	Dolomitic
Iron oxide, Fe_2O_3, FeO.OH	Ferruginous

strong, siliceous sandstones of the Stiperstones Quartzite (Ordovician age) that are used as a building stone in Shropshire (Scard 1990). Calcareous and ferruginous cements are very common and act as true binding agents. Other kinds of cements occur in addition to the common types listed in Table 2.11; for instance barite ($BaSO_4$) occurs in a British Triassic red sandstone in Nottinghamshire and contributes significantly to the strength of the rock. Ferruginous cements are associated with strong colours and colour changes in sandstones. The Old Red and New Red Sandstones, for instance, owe their bright red colour to the ferric oxide, hematite. The well known formations of Greensand are so called because of the presence of ferrous minerals in their unweathered state, the green mineral glauconite being particularly common. In the weathered zones these minerals are transformed to ferric minerals, amongst which the deep brown limonite is prominent. While old exposures of Greensand are almost invariably brownish, the rate of oxidation is variable and some building sandstones from the Lower Greensand have preserved their greenish tinge.

Impure sandstones and arkoses. The mudrocks (see Table 2.10) need not concern us, although volumetrically they are far more abundant than the coarser siliclastic rocks, since they are generally unsuitable for use as building stone. However, we do need to notice that many rocks can contain both coarse grain and clay size particles and that some classification is needed for these transitional materials. Figure 2.34 provides such a classification scheme for the sandstone/mudstone transition (McLean & Gribble 1985). The mixed rocks known as greywacke occur commonly in the older Palaeozoic rocks of the UK and some have been used as building stones in the north of England and the southwest. The Pennant Sandstone of Carboniferous age in southwest England and in South Wales is a greywacke which is used as a building stone, 'Pennant Blue', and as high-quality aggregates by the construction industry in the special application of conferring skid-resistance to a road surface.

Figure 2.34 also incorporates a classification of sandstones based on the mineralogy. While most of the younger and well used sandstones of the UK are dominantly quartz rich, that is, either quartz-arenites or near to this in the terminology of Fig. 2.34, some of the older sandstones may be relatively rich in felspar,

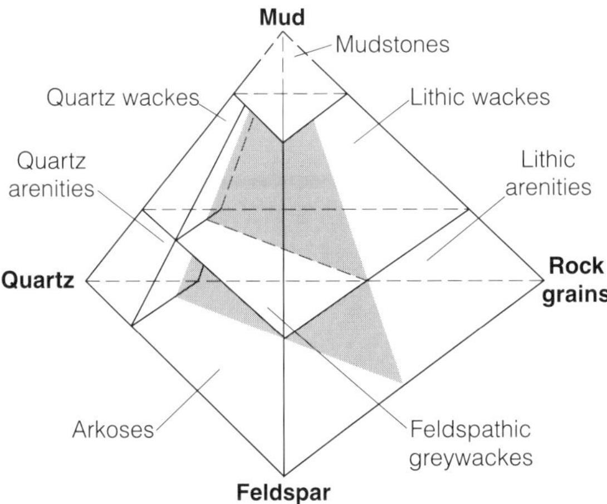

Fig. 2.34. Classification of arenaceous sedimentary rocks based on their composition. (taken from McLean & Gribble 1985)

that is, arkoses. The Torridonian sandstone of Precambrian age, occurring in northwest Scotland, is an example of an arkose which has been used for building and walling.

2.6.2.4. Carbonate rocks

Within the stone industry, all the carbonate rocks may be simply described as limestones. In fact, these rocks consist predominantly of the three minerals: calcite (calcium carbonate $\{CaCO_3\}$ crystallized in the rhombohedral form); aragonite (calcium carbonate crystallized in the orthorhombic form) and dolomite $\{CaMg(CO_3)_2\}$. The latter name is used by geologists for both the mineral and the rock consisting largely of this mineral which is a mixed carbonate of magnesium and calcium. The term 'limestone' is reserved by geologists to describe a rock mainly comprising calcium carbonate.

Thus, the group includes all the rocks which may have been deposited as calcareous muds but became indurated to form the rocks called limestones and dolomites. Thereby, the group also includes chalk, which may range from a poorly indurated, weak rock to being a well-indurated rock as, for instance, the Totternhoe Stone of the Lower Chalk or the Melbourn Rock of the Middle Chalk both of which exhibit a strength exceeding that of a good many limestones.

Limestones are typically the product of deposition of calcium carbonate, in a tropical or sub-tropical climate, as reefs or in lagoons and warm, shallow seas. An additional, important, condition of their formation is that at

Fig. 2.35. Photomicrograph of bioclast wackestone, Carboniferous, Anglesey.

the time the erosion of the land mass is not contributing a significant quantity of siliceous detritus and clays to the sediments. Their chemistry and fossil contents provide a rich source of information for geological studies (Bathurst 1975; Moore 1989; Scoffin 1987). Dolomites were often formed by later alteration of the limestone when magnesium replaced some of the calcium.

Informal classifications. Limestones which are employed as building stones are often described either by their geological age, such as Carboniferous limestone or Cretaceous limestone, or by their fossil or particle content, such as coral limestone, shelly limestone (Fig. 2.35) and oolitic limestone. In some countries producing limestones the rocks may be described by their colour and origin. Thus, Belgian Black is a black, impure limestone with very few fossils and Brescia Brown is a limestone from the Brescia region of southern Italy which has a brown cement and few fossils although both can be ascribed to a particular period of geological time.

From the point of view of their use as construction materials, limestones can be classified into three groups; crystalline limestones, oolitic limestones and chalk. Crystalline limestones are carbonate rocks consisting predominantly of fine-grained calcium and magnesium carbonate minerals and having a well defined crystalline texture, as shown in Fig. 2.36, which is a photomicrograph of Carboniferous limestone from Derbyshire, England. Crystalline limestones have a low porosity and relatively high density and are the strongest of the limestones. Usually they are of Palaeozoic age.

Oolitic limestones are carbonate rocks that are generally less strong and dense than crystalline limestones. The round grains that compose the rock are known as ooliths ('stone eggs'), giving the type of limestone its name. They are mainly sand-sized, spherical grains of calcium carbonate having a layered internal structure as seen in Fig. 2.37 which is a photomicrograph of a Jurassic limestone from France. It is thought that ooliths form by deposition of concentric layers of calcium carbonate and other minerals dissolved in water upon a nucleus and ooliths are often found to have a nucleus of a grain of quartz or shell fragment. The oolitic limestones can be highly porous unless the ooliths have been compressed or the pore space filled with later cement. The strength and durability of the rock are also greatly affected by the size of the pores and the quantity and type of cement, if any, bonding the particles together.

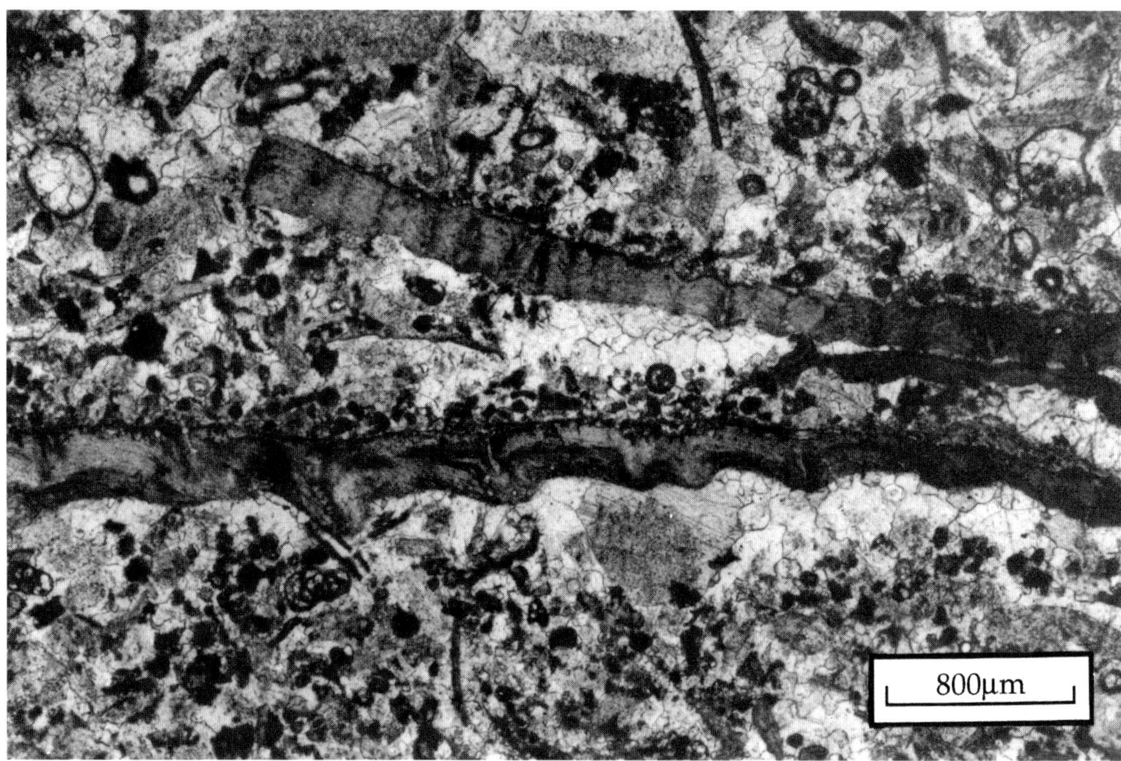

Fig. 2.36. Photomicrograph of grainstone, Carboniferous, Derbyshire.

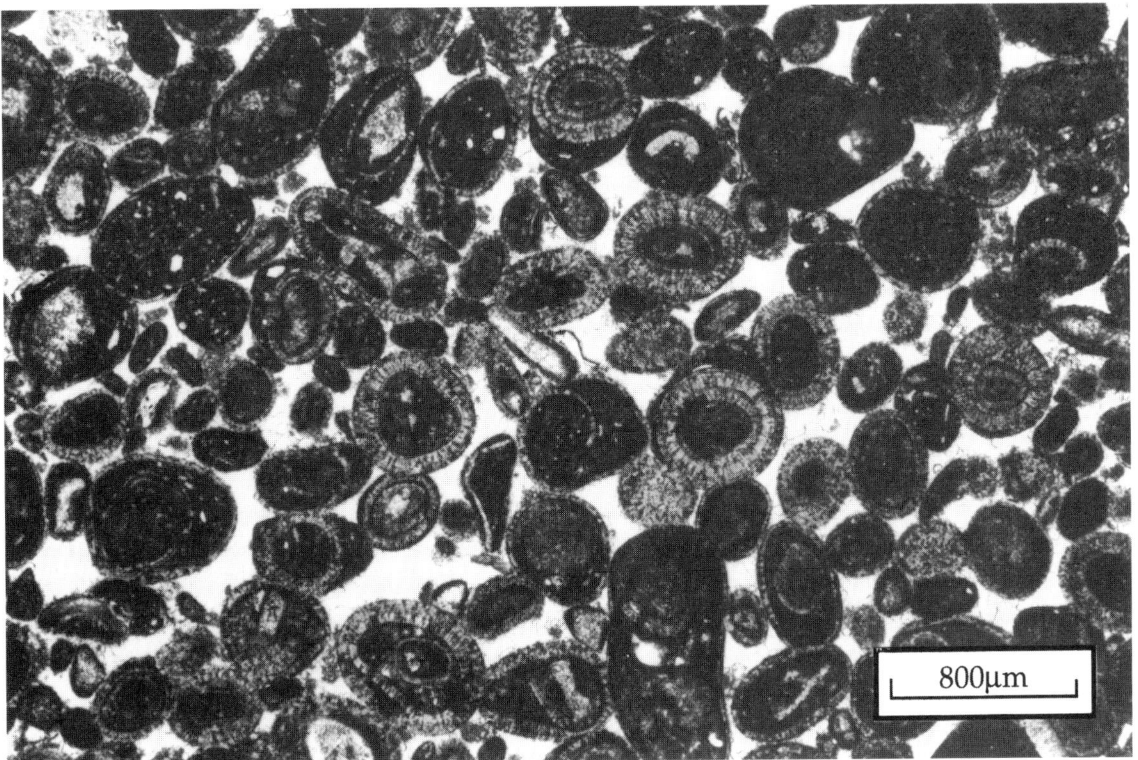

Fig. 2.37. Photomicrograph of oolitic limestone (grainstone), Jurassic, Burgundy.

Chalk is a very fine-grained carbonate rock composed of the silt-sized detrital remains of the exo-skeletons or shells of tiny marine organisms called coccoliths that lived in the sea when the chalk was forming. Chalk is very porous and has both a lower strength and density than the two limestones described above. Indeed, in southern England the Chalk is a major aquifer supplying water to cities such as London. The texture of chalk is well shown in Fig. 2.38, which is a scanning electron microscope (SEM) photomicrograph of the Cretaceous Chalk from England. Chalk is such a familiar rock in England, see Fig. 1.1, that the ability to distinquish it from cheese is the traditional test of sanity and the rock has given its name to the Cretaceous period.

Geological classification. Geologically, the carbonate rocks can have such highly complicated compositions and modes of development that they preclude single, simple systems of classification. Description and understanding of this important group of rocks requires a minimum of at least two systems of classification, the most widely used of which are the systems of Folk (1959) and Dunham (1962) both of which are in current use.

The basis of Folk's system is that the rock may be represented on a triangular chart whose three end members are grain, microcrystalline matrix (or micrite) and crystalline (or sparry) cement as shown in Fig. 2.39. The grains (or allochemical constituents) may consist of one or more of the categories listed in Table 2.12 and the resulting rock names are shown in the classification scheme given in Fig. 2.40. An additional term, 'biolithite', is used in the Folk scheme for limestones which grew *in situ* as reefs.

The classification scheme of Dunham considers the 'framework' within the rock: making a distinction between a mud-supported framework and a grain-supported framework, as opposed to the mud-matrix versus cement-matrix of Folk. Mud-supported frameworks are mudstones or wackestones while grain-supported frameworks are packstones or grainstones (see Table 2.13). The boundstone category is equivalent to the biolithite of Folk.

The Dunham scheme, like that of Folk, has disadvantages when finer details and boundary categories are examined but the scheme as a whole has merit in describing the physical character of limestones and

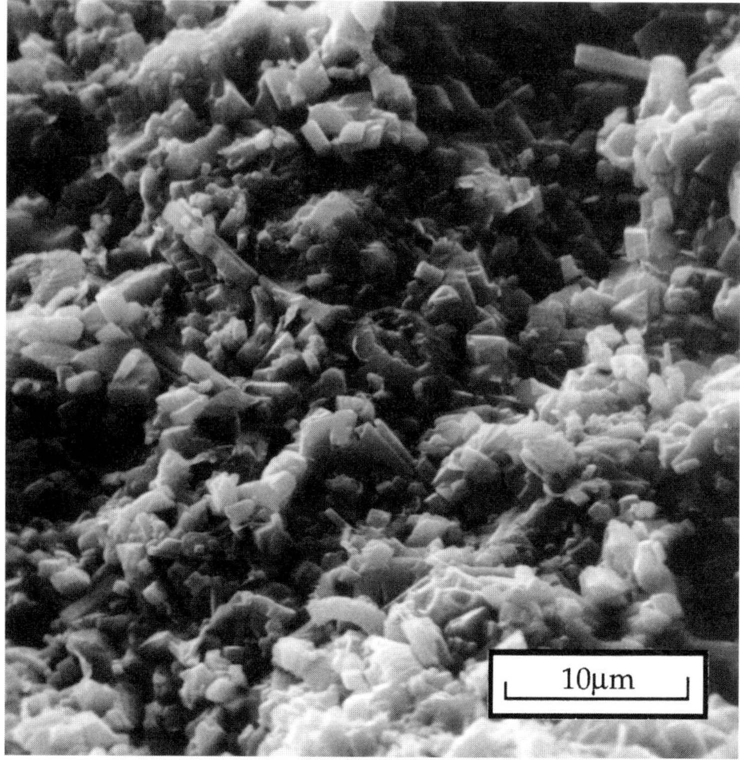

Fig. 2.38. Scanning electron microscope (SEM) image of surface of chalk showing coccolith fragments, Cretaceous, Yorkshire.

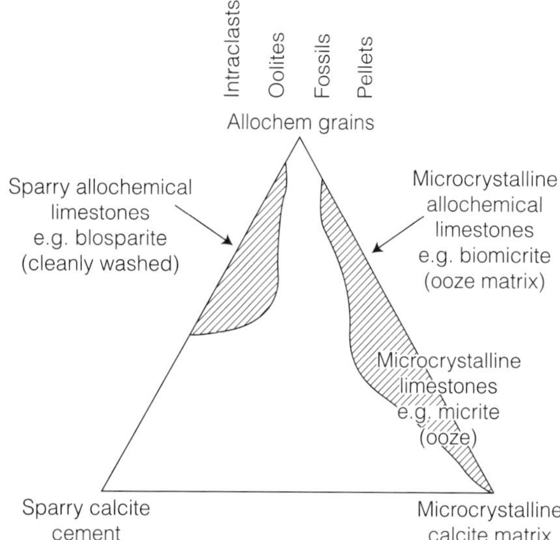

Fig. 2.39. The three end members forming the basis of the Folk (1962) classification scheme for limestones.

Table 2.12. *Categories of 'grains' (or allochemical constituents) found in limestones*

Component	*Prefix for use in Fig. 2.40*	*Mode of origin*
Fossils	bio-	Skeletal parts of carbonate secreting organisms
Peloids	pel-	Spherical or angular grains without internal structure, mostly of faecal origin
Ooids	oo-	Spherical, or sub-spherical grains with a concentric internal structure, probably of biochemical origin
Aggregates	clastic-	Aggregates of several carbonate and other particles cemented together
Intraclasts	intra-	Fragment of previously lithified, or partly lithified, sediment incorporated in the new sediment

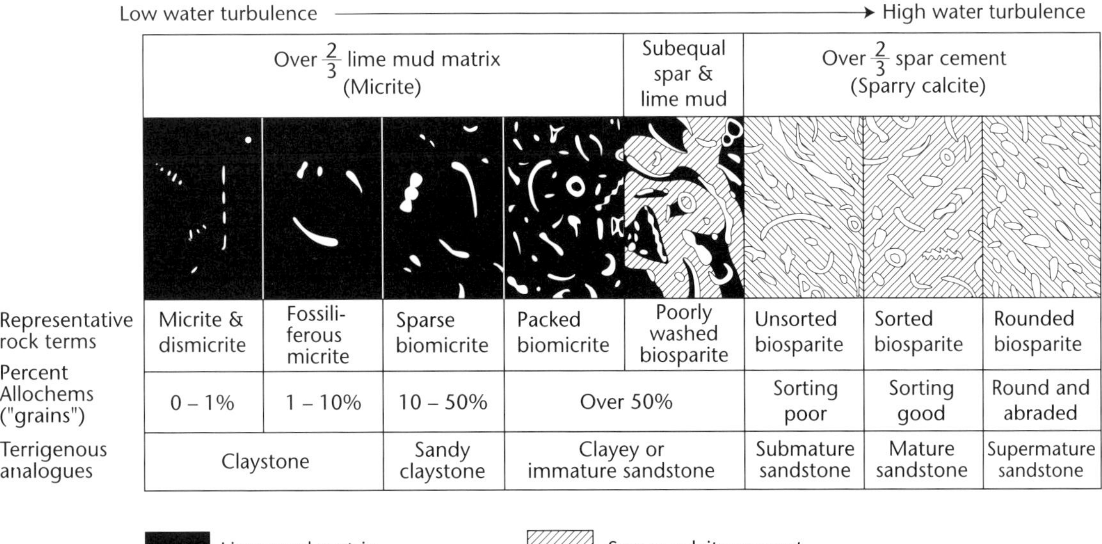

Fig. 2.40. Classification system for limestones devised by Folk (1959). The terms shown above are appropriate for fossiliferous limestones: other granular components (with appropriate prefixes) are listed in Table 2.12.

contributes to the understanding of their engineering properties and behaviour. Likewise the scheme of Folk has considerable merit in understanding the origin, composition and appearance of a limestone.

Dolomites can be formed directly but more frequently they are produced during the alteration of calcite to dolomite known as dolomitisation. In this alteration, which is an example of metasomatism, the calcium in calcite is partly replaced by magnesium contained in solutions permeating the rock but the reverse process can also occur. For this reason the partially dolomitised limestone of Permian age which outcrops in the UK along a line stretching from the Midlands northwards to the coast of Durham is known as the Magnesian

Table 2.13. *Dunham's classification of limestones*

<table>
<tr><td colspan="5">Depositional texture recognizable</td><td rowspan="2">Depositional texture not recognizable</td></tr>
<tr><td colspan="4">Original components not bound together during deposition</td><td rowspan="2">Original components were bound together during deposition. As shown by intergrown skeletal matter or lamination contrary to gravity</td></tr>
<tr><td colspan="3">Contains mud (particles of clay and fine silt size)</td><td rowspan="2">Lacks mud and is grain-supported</td><td rowspan="4"></td></tr>
<tr><td colspan="2">Mud-supported</td><td rowspan="2">Grain-supported</td></tr>
<tr><td>Less than 10% grains</td><td>More than 10% grains</td><td rowspan="2"></td><td rowspan="2"></td></tr>
<tr><td>Mudstone</td><td>Wackestone</td><td>Packstone</td><td>Grainstone</td><td>Boundstone</td><td>Crystalline carbonate</td></tr>
</table>

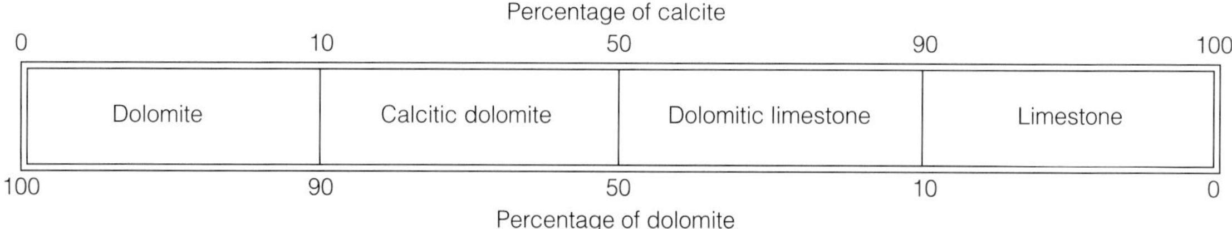

Fig. 2.41. Classification scheme for mixtures of dolomite and calcite.

limestone (Fig. 1.1). It is found that the ratio of dolomites to limestones increases with geological age: with a preponderance of dolomites in the Precambrian and an increasing preponderance of limestones from the Palaeozoic onwards. A simple system for the classification of mixtures of dolomite and limestone is shown in Fig. 2.41.

Impure carbonate rocks. A classification scheme is needed to allow for the transition from limestones to terrigenous siliciclastic rocks. A simple and convenient scheme for this is that of Fookes & Higginbottom (1975) shown in Fig. 2.42. This takes account of both the percentage of carbonate and the grain size categories of the siliciclastic rocks. Where clay grade grain sizes are involved, the scheme incorporates the use of the traditional term 'marlstone' commonly applied to calcareous mudstones.

2.6.2.5. Other sedimentary rocks

Ironstones. There are two main groups of sedimentary ironstones and iron-rich formations. The first of these are the Precambrian iron formations, frequently thinly banded, or laminated, with cherts, of uncertain origin. The second are Phanerozoic ironstones frequently of marine origin with an oolitic texture, the oolites being composed of an iron silicate, chamosite, set in a matrix rich in iron carbonate, siderite, and limonite. The oolites are often flattened and called 'spastoliths' testifying to their colloidal and, therefore, compressible, origin. The Jurassic ironstones of Northamptonshire, formerly worked as iron ores, have long been used as a local building stone (Hudson & Sutherland 1990) with their dark reddish-brown colouring providing an attractive feature of the landscape and contrasting with the paler colours of the local oolitic limestones.

Cherts and Flints. These belong to the group of siliceous, sedimentary rocks of Table 2.9. This group also comes in two main forms. The first of these is the bedded cherts, examples of which include the Precambrian banded formations, referred to amongst the ironstones, and ophiolites, where the cherts are interbanded with volcanic and volcaniclastic rock, common in orogenic regions. The bedded cherts may have a biogenic origin having been produced by silica-secreting organisms such as radiolaria and diatoms similar to the deep sea oozes being formed at the present time.

The second main form of siliceous rocks is the nodular cherts where the nodules commonly form in

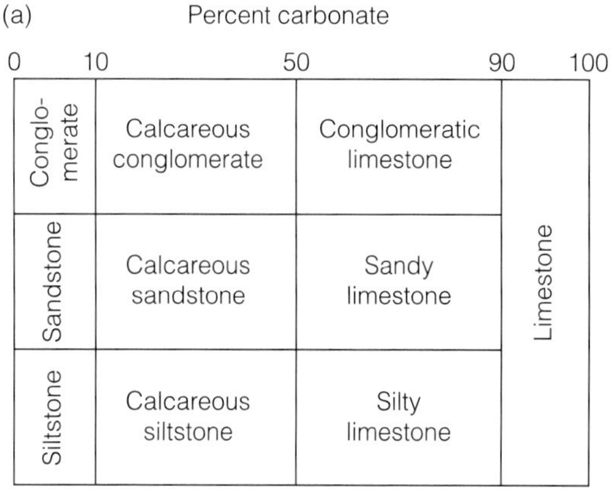

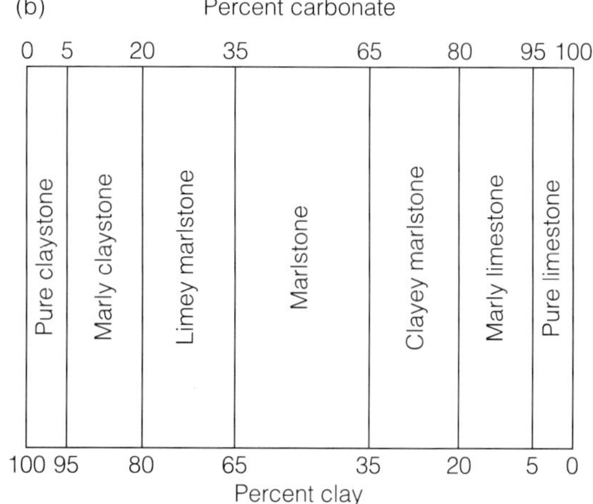

Fig. 2.42. Classification of impure carbonate rocks (from Fookes & Higginbottom, 1975).

carbonate host rocks. Occasionally the nodules may be so close as to link up and form complete layers of chert. Siliceous nodules in the Chalk are known as flints.

Flints provide an attractive source of building stones, particularly in areas short of other suitable supplies such as East Anglia. Shepherd (1972) provides an excellent account of flint and its use as a building stone. Flint is composed largely of microcrystalline quartz together with some chalcedony, an amorphous form of silica. The microcrystalline quartz contains a very small amount of adsorbed water and is usually dark grey or black in colour. The white outer layer of flint is known as the cortex and forms where the microcrystalline silica has been dehydrated. Flints may be used in their natural state, retaining the cortex, or they may have it removed as in dressed flint walling.

Duricrusts. Duricrusts are not commonly thought of as a separate group of sedimentary rocks since they form in the weathered surface zones of arid, or semi-arid, regions. Thus, they are commonly considered under the heading of weathering although it would be reasonable to consider them as a special class of evaporites. Duricrusts are formed by the precipitation of either calcite or silica from groundwater which evaporates as it is drawn towards the surface. Where the surface rocks are granular soils, such as sands or otherwise disaggregated weathered rocks, the calcite or silica can fill up the pore spaces and produce a hard, completely cemented rock: becoming either calcrete or silcrete respectively. In arid and semi-arid regions, where other hard rocks may be absent, the duricrusts can provide a useful source of stone for construction purposes.

The *sarsen stones* of Southern England are thought to have originated as silcretes (Summerfield & Goudie 1980). They represent the cementation of the surface zones of Tertiary age sand beds, possibly occurring in Miocene times. They were famously used by the Neolithic builders of henge monuments such as Stonehenge itself but have also been used during later, more urbanized times for buildings such as churches and domestic dwellings.

2.6.2.6. Occurence of sedimentary rocks

Sedimentary rocks are extremely widespread and can be found in all countries and every continent except the Arctic which is a mass of floating ice. Nevertheless, there are regions in which sedimentary rocks are unlikely to occur. Foremost amongst these are the Shield Areas of the continents.

The present continents are generally founded upon a stable plate of ancient rock of Precambrian age, sometimes called a basement, over which the more recent sediments have been deposited as explained in §2.5.1. The basement rocks themselves are generally mixtures of igneous rocks with highly metamorphosed sediments. In many areas of the World these basement rocks have been exposed by uplift and subsequent erosion to create 'Shield Areas' and no sediments will be found. This applies to well recognized areas of Sweden, Finland, Eastern Canada, India, China, Western Australia, Brazil, Western Arabia and much of Southern Africa plus many smaller areas (Blyth & de Freitas 1984*b*).

Furthermore, sediments are not likely to be found in an unaltered or unmetamorphosed state near centres of tectonic and igneous activity especially destructive plate boundaries or subduction zones and collision zones. Therefore, mountainous terrain such as that of the Alpes, Andes, Himalayas and Rockies is more likely to be composed of metamorphic and igneous rocks than sediments.

Although sediments are so widely distributed, the age of a sedimentary rock is important in determining its utility as a building stone or construction material. In contrast, the age of igneous and metamorphic rocks is of little direct consequence to their use as a construction material. Therefore, knowledge of the chronostratigraphy of a region will be found very useful in the identification of potential occurences of building stone as discussed in §2.2. The reason is that, in general, greater age promotes induration and cementing of sediments, thereby producing strong, durable rock which would certainly be suitable for, say, armourstone. Although this could be thought to be desirable in all cases, very great strength and induration may incur excessive costs of extracting and processing stone and, indeed, may preclude the stone being shaped as a freestone for dimension stone. Greater age also provides greater opportunity for metamorphism to affect the stone, converting it either to a useful but different rock type, for example slate and marble, or less useful rock, for example schist. Conversely, very young sediments tend to be weak and exhibit low durability. This fact is well illustrated by reference to Fig. 1.1, which shows the solid geology or bedrock of the United Kingdom. The principal sedimentary building stones are obtained from sediments of intermediate geological age, namely Carboniferous, Permian, Triassic and Jurassic. Only a little is produced from the Devonian and Cretaceous rocks at the extremes of this range of ages. Rock fill has been produced from rocks of a wider range of ages but armourstone is generally obtained only from the oldest sedimentary rocks. It should also be noted that a large proportion of the older sediments, i.e. Silurian and older, which outcrop over much of Wales and Scotland have, in fact, been metamorphosed to slates and schists. Indeed, the oldest, Precambrian rocks are the gneisses forming the northwest coast of Scotland and the Hebrides.

2.6.3. Metamorphic rocks

2.6.3.1. Petrography

This third major group of rocks consists of rocks in which the original textures, mineralogy, and sometimes chemistry, have been altered by changes in temperature

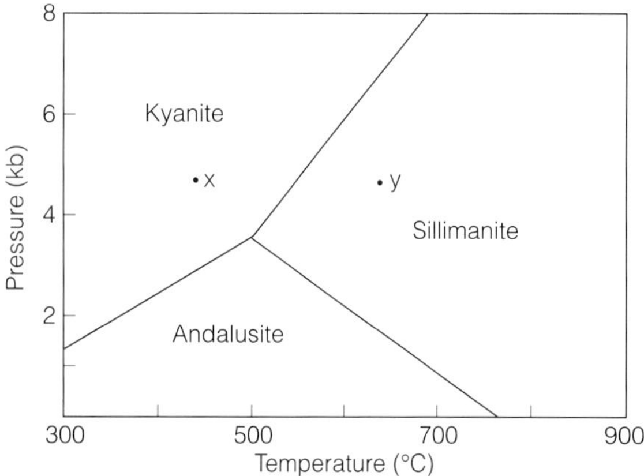

Fig. 2.43. Stability relations of the three polymorphs of aluminium silicate; andalusite, kyanite and sillimanite. In this diagram the black lines represent phase boundaries. A rock containing kyanite is under a pressure of 5 kbars and a temperature of 450°C at point X. As pressure and temperature increase during regional metamorphism from X to Y (pressure 5 kbars, temperature 650°C) the mineral kyanite inverts (changes) to sillimanite as the boundary between kyanite and sillimanite is crossed. Inversion can occur as pressure and temperature decrease as well as increase.

and/or pressure subsequent to their original formation. The constituent minerals of metamorphic rocks are more or less in equilibrium at the new conditions of temperature and pressure. Typical metamorphic minerals include chlorite, biotite and garnet, and a group of minerals found exclusively in metamorphic rocks, particularly staurolite, cordierite, andalusite, kyanite and sillimanite, most of which are rich in aluminium oxide, alumina (Al_2O_3). Under certain conditions these are called index minerals since their occurrence is controlled by temperature and pressure and will thus indicate the conditions under which they were formed. For example, andalusite, kyanite and sillimanite are identical in composition (Al_2SiO_5) but appear in rocks subjected to different temperatures and pressures: andalusite is found in rocks subjected to low pressures and low to moderate temperatures; kyanite in rocks subjected to moderate to high pressures and low to moderate temperatures; and sillimanite in rocks subjected to moderate to high pressures and high temperatures. The stability of the three minerals can be represented on a diagram with pressure plotted against temperature as shown in Fig. 2.43. The presence in metamorphic rocks of the other two minerals, namely staurolite and chloritoid, depends upon a high Fe^{3+}/Fe^{2+} ratio in the rocks undergoing metamorphism.

2.6.3.2. Fabric

The internal fabric of all metamorphic rocks is produced by increases in pressure and temperature which occur at considerable depths in the Earth's crust. The important factors controlling metamorphism are:

(1) confining pressure, which includes the pressure due to depth in the crust and fluid pressure which is the pressure exerted by fluids in pore spaces;
(2) strain, which is a measure of the change of shape and volume due to stress during deformation;
(3) temperature – the rate at which temperature changes with depth is known as the geothermal gradient.

Metamorphic rocks possess directional fabrics in which minerals are arranged in parallel alignment due to conditions of high stress. Platy minerals (micas etc.) may define a planar fabric or foliation, whereas prismatic or elongated minerals may define a linear fabric or lineation. Commonly used fabric terms are slaty cleavage in fine-grained rocks such as slates or phyllites (Fig. 2.12), schistosity in medium grained rocks such as schists (Fig. 2.13), and banding in coarse grained rocks such as gneisses or migmatites (Fig. 2.44).

Slaty cleavage is a discontinuity in low-grade metamorphic rocks parallel or sub-parallel to the axial planes of folds affecting these rocks. In slates, which are composed of clays, the cleavages may cut across the original bedding planes at high angles. Phyllites show the same fabric as slates but the cleavage planes appear shiny or more reflective due to the presence of chlorite and muscovite which have developed in the cleavage planes. Schistosity or foliation refers to continuous bands of aligned minerals, usually mica-rich, appearing in medium-grained schists. These bands may be sinuous if garnets or other high-temperature minerals are present which push the foliation aside (Fig. 2.45). Banding in the highest grade metamorphic rocks, such as coarse grained

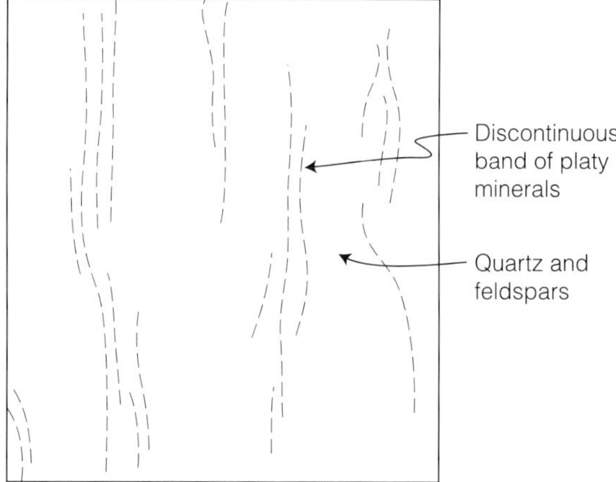

Fig. 2.44. Texture of a high grade metamorphic rock such as gneiss showing discontinuous foliation. The rock is coarse grained and looks like a banded granite.

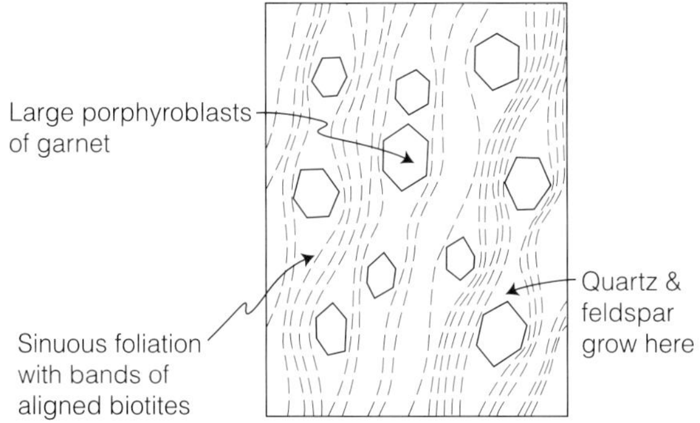

Fig. 2.45. Texture of a garnet-mica-schist showing sinuous foliation and large garnet crystals (porhyroblasts).

gneisses, is usually discontinuous with bands of aligned minerals unable to be followed for any distance across the surface of the rock (Fig. 2.44).

2.6.3.3. Classification

Types of metamorphism include thermal metamorphism where rocks have been subjected to increases in temperature only, such as would occur close to an igneous intrusion. This is also called contact metamorphism. Some distance from the intrusion the rocks are hardly affected, although in some cases they may show hardening, but close to the intrusion the rocks have undergone recrystallization and a new, very tough, rock called a hornfels is formed in which the minerals are more or less randomly orientated. The term hornfels is applied to any rock formed in the innermost zone of thermal aureoles regardless of composition. Extensive metasomatic zones occur around some intrusions due to movement of dissolved compounds in hydrothermal solutions circulating through the country rock. In limestones such zones are called (metasomatic) skarns.

Dynamic metamorphism occurs where stress is the dominant agent acting on the rocks, such as would occur under conditions of strong shearing stress, along fracture belts and low-angle faults or thrusts in the earth's crust. The most changed rock in such a regime is called a mylonite, formed by pervasive ductile flow.

In all metamorphic conditions, progressive increases in temperature and/or pressure will change the metamorphic grade of the new rocks forming and also increase their grain size, the grain size coarsening as the grade increases. Table 2.14 gives a simple classification for rocks produced by regional metamorphism.

At the highest grades of metamorphism, melting may occur and granitic melts of low melting point may form in metamorphic rocks at appropriate temperatures. These appear as veins in a migmatite, which is a coarse grained, mixed rock consisting of these veins intermixed with, or invading, the original metamorphic rock material.

Table 2.14. *A classification scheme for the main regional metamorphic rock types*

	Regional metamorphic rock groups		
	Low grade	Moderate grade	High grade
Grain size	$\ll$1 mm	1–3 mm	>3 mm
Temperature	<300°C	300–550°C	>550°C
Pressure	<3 kb	3–5 kb	>5 kb
Rock fabric	Slaty cleavage	Foliation	Discontinuous banding
Rock types	Slates Phyllites	Schists of all types	Gneisses Migmatites Granulites

Metamorphic rocks which have formed under very high temperatures and pressures, such as occur at the base of the crust or in the upper mantle, are called granulites and are composed almost entirely of minerals such as pyroxenes and feldspar in a granular texture.

Metamorphosed sandstones and limestones give rise to quartzites and marbles respectively.

2.6.3.4. Occurence of metamorphic rocks

The occurences of metamorphic rocks can be categorized under four headings as described below. The principal metamorphic building stones, namely slates, quartzites and marbles, occur in the first two groups described. Slates are formed during low-grade metamorphism and are found within greenschists in orogenic belts. Quartzites and marbles also tend to occur in the same regimes but usually form under medium grades of metamorphism. No building stones occur in the latter two groups.

Regional metamorphism in orogenic belts. Metamorphic rocks are created within mountain belts (orogenic belts) on the Earth's crust produced by the compressional forces generated during convergence and collision of lithospheric plates. The metamorphism is characterized by the presence of low-grade rocks containing chlorite, the so-called greenschists, medium-grade rocks such as schists, amphibolites and gneisses and other high grade, anhydrous rocks containing quartz, feldspars and pyroxene with or without garnet, the felsic or mafic granulites. Regionally extensive migmatite complexes may also occur within some orogenic belts.

Paired metamorphic belts. In the Mesozoic–Cenozoic terranes of the Pacific rim, paired metamorphic belts are recognized. These involve a high-pressure (high-temperature), blueschist belt associated with ophiolites and trench sediments lying adjacent to the oceanic trench (i.e. the subduction zone); and a low-pressure metamorphic belt with greenschists and amphibolites found further inland, associated with calc-alkaline intrusive igneous bodies such as granites.

Sub-sea floor metamorphism. Mineral assemblages in the altered oceanic crust are dominantly of a very low pressure type, including zeolite-bearing rocks (lowest grade), and greenschists (slightly higher grade). In this environment, ophiolite complexes represent ancient, metamorphosed, oceanic crust. The chemical reactions involved in this process, besides producing metal oxides, sulphides and carbonates, also release silica to add to deep marine cherts. The basic oceanic crust is leached of elements such as Mn, Fe, Co, Cu, Zn, Ag and Au which are removed as chloride complexes. The eventual deposition of these leached elements in various forms creates potentially exploitable ore deposits.

High-pressure blueschist metamorphic belts. Submarine pillow lavas and related ophiolite suites are intimately associated with arc-trench greywackes, deep marine sediments, and blueschist belts containing high-pressure mineral assemblages. A blueschist belt forms in subduction zone – ocean trench settings, and derives its name from a blue variety of amphibole called glaucophane. Other typical minerals include jadeite and garnet. These blueschists have formed deep within the sediments of the trench. Although formed at deep levels, blueschists are frequently found as clasts (fragments) within a sedimentary heterogeneous rock called a mélange, which may form by faulting, shearing or some other mechanism. Ancient ophiolites are intimately associated with mélanges which seem to be a diagnostic feature.

2.7. Igneous rocks as building stones

2.7.1. Granites and porphyritic granites

Granites and their closely associated rock types, granodiorites, diorites and tonalites, are by far the most abundant igneous rock types used in the blockstone industry. Of the 27 quarries working igneous rocks in the UK and Eire, no fewer than 24 produce granite. The principal outcrops of granite in the UK are indicated on Fig. 1.1. Granites are crystalline rocks possessing the minerals feldspar, quartz and biotite which have crystallized from a liquid rock or magma and the rock structure contains very few voids. The crystals have long grain boundaries and possess excellent bonding strength between adjacent mineral grains. Such a structure is strong and most commercial granites have a uniaxial strength greater than 100 MPa with a specific gravity of around 2.65 and water absorption of less than 1%.

Those granites worked are mostly grey or pinkish in colour, although some very pale coloured types occur, and a few porphyritic varieties are also worked.

The texture of these granites is usually granular, that is all minerals occurring are approximately the same size, and predominantly coarse grained with the individual minerals being about 5 mm in size, although a few medium-grained types occur with grain sizes of 1 mm to 5 mm. Two fine grained types occur in Cornwall with mineral grains less than 1mm in size, and two microgranites are worked, one in Wales, and the other at Ailsa Craig, a small rocky island 15 km off the Ayrshire coast of Scotland where the rock was extracted and fashioned into curling stones in the past. It is now being worked again after a quarry in Wales became depleted and could no longer supply stone for this purpose. The famous Shap granite of Cumbria is a porphyritic granite with large crystals of potassium feldspar, called phenocrysts, up to 50 mm in length held in a coarse-grained matrix. This beautiful and unusual rock shows these large pinkish brown crystals in a greyish matrix (Fig. 9.28).

The mineralogy of all the granites used by the industry is remarkably similar. The list of working quarries shows that the majority of the granites contain feldspars, both potasssium feldspar and sodium (plagioclase) feldspar in the ratio of about 2:1 which constitute about 75% or more of the rock, micas (always biotite with occasional muscovite, particularly in the grey types), and quartz, which comprises about 15% to 20% of the granite by volume. Any remaining constituents are small in amount and include iron oxides and rare hornblende, although some granites have another major constituent, for example, the microgranite of Ailsa Craig, has a dark blue, sodium-rich amphibole (riebeckite).

Many of the minerals present in granites can be affected by weathering processes, particularly the feldspars which eventually degrade to clay minerals. Indeed, several of the Cornish granites have been weathered or altered almost completely to claystones and are now worked by the English China Clay Company for kaolinite, known commonly as china clay. However, all granites now worked commercially for blockstone are invariably fresh and have not been weathered and this includes those granites which are worked in Cornwall.

From the Table their uses in the UK include building stone, setts, kerbstone, cladding, paving, monumental, and as armourstone where the fine-grained varieties or microgranitic types are the best.

Other granites and related igneous rocks are available from other parts of the world. Scandinavia supplies several granitic types and is by far the largest supplier of granite block to the UK, accounting for over 90% of all imports (which average 250 000 tonnes per annum) in the early 1990s. A handsome orbicular granite is very popular in which the feldspars occur as pale concentric spheres in a coarse pale brown matrix, see Fig. 2.21. The texture of this rock is directly attributable to its history of crystallization, during which various feldspars and quartz appear as the temperature drops. This granite is similar to the famous Rapakivi granites which were originally recognized in Finland. Another popular igneous rock is an alkaline 'granite' from Norway called a Larvikite. This is a very coarse grained dark grey to black stone, commonly found as cladding panels, in which very large feldspars, more than 2 cm in length, occur which refract the light to produce irridescent colours of blue and green on the polished face. In the late 1960s and early 1970s many shops, banks and commercial properties in the high street were clad with this decorative stone. Strong red granites come from Bolivia, and many coloured and textured granites come from other countries of which South Africa and central Europe are important suppliers. The colour of granites is directly attributable to the colour of the feldspars, usually the potassium feldspars, present and the colours exhibited by these minerals are related to small amounts of trace elements which may be present. Thus, minute traces of titanium, manganese, iron, and other elements can have the effect of colouring feldspars brownish, dark brown, pink, red and green in addition to their usual colours of white and grey.

Information on granite dimension stone in the UK and Eire is given in Table 2.15 and the reader is referred to other publications for information on sources of granites and related rocks from European and other countries. The Norwegian and Swedish Geological Surveys publish details of the rocks produced in their countries and more general texts include Shadman (1976), O'Neill (1965) and Ashurst & Dimes (1984).

2.7.2. Other igneous rock types

In the UK only three other igneous rock types are recorded as being worked for dimension stone in addition to granites. In Devon a quarry was recently opened for producing building blocks in a tuff of Devonian age. A tuff is a pyroclastic rock consisting of fine particles of volcanic ash, minerals and pieces of lava thrown out by a volcano during eruption, eventually combining to give a heterogeneous rock when these particles fall to the Earth's surface. A tuff can form on land or in water depending upon where the particles settle. A typical tuff is fine grained and either dark or reddish in colour if land-based, or greenish in colour if water-based. Tuffs consist of materials which have been compacted during geological time and may be friable. Water-laid tuffs are usually stronger and frequently bedded, but most tuffs are not capable of withstanding weathering processes and blocks of this rock type will eventually weather and degrade, especially in the UK climate.

A felsite is a hypabyssal rock, pale buff in colour and with a medium grain size having mineral grains of 1 mm to 5 mm in size. It occurs in minor intrusions such as sills or sheets and has a granular texture of interlocking potassium feldspar crystals, which comprise more than 80% of the rock, with quartz and occasional epidote

Table 2.15. *UK & Irish granite sources of supply*

Location	*Colour*	*Minerals*	*Product*	*Uses*
England Cornwall & Devon	brown, grey silver, c.g.	feldspars, biotite, quartz, muscovite	blocks, slabs (incl. polished)	memorials, setts restoration, cladding, sea defences, paving monumental
England Cumbria	light pink or buff in grey matrix, also brownish, c.g.	large crystals of buff K-feldspar in ground-mass of feldspars, quartz biotite, musc., rare pyrite	blocks	hydraulic stone building, setts
Scotland NE Scotland, Mull	silver grey, pink, reddish m.g. to c.g.	feldspars, biotite, quartz, muscovite, occasional hornblende	blocks, slabs, (incl. polished)	cladding, paving, setts, kerbstones hydraulic stone, memorials
Scotland Ailsa Craig	pale green very f.g.	feldspars, biotite, quartz, riebeckite	columns	curling stone
Wales Pwllheli	grey brown, very f.g.	feldspars, micas, quartz	blocks split by hand	memorials hydraulic stone
Northern Ireland Mourne	pinkish, c.g.	feldspars, micas, quartz	blocks, slabs	building, monumental
Eire Donegal, Mayo, Wicklow	grey, white, pink, various colours, m.g. to c.g.	feldspars, micas, quartz	blocks, slabs (incl. polished)	cladding, building monumental, ashlar, paving, ecclesiastical

c.g., course grained; m.g., medium grained; f.g., fine grained.

Table 2.16. *Three unusual igneous building stones quarried in the UK*

Location	*Colour*	*Minerals*	*Product*	*Uses*
England Devon Tuff	greenish blue fine grained	volcanic ash, fine basaltic minerals	blocks	building
Scotland Fife Felsite	light red, pink fine grained	K-feldspars, quartz	rough blocks	landscaping
Scotland Lanarkshire Qz dolerite	black, dark grey, medium grained	plag. feldspars, quartz, pyroxenes, ores	blocks, slabs, (incl. polished)	cladding, paving, setts, kerbstones memorials

forming the remainder. The felsite from Fife is mainly produced as rough blocks for gardens and landscaping since the natural block size is too small for any other engineering applications.

Hillend Quarry in Scotland produces quartz dolerite which is the main rock quarried for aggregate all over Central Scotland. Dolerite is a medium-grained, dark grey hypabyssal rock occurring in dykes and thick sills which has a strong texture of interlocking laths of feldspar and pyroxene, called an ophitic texture. It has a simple mineralogy of elongate laths of plagioclase feldspar (calcium-rich) in a felted arrangement enclosed in large spongy (poikilitic) crystals of augite (the pyroxene), with the interstices filled with crystals of quartz. Augite and feldspar each comprise more than 40% of the rock with the remainder being quartz and iron oxide (up to about 10%). Quartz dolerite is a very strong rock and in Scotland is frequently used for setts, kerbstones and monuments and the dark colour of the rock makes it very popular for gravestones.

2.7.3. Summary

Although local igneous rocks may be used for building purposes in a large number of locations throughout the world, granites are invariably the most commonly used igneous rocks for commercial exploitation. They are invariably light-coloured and strong with a coarse grain size although medium and fine grained granites are also worked. Setts, kerbstones, and building stones are made from granite blocks and cladding panels, paving stones, coping stones and thin, flat slabs for various uses are produced from rough granite slabs.

Granites from quarries in the UK and Eire have been described in some detail in this section but granite dimension stone is produced by many other countries such as Norway, Sweden, Finland, France, Spain, Italy and Portugal. Other world countries producing granite blockstone include South Africa, Zimbabwe, the eastern United States and Brazil.

Provided that the rock is unweathered and unaltered, igneous rocks are most likely to provide a satisfactory source of rock fill.

With respect to armourstone, the principal concern is that the rock should be unweathered and unaltered. Otherwise, igneous rocks, particularly the basic rocks of higher density, are likely to be suitable provided that the block sizes and shapes are acceptable, see Chapter 8. Fresh granites, syenites, gabbros and basalts are in common use as armourstone.

2.8. Sedimentary rocks as building stones

2.8.1. Previous studies

Two sedimentary rocks which are of pre-eminent importance are limestones and sandstones. It is estimated that well over 90% of the stone and stone-faced buildings in England consist of one or other of these two rock types, with flint making up a substantial portion of the rest (Clifton-Taylor 1972). The qualities of limestones and sandstones which befit them for building purposes, their availability and previous use in the United Kingdom are well covered in the literature. Particularly valuable are reviews by Leary (1983, 1986) for UK limestones and sandstones respectively, Hart (1988) for UK magnesian limestones and Honeybourne (1982) for French limestones. The volume on UK limestones (Leary 1983) gives descriptions of 48 individual stones ranging in age from Silurian to Cretaceous. Crystalline limestones mainly come from Palaeozoic rocks, notably those of the Devonian and Carboniferous systems.

Oolitic limestones come from the Jurassic system, notable amongst which are the oolitic limestones of the Cotswolds, including Bath and Guiting Stones, the Lincolnshire oolitic limestones, including the famous Ancaster, Clipsham, Ketton and Weldon Stones and the Portland and Purbeck limestones. Chalk comes from the Cretaceous system as the name itself implies. As well as providing brief descriptions and properties of the limestones, Leary (1983) also includes coloured plates, at actual size, which reveals the colours of the main beds then being quarried or still available. The texture of limestones to a great extent determines their properties as building stones.

The crystalline limestones are dense and of low porosity, giving rise to strong, durable building stones. Some of the coral and shelly varieties will also take a polish and are used as decorative internal cladding and flooring being described, incorrectly, as marbles. However, the crystalline limestones may be more expensive to extract and difficult to work than the other types of limestones.

The texture of oolitic limestones is less dense and more porous, giving rise to less strong and durable stones but they are relatively easy to extract and often easy to work, that is, freestones. The oolitic limestones of Jurassic age are important sources of building stone in the UK and outcrop over a large area extending from the Isle of Portland to the Humber estuary (Fig. 1.1).

Chalk is the most porous and generally the weakest form of limestone and, owing to these properties, it is not commonly used as a building stone in the UK because frost will damage the stone when wet. However, in the past, the stronger, or 'harder', chalks have been used in small, rustic buildings, local churches and even cathedrals. Important examples are Beer Stone, notable for its use in Exeter and Winchester cathedrals, Totternhoe Stone, notable for its use in Westminster Abbey, and a type of chalk known as 'Clunch' quarried especially in Cambridgeshire. The lack of durability in a climate of frosts precludes its exterior use today except for restoration work and exceptional situations. Nevertheless, chalk is an extremely important source of rock fill in southern Britain where care is taken to prevent excessive breakdown or wetting of the chalk during excavation, placing and compaction and the material is buried at such a depth so as to be protected from frost action (Burland 1990). A comparison of the properties of these limestones is given in Table 2.17.

Leary (1986) provides descriptions of sandstones from 78 quarries, ranging in age from Devonian to Cretaceous. She suggests that those of Carboniferous age may be the most well used. Their main sources are in the north of England and thus complement the most well used limestones, which tend to be in the south, in part because the older limestones of the North, such as the Carboniferous limestone, are too hard to be easily worked as a freestone. This work similarly provides actual scale colour plates of the principal sandstone beds then being worked. More up-to-date information showing which of the quarries are still in production, with information on all rock types in production in the UK and Eire, is given in the Natural Stone Directory (Stone Industries 1993).

Ashurst & Dimes (1990) provide extensive descriptions of the geological background to building and decorative stones including those much used in the past as well as those currently available. Another source of useful geological information, albeit in an architectural context, is Clifton-Taylor (1972). His text describes the qualities of English building stones and the uses to which they have been put. It is a work of immense charm, extolling the visual benefits of using masonry especially where used to conserve and reinforce local character. Clifton-Taylor (1972), Parsons (1990), Jefferson (1993) and Robinson (1995) cover the history of quarrying and building and reveal that because of the intrinsic lithological variability of sedimentary formations, stones which were formerly available may not be so now due to the loss of the quarry and/or working out of the stone. This is a factor which may be especially serious where repairs or replacement of weathered or damaged stones may be required. Even where the basic texture and mineralogy of a stratum may be continuous, the finer details which govern the colour, or colours, may not.

Information specific to particular formations or even more specifically to particular quarries is available from the various publications of the Geological Survey, especially the District Memoirs. These give details of the lithology, structural relations and usually an indication of previous uses. Occasional works which do the same for particular districts also exist, of which Arkell (1946), Purcell (1967) and Scard (1990) are particularly to be recommended.

Table 2.17. *Comparative, approximate physical and mechanical properties of limestones*

Property	*Crystalline limestones*	*Oolitic limestones*	*Chalk*
Strength (UCS, MPa)	>70	20–50	<30
Dry density (tonnes/m^3)	2.50–2.75	2.00–2.50	1.40–2.40
Porosity (%)	<7	10–20	17–50
Water absorption (%)	<5	<10	<25

2.8.2. Discontinuities: joints and bedding planes

The principal discontinuities governing the sizes of the intact material (or the dimensions of the 'dimension' stone) are joints and separable bedding planes. Not all bedding planes act as discontinuities. Those which do usually represent either slight changes in lithology or a break in sedimentation which afforded a time-gap during which the underlying bed may have consolidated or hardened in some way to prevent the 'bedding-in' of subsequently deposited material. Bedding may often be seen visually from mineralogical or textural changes but need not act as a surface of separation (or bedding

Table 2.18. *Descriptive terms for the frequency of bedding planes (after BS 5930, Anon 1981)*

Term	*Spacing*
Very thickly bedded	greater than 2 m
Thick bedded	600 mm to 2 m
Medium bedded	200 mm to 600 mm
Thin bedded	60 mm to 200 mm
Very thin bedded	20 mm to 60 mm
Thickly laminated	6 mm to 20 mm
Thinly laminated	less than 6 mm

controlled joint). Table 2.18 gives descriptive terms appropriate to the frequency of the bedding, irrespective of whether or not these planes act as joints.

Where large dimension stones are required, the ideal sediment will have been deposited in a continuous process without breaks, or significant changes of lithology, preventing the subsequent development of bedding joints. With more frequent bedding joints, in the thinly bedded category of Table 2.18, the bedding may be described as flaggy or tabular. Rock won from such sequences may yield paving or coping stones and with still more frequent bedding joints, i.e. becoming fissile, the rock could yield stone 'tiles' for roofing as, for instance, with the sandy limestones known as the Collyweston 'slates' and Stonesfield 'slates'.

2.8.3. Facies and trade names

Facies is a very useful geological term to indicate the particular style to which a rock mass belongs. It can refer to

- the lithology, that is, lithofacies as in a sandy or a clayey facies
- depositional environment, that is, environmental facies as in shallow or deep water facies
- mineral or fossil content, that is, mineral facies or biofacies respectively
- other respects, for example, diagenetic facies.

A particular sedimentary formation may vary both vertically and laterally in one or more of its facies characteristics even over quite small areas. From the dimension stone aspect, the lithofacies is usually of most concern. Thus, one type of lithofacies may provide suitable building stone while another may be of scant use. The 'rag' and 'hassock' facies of the Hythe Beds in Kent are an example with the rag providing the hard and previously well-used building stone known as 'Kentish Ragstone' while the hassock is generally only a soft and friable sandstone.

Quarry trade names more appropriately refer to a particular type of lithofacies rather than to a precise geological stratum, although in many instances these could be the same. The trade named lithofacies could represent a local variant of a particular stratum, as with the innumerable varieties of the Lincolnshire limestone or other Jurassic oolites, a lenticular development within the quarry or a repeated facies within a varying sequence of beds.

2.8.4. Cross bedding: from quarry to building stone

A common feature of many sediments and an almost ubiquitous feature of coarse detrital deposits that stems from the need to have an appreciable current velocity to move the individual grains, is deposition as current ripples, sand waves and dunes. In the face of an exposure, these features show up as cross-bedding: see Figs 2.11, 2.46 and 2.47 which show the essential forms of this feature. Cross-bedding may be observable from slight changes in mineralogy picking out the cross-bedding planes or from variations in grading, from coarse to fine, within the individual cross-beds. Such variations in grading affect the permeability and allow later differential straining, usually an iron oxide stain, to further emphasize the cross-bedding. Not only are cross-beds prominent in exposed quarry faces of many sandstones and some limestones but are subsequently seen within dimension stones when used in a building.

2.8.5. Polishable limestones (trade-'marbles')

Certain of the harder limestones, which are true sedimentary rocks, will take a polish. Well known in this respect are some of the Purbeck limestones and Carboniferous limestones, such as the black Tournai 'marble' from Belgium (Ashurst & Dimes 1990). The resulting polished stone is referred to in the industry as 'marble' but geologists consider this to be a misuse of the word because in geological terms a marble is a metamorphic rock, produced by the complete re-crystallization of an original limestone or dolomite subjected to very high temperatures and pressures. The usage has become deeply entrenched in the industry and is unlikely to be easily changed but, nevertheless, the phrase 'polishable limestone' should be substituted wherever possible to avoid confusion.

2.8.6. Weathering

Weathering as a geological process has been described in §2.4. The rate of weathering depends on the initial mineralogy and texture of the rock, including the stability of the minerals of the rock, which may have formed under very different conditions, towards the new

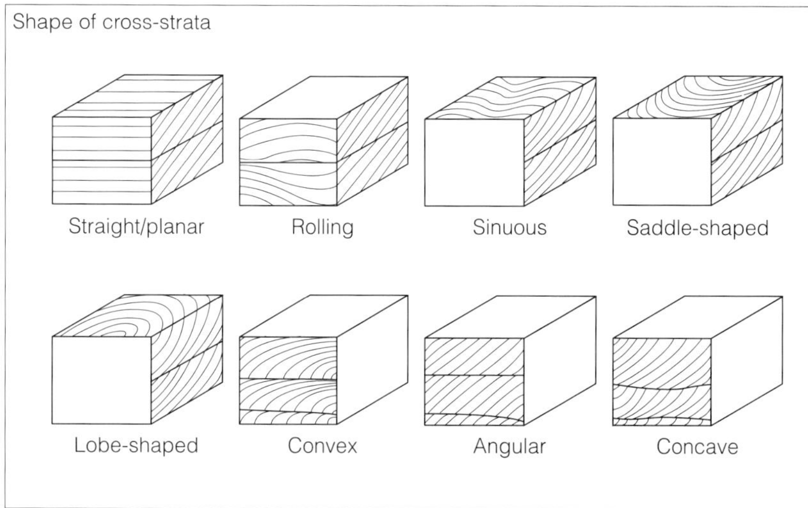

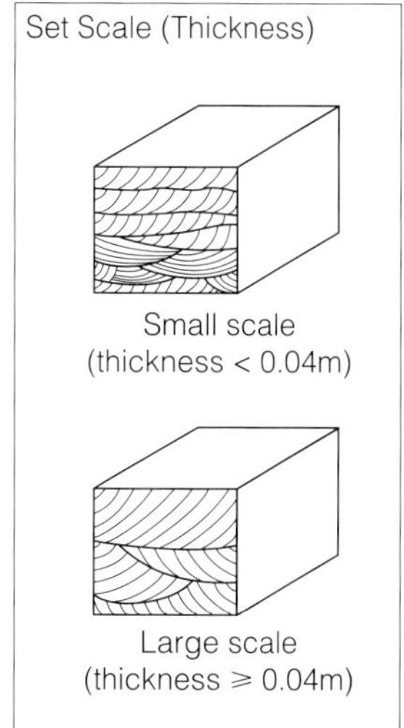

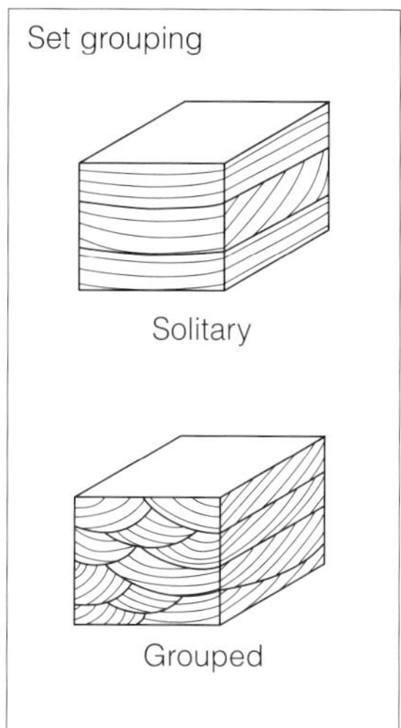

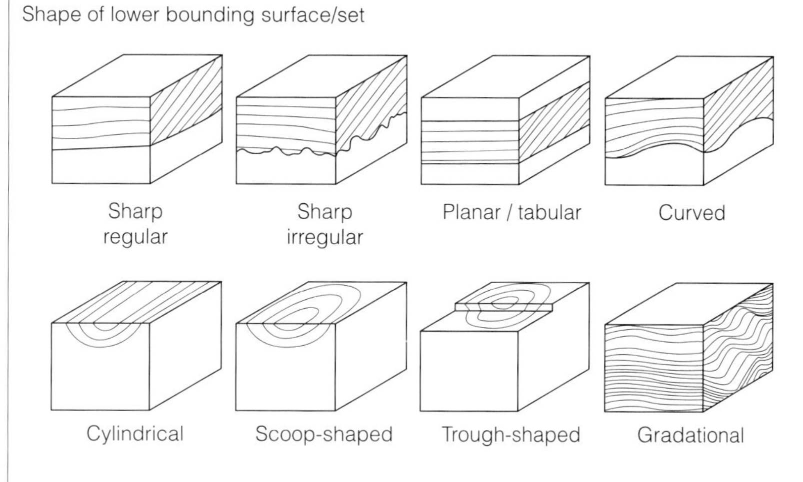

Fig. 2.46. Different forms of cross-bedding.

environment in which the rock is exposed. While many of the weathered profiles seen in geological outcrops have taken geological time to form, there will also be cases of more rapid response where human influence has exposed susceptible rocks to the atmosphere. Since dimension stones are almost invariably quarried from the unweathered part of a rock profile, the danger always exists that this accelerated weathering response may occur to the stone when emplaced in a building. Thus, when a building conservator attempts to stop or slow the weathering, the conservator is, in the dramatic but accurate words of Jefferson (1993), 'actually attempting to combat the forces which shaped the planet'.

Rates of weathering can be accelerated in the polluted atmospheres of urban areas. Thus, the calcite and dolomite of limestones and dolomitic limestones and the cement of calcareous sandstones will be actively dissolved by acid rain and acidic condensations (Schaffer 1932). The effects may prove worse for the calcareous sandstones rather than the limestones (Leary 1986). The calcite in the former is providing a cement to hold the grains together so the dissolution and loss of the small quantity of calcite present as cement allows the grains to crumble from the stones. In the case of a limestone, which is made up almost entirely of calcite, much greater dissolution must occur before it too becomes friable.

Fig. 2.47. Masonry constructed of sandstone showing evidence of current bedding (Public Library, Middlesbrough).

An example of the former is the Reigate stone from the Upper Greensand of Surrey. It is a sandstone cemented with both siliceous and calcareous cement which was well used in medieval London and later because of its ready availability. However, it weathers badly in the urban environment: a fact noted by Sir Christopher Wren in his 1713 survey of the Henry VII Chapel at Westminster Abbey. In a memorable phrase, Wren noted that the Reigate stone was 'so eaten up by our weather that it begs for some compassion' (quoted by Clifton-Taylor 1972).

2.8.7. Summary

Limestones and sandstones are very important building stones especially in England owing to their wide distribution, see Fig. 1.1, and relative ease of extraction and processing. Furthermore, they offer a wide range of colours and textures to the architect .

However, the strength and durability of limestones and sandstones varies greatly and needs to be carefully assessed with respect to the intended use. Moreover, their suitability for use as building stone is determined by several features peculiar to sedimentary rock such as bedding planes and cross and current bedding textures.

A sedimentary rock may be a suitable source of rock fill provided that the rock is well cemented or highly indurated (lithified) although even chalk can be used under certain circumstances.

Similarly, the Carboniferous limestone and highly lithified sandstones have been used successfully as armourstone. The most common limitation is the presence of bedding planes which causes the block to exhibit an unsatisfactory, tabular shape. The cement, if present, of some sedimentary rocks may also degrade in the aggressive environment of salt water or under the influence of repeated cycles of wetting and drying.

2.9. Metamorphic rocks as building stones

Three main metamorphic rock types are commonly used as dimension stone. In order of importance these are marbles, slates and quartzites, although marbles and slates are of far greater importance than quartzites.

2.9.1. Marbles

To the geologist marbles are metamorphosed limestones and do not include polishable limestones, which are described in §2.8.5. The type of marble obtained after metamorphism depends upon the type of carbonate present in the original rock and the purity of the rock. Thus, a pure calcitic limestone will produce a white marble, but any minute impurites in the calcite may allow a black or streaky marble to form. A marble with intercalations of mudstone or clay will produce a banded marble after metamorphism and coloured marbles usually require the presence of minute amounts of certain elements, such as for example manganese which gives rose-coloured marbles and brucite, magnesium oxide, which alters to give yellowish marbles. These coloured marbles are invariably banded so that the colouring is not uniform but appears as bands and wisps across the polished surface of a marble slab. In some countries such as Italy and Belgium marble breccias are commercially worked. These rocks represent marbles which have been broken and reconstituted so that they appear similar to a coarse terrazzo. Another popular product from Italy is travertine which may be marketed as a marble but is, in fact, a highly porous, banded, brownish limestone, often containing cavities, deposited as a precipitate from hot, carbonate rich springs. It is commonly used as cladding panels in foyers and bathrooms as well as non-slip tiles on pool surrounds, see Fig. 2.48.

The metamorphic processes change the original limestone from a porous rock with voids to a more crystalline product possessing medium to coarse grain size, where the minerals form a mosaic-like structure and the percentage of voids are greatly reduced. The rock is stronger and can be cut into thin panels (about 20 mm thick) which can be polished without fear of breakage. Marbles, although chemically identical to limestones, have formed in quite different ways and have quite different engineering properties. Only two genuine marbles are quarried in the UK (from the same Scottish quarry) although several are worked in Eire, and these are described in Table 2.19.

There are two aggregate quarries in Scotland which work black Dalradian marbles. These are located at Blair Atholl in Tayside Region, and on the Island of Islay. They do not produce blockstone at the moment but there is no reason why they should not do so in the future.

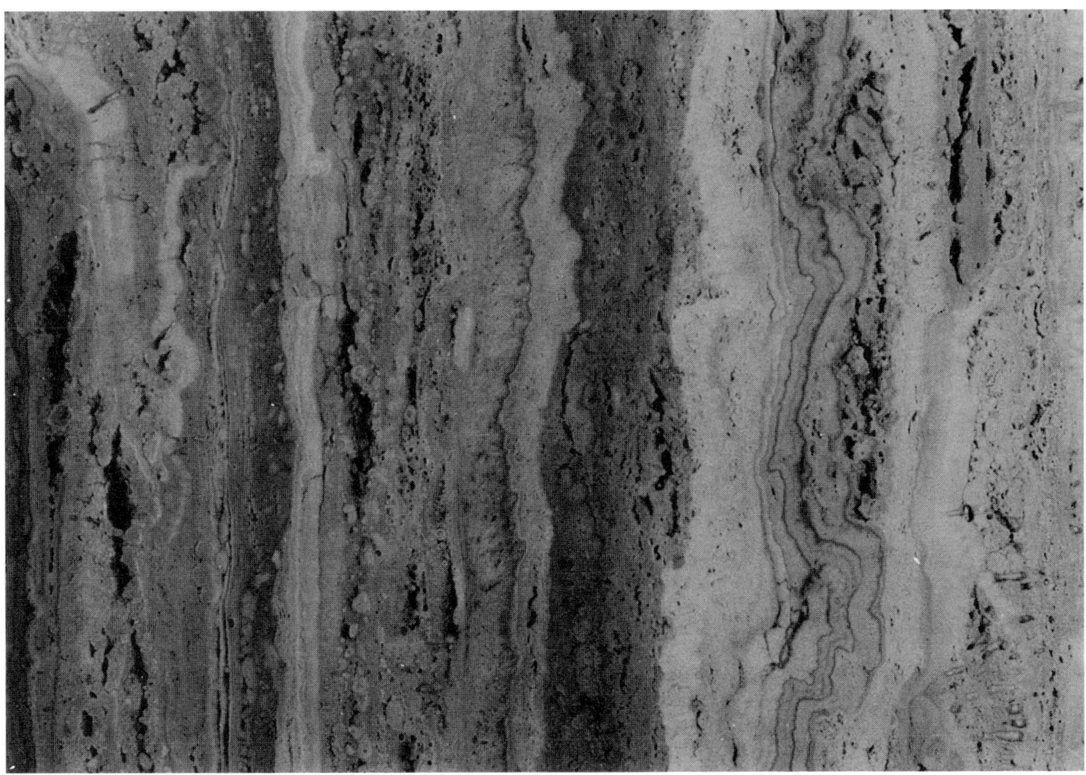

Fig. 2.48. Photograph of the sawn surface of travertine.

Table 2.19. *Marbles quarried in the UK and Eire*

Location	*Colour*	*Minerals*	*Product*	*Uses*
Scotland Highlands	white, grey, yellow, brown banded	calcite, quartz, brucite, serpentine	sawn slabs	cladding, tiles
Eire Connemara	white, green black, banded	calcite, quartz, ophicalcite	thin slabs	wall linings, souvenirs

2.9.2. Metamorphic quartzites

Metamorphic quartzites are the metamorphosed products of sedimentary quartzites, quartz arenites and so on. They are composed essentially of quartz in a 'mosaic' texture with low porosity and exhibit a high compressive stength and great durability. Because they are fairly brittle materials and highly abrasive, they are not commonly used by the industry. Their colours range from white to yellowish brown although occasional impurites yield other colours such as green, and they are medium to coarse grained. In the UK and Eire metamorphic quartzites are usually found in geologically old formations and may have taken part in more than one metamorphic episode. Their complex geological history has often given them a small natural block size which reduces their uses to industry.

All the operating metamorphic quartzite quarries of the British Isles occur in Eire, and Table 2.20 gives details.

2.9.3. Slates

Slates are low-grade, regionally metamorphosed rocks which have been baked and hardened, as well as folded. The original rocks undergoing these processes were shales or mudstones. The metamorphic processes impart a slaty cleavage, which is parallel or sub-parallel to the axial planes of the folded rocks and which allows the slate to be split into flat sheets. The rocks are still composed of clay minerals and rock flour, which is minute particles of feldspars, quartz etc., and the grain size is very small, probably less than 0.01 mm, and too small to be seen with the naked eye. The rocks have been considerably strengthened by the metamorphism, their porosity has been lowered and permeability is virtually nil. These properties explain the suitabililty of slates for roofing purposes and also for sea defence walls. Slates and phyllites are used very successfully for this in Shetland. Because of the presence of slaty cleavage that *all* slates possess, slate and related rock types (phyllites) can be used for any purpose requiring flat, tabular slabs such as roof tiles, table tops, cladding panels, for which green Cumberland slate is popular, and hydraulic stone but not for building blocks or where equidimensional stone is required.

Most slates tend to be dark grey in colour because they are composed of clay minerals, but coloured slates do occur. In the UK Cumberland slates are green because they are composed of volcanic ash and contain green minerals such as chlorite.

A large number of slate quarries occur in the UK and these are described in Table 2.21.

2.9.4. Summary

Metamorphic rocks are not commonly used as dimension stone except for marbles, slates and occasionally quartzites. Marble is used for cladding panels, tiling, paving, monumental and memorial work, and carved ornamental stone. In Mediterranean countries it is used for building purposes but in the northern countries the climate is too severe and it is almost exclusively used for indoor purposes.

Slate is used for cladding and ornamental purposes but its greatest use is still as roofing slate. Nowadays the common dark grey or black slates of Wales and Scotland, and the green slates of Cumberland are augmented by the imported slates from Spain which are available in several colours including red. In the early 1980s UK did not import slates as it could supply sufficient quantities from local quarries in the South

Table 2.20. *Details of Irish quartzites quarried as building stones*

Location	*Colour*	*Minerals*	*Product*	*Uses*
Eire Mayo, Donegal	brown, gold, green, grey m.g to c.g.	quartz	blocks, slabs	cladding, paving, building, fireplaces

Table 2.21. *The main slate quarries in the UK*

Location	*Colour*	*Minerals*	*Product*	*Uses*
England SW England	grey brown, rusty, reddish multicoloured	clays, rock flour very f.g. minerals	sawn slabs, slabs, sheets dressed and polished stone	roofing, flooring paving, walling, tiles, cills, cladding
England Cumbria	black, grey, blue black, light green, mottled green	clays, rock flour volcanic fragments, ash, graded bedding	sawn and polished slabs, blocks of varying thicknesses	roofing, flooring paving, walling, tiles, cladding, fireplaces, cills, copings
Scotland Caithness Stranraer	black, grey, blue black, red, green multicoloured	clays, muds, rock flour	sawn and polished slabs, blocks of varying thicknesses	paving, cladding, fireplaces, floor tiling
Wales Blaenau Ffestiniog Penrhyn	blue-grey, heather-coloured	clays, rock flour, very fine grained minerals	sawn slabs, slabs, sheets dressed and polished stone, riven slabs, coring etc.	roofing, tiles, flooring, paving, walling, cills, cladding, copings fireplaces
Wales Caernarfon	greenish and coloured	clays, rock flour, very fine grained minerals	as above	as above

West and Cumbria. However, slates were expensive to produce at about £400 per tonne and Spain started exporting slates to the UK at less than half the UK price. In 1983 only a few hundred tonnes were imported but this amount had risen to over 50 000 tonnes by the late 1980s and this level of exports continued into the 1990s with 40 000 tonnes imported into the UK during 1992 at a cost of nearly £10 million.

Metamorphic quartzites have a limited use as a building stone and the amounts produced for this purpose are very small indeed. The occurrences in Eire have been discussed in some detail in this section.

Most metamorphic rocks will be suitable for rock fill although rocks that exhibit pronounced cleavage may be difficult to compact owing to the tabular shape of particles.

Again, most metamorphic rocks will be suitable for armourstone provided that the shapes and sizes of the blocks are acceptable. Most examples of use of metamorphic rock as armourstone are gneisses although schists have been used. Indeed, even tabular blocks of slate have been employed in sea defences at Holyhead, Anglesey.

2.10. Conclusions

Although a large number of rock types, their forms, textures, compositions and the structures that affect them, have been described in this Chapter, the principal rock types used as dimension stone in building are only five in number, namely granites, sandstones, limestones, marbles and slates (Fig. 2.49 and Table 1.1). The UK produces about 200 000 tonnes of sandstone and between 200 000 and 250 000 tonnes of limestone each year, and is self-sufficient in these rock types. This fact is borne out by the import figures for 1992 which show that sandstone imports amounted to a mere 1000 tonnes and limestone about 4000 tonnes. The situation is quite different for granites where the figures for 1992 show that approximately 130 000 tonnes were imported, a total virtually identical to that quarried in the UK for building stone use. Granites from Scandinavia, South Africa, France, Eire and India all figured prominently with Scandinavia supplying about 60% of the total imports (Table 1.2). The UK exports virtually no granites. In the early 1980s imported granites enjoyed a huge price advantage over the home-based product but the price gap is now virtually closed and the reason for the continuing demand is the variety of types of granites available. For example, Scandinavia produces Rapakivi and orbicular types (Fig. 2.21) as well as large feldspar Larvikitic types. South Africa exports basic igneous rocks, incorrectly called 'black granites', and India very homogeneous pale grey types none of which types are available in this country. The cost of granite imports has recently increased, which may be due to many of the granite types now being sent to the UK as polished slabs rather than rough block, and there is also a much greater diversity of types being imported now than in the past.

The only other rock types to figure prominently in imports are marbles and slates. In 1992, 31 000 tonnes of marbles, including some limestones and travertines, were imported, mainly from Italy, Portugal and Turkey, at a cost of nearly £20 million. Britian produces virtually no genuine marbles or travertines, so the reason for the

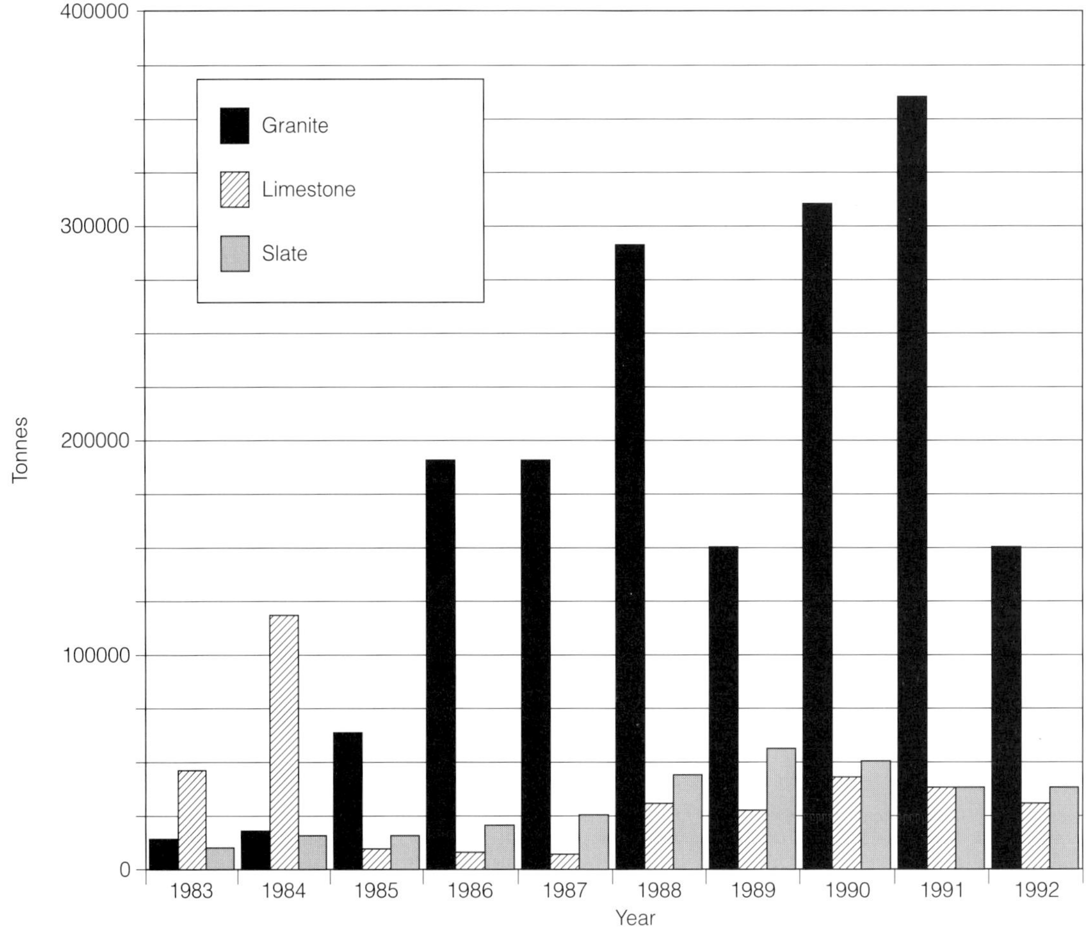

Fig. 2.49. UK import figures for granite, slate and marble for the ten years 1982–1992.

demand is simply that there is no home-based supply of this material. Furthermore, most of this imported material has been shaped and polished for a particular application which explains its very high price of between £600 and £1000 per tonne.

With slates the situation is quite different. Section 2.9.2 showed that the UK has significant workable deposits of slates available and, in fact, produces about 120 000 tonnes per year for building purposes - such as roofing slate.

Most other countries employ the same restricted group of natural building stones for construction and other purposes. In warmer countries, such as those around the Mediterranean, marbles and limestones are used more frequently in outer building walls where they are relatively unaffected by the climate and atmospheric pollutants there. This is because the climate is not as severe in those countries as in the more temperate northern countries and the amount of atmospheric pollutants is usually much less. Thus, the softer rocks, limestones and marbles, can easily survive.

Although the UK has been used as an example for building stone imports, the situation is not very different in other countries where natural building stones are imported for similar reasons: either because they enjoy a price advantage over home-produced rock, or because the imported material is unlike anything that is available on the home market and has been chosen for architectural purposes or for aesthetic reasons.

2.11. References

Allaby, A. & Allaby, M. (eds) 1990. *The Concise Oxford Dictionary of the Earth Sciences*. Oxford University Press, Oxford.

ANON 1996. *Classification schemes for rock weathering*, Geological Society, London.

ARKELL, W. J. 1946. *Oxford Stone*. Faber and Faber, London.

ASHURST, J. & DIMES, F. J. (eds) 1990. *Conservation of Building and Decorative Stones*. Butterworth-Heinemann, London.

BATHURST, R. G. C. 1975. *Carbonate Sediments and their Diagenesis*. Elsevier, Amsterdam.

BIENIAWASKI, Z. T. 1989. *Engineering Rock Mass Classifications*. Wiley, New York.

BLYTH, F. G. H. & DE FREITAS, M. H. 1984*a*. *A Geology for Engineers*, Chapter 1, Edward Arnold, London.

—— & ——1984*b*. *A Geology for Engineers*. Edward Arnold, London, p. 17.

BOGGS, S. JR. 1992. *Petrology of Sedimentary Rocks*. Macmillan, New York.

BRITISH STANDARDS INSTITUTION 1981. *Code of Practice for Site Investigations* (formerly CP2001), BS5930: 1981. British Standards Institution, London.

BURLAND, J. B. (ed.) 1990. *Chalk: Proceedings of International Chalk Symposium, Brighton*, Thomas Telford, London.

CHILINGARIAN, G. V. & WOLF, K. H. 1988. *Diagenesis I, II & III*. Elsevier, Amsterdam (Developments in Sedimentology 41, 43 & 47).

CLIFTON-TAYLOR, A. 1972. *The Pattern of English Building*. (3rd edn) 446pp., Faber and Faber, London.

DEER, W. A., HOWIE, R. A. & ZUSSMAN, J. 1978 *et seq*. *Rock-forming Minerals* (various volumes). Longman, London.

DUDLEY STAMP, L. 1962. *Britain's structure and scenery*. The Fontana Library, Collins, London.

DUNHAM, R. J. 1962. Classification of carbonate rocks according to depositional texture. *In*: HAM, W. E. (ed.) *Classification of Carbonate Rocks*. American Association of Petroleum Geologist, Memoir, **I**, 108–121.

FOLK, R. L. 1959. Practical petrographic classification of limestones. *AAPG Bulletin*, **43**, 1–38.

——1962. Spectral subdivision of limestone types. *In*: HAM, W. E. (ed.) *Classification of Carbonate Rocks*. American Association of Petroleum Geologists, Memoir, **I**, 62–84.

FOOKES, P. G., DEARMAN, W. R. & FRANKLIN, J. A. 1971. Some engineering aspects of rock weathering with field examples from Dartmoor and elsewhere. *Quarterly Journal of Engineering Geology*, **4**, 139–185.

—— & HIGGINBOTTOM, I. E. 1975. The classification and description of near-shore carbonate sediments for engineering purposes, *Géotechnique*, **25**, 406–411.

FRANCIS, E. H. 1961. *The Economic Geology of the Fife Coalfields*. HMSO, London, 113.

GREENSMITH, J. T. 1978. *Petrology of the Sedimentary Rocks*. George Allen & Unwin, London.

GRIBBLE, C. D. 1988. *Rutley's Mineralogy* (17th edn). Chapman & Hall, London.

—— & HALL, A. K. 1992. *Optical Mineralogy Principles and Practice*. UCL Press, London.

HARLAND, W. B., SMITH, A., GILBERT & B. WILCOCK, B. 1964. *The Phanerozoic Time-scale*. Geological Society, London.

HART, D. 1988. *The Building Magnesian Limestones of the British Isles*. Building Research Establishment Report, BRE, Watford.

HOLLAND, C. H. 1978. *A Guide to Stratigraphic Procedure*. Geological Society, London, Special Report 10.

HOLMES, A. 1947. *Principles of Physical Geology*, Thomas Nelson, London.

HONEYBORNE, D. B. 1982. *The Building Limestones of France*. Building Research Establishment Report, HMSO, London.

HUDSON, J. D. & SUTHERLAND, D. S. 1990. The geological description and identification of building stones: examples from Northamptonshire. *In*: PARSONS, D. (ed.) *Stone: Quarrying and Building in England AD 43–1525*. Phillimore, Chichester, 16–32.

JEFFERSON, D. P. 1993. Building stone: the geological dimension. *Quarterly Journal of Engineering Geology*, **26**, 305–319.

KENNETT, J. P. 1982. *Marine Geology*. Prentice-Hall, New York.

LARSEN, G. & CHILINGAR, G. V. 1979. *Diagenesis in Sediments and Sedimentary Rocks, Part I*. Elsevier, Amsterdam.

—— & ——1983. *Diagenesis in Sediments and Sedimentary Rocks, Part II*. Elsevier, Amsterdam.

LEARY, E. 1983. *The Building Limestones of the British Isles*. Building Research Establishment Report. HMSO, London.

——1986. *The Building Sandstones of the British Isles*. Building Research Establishment Report. HMSO, London.

MCLEAN, A. C. & GRIBBLE, C. D. 1985. *Geology for Civil Engineers*. Spon, London.

MOORE, C. H. 1989. *Carbonate Diagenesis and Porosity: Developments in Sedimentology*, **46**, Elsevier, Amsterdam.

O'NEILL, H. 1965. *Stone for Building*. Building Stone Federation, London.

PARSONS, D. 1990. Review and prospect: the stone industry in Roman, Anglo-Saxon and Medieval England. *In*: PARSONS, D. (ed.) *Stone: Quarrying and Building in England, AD 43–1525*. Chapter 1. Phillimore, Chichester.

PETTIJOHN, F. J. 1975. *Sedimentary Rocks* (3rd edn). Harper & Row, New York.

——, POTTER, P. E. & SIEVER, R. 1987. *Sand and Sandstone* (2nd edn). Springer, New York.

PRESS, F. & SIEVER, R. 1994. *Understanding Earth*. Freeman, New York.

PURCELL, D. 1967. *Cambridge Stone*. Faber and Faber, London.

ROBINSON, E. 1995. A pattern of English building: a challenge. *Proceedings of the Geologists' Association*, **106**, 161–170.

RONOV, A. B. 1983. The earth's sedimentary shell. *Am. Geol. Inst. Reprint Ser*. (V. Am. Geol. Institute), Falls Church, Va., USA.

SCARD, M. A. 1990. *The Building Stones of Shropshire*. Swan Hill Press, Shrewsbury.

SCHAFFER, R. J. 1932. *The Weathering of Natural Building Stones*. DSIR, Building Research Special Report **18**, HMSO, London.

SCOFFIN, T. P. 1987. *Carbonate Sediments and Rocks*. Blackie, Glasgow.

SHADMAN, A. 1976. *The Development Potential of Dimension Stone*. United Nations (ST/ESA/34), New York.

SHEPHERD, W. 1972. *Flint: its Origin, Properties and Uses*. Faber and Faber, London.

STONE INDUSTRIES 1993. *Natural Stone Directory*, **9** (for 1994/5). Herald House Ltd, Worthing, Sussex.

SUMMERFIELD, M. A. & GOUDIE, A. S. 1980. The sarsens of southern England: their palaeoenvironmental interpretation with reference to other silcretes. *Inst. Brit. Geog. Spec. Pub*., **11**, 71–100.

TUCKER, M. E. 1981. *Sedimentary Petrology: an Introduction* (2nd edn). Blackwells, Oxford.

—— & WRIGHT, V. P. 1990. *Carbonate Sedimentology*. Blackwells, Oxford.

WINDLEY, B. P. 1984. *The Evolving Continents*. Wiley, London.

Appendix 2.1. Mineralogy

A *mineral* is a naturally occurring, usually inorganic substance which typically has a defined crystalline structure. Each mineral has a characteristic chemical composition. Rocks are composed of minerals which can be divided into *silicates* and *non-silicates*. In the Earth's crust the most common elements in decreasing order of abundance are oxygen, silicon, aluminium, iron, calcium, sodium, potassium and magnesium. The strong affinity that silicon has for oxygen leads to the formation of a 'bonded-unit' where one atom of silicon is bonded to four oxygen atoms in a tetrahedral arrangement. The various types of silicate minerals which crystallize from liquid rock magma reflect the different ways that these tetrahedral units link together. In some minerals they occur as separate units, whereas in others they occur as chains, sheets and complex three-dimensional structures. Other atoms such as magnesium, iron and calcium help to bond the linked Si–O units together.

Planar fractures occur through most silicate structures along which the mineral will preferentially cleave or split. These cleavages are related to particular directions within each mineral and the set of cleavages for any mineral is peculiar to that mineral. Some minerals possess no cleavages (quartz, garnet) whilst others possess one (micas, clays), two (feldspars, pyroxenes, amphiboles) or three (calcite). Cleavages are discontinuities in minerals along which fluids and weathering agents may enter and effect changes in the minerals. These changes will affect the properties of rocks, for example by increasing porosity and decreasing specific gravity.

The main silicate minerals are briefly described although the reader is referred to *Rutley's Mineralogy* (Gribble 1988) or other mineralogical texts for fuller details. Hardness in a mineral refers to a scale (called *Mohs' scale of hardness*) in which ten minerals are listed in order from softest = 1 (talc) to hardest = 10 (diamond) and all other minerals possess a hardness value within this scale.

The other main group of minerals is simply the non-silicates, and this group includes the carbonates, sulphides and oxides as well as other compounds and native elements.

A2.1. Silicates

Olivine $(Mg, Fe)_2SiO_4$ Specific Gravity 3.5–4.5; Hardness 6.5

Olivine crystallizes as short prismatic green crystals at a high temperature early in the cooling of a liquid rock magma. As the magma cools down pyroxenes and plagioclase feldspars crystallize along with olivine. It often alters to serpentine, a change caused by hot hydothermal solutions entering the rock at a late stage and, since serpentine requires a larger volume than the original olivine, cracking often occurs around olivine crystals reducing rock strength and making the rock more susceptible to weathering. Olivine is found in gabbros and ultrabasic rocks.

Serpentine, which has the composition $(Mg_6[Si_4O_{10}](OH)_8)$, is a greenish mineral which may occur in marble; the famous Iona Marble is a serpentine-bearing rock. The pure serpentine rock called serpentinite is often used as decorative cladding.

Pyroxenes $(Ca, Mg, Fe)Si_2O_6$ SG 3.3; H 5.5

Pyroxenes are black prismatic minerals which crystallize from a magma after olivine. Often two pyroxenes form although only one remains as the temperature drops. The main rock-forming pyroxenes are augite, orthopyroxene and diopside. They usually crystallize along with plagioclase feldspar and occasionally olivine and alter at a late stage in the presence of water to chlorite, a clay-type mineral. Pyroxenes occur in gabbros and a few ultrabasic igneous rocks.

Amphiboles $(Na, Ca)_{2\text{–}3}(Mg, Fe, Al)_5(Si, Al)_8O_{22}(OH)_2$ SG 3.3; H 5.5

Amphiboles are black elongate prismatic minerals which crystallize after the pyroxenes. The principal amphibole is hornblende which is found in diorites and intermediate igneous rocks. It crystallizes from more water-rich magmas along with plagioclase feldspar and alters at a late stage in the crystallization of a magma, in the presence of water, to chlorite.

Micas

Biotite $K_2(Mg, Fe)_6(Si, Al)_8O_{20}(OH)_4$ SG 3.0; H 2.5

Muscovite $K_2(Al)_4(SiAl)_8O_{20}(OH)_4$ SG 2.7; H 2.5

Biotites are brown platy minerals which crystallize from a magma at lower temperatures than amphiboles. The magma is more water-rich by this time so biotite and the micas contain hydroxyl ions in their structure. Micas occur in diorites and granites and are common in veins. Biotite alters in the presence of water to chlorite. Muscovite is a low-temperature mineral occurring after biotite has crystallized and is a common constituent of granites and pegmatites. It is a colourless platy mineral which does not alter. Both micas are common constituents of many sedimentary rocks (sandstones, siltstones) and metamorphic rocks (mica schists, gneisses) where their platy character often imparts an internal foliation or banding to the rocks that contain them. Gold-coloured veining in some marbles has been attributed to the presence of bands of muscovite.

Feldspars

Plagioclase feldspar $NaAlSi_3O_8\text{–}CaAl_2Si_2O_8$ SG 2.8±; H 6

Alkali feldspars $KAlSi_3O_8\text{–}NaAlSi_3O_8$ SG 2.7±; H 6

Feldspars are pale-coloured prismatic minerals and are the commonest of all the silicate minerals, occurring in most igneous rocks where they comprise anything up to 50% of the total volume of the rock. They display a variety of colours with white and pink common, although grey, red, blue and green varieties may also occur. Plagioclase feldspars comprise a series of minerals, from a calcium-rich variety which crystallizes at high temperatures along with olivine and pyroxenes in basic igneous rocks, to a sodium-rich variety which crystallizes at lower temperatures along with amphiboles and biotites in intermediate igneous rocks (diorites) and acid igneous rocks (granites). The alkali feldspars crystallize are essential constituents of diorites, granites and pegmatite veins. Feldspars are common minerals in sedimentary rocks such as sandstones, arkoses and greywackes and also occur in metamorphic rocks such as schists, and especially high-grade gneisses. Feldspars hydrothermally alter at late stages to hydrated muscovites and eventually alter to clay minerals during weathering. Feldspar alteration is the main source of clay minerals in the world and, in the UK, altered feldspars in granites are mined in Cornwall for kaolinite (china clay).

Quartz SiO_2 SG 2.65: H 7

Quartz is a low-temperature mineral crystallizing with sodium feldspar and biotite in granites and pegmatites. It is colourless or white and prismatic and does not alter. It is hard and durable and is an important constituent of acid igneous rocks and is ubiquitous in many types of sedimentary rocks; it is also common in metamorphic rocks.

Clays (K, Na) $[(Al, Fe, Mg)_{4-6}(SiAl)_8O_{20}(OH)_4]$ SG 2.7–2.9: H 1–2.5

Clays comprise a large group of minerals which include kaolinite, illite, montmorillonite (and other smectites); and the minerals chlorite and serpentine are closely related to the clay minerals. They form from the alteration of pre-existing silicate minerals especially feldspars, although other minerals also change to clays under prolonged weathering. Chlorite and serpentine are often the cause of the green colour in marbles and slates. Table 2.3 shows the relationship of clays to the other minerals mentioned here, and reveals that most clays alter eventually to kaolinite which is the final product of alteration. However, in tropical regimes kaolinite may not be stable and through time will alter further to gibbsite $[Al(OH)_3]$, a major constituent of bauxite and lateritic soils.

The only other silicate mineral of importance is **garnet** $(Ca, Mg, Fe, Mn)_3(Al, Cr, Fe^{3+})_2Si_3O_{12}$ with a density of about 4 and a hardness of 7. It is a major constituent of garnet schist – a metamorphic rock – and may occur in some unusual igneous rocks obtained from great depths. It is durable and does not alter but it is rare and is an uncommon mineral in sediments and sedimentary rocks.

A2.2. Non-silicates

Carbonates

Calcite $CaCO_3$ SG 2.7; H 3.0
Dolomite $CaMg(CO_3)_2$ SG 2.85; H 3.5

Calcite and dolomite are essential constituents of limestones and dolomitic limestones as well as carbonate-bearing sandstones and other sedimentary rocks. They are also found in marbles and other metamorphosed carbonate-bearing sedimentary rocks. Calcite commonly occurs as a cement in sandstones (the building sandstones of Carboniferous age of the Glasgow area contain a calcite cement as an essential constituent), and often occurs as an infilling in joints and cleavages in slates.

Calcite and dolomite are colourless or white (dolomite is often buff-coloured) prismatic minerals. They are relatively soft and a test of recognition for carbonates is their reaction with dilute HCl acid in which the gas carbon dioxide is given off.

Oxides

Hematite Fe_2O_3 SG 5.0±; H 5–6
Magnetite Fe_3O_4 SG 5.0±; H 5–6

Sulphides

Pyrite FeS_2 SG 5.0±; H 6+

These minerals are usually termed ore minerals and occur in many rock types either having formed by crystallization from the magma in igneous rocks or by being detrital minerals in sedimentary rocks or by mineral reactions producing iron ores in metamorphic rocks. They are metallic, cuboid minerals with hematite dark being brown, magnetite black and pyrite brassy yellow (Fool's gold). In marbles and limestones, hematite is the major cause of red veining and red colouration and pyrite is a major cause of blue-grey veining and colouration.

Other non-silicates of importance include **halite** (NaCl) and **barite** ($BaSO_4$), but the reader is referred to well known mineralogical texts such as Gribble (1988), Gribble & Hall (1989) or the various advanced books by Deer, Howie and Zussman (1978 *et seq.*) if more information is required.

3. Exploration

3.1. The aims and objectives of exploration

3.1.1. Aim

Although the purpose of geological exploration in the broadest sense is to build up a three-dimensional picture of the rocks beneath the earth's surface, in the context of industrial minerals and rocks it is more specific, being to determine if useful materials can be extracted at acceptable cost. Rocks and minerals of suitable quality and in suitable quantities for industrial, engineering and others uses occur extensively throughout the world. Only a very small proportion of these *resources* can be worked and processed economically; that is very few can be considered as *reserves*.

There are various definitions of reserves and resources, some being outlined in the text box. The frequent subdivision of reserves and resources into such groups as 'inferred reserves' or 'probable resource' have come about as a result of the conflict between financial institutions, who wish to define precisely the potential risk of an investment, and the uncertainties which always accompany geological information.

The international nature of exploration, extraction and production has, in recent years, highlighted the problems created by different definitions of reserves and resources. Since 1993 the member institutions of the international Council of Mining and Metallurgical Institutions (CMMI) have been working on an acceptable international standard for the classification of mineral reserves and mineral resources. In October 1997 an agreement was reached on a set of proposed international standard definitions. These proposals, now referred to as the 'Denver Accord' after the location of the meeting where agreement was reached, are currently (1998) the subject of discussion by the CMMI member institutions. The proposed definitions are discussed in detail by Riddler (1998).

Fortunately when considering rock products such as dimension stone or armourstone, the capital cost of the plant used for extraction and processing is relatively low and its write-off period normally short, compared to bulk products such as aggregate or cement. Moreover the value of the market can be fairly accurately assessed beyond this pay-back period. The financial parameters can, therefore, be quantified and the required reserves clearly defined as 'material whose physical and chemical properties have been proven, to an acceptable level of confidence, to be within the limits of variability of the product or process, and which can be extracted and processed at a cost which does not jeopardize the viability of the total process'. The aim of exploration and assessment is, therefore, to prove sufficient raw material which will satisfy this definition of a reserve and examples of resource assessment, albeit not of stone quarries, have been provided by Annels (1992) and Whateley & Harvey (1994). The close relationship between raw materials, process and product should be noted.

3.1.2. The stages of proving a mineral reserve

In order to accomplish this aim, a number of objectives must be achieved:

- locate a target resource
- determine the quantity and quality of the resource
- determine the economics of extraction of the mineral
- determine the cost of processing up to the feed-stock stage, if the mineral extraction is part of an on-going process, or up to the quarry gate where no further processing is involved or the mineral is processed elsewhere

---

Resources and Reserves

Mining companies, investors, the stock market and others involved with the risks of mineral extraction, require some form of classification of deposits in order to help quantify the risk. This has resulted in a number of schemes which define the level of knowledge about a mineral prospect. Although all tend to use the terms ***Resource*** and ***Reserve***, variations in the definitions of these terms occur, and they are often subdivided into different confidence levels. The summary of some of the major classifications below is based upon the discussion by Armitage & Potts (1994).

United States Bureau of Mines/United States Geological Survey

Identified Resources
The ore grades, tonnages and geological continuity have been estimated. On the basis of economic criteria they are divided into:

Economic Reserves and ***Marginal Reserves***
Depending upon the degree of geological confidence, these in turn can be divided into:

Measured, in which the continuity is so well defined that the size, shape and mineral content of the deposit are well established.
Indicated, when the data is insufficient to outline the ore completely or to establish its grade throughout.
Inferred, where the reserve is based on assumed continuity or repetition for which there is geological evidence.

Subeconomic Resources
are those identified resources which could not be economically extracted at the time of determination.

Undiscovered Resources
Are based on geological interpretation and guesswork. The level of geological confidence allows these to be divided into:

Hypothetical and
Speculative

Australasian Institution of Mining and Metallurgy/Australian Mining Industry Council

A **Resource** is an identified *in situ* mineral occurrence which has reasonable prospects for eventual economic exploitation. An **Ore Reserve** is that part of a 'Resource' which feasibility studies has shown to be economically recoverable under conditions appertaining at the time of reporting. 'Resources' are divided into:

Measured Resources have, on the basis of a firm understanding of the geology and the mineralization, a confirmed continuity. Economic input may allow part of the resource to be classified as:

Proved ore reserve if shown to be economically mineable, even after dilution.

Indicated Resources have a reasonable indication of continuity. Economic input may allow part of the resource to be classified as:

Probable ore reserve if shown to be economically mineable.

Inferred Resources are estimates where the geological framework and continuity of mineralization are insufficiently known to be confidently interpreted, although continuity of mineralization can be reasonably assumed.

Pre-resource Mineralization relates to specific mineral occurrences where there is insufficient data to enable classification as a 'Resource'.

The Institution of Mining and Metallurgy

Both **Mineral Resources** and **Mineral Reserves** are similar to those defined under the Australian scheme. However they can be either an in situ mineral occurrence or a 'mineable' deposit depending upon whether or not the yield estimates take into account mining dilution and losses. 'Mineral Resources' are divided into:

Measured Mineral Resources have, on the basis of a firm understanding of the geology and the mineralization, a confirmed continuity. Economic input may allow part of the resource to be classified as:

Proven mineral reserve if, as the result of a full feasibility study it is shown to be economically mineable, even after dilution.
Probable mineral reserve if only economic studies, rather than a full feasibility study, have indicated that the mineral would be mineable.

Indicated Mineral Resources have a reasonable indication of continuity. Economic input may allow part of the resource to be classified as:

Probable mineral reserve if economic studies have indicated that the mineral would be mineable.

Mineral Potential is a category which is equivalent to the 'Pre-resource mineralization' of the Australian system.

- assess the planning and environmental costs of extraction, together with the cost of restoration and processing
- assess the cost of further processing to produce a marketable material if this is necessary

An important point to note is that, once a resource has been shown to be present, all the stages of the investigation which follow have financial implications. At this stage of the investigation, although information such as the cost of plant, together with historical data on markets and prices, will be available, most of the decisions will be made on a subjective basis. Close cooperation between those assessing the mineral reserve, management and accountancy staff is, therefore, essential. It is not appropriate to discuss, in this chapter, the financial management techniques which are available to estimate the economic implications of the various quarrying and processing activities which may be required. The interested reader is refered to §4.4.2 and should consult a good text on financial management, such as that by Hingley & Osborn (1989).

The objectives listed above will be achieved sequentially, as illustrated in Fig. 3.1. It is clear that the process of exploration and assessment could be halted at any stage. For example, should the quantity of overburden indicate that the cost of its removal would be so high as to make extraction by quarrying uneconomic, and the geotechnical properties of the ground make the alternative of mining untenable, there is no point in calculating the financial aspects of dressing the stone to produce ashlar, even if a major market exists.

Although these comments relate to the development of a new mineral prospect, it is occasionally possible to utilize the by-product of an existing mineral operation to satisfy a market need. Alternatively it may be possible to modify an existing process to produce the raw material required. In either instance the studies of the economics of extraction, processing, planning and environmental impact would have to take into account the effect on the primary process. For example, an alteration to the method of blasting in an aggregate quarry in order to produce large blocks for armourstone, could well have a detrimental affect on the

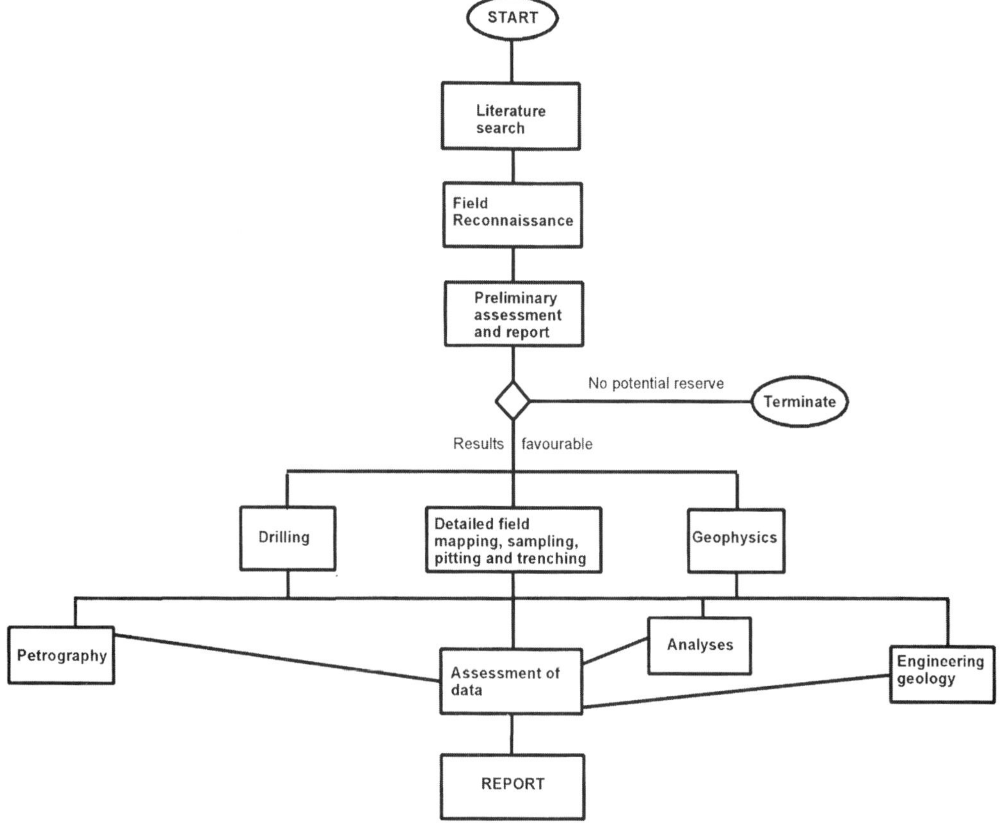

Fig. 3.1. The interelated aspects of mineral exploration.

profitability of the quarrying operation, if the result was a serious reduction in the throughput of the primary crusher on the aggregate plant. If the additional income from the armourstone offset the loss from reduced aggregate sales, the production of armourstone may be found to be viable. A detailed financial study, as well as technical study, would be required to determine the overall effect of such a change.

3.2. Feasibility studies

3.2.1. Literature search and desk-top studies

Field exploration is expensive since it is usually necessary to pay for accommodation and subsistence in addition to normal salaries. Moreover, there are often additional transport and labour costs involved, especially when working overseas. Total mapping of a large area in the search for resources is therefore impractical. Target areas must be defined before field work commences.

3.2.1.1. Sources of data

Over the past hundred years, most of the land surface of the earth, and much of the continental shelf, has been topographically and geologically surveyed. Most of the data that have been acquired have been presented on maps, in scientific papers and books and so are available from Geological Surveys, universities and libraries throughout the world. The collation of existing data can be a complex task since there is not only a considerable quantity of data already available, but geological information in the form of papers, reports and maps is being published continuously. GEOARCHIVE, an on-line geoscience database, contains references from over 5000 serials, books, geological maps and doctoral dissertations (Dialog Information Services 1991), and it is probable that the number of publications worldwide which contain potentially relevant geological information is well in excess of this figure. New papers and articles are appearing at the rate of at least 1000 per week (McKay 1994). Fortunately a number of computer-based abstracting services are available on-line and these enable very rapid and specific searching to be

Fig. 3.2. An ancient tilestone quarry, probably of late medieval age, in the Hoar Edge Grit near Kenley, south of Shrewsbury. The distribution of the old workings in this area has been used to help identify new sources of stone roofing materials for restoration work.

undertaken. With the advent of CD-ROM technology, the facility for searching the world's geological literature is now starting to be available even on portable 'notebook' computers. A useful starting point for UK sources of information has been given by Perry & West (1996).

3.2.1.2. Historical sources

Although the geological literature may well identify a possible resource area for potential building stone, it is advisable to consult the historical literature within the search area for even more precise targeting of possible sources of raw materials. Quarrymen and stonemasons have always tended to exploit the most appropriate sources of stone. Often their quarries became overgrown and lost well before the geological surveys started collecting the information and presenting it in reports and on maps (Fig. 3.2). A study of historical as well as modern plans, in order to determine if such names as 'Quar Lane' or 'Big Pits Wood' are present, is an obvious example of historical data assisting exploration. The search for place-names compounded with Old English words such as *stan* (stone) or *delph* (excavation) is perhaps less obvious (Parsons 1990). For example, paving stone supplied to All Souls College in Oxford in the 18th century, was extracted from upper Portland Beds at Standhill east of Oxford. This name is an Ordnance Survey corruption of 'Standel', which itself is derived from *stan gedelf* meaning 'stone quarry'; evidence of ancient workings being present in the area (Arkell 1947).

3.2.1.3. Remote sensing techniques

When radiant energy strikes the surface of the earth it may be reflected or scattered. Detection and interpretation of this energy, which may occur throughout the spectrum from the ultraviolet to the microwave regions, can be related to the geology of the surface. Where natural phenomena are producing thermal infra-red or microwave radiation, this can also be detected. These effects are the basis of the remote sensing techniques often used in the search for minerals and fuels. However, apart from the most familiar of the techniques, that of aerial photography, the surface detail that can currently be determined by remote sensing is not normally sufficient for it to be used in the search for stone for construction purposes. Only outline details are therefore provided here and the interested reader should consult works such as that by Drury (1993) for more detailed information on the role of remote sensing in geology.

3.2.1.4. Aerial photography

The study of aerial photographs can be of considerable value. Traditionally used as an aid to geological mapping, aerial photographs can be of considerable value when locating sources of traditional building stone. Although the techniques of photo-interpretation are similar both in geology and archaeology, the additional features which the archaeologist seeks out, such as crop marks, can be of great assistance when locating sites traditionally used to supply building stone.

Aerial photographs can be either vertical or oblique, the latter being divided into low angle, where the horizon cannot be seen, and high angle which show the horizon (Compton 1962). Although useful for structural and geomorphological studies, as well as placing a site in its geographical context, oblique photographs suffer from the problem of perspective, which makes accurate measurement extremely difficult. Vertical photographs are therefore normally used for geological work. A further advantage of vertical aerial photography is that adjacent photographs normally overlap. This enables three-dimensional or stereoscopic images of the terrain to be obtained.

Even the best topographic maps produced cannot show the subtleties of changes in vegetation, slight changes in slope or changes in ground level of a few centimetres. Good aerial photography, even in black and white, will record these small changes, especially when the photography has been undertaken with the sun at a relatively low angle producing long shadows from smallest features. The use of stereoscopic pairs of photographs will reveal minor features in even greater detail, since stereoscopes tend to magnify the image and exaggerate the relief.

Due to the quantity of detail contained in aerial photographs compared to topographic maps, it is often preferable to map areas using photographs in conjunction with maps, or even photographs alone, rather than rely solely on traditional large-scale plans (West 1991). This is especially true in areas where features such as walls or buildings are sparse. Individual exposures and features can often be located exactly on a photograph. Although it is difficult to write field notes on the face of a photograph, it is easy to make a small hole with a pin at the site of the exposure and write the relevant notes on the reverse of the print. Although there are well established methods of transferring field data from photographs onto accurate topographic maps (Compton 1962), a rapid method involves transferring the photograph onto a transparency, using a photographic, computer or photocopying method, and then projecting the resulting picture directly onto the topographic map. Although, for optical reasons, it is impossible to match up all the points on a photograph with the same points on the map simultaneously, careful adjustment of the projector allows a very accurate transference of the field data.

3.2.1.5. Other aircraft-borne sensors

These techniques are largely geophysical in nature and similar to those discussed in §3.5. They provide a rather generalized view of the geology of an area and are used more to identify geological structures rather than individual rock units. Moreover, the cost of using aircraft-borne sensors is high when compared to the typical expenditure involved in exploration for stone for construction use. However, despite the cost of aerial prospecting, electrical methods have been used for the detection of sand and gravel deposits, as has the use of thermal imagery using an airborne infra-red linescanner (Smith & Collis 1993). However, this latter technique could perhaps be considered as a specialised form of aerial photography as the electromagnetic radiation used is at, or very close to, the visible spectrum.

3.2.1.6. Satellite-borne sensors
The data obtaining by remote sensing using satellite-borne equipment can be utilized in two ways for geological exploration. The first of these uses the spectral characteristics of the electromagnetic radiation which is reflected or emitted from the surface. Different rocks will have different spectral characteristics and, if these are known, the possible composition of the surface can be suggested from the satellite data. However since the remote detectors only collect data for certain specific wavelengths and not over the whole spectrum, similar spectral characteristics may be produced by different rock types and are, therefore, not necessarily rock-type specific. Nevertheless, since the data are in digital form, computer techniques can be used to assist in producing the best estimates possible of the nature of the ground surface detected by the sensors. Use of this technique is only an aid in planning an exploration strategy and will merely highlight targets for field investigation. Even if the spectral 'signature' of the various rock units is not known, the analysis of multispectral data can be used to distinguish between different geological or vegetation units on the ground. Another important factor is the fact that the satellites produce a very consistent data source worldwide, so that interpretations of data in one area can be applied, not only in adjacent areas, but even from continent to continent (Press 1983).

In the second technique the weathering and erosional characteristics of different rock types are used to identify the presence of geological structures at the surface and then to predict the structure at depth by projection of this information into the subsurface. Information contained in an image from almost any type of remote sensing data can be useful for this type of analysis.

The main problem with satellite-borne sensors is that, unlike photography undertaken from aircraft, where the resolution is about one metre on the ground, current commercial satellite-borne sensors produce data with considerably less resolution. For example the instantaneous field of view (IFOV) of the multispectral scanners in the first three Landsat satellites, is about 80 metres. Although this is too coarse for specific site studies, it can be of value in semi-regional reconnaissance applications in areas, particularly overseas, where the geological map coverage may not be comprehensive. This may be of importance in major engineering projects in developing countries where large quantities of rock fill and armourstone may be required. Maps with scales down to about 1:250 000 can be produced from these data. Moreover the data are relatively cheap, individual pre-1988 scenes covering 34 000 km^2 costing about $200 (Lamb & Lawrence 1993). The Thematic Mappers (TM) carried by Landsat-4, 5 and 6 have an IFOV of 30 metres which can result in map scales down to 1:50 000. The French SPOT satellite has a resolution of 20 metres for multiband images or 10 metres for single band. In addition it can produce stereoscopic images.

Even with an IFOV of 20 metres the resolution is too low for detailed ground studies, especially of deposits suitable for building stone or other construction materials which may only cover a small area. However, it is reported that there are signs that some surveillance photographs from the former Soviet intelligence satellites, and possibly from United States sources, are becoming available (Drury 1993). Since it is believed that military satellites can have a resolution of better than 1 metre, there would appear to be considerable potential for this type of reconnaissance in the future.

Despite the limitations of resolution, remote sensing has been used in the identification of calcretes for construction purposes in Botswana (Beaumont 1979) and in the location of sand and gravel in Italy using multispectral satellite photographs taken from Skylab (Cassinis 1977). The Skylab data have a much higher resolution than the images obtained from the Landsat data.

3.2.2. Field reconnaissance

The main aim of this stage of the exploration is to assess rapidly those aspects of the geology of an area which are potentially of major economic importance to the project. This will involve the preparation of a basic geological map and carrying out initial sampling. Although the mapping will determine the stratigraphy and structure of the area, as discussed in Chapter 2, it will tend to be thematic and project orientated. It is more important at this stage to note that a bed of limestone is cross-bedded and has a maximum bed thickness of 50 mm, than to identify the stone as a biopelmicrite containing a variable quantity of silica grains; such information, which may have a bearing on the durability of the stone, would only be relevant if the limestone had been shown to be potentially viable as a raw material source. Similarly, apart from their value as aids to correlation between exposures, the fossil content of the rock is considered, not from the point of view of stratigraphy, but for its effect on the appearance and durability of the stone.

During the reconnaissance survey it is not sufficient merely to locate resources of stone which would form the basis of a more detailed investigation. The economic aspects of the project must always be borne in mind. Thus, once a deposit which appears worthy of a more detailed study has been located, the other factors which may affect the viability of the scheme must be assessed. These include the possible quantity of waste stone and overburden, potential environmental problems (§5.2.3), the existing and required infrastructure, and the potential value of any possible by-products.

3.2.2.1. Use of the built environment

In the more developed parts of the world, exposures are often limited or inaccessible. However, those areas which are likely to provide stone for building or engineering use have often provided stone for these purposes for many hundreds of years. Transport of bulk materials on land has always tended to be difficult and expensive. The source of stone used for construction is, therefore, very likely to be close to the building for which it was used and, although lacking such information as horizon thickness and structure, the building can be used as a substitute exposure. Similarly the stone used in dry stone walling has rarely been carried more than a few metres. For example, fossil bands in the Carboniferous limestone of north Yorkshire can be mapped for considerable distances using the occurrence of blocks of the fossiliferous horizon in the dry stone walls that occur extensively in the area.

When carrying out a survey for building stone, the existing buildings can provide valuable information, not only on the type of stone available, but also on the thickness of the strata. The pattern of course heights in an old building, especially if built in a vernacular style, is not normally the result of an architectural whim, but is a reflection of the actual bed thicknesses present in the horizon which was worked (Fig. 3.3). If a building consists of two 100 mm courses of limestone for every 200 mm course of stone, this will reflect the fact that there are twice as many thin beds in the limestone as there are thick ones. If the maximum thickness of stone found in any old building in an area is 150 mm, the chances of locating a building stone 300 mm thick is extremely remote; if suitable stone did occur with this thickness, the original stonemasons in the area are likely to have utilized it. As well as providing information on the thickness of the stone which may be available, existing buildings also give an indication of the durability of the stone. It should be borne in mind when considering this latter feature that information on weathering resistance should only be taken from traditional buildings in which the stone has been used correctly, which still retain their roofs, and never from buildings which have been pointed with Portland cement-based mortars. This latter point is important since it is likely that, due to the hardness and impervious nature of such mortars, the build-up of moisture, coupled with stresses on the stone, will have accelerated its decay.

Fig. 3.3. A building of coursed iron-rich Marlstone Rock Bed from Jurassic Middle Lias near Grantham. The thickness of the stone courses is dictated by the thickness of the beds from which the stone was obtained. Since the local stone from which the building was built is not particularly durable, the dressings are of Lower Lincolnshire Limestone which outcrops about 1.5 kilometres to the south.

3.2.2.2. Geomorphological information

An indication of the possible durability of a potential building stone can also be assessed during the reconnaissance phase of exploration, by studying the landforms in the area (§2.5.2). Lack of exposure is always a major problem when preparing a geological map. However, in the context of building stone or armourstone, the absence of exposure, often coupled with a subdued topography, could signify a low resistance to weathering, a potentially undesirable feature.

In contrast, areas such as the Arabian Peninsula which have an arid climate and an often mountainous terrain, can provide information which elsewhere has to be obtained by time consuming field measurements. The nature of the erosion in these area often results in steep-sided wadis. Natural erosion of the sides of these valleys tends to release blocks of stone which break off along the natural discontinuities. The size and shape of the blocks which fall to the wadi floor, may provide an indication of the size and shape of blocks of armourstone or dimension stone which it might be expected to extract from a quarry.

3.2.2.3. Potential environmental factors

The environmental information which is required at the reconnaissance stage includes details on the nature and use of the existing terrain. Although in many highly developed countries, stone resources frequently occur beneath farmland, much of this countryside can also be used for recreational use or be located in a Green Belt, and plans to extract minerals are often perceived as an environmental problem by many people in such areas. Many hard rocks, which are ideal for construction use, form upland areas, often of great beauty, which may have been classified as areas of Special Landscape Value or even a National Park. Even in areas which do not suffer from these potential problems to extraction, it is necessary to determine the location of the nearest habitations and roads and to estimate how much landscaping would be required. In this context the availability of materials to construct necessary landscape bunds must also be ascertained.

Information on both surface and underground water will also be obtained, since not only is there always a danger of polluting watercourses during mineral extraction, the cost of diverting streams and pumping groundwater from a quarry can significantly increase the cost of the final product.

The likelihood of encountering archaeological features in the potential extraction area must also be assessed (Fig. 3.4). In areas rich in archaeological features the cost of the detailed studies which may be required before an area can be quarried can be very high. This cost will normally have to be borne by the developer and experience has shown that it could add as much as £1.50 per tonne to the extraction cost of the stone.

Conservation areas can also add considerably to mineral extraction costs. In the United Kingdom quarrying and carefully planned restoration near to geological Sites of Special Scientific Interest (SSSIs) and

Fig. 3.4. An aerial view of an archaeological excavation being undertaken ahead of the quarry face at Ham Hill stone quarry in Somerset. The quarry is situated on Hamden Hill, a Scheduled Monument (courtesy of Wessex Archaeology).

Regionally Important Geological Sites (RIGS) can often result in enhancement of such sites. However, biological SSSIs, especially those where ponds or wetlands are involved, can require considerable expenditure ensuring that ecosystems are not disturbed by the mineral extraction or processing.

3.2.2.4. Infra-structure

Although not normally a problem in the more developed parts of the world, lack of infra-structure can seriously affect the viability of even a simple building stone quarry in certain parts of the world. Electricity can be supplied by means of a generator and water can be supplied by diesel pump and surface pipeline, or using a bowser. However, should the potential site be ten kilometres from the nearest road across rough terrain, the cost of providing access could easily make the development of a site, which may produce only relatively low value stone, completely uneconomic. Even if a main road or a railway is close to the prospect, if the market is a considerable distance away the transport costs could still result in the project being unviable. It is not only the infrastructure required for the quarry which must be considered. There must also be a workforce to operate the quarry, and they must either be transported to the site or be housed on the site itself. Should the latter be necessary the infrastructure requirements will then become a major issue.

Fig. 3.5. The 'Silver Bed' and other building stone, seen at the base of the face in Lincoln Cathedral quarry, is overlain by a sequence of limestones and shales. When this overburden is being removed the thicker limestones are separated and stockpiled in order that the stone can be hand-dressed for use as walling stone.

3.2.2.5. Secondary products

Although it was suggested above that reconnaissance mapping must be *project* orientated, this must not be confused with being *product* oriented. It is unfortunately true that most geological horizons with a potential economic value do not occur in the form of horizontally bedded strata located at the ground surface. The strata which occur above, and sometimes below, the beds of interest have normally to be removed as overburden. The cost of moving stone is high. Having gone to the expense of breaking the material out of the ground, the question of its potential value should always be addressed.

Frequently the requirement to backfill and restore worked-out portions of quarries dictates that the bulk of the stone removed as overburden is returned immediately to the void. However, it is essential that the nature of the strata which enclose the potential resource are assessed, not only from the point of view of overburden removal, but also to determine if it contains material with an economic potential. It is not uncommon to find that massive beds of stone, suitable for the production of blocks of dimension stone, are overlain by thinner and more variable beds of similar stone, a typical example being shown in Fig. 3.5. Assessment of the possible removal of some of these thinner beds for use as building or walling stone must be undertaken at the reconnaissance stage. Offsetting some of the overburden removal costs by sale of such material could allow more overburden to be removed. The quantity of freestone available for extraction could, therefore, be increased and this could improve the economics of the deposit in such a way as to change an unworkable resource into a successfully exploitable reserve.

3.2.3. Preliminary assessment and report

The assessment and presentation of the results of the reconnaissance survey are possibly the most important stage in the development of a relatively low-value material such as stone. Unlike metals, fuels or even such industrial minerals as cement, lime or china clay, the size of the final extraction and processing operation will normally be relatively small, unless the process is associated with aggregate or the production of some other bulk mineral. However, the cost of detailed exploration, sampling and testing is not directly proportional to the size of the deposit or the project. This is a result of both the cost of mobilization of exploration equipment, and of the assessment of the data, often being the same for both large and small projects. Large projects will certainly require more drilling and testing. However, the time taken to assess the data, produce development plans and prepare planning applications need not be greatly different for a small building stone quarry or a large aggregate quarry. This results in the necessary detailed investigation requiring a major capital outlay, which will form a relatively large proportion of the operating costs of the resulting operation, at least in the early years. In contrast, such costs are much less significant, although still important, in the context of an aggregate quarry which may well have a daily output in excess of the annual output of the building stone quarry.

As well as providing the results of the initial survey, the report will also include the details and costs of the various steps which would be required to prove the quality and size of the deposit, and plan its development. It will also provide information which would give an indication of the type of processing equipment which would be required. The report will also indicate how each of the further stages of the investigation will provide additional information in such a manner as to confirm, or alternatively throw doubt on, the viability of the scheme. This will enable any losses, which may result from expected problems terminating the project, being minimized.

Not only does the importance of the reconnaissance report lie in providing enough information for the stone company to make the decision on whether or not to spend money on further expensive investigative work, but it may also be used as a means of obtaining funding from financial institutions, in order that the exploration and development can be undertaken. Thus great care must be taken to ensure that the contents of the report reflect not only the actual findings of the survey, but also that the financial implications of the shortcomings of a reconnaissance survey are clearly highlighted. The report on the reconnaissance survey and assessment is, therefore, essentially a feasibility study.

3.3. Detailed field investigations

3.3.1. Aim

The detailed exploration must produce a complete three-dimensional picture of both the quantity and quality of all the materials within the block of ground which has been selected for exploitation. This will enable a detailed plan for the extraction of the stone to be developed. Such a plan will ensure that adequate quantities of each of the products produced from the deposit, are always available to satisfy the predicted market requirements.

Unlike metal ores and to some extent industrial minerals such as ceramic clays, it is not possible to work various grades of ore and blend them to produce the required product. Although it may be possible to stockpile armourstone extracted from a large aggregate quarry, the relatively small size of most building stone quarries limits the area which can be given over to stockpiling the various grades of stone. Apart from maintaining a stock of block stone, which enables purchasers to select blocks of the correct size and quality, the only stockpiles to be found in most stone quarries are those of materials waiting to be processed, together with buffer stocks of walling and similar products. Moreover, once out of the ground many building stones deteriorate rapidly if left in the quarry due to the absorption of moisture and the effect of the weather; this effect is, of course, much less of a problem once the stone has been incorporated in a correctly designed building. The stones must be stored in a sheltered area, a procedure which is normally only possible on a small scale due to the high cost of covered storage. There could also be problems of obtaining planning permission for large storage facilities at many extraction sites. Despite the potential storage problems, in situations where more than one product is produced, for example, building stone and block stone, there cannot be extensive periods where the raw materials for one or more products are not available or, an even worse situation, where no stone is available due to the necessity to remove overburden.

3.3.2. Field mapping

The basis for all detailed raw materials assessments is the accurate geological map. From it the basic three-dimensional model, later to be refined by pitting and/or borehole drilling, will be developed. During the field mapping the samples will be collected which will provide basic information not only on the overall quality of the stone, but just as important, upon the amount of variation in the stone. It is from this variability information, coupled with the structural information also collected during the field mapping, that any drilling programme will be formulated. It must be borne in mind, however, that surface exposures can only provide a limited amount of information about the strata at depth and, as is discussed in §4.1, the results of the initial boreholes may alter the interpretation of the geology based on the surface exposures, with a resulting modification to the drilling programme.

3.3.2.1. The base map

Although the initial reconnaissance mapping can, and often is, undertaken with the aid of small scale maps with scales between about 1:25 000 and 1:250 000, geologists having even been known to use Michelin road maps when nothing else was available, detailed field mapping requires accurate plans. The Ordnance Survey, the National Mapping Agency of Great Britain, can supply maps with scales of 1:10 000 and 1:2 500, the former covering the whole country, the latter most of the country except for mountain and moorland areas. Urban area mapping is also available at a scale of 1:1 250. Although currently available in printed form, the Ordnance Survey is steadily converting their mapping to digital form which will enable base maps to be supplied either as completely up-to-date prints or in computer readable form for loading directly into mapping and assessment software. In less developed parts of the world large-scale maps do not occur in any form, especially in rural areas. In these circumstances it is necessary to prepare a contoured plan of the site prior to undertaking the geological mapping. All geologists working in such areas should be sufficiently conversant with topographic surveying techniques, to prepare a base plan accurate enough to enable detailed estimates of areas and volumes to be made (Fig. 3.6). However, much work can be done with a prismatic compass, measuring tape and Abney level (West 1991). Once it is clear that the project is likely to proceed to a successful conclusion, an accurately contoured plan would then be produced by qualified surveyors.

Major changes are taking place in surveying technology with the development of satellite-based Global Positioning Systems (GPS). Although sophisticated equipment is still required to determine the location of a ground-station to accuracy of less than 10 mm in both the horizontal and vertical directions, completely portable systems with an accuracy of 1 to 2 metres are now available (Fig. 3.7). However, even these latter systems are expensive, the cost being at least five times that of an optical theodolite. Equipment the size of a cell-phone is now available for about £3000, which can be used to locate a position to within about 10 metres. The accuracy of GPS has been demonstrated in southern California where monitoring stations collect data from all visible GPS satellites every 30 seconds. This allows a daily determination of the position of each sensor to be calculated with a precision of 2–3 mm horizontally and 5–10 mm vertically (Bock 1994). A GPS system mounted on a four-wheel drive vehicle has been used for volumetric surveys of mine-waste tips and for the collection of

Fig. 3.6. Modern topographical surveying equipment can record all survey data digitally. When downloaded into a computer, this enables topographical maps to be prepared rapidly and efficiently, and also allows survey data to be passed directly to geographical and mining assessment software. (Courtesy of West Country Surveys).

Fig. 3.7. A hand-held GPS system being used to locate boreholes in an exploration site in the Caribbean.

Fig. 3.8. Lightweight and even hand-held drilling machines are available for sampling during reconnaissance surveys (Courtesy Atlas Copco).

data for the preparation of three-dimensional computer-generated models for use with planning applications (Simmons 1994).

3.3.2.2. Exposures

The procedures followed when carrying out detailed field mapping are similar to those in the reconnaissance survey, but are carried out in much more detail and almost invariably cover a smaller area. The techniques used are well documented elsewhere and will not be discussed in detail here (for example, Barnes 1982; McClay 1987; West 1991; Compton 1962). What must be emphasized, however, is the importance of good record keeping. In most parts of the world where stone is being sought for commercial purposes, exposures are limited. In contrast, there tends to be very little demand for building stone or armourstone in barren and unvegetated parts of the world. Every possible exposure must therefore be recorded in detail. It is not normally practical to return to the field to check the stream section which was missed, or measure the un-recorded dip at an exposure. The missing data could, however, be a vital part of the information upon which an expensive drilling investigation will be planned, or possibly the site purchased. Where exposures are not available they must be made, hand augering being the normal method although lightweight hand-held drills are also useful in some instances (Fig. 3.8).

3.3.2.3. Methods of recording field data

Field work is often undertaken by more than one geologist. This can result in problems of correlation between areas mapped by different personnel since one person's 'off-white medium-grained sandstone' can quite easily become another's 'pale grey arkose'. Use of standard recording sheets, preferably developed for the specific project being undertaken, are of considerable help in overcoming such problems. Such systems are now becoming very sophisticated, utilizing barcode readers connected to notebook or pocket computers; a typical system is illustrated in Fig. 3.9. In these systems the descriptive codes for the rocks, together with

Fig. 3.9. Field data-capture systems, using bar-code readers and notebook computers are becoming common, especially where computer systems are used to process the field data. (Courtesy Field Data Systems Ltd.)

numbers for recording dips or joint directions, can be generated in the form of sheets of barcodes which can be then encapsulated in plastic. The location of an exposure together with its description can then be entered directly into the computer with a few strokes of the barcode reader. The data file which has been stored in the portable computer can then be transferred, either directly or by means of a telephone connection, to the main processing computer. Modern mobile digital phones and satellite communications even remove the necessity for access to a terrestrial telephone network.

Not only do such systems reduce the time, and therefore cost, required for data acquisition, they are also much easier to use in poor weather conditions than traditional notebooks and field map-sheets. However, unlike written field notes, which may be damaged by rain or wind but are rarely lost, electronic storage can be incorrect due to faulty input or equipment problems in a harsh environment. Frequent checks should, therefore, be made to ensure that the data entered into the final database are correct.

As with the reconnaissance survey, the detailed field mapping must be project-oriented. The fact that the minerals in a granite tend to be aligned giving a lineated fabric is much more important in the dimension stone industry than accurate measurements of the directions of those lineations. What is considerably more important, when the granite is being considered for engineering use, is the fact that it may show signs of weathering down to a depth of ten metres beneath the surface. Similarly the spacing of joints and bedding planes is much more important than the origins of the discontinuities themselves.

3.3.2.4. Recording discontinuity data

Where deposits which may be suitable for armourstone or dimension stone are being sought, the recording of the discontinuity information is extremely important, since it is the joints and bedding planes which will largely determine the size and shape of the blocks of stone. For engineering and slope stability studies it has been suggested that, in order to characterize a site, between 150 and 350 discontinuities should be measured at between 5 and 15 sample locations (Priest 1993). Although the resulting 1000 to 2000 measurements may be in excess of the number required to estimate the potential block sizes to be obtained from a quarry, sufficient information must be recorded to enable a reliable estimate of the size and shape of the blocks of stone to be estimated in order to allow a reliable business plan to be developed.

A range of parameters can be measured on discontinuities (ISRM 1978*b*; Hudson 1989). Typical factors are:

Orientation	The attitude of the discontinuity in space.
Spacing	Perpendicular distance between adjacent discontinuities.
Persistence	Trace length of a discontinuity as observed in an exposure.
Number of sets	The number of joint sets comprising the total joint system.
Block size	Rock block dimensions resulting from the mutual orientation and spacing of the individual sets of discontinuities.
Roughness	Inherent surface roughness and waviness relative to the mean plane of the discontinuity.
Wall strength	Equivalent compression strength of the adjacent rock walls, which may be less than the block strength due to weathering or alteration along the discontinuity.
Aperture	Perpendicular distance between the walls of a discontinuity.
Filling	Material that separates the walls of the discontinuity.
Seepage	Water flow and free moisture in the discontinuities.

The relative importance of the various factors is dependent upon the purpose of the survey. When studying the stability of a rock mass, seepage, filling and roughness are probably just as important as orientation and number of sets. When determining the potential usefulness of a rock mass as a source of construction stone, orientation, spacing, number of sets and persistence are the most important considerations, since it is these factors which will decide the size and shape of the blocks which can be extracted. The roughness and wall strength of discontinuities should, however, be noted, since both these factors could be important in determining how much material will be have to be removed when the ex-quarry blocks are dressed to form sawn blocks or slabs of stone.

Information relating to discontinuities in surface exposures is recorded using scanline sampling or window sampling techniques (ISRM 1978*b*; Priest 1993). In the former, a tape is stretched along the exposure, or pinned to it, and the position, orientation and nature of every discontinuity encountered along the tape is noted. Pre-printed logging sheets, such as illustrated by Priest (1993), help to ensure that all the relevant information is recorded. As both natural and man-made exposures such as quarries are rarely smooth, this procedure can be difficult and, in many locations, potentially dangerous. A major problem associated with scanline sampling, especially where limited exposures are available, is the fact that discontinuities occur in three dimensions. High-angle planar discontinuities parallel to the exposure will not cut the face being measured. In fact in many

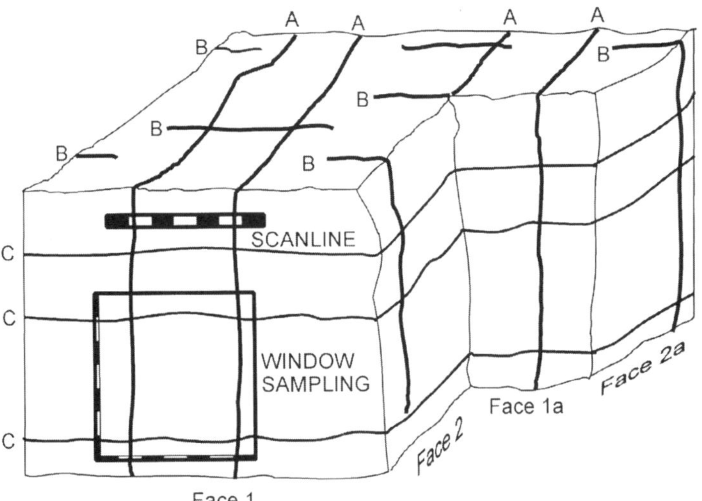

Fig. 3.10. Care must be taken to ensure that the method used to measure and record discontinuities captures all the necessary information. Use of scan-lines on faces 1 and 1a would only record data from joint set A. Even use of window sampling will only add information from the bedding planes unless additional data are obtained from faces 2 and/or 2a. Even complete recording from the faces will not identify the fact that joint set A is continuous whereas set B is not.

building stone quarries or natural exposures, such planes actually form the face, since the stone has been removed by man in the case of the former and by nature in the latter, along such a surface. In horizontally bedded strata, a horizontal scanline will not intersect any bedding planes, which are clearly discontinuities of major importance when considering the extraction of block stone. Two faces approximately at right angles to each other, together with a vertical traverse, are therefore required to successfully record discontinuity data using the scanline technique. The recording methods are illustrated in diagrammatic form in Fig. 3.10.

The potential problems associated with a vertical scanline, which may possibly require abseiling or bosun's chair techniques, are partially overcome using the window sampling method (Priest 1993). In this procedure, large rectangles are marked out on the exposure and all the discontinuities within the marked area are measured. In relatively homogenous materials such as granites, or in some highly inclined or contorted strata, random placing of the rectangles will provide adequate sampling. In the case of strata which is relatively horizontally layered, care must be taken to ensure that all the strata from the top to the base of the exposure are sampled at some point. Care must also be taken to record every discontinuity in the sample rectangle, some form of marking being required if a large number of features are present. Although window sampling addresses the vertical and horizontal variation in any one plane, an exposure at right angles to this is still required to sample those discontinuities which may be approximately parallel to the first sampling plane.

Although sampling and recording of discontinuities tend to be undertaken on quarry faces or natural exposures, which are essentially two-dimensional surfaces, it is possible to use this information to determine the size and shape of the three-dimensional blocks of stone that could be extracted from the deposit. Wang *et al.* (1991*a*) have developed a program, based upon the block theory of Goodman & Shi (1985), that uses the dip direction, dip angle and intercept of each discontinuity measured with an oriented tape, to predict the sizes and shapes of the population of blocks within the mass. The main limitation of the method lies in the assumption that all the discontinuities are persistent. This could result in an underestimation of block size.

3.3.2.5. Photographic recording

Even with extensive field descriptions and sketches, it is often difficult to record all the pertinent features of an exposure or the relationship between exposures. A photographic record of exposures is, therefore, an extremely useful supplement to the data collected in the field. Although it is normally adequate to take only individual photographs of specific features, photogrammetric methods may assist in mapping the discontinuities. It is possible to achieve this using a normal camera to produce overlapping stereo-pairs of photographs. However, if these are to be used for any form of measurement, great care and accuracy must be used in setting up the camera to produce the photographs (ISRM 1978*b*).

In order to ensure that the correct photograph can be related to field notes and map, each exposure photographed should include its identification code, normally written on a large piece of paper or card, not painted onto the rock face, as well as a scale-rule, hammer or other item included to provide the scale of the photograph. Colour photographs rarely reproduce the true colour of a rock exposure or sample. The colour of the stone in the exposure should, therefore, be recorded using the *Rock Color Chart* published by the Geological Society of America (1991) and distributed in Europe by the Geological Society of London. Based on the widely used Munsell® colour system, the chart provides a standard method of describing the colour of a stone, which allows the exact colour to be recorded without the necessity for specialist colour photography. As the colour of a stone may vary depending upon whether it is wet or dry, both colours should be recorded if the stone is being investigated for building, monumental or ornamental use.

3.3.2.6. Interpretation

The result of the detailed field mapping will be a three-dimensional model of the deposit being studied. This will, of course, only be a best estimate, since there will always be areas within the deposit in which, even with the most careful and detailed fieldwork, the structure and nature of the strata is unknown. These problematical areas will determine the scale and form of the borehole or pitting investigation that follows.

Once the fieldwork is completed, a start can be made on assessing the economic viability of the deposit since, although some parts are unknown, it should be possible to suggest likely structures for such areas and evaluate them accordingly. It may be found that certain of the unknown areas are more critical to the potential viability of the stone than others; these would then become the initial target areas for drilling or pitting.

3.4. Sampling

3.4.1. Aim of the sampling

The nature of the raw materials, mineral extraction plan, and the choice of plant both to win the material and to process it, all have to be determined whilst the stone is largely unseen in the ground. Only the samples which have been obtained from exposures or by borehole drilling are available for study. Throughout the world, in every rock or mineral-based industry, there are examples of financial and natural resources being wasted on a vast scale due to bad or inappropriate sampling. These errors are often compounded by the use of incorrect sample preparation methods during the exploration and assessment stages of a project. The financial cost of such errors can range from relatively minor losses such as those incurred when diamond-tipped saw blades with the wrong type of setting and matrix are purchased to cut blocks of dimension stone, to major miscalculations involving the construction of multi-million pound processing plants being built to the wrong design or in the wrong location, the raw materials being found to be unsuitable, or present in insufficient quantity, after the project had been completed.

3.4.2. Sample and population size

Although quarries vary considerably, experience has shown that even a small building stone quarry in the UK will have to produce and sell about 15 000 tonnes of finished stone products merely tc recoup the initial investment which is required to establish the business. In order to ensure a reasonable return on the investment, the life of the deposit would have to be at least ten years. This probably represents the exploitation of at least 60 000 tonnes of stone, excluding the overburden. The economics of this type of operation in Western Europe limit the amount of exploration which is possible. It is likely that, at the very best, samples totalling no more than two cubic metres of stone will have been collected. This represents less than 0.008% of the deposit. Sub-samples will have been selected from this material for studying the properties of the stone. In the best cases about 25 kg of samples will have been tested, half for physical properties, half for durability. Thus the assessment of the durability of the stone will have been based upon samples which represents 0.00002% of the deposit, or 1 in 50 000. This is comparable to estimating the overall variation in the population of Cardiff on the basis of a sample of about six people, or Washington DC with a sample of about 75 people. It should be noted that these figures are based upon dimension stone assessment. When assessing mineral deposits for use as feedstock for such processes as bricks, refractories, lime or cement, the amount of material actually tested can be as low as about 1 part in 10 million.

The results of any sampling scheme will only provide an estimate of the quality and quantity of the material present. In order to provide a 100% guarantee of the nature of the mineral, the sample would have to consist of all the mineral present! Sampling a deposit will provide information to a certain accuracy. This can then be translated into a degree of financial risk. Should this risk be accepted, the assessment would be undertaken on this basis. Should the financial risk be considered too high, additional sampling would be required to lower it to an acceptable level.

3.4.3. Sampling theory

In order to provide an acceptable estimate of the overall properties of a deposit, samples must be representative of the rock and its normal variations. Three main factors affect the accuracy of sampling: the size of the particles within the sample, the size (mass) of the samples, and the number taken. All these factors are related. For example, considering a material with a given variation, the larger the particles in the sample, the greater the number of samples of a given sample size which have to be taken; alternatively if a fixed number of samples is taken, each sample must be larger in order to compensate for the larger particles.

Many studies have been undertaken on the subject of accurate sampling, for example Gy (1967, 1971, 1979), Goodsall & Mathews (1970), Sedman & Stanley (1990). Numerous guidelines, including national standards, aim at assisting in taking representative samples. Practical experience suggests that the majority of these underestimate, often considerably, the quantity of sample required for both accurate resource assessment and for production control once the deposit is brought on-line. Many schemes are based upon conventional statistics, as if a rock is made up of so many random billiard balls, whereas in reality there are always relationships between different parts of a deposit. In a sedimentary rock, it is the original depositional environment that relates different parts of the rock. In igneous rocks, the parent magma and the mode of emplacement will result in mineralogical relationships within the resulting rock mass. Later diagenetic and structural changes will superimpose other patterns upon those related to the formation of the rock and thereby complicate the final pattern. However, spatial relationships will always exist, even if they are extremely complex.

Sampling schemes will provide the point data upon which the assessment of the deposit as a whole will be based. This evaluation of the rock or mineral deposit may well involve precise mathematical procedures, such as geostatistics, which take the spatial relationships between samples into account. However, for these numerical techniques to be of value, the number and spacing of samples if often crucial. This should be borne in mind when planning a sampling scheme. Since such mathematically based techniques also allow estimates of the errors in the predictions of the quality of the stone to be made, immediate analysis of samples enables sampling to continue until these errors are reduced to an acceptable level. This is an important factor when investment decisions are to be made on the basis of the sample results.

3.4.4. Sampling schemes

Probably the greatest danger in sampling is that of not taking a representative sample. Even when sampling

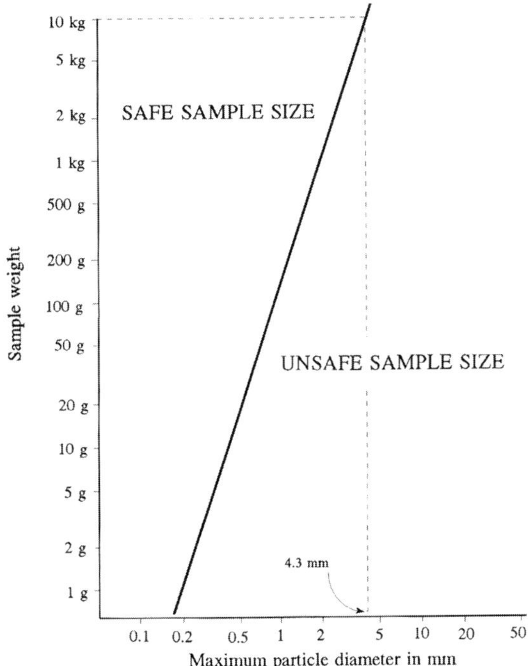

Fig. 3.11. Gy's safety rule for sampling particulate materials (Gy 1979).

particulate materials such as aggregate, the sample size necessary for reproducible results is often underestimated. A good estimate of the size of sample which is required is obtained by applying Gy's 'safety rule' of:

$$M_S \geq M_{So} = 125\,000d^3$$

where the sample weight M_S expressed in grams, should always be larger than a certain value M_{So}, which is equal to 125 000 times the cube of the diameter of the largest particle expressed in cm (Gy 1979). Thus when sampling stone which has been crushed to 25 mm, a minimum of two tonnes is required if a representative sample is to be taken. This would be for material of average grade variation; should a high variation occur, this sample size might have to be doubled. The 'safety rule' is illustrated in Fig. 3.11.

The calculation of sample size for particulate materials is relatively easy. However, when sampling stone to be used as armourstone or dimension stone, the problem is made difficult by the size of the blocks produced. What is required is an estimate of the variation within the beds from which the blocks are taken, on a scale which is similar to the size of the blocks. This would result in an estimation of the variation between the blocks themselves. Clearly Gy's 'safety rule' cannot be used when the smallest particle weighs about 0.5 tonne. Jefferson (1993) has suggested that, as the properties of a block of stone, such as durability, are determined by the

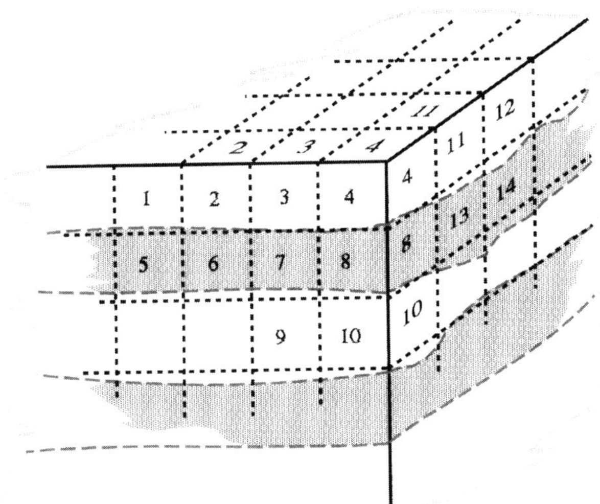

Fig. 3.12. Features such as thin lamina in a test sample, indicated by shading, can be used to provide an estimate of the number of samples which should be tested. The surface of the test cube can be considered to be made up of a large number of smaller cubes, for example those numbered 1 to 14 in the diagram, the size of which is determined by the size of the feature such as the lamina.

properties of the constituent parts of the stone, the size of these constituent parts can be used as a guide to determining the sample size. For example in a laminated stone, where the individual lamina could have appreciably different properties, the thickness of the largest lamina could be used as the unit size. This is then related to the size of the sample being tested. This is illustrated in Fig. 3.12. As an example, if 40 mm cubes of stone were to be tested for weathering properties, and the maximum thickness of any lamina was 4 mm, the surface of the test block could be considered as being made up of a stack of 488 four millimetre cube samples. Using Gy's rule, if the maximum particle size is 4 mm, 8 kg of sample are required. This suggests that about 100 cubes, each of 40 mm side, would have to be tested.

This is a large number of samples for what are often expensive tests. However, as the samples taken for sampling will almost certainly have been taken from a bed of stone already selected as appearing uniform, and therefore being potentially suitable for dimension stone or armourstone, it is likely that the variation both within and between blocks will be small. This allows the 'low cost' version of Gy's rule, which replaces the 125 000 multiplier with 60 000, to be used. This would halve the sample requirement to about 50 in this example. It should be possible for any suitably equipped laboratory to test this number of samples as a single batch, thereby keeping costs to a minimum.

In practice, the number of samples required for assessing a single bed of potential building stone over an area of about one hectare, will probably be of the order of fifteen or twenty. Where the stone is truly uniform and fine-grained, as is the case with materials such as Ketton stone, this figure may be as low as six samples. However, in variable strata, such as the bank of sandy Jurassic shell debris from which Ham Hill stone is obtained, it may be necessary to test up to 50 samples, as in the example above, in order to characterize the stone fully.

3.4.5. Surface sampling

Apart from stream, river or coast sections, where all the surface strata tend to be subjected to high-energy erosional forces, surface outcrops are the result of continual but slow weathering. The result is a tendency for harder and more resistant strata to stand out as elevated features, whereas the softer material erodes and becomes covered, either with erosional debris or vegetation. These aspects of geomorphology are discussed in more detail in §2.5. The result is that, in any given area, the geological exposure is not representative of the geology as a whole. In the case of dimension stone this may not be significant, since any rock which has suffered excessive weathering *in situ* is unlikely to be suitable for construction purposes. However, where softer patches and bands occur within an otherwise hard band of stone, great care must be taken to sample the whole band in a representative manner in order to determine the reason for the variation and its implications both on the quality of the stone and the probable amount of waste in the bed.

Care must also be taken to ensure that surface samples are truly representative of the material as a whole. Weathering involves chemical as well as physical changes, and the stone exposed at the surface can be rather different from that which will be worked, even from a shallow quarry. Although these surface effects may only affect the outer one or two centimetres, experience has shown that well weathered natural exposures should always have the surface layer removed before a sample is taken. Small but important variations within a bed can also be reflected in the weathering. A thick bed of sandstone or limestone can weather to give an irregular surface and there is always the temptation to sample only those areas which stand proud of the general surface and which are, therefore, easily removed. However it is likely that, even if the bed appears to be uniform in composition, those areas that project out from the weathered surface do so because of some variation in the stone. It may be that they are slightly more lithified or perhaps contain above-average amounts of silica.

Sampling should always be on a regular basis. For example, if it has been determined that four samples are to be taken for durability tests between the top and base of a 1-metre thick bed, the aim should be to take samples, approximately 10 cm in size, every 20 cm across the bed. Moreover, in the case of dimension stone, it is necessary to take orientated samples. This is due to the manner in which building stone should be used, that is reflecting its original orientation in the ground. Sample testing will take this into account.

When designing a sampling programme, it should be remembered that surface weathering may extend many tens of metres into the stone from the surface, this feature being discussed in §2.4. The level of the groundwater, both at the present time and in the past, will also have an effect on the stone. Except in the case of igneous rocks such as granite, where the degradation of the stone due to weathering can extend for many metres into the outcrop, resulting in high overburden ratios, these effects will not normally affect quarries for building stone, although they can be important in larger quarries which may be being considered as a source of rock fill or armourstone. These deeper weathering effects can be startling. The cream, buff or yellow Jurassic limestones which stretch in a belt from Yorkshire down to Dorset and the south coast of England, and from which many of our traditional building stones such as Ancaster, Weldon, Bath, Guiting and Portland are extracted, appear to be dark blue or grey at depths greater than about 20 metres, although the actual depth at which the change takes place varies. There normally appears to be a transition zone in which weathering to a yellowish colour has occurred adjacent to joints and bedding planes, the blue colour remaining in the body of the stone. It is, therefore, possible to obtain large blocks of apparently high quality cream coloured dimension stone which may be of limited value, since they are 'blue-hearted' and cannot be cut into smaller pieces of a similar uniform colour. Only if a mottled blue and cream stone was aesthetically acceptable, would such material be worth working. If, therefore, it is proposed to follow a seam of dimension stone and extract it by underground methods, borehole cores will almost certainly be required to ensure that the nature of the stone is similar at depth to that seen at the surface.

3.4.6. Pitting and trenching

Both building stones and armourstone are required in large blocks. An important feature of the field studies is to determine the size of the blocks which could be extracted from the deposit, without the requirement for blasting, in the case of armourstone (Wang *et al.* 1991*b*). At outcrop this is easily determined by the measurement of joints and other discontinuities, as has been described in §3.3.2.4. However, in areas which are unexposed, pits or trenches have the great advantage over boreholes in that they can be made large enough to determine joint spacing and allow visual examination of the strata *in situ*. In hard materials, it is normally only possible to excavate a pit or trench down to the top surface of the rock, although this will allow the joint pattern to be studied. In softer materials, it is often possible to extract large pieces of stone which will enable a much better impression to be gained of the appearance of the material when broken or cut into the relatively large pieces used in construction or cladding. This is particularly important in ornamental stones such as some marbles, where the overall effect is due to the larger-scale variations in pattern or colour within the material (§2.9.1).

Since pits and trenches are only temporary exposures, their faces should be photographed in colour to provide a permanent record. As with surface exposures the pit number and a scale must be included on each photograph. The colour of the stone exposed in the excavation should be recorded, both wet and dry, using a colour chart such as that described in §3.3.2.5.

3.4.6.1. Machine excavation

Pitting would normally be undertaken with an hydraulic excavator. These can range from the backhoe attachment on a small JCB wheeled loading shovel, to large tracked excavators with a digging depth of about 8 metres. Although even a small machine can theoretically excavate to three or four metres, it may still be necessary to employ a much larger machine since, in the type of rock which would be suitable for building or engineering use, the break-out force required can only be applied with heavy mobile plant. The main limitation of pits and trenches is the problem of breaking through thicker, and therefore potentially valuable, beds of stone using only the teeth on the bucket of the excavator. It is possible to drill the site of the pit first and loosen the ground will small explosive charges. However great care is then required in interpreting the fractures in the wall of the excavation, since many of these could be the result of the explosive charges rather than being natural features.

3.4.6.2. Hand excavation

In those parts of the world where suitable equipment may be unavailable for the excavation of pits, it is often possible to excavate them by hand. Unlike the trench produced by a mechanical excavator, due to the digging arc the boom, hand excavated pits can take the form of vertical shafts. Constant supervision is required to ensure that such shafts remain stable.

Care should be taken to ensure that once the excavations, be they machine or hand excavated, have served the purpose for which they were made, they are filled in. Such features, especially if they become flooded, can be extremely dangerous to the local population, especially children.

3.4.6.3. Sampling

When logging and sampling the strata exposed in pits and trenches, care should be taken to ensure that the walls of the excavation are safe. Unfortunately, legislation in the UK now requires that such pits are shored up before work is undertaken in them, even if the pit is inherently stable and is only open for the time it takes to log and sample the exposed strata. However, limited access to the face can still be achieved by means of removable shuttering.

In the UK, planning law limits both the size of pits and the number which can be excavated within a given area without previously obtaining planning permission. This restriction does not apply to normal exploration drilling, except in National Parks, areas of outstanding natural beauty, sites of archaeological or special scientific interest, or where the site is within 50 metres of a residential, or other specified, building (S.I. 1995 No.418). Although drilling rigs in excess of 12 metres high do require planning permission, such equipment would not normally be used during the exploration for stone for construction purposes.

3.4.7. Borehole drilling

Where the bedrock is hard or individual beds are thick, or where there are more than a few metres of overburden, it will be necessary to drill boreholes. The aim of a drilling programme is to determine the configuration and quality of the rock resource at depth. However, the current cost of a 20-metre cored borehole, including rig mobilization, could well be in excess of £1000. The planning of the positions of the optimum number of holes is, therefore, extremely important.

When determining the structure of a deposit, borehole locations will depend, in the first instance, on the model of the deposit built up from the surface mapping. This initial view of the deposit may well be modified as more information is obtained from the early boreholes. Drilling to confirm quality is, however, more complex. The core from a single borehole is obviously no more representative of the strata penetrated than a single grab sample taken at outcrop. If the deposit is to be characterized, a number of samples must be used to determine the variation in the material to a given confidence level. The actual number of samples, and therefore boreholes, depends upon the variability of the deposit and the confidence level required.

3.4.7.1. The size of the drilling programme

In practice the number of boreholes frequently depends upon the finance available. Although the realistic expenditure on exploration and assessment for a new project would be between 1% and 2% of the total capital cost of the project, it is rare for companies in the industrial minerals sector to spend this amount; often with inadequate results. In the context of building stone the investment is often low, perhaps only between £100 000 and £150 000 to equip a 3000 tonne per year block stone quarry. At even 2% of the capital involved the amount available for exploration is minimal. Fortunately the small output and low rate of working allow for flexibility in the quarry should problems arise. Moreover it will only be necessary to prove the existence and quality of about 20 000 m^3 of building stone in order to ensure, assuming market predictions are fulfilled, that sufficient raw materials exist to cover at least the initial investment in the project. Even if the building stone horizon is only one metre thick, the minimum area to be brought up from resource to reserve status is only about two hectares. If, for example, four boreholes are considered necessary to prove the necessary minimum reserve, the total cost of the exploration and assessment could still be less than 5% of the total capital cost. However, it should be emphasized that with a limited amount of drilling, the geologist will only have ensured that, on the basis of all the available evidence, there is a high probability of the deposit extending beyond the initial proven area. Future exploration will then become an operational cost and be absorbed in the annual turnover. This low level of expenditure on exploration should be compared with those bulk industrial minerals used as raw materials for cement, lime or clay products, where a capital outlay approaching £100 million, or even more, would be accompanied by exploration costs of the order of £250 000. It should be noted that this latter figure falls well short of even 1% of the total project cost.

3.4.7.2. Design of the drilling programme

From time to time, major projects will require considerably more drilling than the traditional dimension stone quarry. For example, a slate quarry producing 10 000 tonnes each year of different products would require a detailed assessment of the raw materials and their variation in the ground. Unlike drilling to determine the structure of a deposit, where boreholes are located individually on the basis of the previous data, drilling to determine variations in grade will normally be based on a grid pattern. The actual shape and spacing of the grid will be dependent upon the trends in variation within the deposit. For example, in a stone which appears to vary equally in all directions, a square grid would be used. In the case of a slate where the change in cleavage is clearly greater in one direction than another, the grid spacing will probably be closer at right angles to the cleavage than parallel to it. However, this rectangular grid could be modified due to changes in lithology which would be greater at right angles to the dip than in the strike direction, neither of which is likely to be related to the cleavage. The actual spacing of the grid would be determined by an analysis of the variation in the deposit, geostatistics sometimes providing a valuable tool for optimizing borehole spacing, when sufficient data is available.

3.4.7.3. Drilling methods

There are two types of exploration drilling, core drilling and non-coring methods. The latter method uses some form of chiselling action to break the ground, the rock fragments being carried to the surface by a flushing medium. Apart from its use in initial reconnaissance drilling, this form of exploration has no place in the detailed assessment of a deposit. Not only does it break up the strata, but there is no guarantee that all the fragments will reach the surface and be sampled. Furthermore, there will be segregation of the fragments as they rise up the borehole, and because of this, and the time taken for the chips to come to the surface, their actual original position in the strata will not be precisely known. Some of these problems have been overcome by the use of reverse circulation techniques, where the fragments are blown up the inside of the drill string and collected in a cyclone located on the drill rig. Even so, important information on jointing, bedding, soft partings in an otherwise solid bed, and textural variation, is all lost.

The only acceptable method for obtaining samples for assessing stone for building or for use as armourstone is rotary core drilling; a typical drilling rig being shown in Fig. 3.13. Non-coring methods are appropriate for determining the thickness of soft overburden or weathered stone above the potentially useable rock, or even for rapidly determining the nature of the bedrock and the stratigraphy in areas where there may be some doubt as to the structure within the deposit. Where the drill-rig is used as a pure exploration tool rather than a

Fig. 3.13. A modern drilling rig, mounted on an all-terrain vehicle, drilling a borehole in a potential dimension stone deposit in Scotland.

means of sampling, it is important that the geologist is on site and monitors the drill chippings as they are discharged from the borehole. An experienced driller will also be able to supply valuable information on the strata being penetrated from the manner in which the rig itself is operating. Such information can be of great value in assessing the amount of soft stone present, which may be lost in the dust ejected from the hole, together with the presence of cavities or broken ground.

The same drilling rig would be used for either cored or non-cored boreholes. The only difference would be the drilling tool itself. Examples of a drill bit used for obtaining borehole core and one used purely to produce rock chips, are shown in Fig. 3.14 (see also §5.3.4 and Fig. 5.28).

3.4.7.4. Choice of core size

As has been indicated previously, it is most important to ensure that samples are representative and of adequate size and number. In the case of armourstone and building stone, which are not only worked as large blocks but are also tested in the form of large pieces, the diameter of the core should be as large as possible. Since it may be necessary to cut 40 mm cubes from the core for stone durability testing, the minimum core size should be 'H' or '412', both of which provide a core of about 76 mm in diameter; the actual core diameter will vary slightly depending upon the style of core-barrel used in the drilling. Although 'N'-size core, particularly NWT, would theoretically produce a core from which a 40 mm cube could just be cut, slight variations in the core diameter and damage to the core surface, both of which can occur during drilling, would result in test cubes that could not be considered representative of the stone. 'P' or 'S'-size core, about 92 mm and 113 mm respectively would be even more satisfactory. However, the cost of drilling is normally an important factor and an increase in core size results in a greater drilling cost. For example the cost of coring at 'P'-size can be about 15% more than at 'H'-size. Thus, the cost of seven 'H'-size boreholes is approximately the same as six 'P'-size ones and the extra borehole may be considered of more value than the larger-diameter core. Every deposit of stone represents an individual case and, as such, must be considered on its merits, a balance between sample/core size and number of samples/boreholes being determined on the basis of the individual deposit and the variation within that deposit.

Fig. 3.14. Drill bits used in drilling boreholes: (**a**) impregnated diamond core bit (or surface set diamond core bit) used for producing borehole cores. (Courtesy of Boart Longyear Ltd.); (**b**) steel toothed triple cone drill bit for non-coring applications.

3.4.7.5. Core recovery

As well as core size, core recovery is extremely important. Drilling contractors normally charge on the basis of the total length of core drilled, the cost per metre reflecting the time taken to drill the stone and the time taken to recover the core from the borehole. The deeper the borehole, the longer the time taken to remove the rods in order to obtain the core. Hence, the cost of drilling a metre of stone tends to be greater, the deeper the borehole. Wireline drilling, where the core is recovered by lifting it up through the drill string, without removing the rods from the borehole, obviously reduces the time taken to recover the core; this is illustrated in Fig. 3.15.

From the point of view of the drilling contractor, the speed with which the borehole can be drilled is an important consideration. Unfortunately, the quality of the core recovered can often suffer in the desire to minimize the time taken to drill a borehole. Modern drilling equipment in the hands of an experienced driller can produce extremely good core recovery in the most difficult strata. However, core loss will occur, and this is often in softer horizons which, in the case of stone for construction use, could seriously affect the performance of the product. It is essential that such materials are recovered during the drilling if an accurate assessment of the deposit is to be made. Experience suggests that a recovery rate of 97% for each and every metre should be considered the minimum acceptable standard for cored boreholes in deposits being assessed for construction materials or industrial minerals.

3.4.7.6. Choice of drilling fluid

Another aspect of drilling which must be specified at the start of a drilling project is the nature of the drilling fluid used to remove the cuttings from the borehole and cool the drill-bit. Air, water, foam and various forms of drilling mud are all available. All can have an erosive

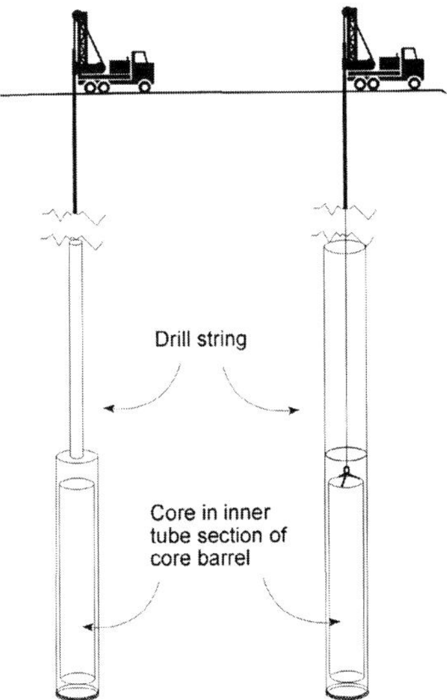

Fig. 3.15. In conventional core-drilling (left) the complete drill string has to be removed from the borehole to recover the core. In wire-line drilling (right) the core can be pulled from the core barrel to the surface through the inside of the drill rods.

effect on the core, removing softer horizons and material from cavities. Chemical foams and muds can contaminate the core, an important factor if the chemical analysis of the core samples is a requirement. Perhaps the most common drilling fluid used in exploration drilling, using mobile drill-rigs, is air. Compressors are often mounted on the drill-rig or can be easily towed on site. If boreholes are dry a small amount of water may be added to the air to assist the drilling process. This procedure also helps reduce any dust which may be blown out of the borehole by the air-flush.

3.4.7.7. Angle drilling

Although the vast majority of boreholes drilled in stone and other industrial mineral deposits are vertical, there is often a case for drilling at least some boreholes at an angle. The two main reasons for drilling in this fashion are, firstly to reduce the amount of drilling required to cut all the beds present in steeply dipping strata, and secondly to assess the quantity and nature of discontinuities, such as joints, which may be present in a deposit; Fig. 3.16 illustrates these points. Although the problem of the borehole deviating from its intended path is not as prevalent in shallow boreholes as in deep holes, there is always the potential problem of borehole deviation in angled holes. It is therefore always good practice in inclined boreholes, to determine how far from its intended path the borehole has deviated during drilling. Good drilling contractors will have the specialist equipment which will allow these calculations to be undertaken.

3.4.8. Core logging

As with information collected from outcrop exposures, the accurate logging of borehole core is extremely

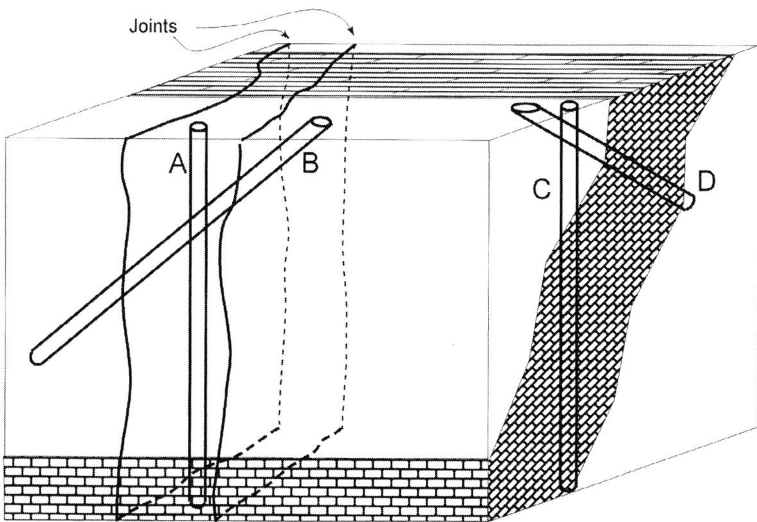

Fig. 3.16. Comparison of vertical and inclined boreholes. Vertical borehole A will not intersect any of the joints which occur in the deposit whereas the inclined borehole B can be used to determine the frequency and nature of the discontinuities. Whereas a very long vertical borehole C will be required to prove the thickness and nature of the limestone stratum, an inclined hole such as D will be considerably shorter and, therefore, cheaper.

important. Moreover, it is just as important to ascertain and log what is missing from the core as it is to accurately describe the core itself.

The borehole core will have been placed in core-boxes by the driller and the top and bottom of each core run will have been labelled with a depth figure. It is not unknown for a driller to place core in a core-box back-to-front or out of sequence. It is the site geologist's responsibility to ensure that the core is sequenced correctly. The depth labels inserted by the driller will indicate the depth of the drill bit when that particular run of core was retrieved. The geologist should maintain a check on the number and length of drill rods, and the length of the core barrel, in order to confirm this figure. Furthermore, the core recovered may well have broken off in the barrel rather than at the crown. It is essential that this fact is borne in mind and, except in uniformly solid ground, it is unlikely that the geologist's depth estimates will match those of the driller. In soft or broken ground the problem is made more difficult by core losses. The core from a one metre drill run could well be laid out in the core box by the driller to occupy a one metre length. However, when correctly re-assembled and packed into the box by the geologist, it may well be found to represent only half a metre.

Where core losses are not uniform, the driller's log may assist in determining where the losses were occurring. Ideally the geologist should be present during the drilling of the borehole in order to make his own observations on such features as loss of drilling fluid, sudden rapid advance of the drill rods or other events which would indicate inhomogeneity in the strata.

3.4.8.1. Logging methods

The core logging should record all the features of the core, lithology, colour, dip, jointing and so on. When undertaking site investigation for geotechnical purposes, engineering geologists would undertake the description of the core using routine procedures such as those laid down in BS 5930. This allows comparison to be made with other materials of similar description, whose engineering properties are known, thereby giving an early indication of the properties which may be expected on the site. Furthermore, the engineer will wish to simplify the results of the exploration into a series of 'uniform' blocks to which he can attribute values for such parameters as permeability or shear strength. The assessment of a mineral deposit requires a more flexible approach, often product-oriented, and involving mathematical modelling methods which reflect continuous variations within the deposit and which will provide predictions, to a known confidence level, of certain features occurring at any point within the deposit. For example, the knowledge that a given proportion of a quarry face will be less than the required quality for 25% of the time during the development of the quarry, is important in planning the quarry; the exact locations of the patches of low-grade material may well be of little importance.

3.4.8.2. Contents of the log

A borehole logging and sampling programme will be planned for the specific mineral and project which is being undertaken. Whereas the engineering geologist may use the approach detailed in the *Code of Practice for Site Investigations* (British Standards Institution 1981; Hawkins 1986), the minerals geologist assessing stone resources will have different aims and objectives, and the borehole log will reflect this. The principal difference will be in the emphasis given to the visual description of the core. Many of the items recorded will be similar to those required in standard schemes such as that in BS 5930. The location, collar elevation, angle of the borehole, drilling method and flushing medium are all recorded, irrespective of the purpose of the borehole. Similarly the level or levels at which water is encountered, together with the position of the water-table, indicated by the rest water level, should be noted on a daily basis. It is preferable to measure the rest water level before drilling commences each day as this will have allowed the water level to stabilize for some hours before the measurement is made. If water is used as the flushing medium this will clearly cause problems as the water in the borehole may be, at least in part, the residue from the drilling fluid. Similarly surface water from overnight rain can result in standing water in a borehole which is unrelated to the groundwater. If possible, the drilling fluid should be blown out of the borehole with compressed air at the end of a days drilling to ensure that any water measured later in the hole is groundwater.

Description of the core must be very precise. The exact depth down the borehole of each change in rock type, change in facies within a rock type, vein, fissure, cavity or other feature must be recorded precisely. Changes in colour or hardness will also be noted. The dip of both the strata and any discontinuities such as joints will also be recorded. Measurement of core recovery and the identification of those areas where core has been lost is essential, since the presence of soft material can have important implications in the viability of a scheme, whether it is in the context of volumes of waste materials, face stability, or harmful impurities concentrated in the softer materials. The rate of penetration of the drill-bit will be dependent upon the hardness of the material being drilled. Observation of the speed of drilling by the site geologist, coupled with the driller's logs, will assist in interpretation of the borehole core, especially where the recovery is not 100%.

The recording of discontinuities in borehole core can present special problems. Although every discontinuity within a vertical section will be sampled by a borehole, the actual process of drilling can introduce artificial discontinuities by breaking the core. Furthermore, the exact nature both of these introduced fractures and real discontinuities, can be obscured by rotation of the core which can cause the stone above and below the fracture to grind together, destroying the natural surfaces of the stone either side of the break. This loss of surface features, together with loss of possible soft infill material, can make identification of the nature of the discontinuity difficult. Similarly the loss of stalactitic material from a discontinuity in limestone, which may indicate water formed cavities, or slickensides on a joint indicating movement, can hinder the interpretation of the discontinuity patterns. Moreover, although the dip of a discontinuity can be obtained from borehole core, rotation of the drilling tools results in the orientation of the discontinuities being lost when the core is withdrawn from the borehole. Special logging tools, as described in §3.5.7.2, are required to obtain this information.

3.4.8.3. Sampling borehole core

The selection of core samples for testing is completely project dependent. In the case of bulk minerals such as aggregates or the raw materials for a processed material such as cement, all the core will be tested. If the core is of an adequate diameter, it is often worthwhile cutting the core in half lengthways in order to retain a complete sample of the material as a record of the sequence or for later testing. When testing of the complete core is undertaken the sample intervals are chosen on the basis of lithology or, in the case of thick beds, on the basis of the known or likely variation in chemistry or physical properties. Normally the maximum sample length for analysis would be between one and two metres, and would rarely exceed three metres. During the assessment of the deposit, it is probable that estimates of the grade of material which would occur in thicknesses equivalent to the height of a quarry bench will be made. Such calculations would be used to determine the optimum location of the benches and, if the individual sample lengths exceeded about three metres, such calculations would be meaningless, since any variation in the material would be lost within the individual analyses.

In the case of dimension stone or other material where only specific horizons were going to yield the product, the sampling of the core would be similarly specific and much of it may never be tested. However, just as the bulk mineral sampling has to be on such a scale to allow the correct design of the quarry, since different benches may provide different grades of material, the strata producing potential building materials must be tested in a similar manner. Although a bed of sandstone may be one metre thick and appear uniform, if there are slight changes in the nature of the cement in the stone, this could result in differential weathering; this could preclude the stone from being used for one metre high pieces of ashlar or cladding, if long-term uniformity in appearance was required. The size of the sample interval must, therefore, reflect both the potential changes in the stone and the probable end uses for the material. Although the full length of core through a building stone would probably not be tested, it is unlikely that the sample interval, at least in the early stages of an investigation, would exceed about 30 cm.

3.5. Shallow geophysics

3.5.1. Overview

Although used extensively in oil and mineral exploration, geophysics is considerably less important in the exploration and assessment of industrial rocks and minerals. Geophysical methods do not actually provide geological data but merely record the changes which take place when some form of energy passes through the material under study. The geologist and geophysicist must interpret the likely meaning of these changes in geological terms, based on a knowledge of the strata being studied.

Geophysics may help in refining the knowledge of the subsurface geology. The changes that the geophysical techniques measure when energy, for example in the form of electricity, sound, or radar waves, passes through the earth, result from changes in the mineralogy or moisture content of the rock, or by discontinuities such as fractures. The limited use of geophysics in industrial mineral investigations is because most such minerals tend to be worked by open-pit methods, and the exploration therefore tends to be restricted to a depth of about 100 metres beneath the surface. The number of changes in the strata caused by weathering in this zone is so great that it is extremely difficult to interpret the resulting altered geophysical signal, of whatever type this may be. At much greater depths the minor variations within a single stratum have little or no effect compared to the major change that can occur between large rock units. For example, the change in velocity of a seismic wave as it passes from Permian limestone into Triassic sandstone, when studied on a regional scale at a depth of about one or two kilometres, is likely to be much more significant than velocity changes due to minor variations caused by small discontinuities in the strata. However, shallow geophysics can be of value in helping to evaluate specific local problems, such as the precise location of a suspected fault, or the amount of fracturing that may be expected in a bed of stone. Methods of interpreting shallow geophysical data are becoming more refined, and a number of geophysical methods are now used routinely in archaeological surveys. Experience of such work has indicated that shallow geological features, of value in the search for stone for construction purposes, can be detected during these site surveys. Joint patterns, especially where the joints are filled with moisture retaining material such as clay, often become apparent amongst the archaeological features detected.

Table 3.1. *Geophysical surveying methods (Kearey & Brooks 1991)*

Method	*Measured parameter*	*'Operative' physical property*
Seismic	Travel times of reflected/refracted seismic waves	Density and elastic moduli, which determine the propagation velocity of seismic waves
Gravity	Spatial variations in the strength of the Earth's gravitational field	Density
Magnetic	Spatial variations in the strength of the geomagnetic field	Magnetic susceptibility and remanence
Electrical: Resistivity	Earth resistance	Electrical conductivity
Electrical: Induced polarization	Polarization voltages or frequency-dependent ground resistance	Electrical capacitance
Electrical: Self potential	Electrical potentials	Electrical conductivity
Electromagnetic	Response to electromagnetic radiation	Electrical conductivity and inductance
Radar	Travel times of reflected radar pulses	Dielectric constant

The density, elasticity, magnetism and electrical properties of rocks and minerals can be used in geophysical surveys. In addition, the chemical properties, in particular radioactivity, can also be used. Eight methods of geophysical survey are commonly used (Table 3.1).

Although all these methods were developed as techniques to be used at or above ground surface, many have now been adapted for use as borehole logging tools. This latter technique also frequently uses radiometric methods, detecting either the natural radioactivity of the rocks, or using a radiation source to excite the minerals in the rock and detecting the resulting radiation.

A detailed discussion of geophysical methods will not be given here, only the general principles being introduced. The interested reader should refer to the many texts available on the subject, for example Kearey & Brooks (1991) and Milsom (1989). The geophysical methods which have been used in the search for aggregates, and which may be applicable when studying deposits of potential rock fill, are discussed in Smith & Collis (1993).

3.5.2. Electrical resistivity/conductivity and electromagnetic methods

3.5.2.1 Principles

Apart from rocks containing quantities of minerals such as graphite or sulphides, the majority are poor conductors of electricity. Electric currents which do pass through rocks and sediments are carried by ions in pore waters or in the hydrous layers of clays. Pure water is also a poor conductor and, if ionized salts are not present, the conductivity of the rock will still be low. Geophysical prospecting using electrical methods does not, therefore, distinguish between different types of rock, only the effect of the contained moisture, or in some methods, the electrical properties of certain minerals within the rock. Since the resistivity of most rocks covers a wide range, they commonly overlap. It is possible, therefore, that two or more rock types in contact with each other could have similar electrical properties. If this were the case, it is unlikely that electrical methods would be able to distinguish between them, the various techniques requiring a contrast between two types of rock if they are to be detected.

3.5.2.2. Resistivity/conductivity

Resistivity or its reciprocal, conductivity, is measured by placing electrodes into the ground and passing a current between them. Due to very high contact resistances the voltage cannot be measured between these electrodes and a second pair connected to a high impedance voltmeter is used for this purpose. The path of the current through the ground is dependent upon the spacing of the electrodes: the wider the spacing the deeper the penetration of the current. By taking readings at progressively wider spacings, deeper penetration can be obtained, the changes in resistivity resulting from varying strata encountered at progressively deeper depths. It should be noted however that most of the current passes through the shallower surface layers and the depth to which the technique is effective, even with wide electrode spacing, may be limited if power sources producing several kilowatts are not available. Details of the more common electrode configurations are given in the text box.

A development of the traditional resistivity survey is electrical tomography or electrical imaging (Barker 1994). Twenty five or more electrodes are laid out in a line and connected by a multicore cable system. A switching module and a laptop computer can then select all possible electrode combinations satisfying a given electrode configuration and automatically record,

Geophysical exploration – Resistivity

There are a number of possible array configurations for the electrodes (Milsom 1989) although two, the Wenner and Schlumberger, are the most common. In the former the four electrodes are equally spaced and increased depth penetration is obtained by expanding the array whilst maintaining the equidistant nature of the electrodes. In the Schlumberger configuration the central two electrodes from which the voltage is read are relatively close together compared to the two outer ones. Depth penetration is obtained by moving these outer two. Another common procedure is the offset Wenner method in which five electrodes are set out with four being used for a reading; a second reading which is averaged with the first, uses the 'second' four.

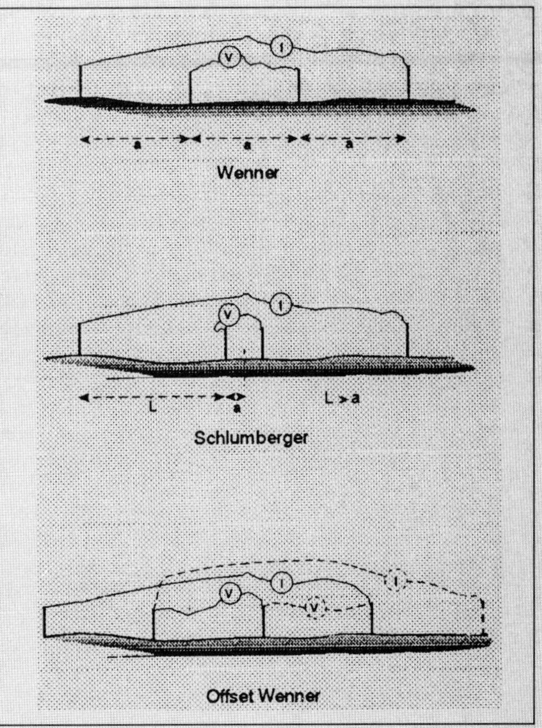

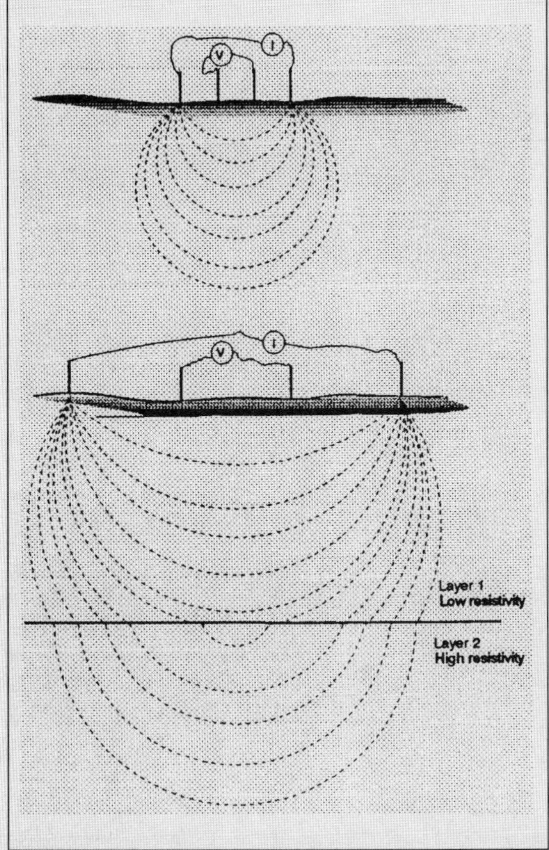

The depth of penetration of the electric current is determined by the spacing of the electrodes. The overall resistance of the ground is determined by the individual conductivities of the different strata encountered by the current. Analysis of the emf measured at different positions on the surface and with different electrode spacing, will enable a three-dimensional model of the ground resistivity to be built up. When combined with the known geological data, this can be used to correlate between geological data points and help to develop a more comprehensive geological model of the deposit being investigated.

interpret and plot the measured resistivity. A 'section' through the deposit along the line of the electrodes is thereby produced. In essence the system is merely carrying out a traditional resistivity survey in which the electrode positions and spacing were altered manually. However, the use of modern electronic equipment now allows the survey to be undertaken very rapidly and to produce the results automatically on site, potentially leading to a much more efficient field survey.

3.5.2.3. Induced polarization

When current flows in the ground, some parts of the rock can act in a manner analogous to a capacitor and the rock becomes electrically polarized. If the current creating this effect is removed, the polarization cells will discharge over a period of a few seconds, producing currents, voltages and magnetic fields which can be detected. Known as induced polarization (IP), the effect is most marked in disseminated sulphide minerals and the technique is widely used in exploration for such deposits. It is, however, of little interest in the study of rock for construction purposes.

3.5.2.4. Electromagnetic methods

Electric current flowing in a coil of wire at, or close to, the surface of the earth will produce a magnetic field at right angles to the coil. This magnetic field can generate electric currents in the ground, together with their related magnetic fields. This latter induced magnetism is detected by a second coil, which can also detect the primary magnetic field. An alternating current is applied to the primary coil. The frequency of this can be varied, as can the spacing between the coils. These two factors can be varied to give an optimum response which will allow the measurement of the electrical conductivity of the ground. The depth of penetration using this method is similar to the resistivity methods being typically a few tens of metres. For shallow work up to about 6 metres, completely portable one-man operated equipment is available. However, as the coils are fixed at either end of a long boom, normally between 3 and 4 metres in length, carried by the operator, the flexibility of the instrument in terms of coil spacing is limited.

As noted above, it should be remembered that the resistivity, induced polarization and electromagnetic/

Geophysical exploration – Electromagnetic

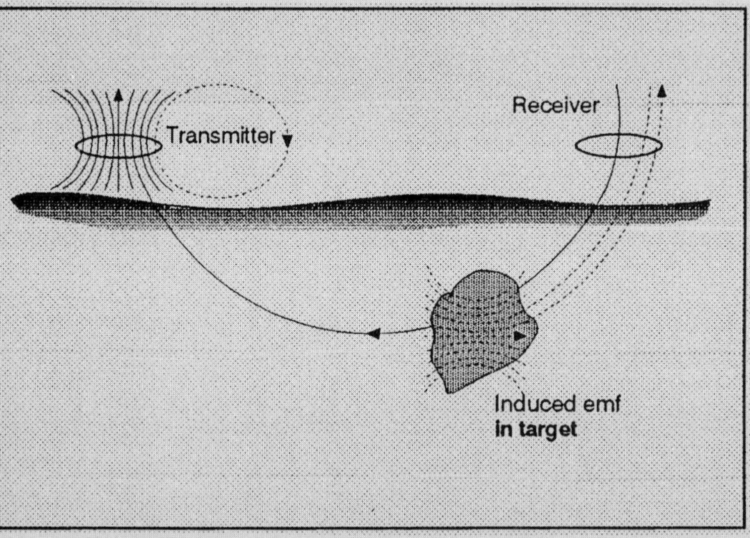

The alternating current passing through the transmitting coil will create a magnetic field which passes through the ground. This will induce an opposing emf in susceptible materials. The magnetic field thereby generated is detected by the receiving coil, which also detects the field set up by the generator. By progressively separating the coils a series of readings incorporating progressively deeper strata can be obtained. Analysis of the conductivities so obtained, when used in conjunction with geological information, will provide an indication of the sub-surface structure.

conductivity methods measure the electrical properties of the ground as a unit. The results are dependent upon moisture, discontinuities, and individual mineral species rather than upon rock type. The methods should, therefore, be used in conjunction with geological information from boreholes and outcrops. For example, resistivity has been used to locate the exact position of faults, known to exist from borehole data, and ground conductivity surveys have been used to determine the distribution of overburden overlying the reserves of a stone quarry (Barker 1983).

3.5.3. Seismic

3.5.3.1. Principles

The speed at which the shock waves from a natural or man-made source travel through the earth is determined by the nature of the rock layers through which they pass. The time taken for this seismic wave to travel from its source to a detector, coupled with a knowledge of the intervening strata, enable the distance to the source to be calculated. Conversely, if the location of the source of a seismic event is known, the time taken for a seismic wave to travel to a detector should provide information on the nature of the intervening strata. This is the basis of seismic surveying. The seismic wave is generated by means of an explosive charge in a borehole, or some form of impact on the ground surface.

When seismic waves pass through the earth, junctions between different rock types will affect their passage, resulting in their reflection or refraction. In the case of refraction, this can be simple, the path of the wave merely being bent as it passes across the junction, or critical refraction where it travels along the interface rather than passing across it. These terms are illustrated in Fig. 3.17.

Since sub-surface exploration demands that both the source of the seismic wave and the detecting equipment are on, or close to the ground surface, the phenomena of reflection and refraction of seismic waves are the basis of seismic surveys.

3.5.3.2. Applications

Although originally developed for assisting in the interpretation of geological structures and stratigraphy at depth, recent developments in digital recording instruments and portable computers capable of being operated in the field have allowed the development of shallow seismic surveying techniques which can be of assistance in the extractive industries. Although some materials such as chalk and peat attenuate the seismic energy so rapidly that the technique cannot be used, very satisfactory indications of the subsurface geology can often be obtained down to depths of between 100 and 200 metres. This is especially true where contrasting materials such as clays and limestones, or glacial deposits overlying bedrock, are involved. A typical profile is shown in Fig. 3.18.

Although modern seismic reflection techniques may provide a higher resolution than traditional shallow refraction methods, the latter have been used widely for groundwater studies (Worthington & Griffiths 1975) and for engineering studies, despite the relatively high cost compared to other geophysical techniques. Engineering uses of seismic refraction include the determination of the rippability of stone (MacGregor *et al.* 1994). Such information could clearly have a bearing on the use of the material as fill, or in the case of a stone quarry close

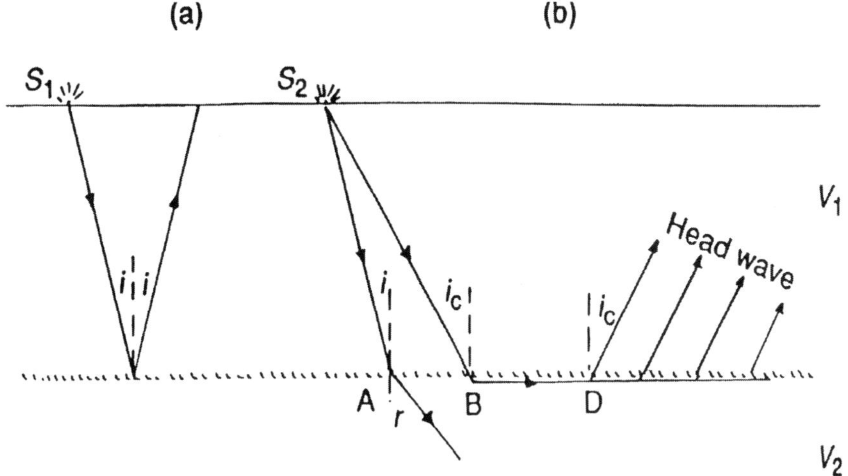

Fig. 3.17. Seismic reflection (**a**) and refraction (**b**). V_1 and V_2 are the seismic velocities of the two layers. At A where simple refraction is taking place, $\sin i/\sin r = V_1/V_2$. At B where there is critical refraction, $\sin i_c = V_1/V_2$. Energy leaves the interface from points such as D to form waves which return to the surface (after Milsom 1989).

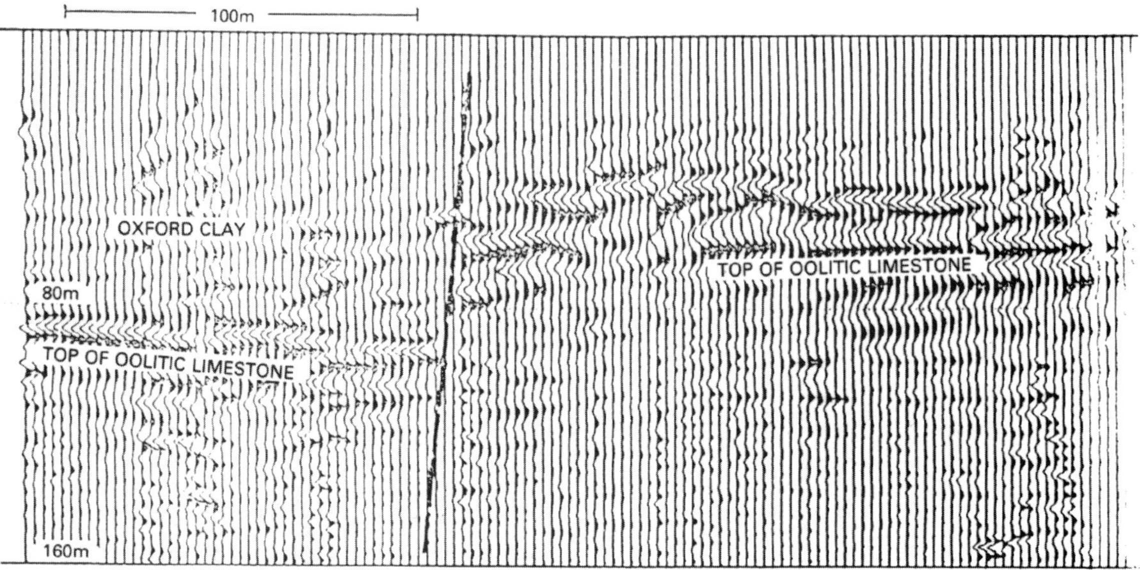

Fig. 3.18. Reflection seismic profile over a fault in sedimentary rocks (reproduced by courtesy of Quarry Management).

to noise or vibration sensitive areas, on the practicality of extracting the material without resorting to the use of explosives. It is also possible to identify zones of weathering from seismic refraction profiles and this can be important in the case of construction materials (Barker 1983).

3.5.4. Gravity

3.5.4.1. Principles

The strength of the earth's gravitational field varies from place to place due to variations in the density of the rocks beneath the surface. By measuring these variations using an instrument known as a gravimeter, it is possible to determine variations in the rock type beneath the surface. Since the gravity variation measured at ground surface is a result not only of the density of the buried rock mass, but also its size, shape and depth, interpretation of the anomalies can be difficult and can require a large quantity of other geological information if major errors are not to be made.

3.5.4.2. Applications

The change in gravity due to variations in a mineral deposit are extremely small, especially when compared to natural variations due to topography, latitude, tidal effects and even nearby walls and buildings. The accurate spatial control of each survey point, coupled with the corrections required for variations in the field due to effects not related to the sub-surface geology, result in the gravity survey normally being an inappropriate tool for surveying rock masses intended as construction materials. It is possible, however, that in circumstances where a qualitative estimate is required of such items as cavities, joints or other discontinuities which contain material of highly contrasting specific gravity to the bedrock, a gravity survey may be justified.

3.5.5. Magnetic

3.5.5.1. Principles

All materials placed in the earth's magnetic field will acquire a magnetization. However this tends to be very small and cannot normally be detected with the survey magnetometers used to measure the earth's field. However a small number of substances are ferri- or ferromagnetic. These are the naturally occurring minerals such as magnetite. Any rock containing such minerals will produce an anomalous magnetic field which will be detectable with a magnetometer.

3.5.5.2. Applications

The quantity of magnetic minerals contained in most rocks used for construction purposes is normally very low. The likelihood of a magnetic survey being of use in locating stone for fill, armourstone or building stone is therefore small. It is possible that, from time to time, a dimension or ornamental stone may be encountered which does contain sufficient magnetic mineral to allow consideration of a magnetometer as an exploration tool. However, the precautions to be taken during a magnetic survey are similar to those encountered during gravity surveys (§3.5.4.2). Local readings can be affected by

The ground penetrating radar scan from A to B has picked up the horizontal discontinuity containing weathered zone which is indicated by the arrows. The height of the face is about 9 metres.

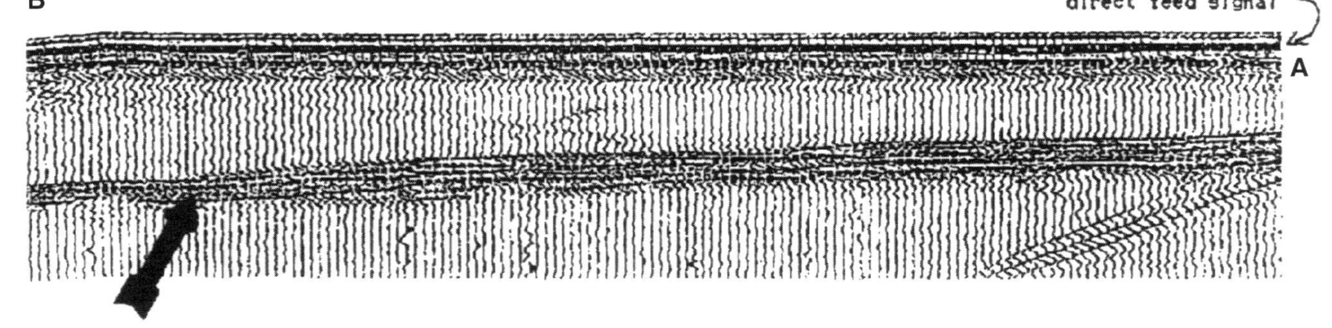

Fig. 3.19. Use of radar in a dimension stone quarry (after Unterberger & Thornton 1990).

non-geological features such as buried pipes or nearby vehicles; even the geologist's hammer could cause errors in the readings. Natural effects such as the diurnal magnetic variation and magnetic storms can also create problems if corrections are not applied to the data that are collected.

3.5.6. Radar

3.5.6.1. Principles
Radar, the acronym of *RA*dio *D*etection *A*nd *R*anging, consists essentially of an electromagnetic radiation generator producing microwaves with wavelengths of a few centimetres, the output of which is pulse modulated at radio frequencies. It is radiated as a beam, and any object in its path will reflect the pulses back to the transmitter. The time between the transmission of the signal and its return is a measure of the distance between the transmitter and the object.

Although normally operating above ground, choice of the correct radar frequencies will allow the beam to penetrate solid materials. Experiments carried out in the United States with special high-power, low-frequency radar have penetrated dry rock salt to a distance of over two kilometres (Unterberger & Thornton 1990). Whereas in air, radar signals are reflected from objects which cut the transmitted beam, in solids the beam is reflected from discontinuities within the material in a manner analogous to the way in which a beam of light is affected by flaws in a block of glass. Measurement of the time taken for the beam to travel from the transmitter to the discontinuity and back provides information on the distance to the reflector.

3.5.6.2. Applications
Although development of ground penetrating radar is still in its early stages, it can now be used routinely for the location of underground pipes, tanks and similar features. Engineering uses include the detection of voids behind tunnel linings and discontinuities in the rock concealed behind engineering structures. Work reported by Unterberger & Thornton (1990) has shown that granite can be penetrated to a depth of about 60 metres. Both veins and fractures in the granite were detected by the radar; this is illustrated in Fig. 3.19. Once the reliability of the systems are proved, the use of radar could well become important in both in the exploration for dimension stone, where it could be used for plotting joint patterns and thereby determining block size, and also in checking the integrity of large blocks extracted from the resulting quarry.

3.5.7. Borehole geophysical logging

3.5.7.1. Principles
Borehole drilling, especially core-drilling, can be expensive. Moreover, in some circumstances the core recovery can be incomplete, raising questions as to the exact nature of the ground. In the case of open hole drilling, where only rock chippings have been retrieved, accurate details of the stratigraphy down the hole can only be obtained using logging devices. Down the hole logging, using various types of detectors, can not only help to provide answers to questions posed by the borehole core, but can also allow the borehole to be used to obtain additional information on the strata penetrated, at very little extra cost. It could be argued that use of such methods should be a routine procedure on all boreholes.

The various methods which can be used to obtain information from boreholes can be conveniently divided into five types:

Direct measurement and visual inspection. Callipers for measuring the diameter of the borehole and television cameras for viewing the wall of the hole, come into this category. Inclinometers and magnetometers can be used to check the orientation of the borehole.

Electrical. The geophysical techniques for measuring electrical resistivity/conductivity, either directly or through induction, described in §3.5.2, can also be applied to the strata encountered in a borehole.

Sonic. The use of seismic data for assisting in determining the *in situ* strength of rock was noted in §3.5.3.2; similar determinations can be made down boreholes using a sonic probe. The method is also used for porosity determinations. The reflected signal from sonic pulses emitted by a rotating transducer, can be used to produce a 'picture' of the wall of the borehole, an example being shown in Fig. 3.20. Such an 'acoustic televiewer' has an advantage over an optical camera in that it can be used even in boreholes containing optically dirty drilling fluid. Indeed, it is necessary that the borehole contains water and that the sonde is submerged even if water is introduced temporarily by pumping.

Gamma ray and neutron. Measurement of radioactivity can be used for a number of purposes. In sedimentary sequences, shales tend to contain more potassium bearing clay minerals than do sandstones or limestones. Radioactive potassium isotopes will be present and gamma rays caused by these can be detected, thereby helping to identify shale or clay-rich areas, an example being shown in Fig. 3.21. If the rock forming the wall of the borehole is subjected to irradiation with gamma rays from a Cobalt-60 or Caesium-137 source, the electrons in the formation will interact with the radiation causing scattering and loss of energy in the gamma rays, proportional to the number of electrons in the formation. From this 'electron density' the bulk density of the formation can be determined. When neutrons collide with atomic nuclei they lose some of their energy. This effect is most marked when the collision is with a hydrogen atom. Since hydrogen in rocks is concentrated in

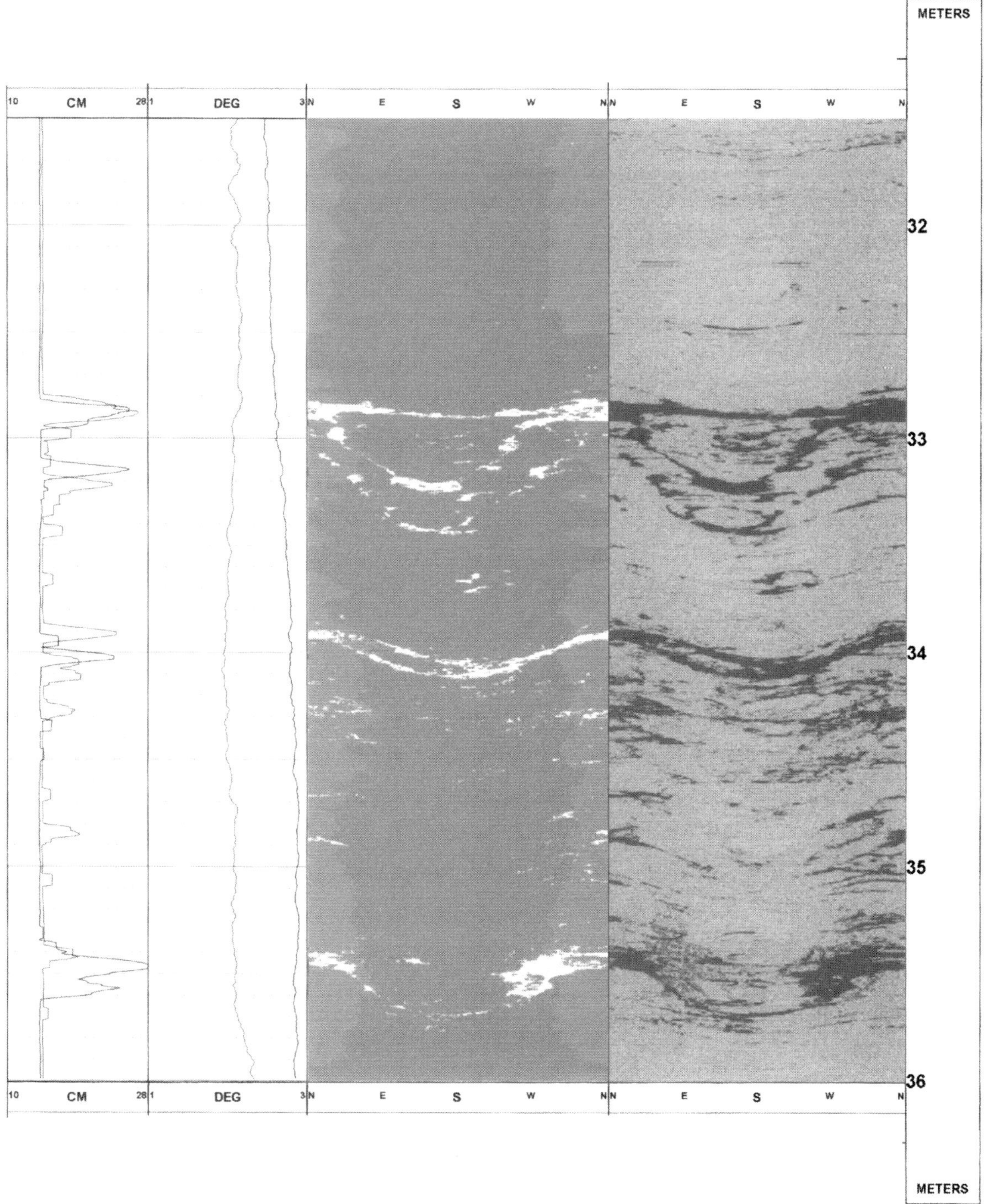

Fig. 3.20. Acoustic log of a borehole wall showing discontinuities. The left-hand column (CM) records the output from two callipers mounted on the sonde. The column labelled DEG records the angle of the borehole and its orientation. The two acoustic records both represent a 360° scan of the borehole. The left-hand trace records the signal travel time and may be considered as an 'acoustic calliper'. A number of discontinuities can be discerned in this record, two of which stand out clearly. One of these is approximately horizontal and is apparent at about 32.9 metres, possibly separating two rock types, the second appears as a set of inclined discontinuities below this level, represented as curves on the trace. (Courtesy of BEL Geophysical Ltd.)

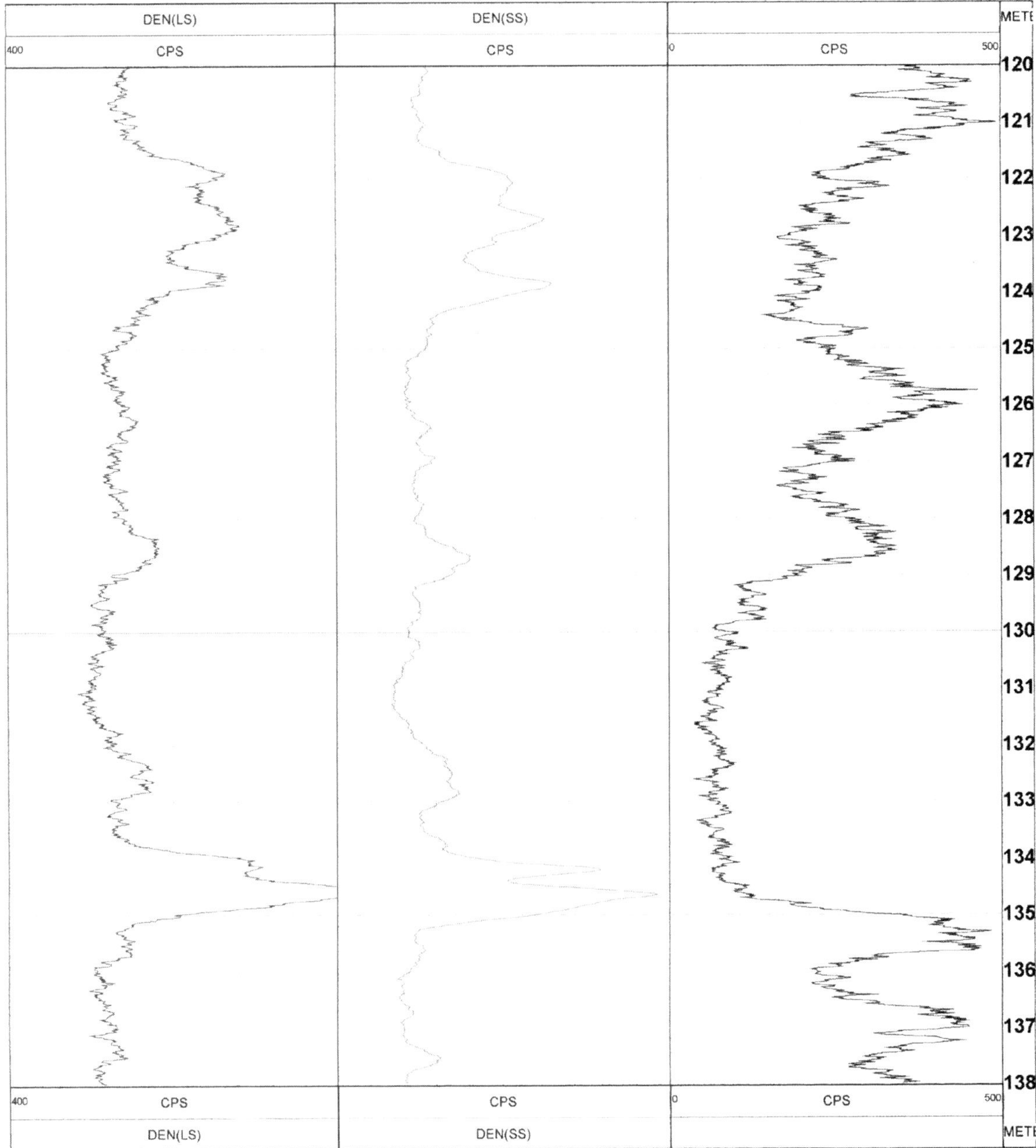

Fig. 3.21. A thick seam of pure limestone identified in a marlstone/limestone sequence. The natural gamma log on the right-hand side indicates the variable quantity of clay mineral in the marlstone, the g count is increasing to the right. Between about 130 metres and 135 metres the limestone is clearly relatively pure. Marlstone reappears at the base of the section. Uniformity of the limestone is suggested by the two gamma density logs on the left (the right-hand of these logs being the measurement over a smaller vertical interval than the record on the left). In these traces high density is on the left. The density reading of almost zero at the base of the thick band of limestone, is interpreted as a natural solution void at the junction between limestone and the clay-rich material beneath. (Courtesy of BEL Geophysical Ltd.)

Fig. 3.22. Borehole logging systems are now available which are self-contained, incorporating a winch, sonde and recording device and which can be mounted on the borehole. This enables the logging to be undertaken either by the geologist or geophysicist or by the driller himself. (Courtesy of BEL Geophysical Ltd.)

water molecules, a neutron source and detector placed in the borehole will be able to assist in distinguishing between water-filled and air-filled voids in the strata.

Water flowrate detectors. Where water is encountered in boreholes, it may be important to determine if any artesian flow is present. Equipment containing impellers can be installed in the borehole to measure the flow. Where the flow is small, electro-magnetic flowmeters or devices which heat the water and detect the time for the heat to reach a sensor, can also be used.

All the instruments used are encased in sondes which are lowered down the borehole by a small winch. Recording devices are relatively portable and, as well as collecting the data transmitted from the probe, receive signals from the winch thereby allowing a simultaneous depth record to be made. Since it is often advantageous to record different types of data from the borehole, many sondes will carry a number of different devices, for example natural gamma and calliper. A typical portable logging system is shown in Fig. 3.22.

For a detailed description of down the hole logging, works such as those by Asquith (1982) and Hurst *et al.* (1990) should be consulted.

3.5.7.2. Applications. Important factors in the exploration for stone for construction purposes are bed boundaries, the presence of discontinuities, the nature of soft horizons, and such physical features as hardness, porosity and permeability. Down the hole logging can assist in providing data which may not be available from the borehole core or chippings.

Determination of dips and the presence of discontinuities. Borehole cameras can be of use in clean boreholes, although there will be a lack of orientation information. Acoustic televiewers have the advantage of operating in conditions where optical equipment might be unsatisfactory. They also have the added advantage of containing an integral compass, allowing orientations to be accurately measured. Orientations can also be obtained from sondes bearing four micro-resistivity pads mounted at right angles to each other on callipers. A planar feature which is not perpendicular to the borehole axis, will be detected at different times by the resistivity units as the sonde is lowered down the hole; its orientation can then be calculated. A magnetometer mounted in the sonde, records the position of magnetic north, and inclinometers will supply information on the verticality of the borehole, enabling orientation corrections to be made if necessary.

Loss of soft horizons. This is a common feature when drilling cored boreholes. The exact nature and thickness of the lost material is often difficult to assess. Callipers mounted on a sonde may help determine the top and bottom of the weaker intercalations, and a natural gamma logger will assist in determining whether or not clayey or shaley material is present.

Bed boundaries. Although it should be possible to determine the position of boundaries exactly in a well-cored borehole, in those drilled by open hole methods, where only rock chippings are available, this is more difficult. The use of a resistivity probe could assist in enabling the position of junctions between beds to be determined.

Porosity and permeability. The neutron probe was designed to help determine these parameters. In common with most probes, the neutron device requires a fluid-filled borehole to operate. In cases where the borehole is dry or lined with plastic casing, the electro-magnetic induction sonde can be used to give an indication of these factors.

Density and porosity. The density logging device, using a gamma ray source is normally used for this purpose. If used in conjunction with a sonic log, which also assists in porosity determination, an indication of rock strength may also be obtained.

3.6. Field analysis

3.6.1. Chemical and mineralogical analysis

The speed with which sample preparation and analysis can be undertaken in modern laboratories, coupled with an efficient world-wide network of commercial courier services for transporting samples, can result in chemical analyses being available very soon after a sample has been collected. Some basic tests, which may influence the direction of the exploration, can however be carried out in the field. Pure limestone can be distinguished from magnesian limestone using dilute hydrochloric acid, the reaction with the former being much more violent than with stone containing dolomite. The same technique can be used to give some indication of the nature of the cement in a sandstone. A carbonate cement will react with acid, whereas other types of cement will not.

The presence of soluble sulphate in stone, which could cause problems if the stone was used for construction purposes, can be rapidly detected using barium chloride solution. The crushed sample is treated with dilute hydrochloric acid, and a few drops of the barium chloride solution added to the resulting liquor. A white precipitate indicates the presence of sulphate.

It has been suggested that radon gas may prove to be a potential health hazard if allowed to accumulate and inhaled over a long period of time. Being formed naturally by the radioactive decay of uranium, which occurs in many rocks to a greater or lesser extent, it is conceivable that there could be a build-up of the gas in enclosed spaces in buildings constructed of such rocks. Field detection of uranium in the rock, using a portable gamma-ray spectrometer can indicate the potential for the generation of radon. It is also possible to measure

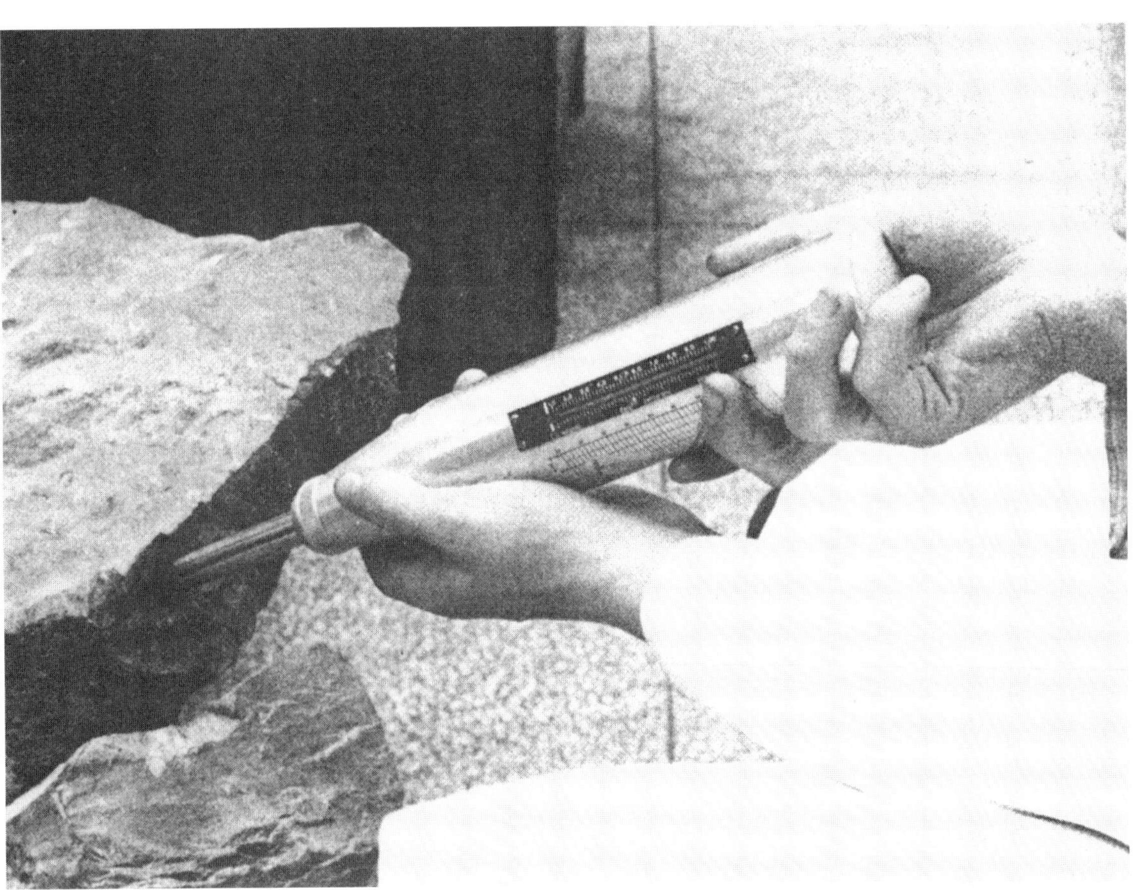

Fig. 3.23. The Schmidt hammer, used for field determination of rock strength.

the radon gas directly by inserting detectors into the soil above the suspect strata.

The identification of the mineralogy of stone in the field is part of the routine field description of the rock. In coarse to medium-grained material, mineral identification can normally be undertaken with the aid of a hand lens. For finer-grained material a field microscope may be required.

3.6.2. Physical analysis

In any exploration for construction materials, the main mechanical property which may be useful in assessing rock quality is that of compressive strength. This can be assessed in a number of ways in the field. A sample of core, or even a hand sample, can be tested in a portable point load tester, and the point load index obtained by loading the specimen across the diameter of the core until disruption occurs. Details of this test are provided in appendices B and C. The instrument produces a set of index values, thereby allowing different samples to be compared. However, its results have to be correlated with accurate unconfined compressive strength values from the same rock, if accurate compressive strength determinations are required. The resistance of potential armourstone to impact can be assessed in the field using the portable point load tester (Latham 1998). The same equipment can also be used to provide information on the possible behaviour of a rock being considered for incorporation in a rock fill, since, as discussed in Chapter 7 the particle strength and hardness of the material will have a significant influence on the behaviour of the stone during compaction.

The competence, or strength, of any exposed rock mass in the field can be tested in a non-destructive manner using a Schmidt hammer (Fig. 3.23). This is a versatile piece of apparatus which is easy to use under field conditions. Not only can it be used to test rock *in situ*, but also blocks of stone and borehole core. The instrument consists of a small metal cylinder containing a piston which is held under compression by a spring. When placed against a flat rock surface, the spring is released. The rebound of the hammer is expressed as a percentage of the forward travel of the piston, and the result is given as a number expressed as the 'rebound number', R. The value of R, which can vary between 0 and 70, can be correlated against both seismic velocity and unconfined compressive strength, high numbers correlating with both high compressive strengths and high seismic velocities. However, maintenance of the hammer at regular intervals is important if reproducible results are to be obtained.

The cone indenter, developed by National Coal Board (later British Coal), is a less suitable indicator of rock strength. It measures the penetration of a tungsten carbide tipped indenter into the specimen under a standard applied load. The unconfined compressive strength can be calculated from the results. Only fine-grained rocks should be tested with the equipment, since there is a danger that, in coarse-grained rock, the indenter will only be acting upon an individual grain.

Practical details of all these methods are provided by West (1991).

3.7. Sample preparation

3.7.1. Sample size

The problems associated with accurate sampling have been discussed at length in §3.4. Sample preparation for testing is often covered in the specification for the tests to be undertaken. Such specifications often indicate the size and/or number of samples to be taken. Unfortunately, the sample size is a function of the variability of the material to be tested, and to quote a fixed sample size could well lead to a seriously inaccurate assessment of the deposit. For example six samples are required for the acid immersion test described by the Building Research Establishment (Ross & Butlin 1989). This may well be adequate for a bed of building stone with low variability, but in some circumstances could result in an inaccurate assessment. Some standards indicate minimum sample quantities, for example BS 812:1975, but do not provide guidance on the actual size required for reproducible results; and there will always be the temptation to use the minimum acceptable quantity of sample. It is always better to over-sample and test than to under-sample. The establishment of even the smallest quarry is probably going to cost at least £100 000 at today's prices. If, once opened up, the stone is found to be unsuitable for the purpose for which it was intended, the initial saving of a few thousands of pounds on sampling and testing will be regretted.

3.7.2. Sample reduction

Since sample testing is often destructive, it is always preferable to retain half the borehole core for future reference during the assessment. The core should be split lengthways, preferably using a diamond saw.

Although most tests on stone used for construction purposes are undertaken on blocks of material, it is possible that chemical tests for impurities may be required. Bearing in mind that only one or two grams of sample are analysed, great care must be taken to ensure that this small amount is truly representative of the bulk of the material. Laboratory jaw crushers can reduce most stone down to about 1 mm. However this can take time and some materials tend to compact on the jaws of the crusher when this level of comminution is attempted. Crushing in a jaw crusher down to about 4 mm, followed by reduction of a portion of this material down to 1 mm using a laboratory crushing roll has been found to be satisfactory. All crushers should be of a design which allows them to be opened up and cleaned between each sample. Assuming a typical sedimentary rock, about 8 kg of 4 mm crusher product will be required if the sub-sample is to be representative. Splitting of samples should always be undertaken using a rotary cascade type of sample splitter. Although riffles are satisfactory if used correctly, they need to be correctly dimensioned for the material being sampled (Gy 1971). Coning and quartering is subject to too many variables and should never be used for accurate sample splitting.

The material which has been reduced to 1 mm or less in size by crushing, is again sampled using a rotary cascade splitter before being milled in a vibratory cup mill, or similar equipment, prior to analysis. In order to minimize any chance of contamination from the equipment, care should be taken to choose the correct type of mill and the most suitable material for the grinding elements. Most rocks, whether igneous or sedimentary, are successfully milled in a vibrating cup mill. However some materials, such as gypsum or coal can be comminuted in a disk mill. Tungsten carbide grinding media are normally preferred for grinding, since the hardness reduces wear, and therefore contamination, and the high density reduces the milling time. Other materials such as agate and zirconia are available, although their wear properties are not as good as tungsten carbide. Although grinding media made from various steel alloys are available, their wear characteristics are such that detectable quantities of iron can often contaminate the sample being ground, especially when the rock contains quartz. New ceramic materials, such as the silicon nitride alloys known as sialons, are now available for grinding media and have a high resistance to wear. However, their relatively low density can result in extended milling times.

Numerous methods of analysis exist, the choice often depending upon the elements whose concentrations are being sought. Most, however, only utilize a small portion of the milled material. Fortunately rotary sample dividers are available which will allow accurate splitting of the powder into portions of the correct quantity for analysis.

3.8. Overview of testing requirements

Testing the samples obtained during exploration is an integral part of the investigation process, since the test results can radically affect the exploration programme. For example, should it be discovered during the field sampling that there was a change in the mineralogical composition of the stone under investigation, and that this change could affect the durability of the material, it may be necessary to change the search area, or even abort the work in that particular location.

As was indicated previously, one of the main reasons for obtaining borehole core is to obtain samples which are suitable for testing. The test results will not only determine if the material is suitable for its intended purpose, they will also provide the information upon which the planning of the extraction will be undertaken. In the context of stone for construction purposes, armourstone and fill, the rock will be tested in order to determine its composition, properties such as density and water absorption, strength, abrasion resistance and durability. The relevant tests are discussed fully in Chapters 7, 8 and 9 which discuss the different uses of stone in construction, and are detailed in Appendix B. Some test results for British natural building stones are given in Appendix C. Only the outlines of the tests in the context of surface and borehole sampling will be discussed here.

3.8.1. Petrography

The manner in which a stone will behave when used for an engineering purpose, be that as fill, as armourstone or as a building material, is dependent, not only upon the macroscopic texture of the rock, but also upon the minerals from which it is composed, and the relationships between those minerals (ISRM 1978*a*). A petrographic study of the stone is, therefore, the most important test which can be undertaken.

Most rocks and minerals are transparent when cut extremely thin, and the microscopic examination of them is undertaken using thin sections mounted on glass slides. Those materials, such as some metal ores, and extremely fine-grained rocks which appear relatively opaque in standard thin section, can be polished and studied using reflected-light microscopy. The methods used for preparing thin and polished sections are discussed fully by Humphries (1992).

The procedures used for a petrographic analysis are well documented in numerous textbooks, for example Cox *et al.* (1988). Not only is it important to identify the various components of a rock, the minerals in an igneous or metamorphic rock, and the fragments or minerals which make up a sedimentary rock, but the state of weathering of these components must also be noted. Figure 3.24 illustrates a typical feature in a sedimentary rock which may cause a problem once the stone begins to weather.

As well as the individual grains in a sedimentary rock, the nature of the cement is also extremely important, since it is often within the cement that the breakdown of the rock due to weathering starts. Similarly the groundmass, which can enclose the larger crystals in extrusive rocks such as basalt, should also be carefully studied to ensure that natural glass, which can be relatively unstable and react with materials such as Portland cement, is not present in undesirable quantities. The presence of other minerals such as feldspathoids and zeolites, which can occur as secondary as well as primary minerals, and which are also potentially highly reactive,

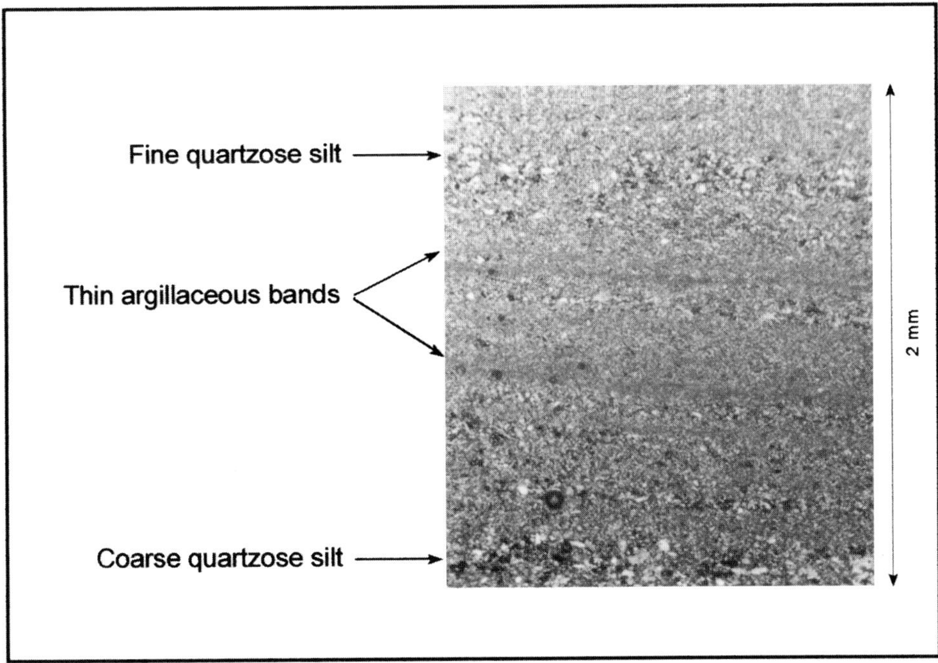

Fig. 3.24. A photomicrograph of a thin section of siltstone which has potential use as a roofing material. Thin layers of argillaceous material could, however, be a source of weakness, resulting in splitting of tiles made from this stone. Detailed testing would be required to determine whether or not this was a problem.

should be noted even if they only occur in small quantities. Identification of these minerals is particularly important when the rock is being considered as a source of armourstone, since the Sonnenbrand effect, which leads to cracking of the stone, is believed to be caused by such minerals (Latham 1996). Basalt, found in many volcanic areas (§2.6.1) and which, being hard, massive and inert, is potentially suitable for armourstone, can, unfortunately, be a common source of such minerals.

The long-term stability of stone, especially that used for rock fill and armourstone, both of which will tend to be located in wet environments, can be seriously affected by layered minerals such as clays. In particular the smectite group of clay minerals, which includes montmorillonite, adsorb moisture and swell, causing disruption to the rock. Petrographic analysis will enable such minerals to be identified at an early stage in the exploration.

As the rate of weathering of stone is often related to its exposure to moisture and the atmosphere, as well as to contaminants carried by these media, an important feature which should be measured during a petrographic study, is the presence of voids and micro-fractures naturally occurring within the stone. Some of these will be completely closed. Others, however, will be interconnected and will therefore have the potential to carry harmful materials deep into the stone. Impregnation of the rock sample with coloured synthetic resin or Canada balsam, prior to thin sectioning and petrographic assessment, will allow the closed voids to be distinguished from those which are inter-connected.

Although the stone under investigation will be described both in bulk and hand sample, most of the petrographic study will be undertaken using thin sections. These normally measure only about 20 mm by 40 mm and great care should, therefore, be taken to ensure that, not only are sufficient samples studied, but also that sections are cut in enough directions to ensure that any lineations, be they physical or crystallographic, are identified. In order to relate any such features found in the rock to the deposit as a whole, it is important that the sections have been prepared from orientated hand samples or borehole core.

3.8.2. Density of the stone

There are a number of ways in which density can be measured. These are discussed in Appendix B. For the purposes of the assessment of a mineral deposit, the density used would be the dry mass per unit volume in the ground, or dry bulk density, this giving a minimum reserve figure. Although many methods of measuring this density exist, probably the most reliable is to thoroughly dry and determine the mass of lengths of borehole core; these should be of the order of one or two metres long. Since, as long as the drilling was to a good standard, the core will be of uniform diameter, the volume of a length of core is easily determined and the mass, being quite high, will provide a very realistic estimate of the density of the stone. It should, however, be noted that, as a variation will exist in the deposit, the calculation should be repeated on samples from as many boreholes as is necessary to provide a consistent average result.

3.8.3. Water absorption

The amount of water which will be absorbed by a stone, together with the rate at which the absorption takes place, may provide an indication of the potential durability of the stone, since it is dependent upon the number and size of the pores within the rock. However, although increased pore space within a rock may produce a greater surface area, this does not necessarily result in increased degradation, nor does it necessarily result in an increased risk of frost susceptibility, unless the pores are completely filled. Even when used in conjunction with the measurement of porosity and saturation coefficient discussed in §3.5.6, it should only be used in a qualitative, rather than a quantitative, manner, or for comparison with similar materials with known properties. The various methods of determining water absorption in building stone are discussed by Yates *et al.* (1994), and in Appendix B.

Although water absorption may only provide an indication of the resistance of a stone to weathering in situations of high moisture content, it should be noted that the water absorption test is recommended in the '*Manual on the Use of Rock in Coastal and Shoreline Engineering*' (CIRIA/CUR 1991), and has been proposed as a mandatory test in the draft CEN (Comité de Europèen Normalization) specification for armourstone (Latham 1998). The British Standard for roofing slates, BS 680 : Part 2 : 1971, also includes the test as a measure of frost resistance, as do some standards from other parts of the world (Table 9.4). Furthermore, consideration is being given to its inclusion in the European Standards, currently under discussion, for a range of natural stone products (§9.6.4). When investigating any deposit as a potential source of construction material, it is always wise to determine the current state of the national standards, as these are always subject to review.

3.8.4. Strength

Although it is not uncommon for the compressive strength of a building stone to be requested by architects, civil engineers or builders, the strength of most rocks used for construction purposes, if used correctly, is commonly greater than that of man-made materials (Jefferson 1993); the strength of the mortar between the stone blocks can however reduce the overall strength of the masonry. Moreover, due to the inherent inhomogeneous nature of all rock, no one figure can represent the strength of a stone. This is acknowledged in ASTM C 170–90, which requires that uniaxial testing is not only carried out wet and dry, but also parallel to, as well as normal to the bedding. Details of the various tests for both compressive and shear strengths are given in Appendix B. The range of tests designed to assess the strength characteristics of potential rock fill and armourstone, are discussed in §§7.3 and 8.5 respectively.

It is important to remember that the strength of rock can decrease dramatically due to weathering (e.g. Geological Society 1995) and great care must be taken to ensure that only fresh rock is sampled, preferably from a recent quarry face or pit.

3.8.5. Abrasion and slip resistance

These tests are used to determine the suitability of a material for paving, but it is unlikely that it would be necessary to carry out the relevant tests, discussed in §§9.6.2.5, 9.6.2.6 and Appendix B, at the exploration stage. If, however, the supply of paving stone was likely to be a major economic consideration of the deposit being investigated, it would be necessary to confirm the suitability of the material for such a use.

Armourstone can also be subject to abrasion through the effect of water borne sand or movement within the structure. Specialized tests to investigate the resistance of potential raw materials to be used in structures where this may occur, have been developed and are discussed in §8.5.4.5.

3.8.6. Durability

All stone will weather, the rate of weathering being dependent upon a large number of factors. The durability of a stone product is similarly dependent upon the stone type, compatibility with nearby materials, geographical location, use and expected lifetime of the stone (Yates *et al.* 1994). Apart from rock type, it is unlikely that any of these parameters will be known when a deposit is being investigated. There are a number of tests which have been devised with the aim of determining the durability of stone. Some of these are standard tests, others have been developed by the Building Research Establishment and have tended to be used by the industry to give an indication of the durability of building stones. The tests are discussed in §9.6.2.4 and in Appendix B.

The testing of building stone for durability has aroused considerable debate. This has arisen mainly because, apart from the freeze–thaw test, the method of testing bears little or no relation to the processes which actually take place when stone weathers. Moreover, there is always an element of 'pass' or 'fail' with any test and this has the unfortunate effect of prejudicing architects and builders against stone which, although completely satisfactory for construction purposes, has 'failed' one or more of the durability tests. For example Ancaster stone, a traditional building stone from the Jurassic limestone of Lincolnshire, has been used extensively in cathedrals and other prestigious buildings, as well as in vernacular architecture, since Roman times. This stone can fail the crystallization test (Leary 1983). Triassic sandstones such as Red St. Bees and Shawk have been used for Hadrian's Wall, Windsor Castle, the docks at Barrow-in-Furness and Cardiff, Manchester Cathedral and many other major works. This stone fails the acid immersion test for sandstone (Leary 1986).

The durability of a stone is controlled by its composition. The petrographic analysis of the rock will, therefore, provide a considerable amount of information on the suitability of the material for different uses. If so-called durability tests, such as the crystallization test are carried out, the results should only be used to compare the material with similar materials whose weathering characteristics are known. Where a stone has been used for a number of years, apparently poor test results can be tempered with visual inspection of such buildings. When a new building stone is being brought onto the market there will be no reference buildings to provide evidence of the durability of the stone. In these circumstances apparently poor test results can have an extremely detrimental effect on the potential sales of the new stone. Great care must, therefore, be taken to explain the significance of the tests in the context of the purpose for which the stone is to be used.

References

American Society for Testing and Materials 1971. *Standard Method of Test for Unconfined Compressive Strength of Intact Rock Core Specimens.* D 2938–71a.

——1987. *Test Method for Modulus of Rupture of Dimension Stone.* C 99–87.

——1989. *Flexural Strength of Dimension Stone.* C 880–89.

——1990. *Test Method for Compressive Strength of Dimension Stone.* C 170–90.

Annels, A. E. (ed.) 1992. *Case Histories and Methods in Mineral Resource Evaluation*, Geological Society, London, Special Publications, **63**.

Arkell, W. J. 1947. *Oxford Stone.* Faber & Faber, London.

Armitage, M. G. & Potts, F. A. 1994. Some comments on the classification of resources and reserves. *In*: Whateley, M. K. G. & Harvey, P. K. (eds) *Mineral Resource Evaluation II: Methods and Case Histories.* Geological Society, London, Special Publications, **79**, 11–16.

Asquith, G. B. with Gibson, C. R. 1982. *Basic Well Log Analysis for Geologists.* Methods in exploration series. The American Association of Petroleum Geologists, Tulsa.

Barker, R. D. 1983. Comparison of geophysical techniques over the Cliffe Hill markfieldite, Leicestershire. *In*: Atkinson, K. & Brassington, R. (eds) *Prospecting and Evaluation of Non-metallic Rocks and Minerals.* The Institution of Geologists, London, 57–68.

——1994. Recent examples of the application of electrical imaging in the extractive minerals industry. *Abstracts Volume.* Extractive industry Geology '94. University of Sheffield. Institute of Mining & Metallurgy and Geological Society.

Barnes, J. W. 1982. *Basic Geological Mapping.* Geological Society Handbook Series. Wiley, Chichester.

Beaumont, T. E. 1979. Remote sensing for the location and mapping of engineering construction materials in developing countries. *Quarterly Journal of Engineering Geology*, **12**, 147–158.

Bock, Y. 1994. Crustal deformation and earthquakes. *Geotimes*, **39**, No. 6, 16–18.

British Government 1995. Statutory Instrument, S.I. No. 418.

British Standards Institution 1971. *Specification for Roofing Slates.* BS 680: Part 2.

——1975. *Methods for Sampling and Testing of Mineral Aggregates and Fillers.* BS 812.

——1981. *Code of Practice for Site Investigations.* BS 5930.

Cassinis, R. 1977. Use of remote sensing from space platforms for regional geological evaluation and for planning ground exploration. *Geophysical Prospecting*, **25**, 636–657.

CIRIA/CUR 1991. *Manual on the Use of Rock in Coastal and Shoreline Engineering.* Construction Industry Research and Information Association Special Publication 83, London. Centre for Civil Engineering Research, Codes and Specifications Report 154, Gouda.

Compton, R. R. 1962. *Manual of Field Geology.* Wiley, New York.

Cox, K. G., Price, N. B. & Harte, B. 1988. *The Practical Study of Crystals, Minerals and Rocks.* Revised first edition. McGraw-Hill Book Co. London.

Dialog Information Services 1991. *Geoarchive Bluesheet.* Dialog File 58, Dialog Information Services Inc. Palo Alto.

Drury, S. A. 1993. *Image Interpretation in Geology.* Chapman & Hall, London.

Geological Society 1995. The description and classification of weathered rocks for engineering purposes. Geological Society Engineering Group Working Party Report. *Quarterly Journal of Engineering Geology*, **28**, 207–242.

Geological Society of America 1991. *Rock Color Chart.* Prepared by the Rock-Color Chart Committee, published by The Geological Society of America, Boulder.

Goodman, R. E. & Shi, G. 1985. *Block Theory and its Application to Rock Engineering.* Prentice-Hall, New Jersey.

Goodsall, G. D. & Mathews, D. H. 1970. Sampling of road surfacing materials. *Journal of Applied Chemistry*, 361–366.

Gy, P. 1967. *L'échantillonnage des Minerais en Vrac – Tome 1: Théorie Générale.* Special issue of Revue de L'industrie Minérale, January 15 1967. Société de l'Industrie Minérale, Saint-Etienne.

——1971. *L'échantillonnage des Minerais en Vrac – Tome 2: Théorie Générale, Erreurs Opératoires, Compléments.* Mémoires du, B. R. G. M., No. 67. Bureau de Recherches Géologiques et Minières, Orléans.

——1979. *Sampling of Particulate Materials, Theory and Practice*. Developments in Geomathematics, 4. Elsevier Scientific Publishing Company. Amsterdam.

HAWKINS, A. B. (ed.) 1986. *Site Investigation Practice: Assessing BS 5930*. Geological Society, London, Engineering Geology Special Publications **2**.

HINGLEY, W. & OSBORN, F. 1989. *Financial Management Made Simple*. 2nd edition. Made Simple Books. Heinemann Professional Publishing Ltd., Oxford.

HUDSON, J. A. 1989. *Rock Mechanics Principles in Engineering Practice*. CIRIA, Butterworths, Borough Green.

HUMPHRIES, D. W. 1992. *The Preparation of Thin Sections of Rocks, Minerals, and Ceramics*. Royal Microscopical Society, Microscopy Handbooks, No. 24. Oxford University Press, Oxford.

HURST, A., LOVELL, M. A. & MORTON, A. C. (eds) 1990. *Geological Applications of Wireline Logs*. Geological Society, London, Special Publications, **48**.

ISRM 1978*a*. Suggested method for petrographic description of rocks. International Society for Rock Mechanics Commission on Standardisation of Laboratory and Field Tests. *International Journal of Rock Mechanics and Mining Sciences & Geomechanics Abstracts*, **15**, No. 2, 41–45.

——1978*b*. Suggested methods for the quantitative description of discontinuities in rock masses. International Society for Rock Mechanics Commission on Standardisation of Laboratory and Field Tests. *International Journal of Rock Mechanics and Mining Sciences & Geomechanics Abstracts*, **15**, No. 6, 319–368.

JEFFERSON, D. P. 1993. Building stone: the geological dimension. *Quarterly Journal of Engineering Geology*, **26**, 305–319.

KEAREY, P. & BROOKS, M. 1991. *An Introduction to Geophysical Exploration*, Second edition. Blackwell Scientific Publications, London.

LAMB, A. & LAWRENCE, G. 1993. 'Remote sensing in oil and mineral exploration' *Geoscientist*, **3**, No. 6, 2–3.

LATHAM, J.-P. 1998. Assessment and specification of armourstone quality: from CIRIA/CUR (1991) to CEN (2000). *In*: LATHAM, J.-P. (ed.) *Advances in Aggregates and Armourstone Evaluation*. Geological Society, London, Engineering Geology Special Publications, **13**, 65–85.

LEARY, E. 1983. *The Building Limestones of the British Isles*. Building Research Establishment Report SO 36. HMSO, London.

——1986. *The Building Sandstones of the British Isles*. Building Research Establishment Report BR 84. HMSO, London.

MACGREGOR, F., FELL, R., MOSTYN, G. R., HOCKING, G. & MCNALLY, G. 1994. The estimation of rock rippability. *Quarterly Journal of Engineering Geology*, **27**, 123–144.

MCCLAY, K. 1987. *The Mapping of Geological Structures*. Geological Society Handbook Series. Wiley, Chichester.

MCKAY, D. J. 1994. Bibliographic reference systems for the earth sciences. *Geoscientist*, **4**, No. 6, 7–8.

MILSOM, J. 1989. *Field Geophysics*. Geological Society Handbook Series. Wiley, Chichester.

PARSONS, D. 1990. Review and Prospect: The Stone Industry in Roman, Anglo-Saxon and Medieval England. *In*: PARSONS, D. (ed.) *Stone. Quarrying and Building in England. AD 43–1525*. Phillimore & Co. Ltd., Chichester in association with The Royal Archaeological Institute, 1–15.

PERRY, J. & WEST, G. 1996. *Sources of information for site investigations in Britain*, TRL Report 192, Transport Research Laboratory, Crowthorne.

PRESS, N. P. 1983. The use of Landsat imagery for industrial mineral prospecting. *In*: ATKINSON, K. & BRASSINGTON, R. (eds) *Prospecting and Evaluation of Non-metallic Rocks and Minerals*. The Institution of Geologists, London, 15–20.

PRIEST, S. D. 1993. *Discontinuity Analysis for Rock Engineering*. Chapman and Hall, London.

RIDDLER, G. P. 1998. Mineral Reserve and Mineral Resource Definitions: The 'Denver Accord' signals progress towards an international reporting standard. *International Mining and Minerals*, **1**, 4, 90–93.

ROSS, K. D. & BUTLIN, R. N. 1989. *Durability Tests for Building Stone*. Report BR 141. Building Research Establishment, Watford.

SEDMAN, J. H. F. & STANLEY, L. 1990. Variations in the physical properties of porous building limestones. *Stone Industries*, **25**(6), 22–24.

S. I. 1995 No. 418. *Town and Country Planning (General Permitted Development) Order 1995*. HMSO, London.

SIMMONS, G. 1994. Kinematic GPS for volumetric survey. *Reporter*. No. 32, Leica AG, Heerbrugg.

SMITH, M. R. & COLLIS, L. (eds) 1993. *Aggregates – Sand, Gravel and Crushed Rock Aggregates for Construction Purposes*. Second edition. Geological Society, London, Engineering Geology Special Publications, **9**.

UNTERBERGER, R. R. & THORNTON, M. 1990. Radar sees through rocks. Research in the US. *Quarry Management*. June 1990, 43–44.

WANG, H., LATHAM, J.-P. & POOLE, A. 1991*a*. Predictions of block size distributions for quarrying. *Quarterly Journal of Engineering Geology*, **24**, 91–99.

——1991*b*. Blast design for armour stone production. *Quarry Management*, Part, 1, July 1991, 17–21, Part, 2, August 1991, 19–22.

WEST, G. 1991. *The Field Description of Engineering Soils and Rocks*. Geological Society Handbook Series. Wiley, Chichester.

WHATELEY, M. K. G. & HARVEY, P. K. 1994. *Mineral Resource Evaluation II, Methods and Case Histories*. Geological Society, London, Special Publications, **79**,

WORTHINGTON, P. F. & GRIFFITHS, D. H. 1975. The application of geophysical methods in the exploration and development of sandstone aquifers. *Quarterly Journal of Engineering Geology*, **8**, 73–102.

YATES, T., LEWRY, A. & BUTLIN, R. 1994. *Stone testing – The use and interpretation of test methods for natural building stone*. BRE Client Report CR44/94. Building Research Establishment, Watford.

4. Assessment

4.1. Introduction

Although, as indicated in Fig. 3.1, the assessment of the rock or mineral deposit utilizes the data obtained from the field work and laboratory studies, the actual process of assessing the data is continuous throughout the raw material investigation. For example, assessment of the initial drilling results or laboratory analyses can radically alter the location of later boreholes. The physical and chemical models of the deposit are therefore being built up and refined continuously during the exploration. This is illustrated in Fig. 4.1. In fact, the exploration phase of the project will only cease once the models are sufficiently refined to enable the economic viability of the project to be determined.

The aim of the assessment is to determine the size and quality of the reserve of raw material and case histories of exploration and assessment of mineral deposits illustrating the methods used have been provided by Annels (1992) and Whateley & Harvey (1994). Invariably the reserve will be less than the resource which is present. Moreover, the size of any reserve will vary with time, since it is dependent upon extraction costs and the market value of the product. If the average production cost of a dimension stone increases due to thick overburden in part of the quarry, but market forces reduce the price of stone for construction, the reserve of stone, calculated using earlier financial criteria, could well be reduced. This would be a result of having to minimize quarrying costs by working only that material with little overburden.

4.2. Determination of the suitability and grade of the stone

Whereas the raw materials for products such as ceramics, lime or cement, can be blended prior to processing, this is not possible with stone for construction purposes. The stone as extracted must have acceptable properties for its final use. Every individual block of armourstone must satisfy the engineering criteria specified for the job to which it is being supplied. Low-grade material cannot be blended with stone which has a higher grade than required and must therefore be discarded as waste.

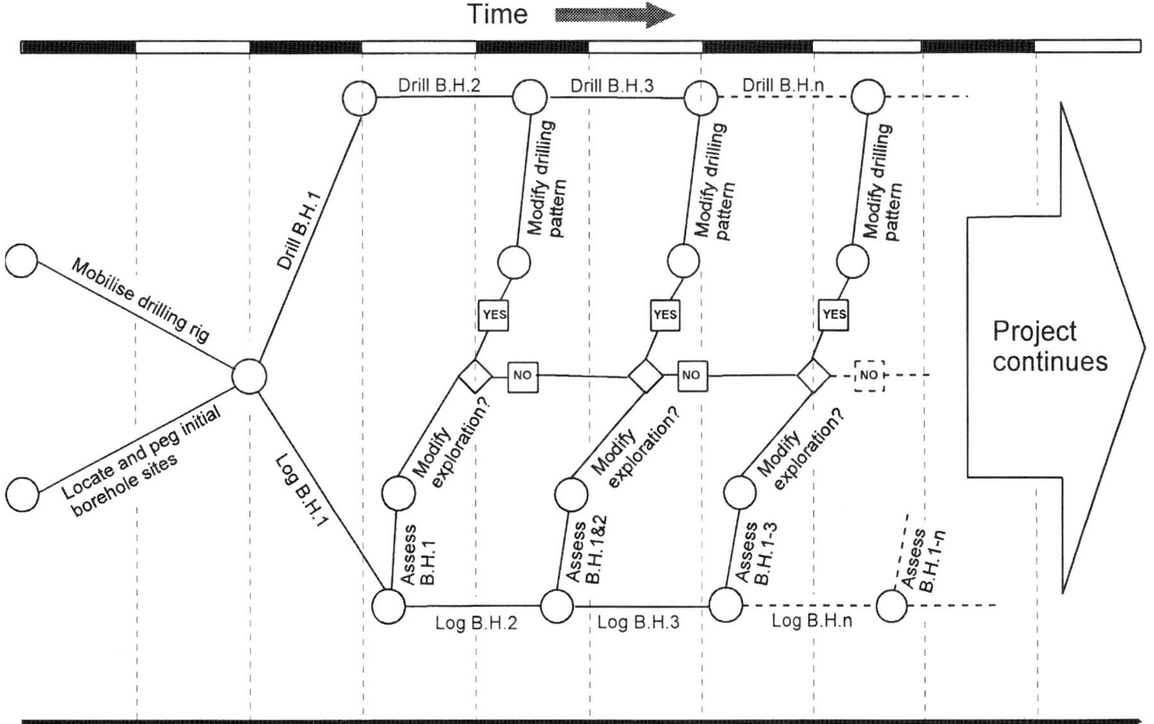

Fig. 4.1. PERT chart indicating how on-going assessment can modify exploration.

The assessment of stone for construction purposes is product based. Some end uses, such as ashlar or cladding require a higher specification than building, walling or rockery stone. This results in some materials being potentially multi-purpose. Block-stone suitable for ashlar can also be used for building stone or rockery. Similarly large blocks of stone suitable for use as armourstone can also be crushed for use as aggregate or even rock-fill. The converse is, however, not normally true. The poorer grade stone which is suitable for walling, building or rockery, cannot be upgraded to cladding or ashlar. An exception to this would be where hard, massive rock is being used for aggregate or some other purpose, the distribution of the discontinuities may result in the production of armourstone or dimension stone being feasible. Clearly no quarry owner is anxious to sell block stone as walling stone, when the value of the latter is only one tenth that of sawn block. However, if the market for the block-stone is limited, or removal of the block will release quantities of other material for which there is a ready market, the resulting cash flow can well over-ride the ideal situation of utilizing the stone for the purpose which it is best suited.

The specifications of the various products for which a deposit is being investigated will have provided the basis for the testing programme which was undertaken during the exploration. The aim of the assessment will be to use the same specifications to divide the deposit up into a series of three-dimensional blocks of ground, each containing stone which conforms in grade to the requirements of one or more of these products.

In the case of dimension stone or armourstone, the size of the individual blocks of stone that can be extracted is of prime importance. In the case of stratified deposits,

Fig. 4.2. The variation in the colours of Ledmore marble is produced by variations in the mineralogy. (Photo courtesy of Fife Silia Sands Ltd.)

there will be a minimum bed thickness from which suitable stone could be obtained. The initial stage of the assessment would be to identify all the beds that satisfy this first criterion. The remaining two dimensions of a potential block-stone or armourstone are limited by natural discontinuities, such as joints, within the deposit. In the case of massive non-bedded bodies of stone, such as granites and some marbles, it is these discontinuities alone which will determine the natural block size. Blocks which result from a wide joint pattern may be too large for use, but can always be split. If there are very few discontinuities, armourstone can be produced by blasting (Wang *et al.* 1991*b*). The generation of blocks of stone by blasting would not normally be acceptable for dimension stone, due to the possibility of generating micro-fractures which may cause early degradation of the stone due to weathering. Where the joints in the stone are close together, the resulting blocks could be too small to be of use. Assessment of the distribution of the discontinuities will enable predictions of the block size distribution to be made (Wang *et al.* 1991*a*). Those portions of the deposit which will probably contain suitably sized blocks can therefore be identified and those areas where all or most of the blocks would be too small can be excluded. Even in the areas containing acceptable material, the range of block sizes present will be such that some of the material will be unsuitable for dimension or armourstone.

Once those parts of the deposit where material of a suitable size may be obtained have been identified, these would again be subdivided on the basis of such properties as strength, potential durability and visual appearance. The actual choice of the properties used would be dependant upon the final end use.

Having determined the location of the areas within the deposit which are suitable for the extraction of the principal product, the material which has been excluded for some reason, for example block size or colour, would then be appraised in order to determine whether or not it could be economically utilized for some secondary product. If blocks of dimension stone were the primary product, the residual stone may be studied as a possible source of building stone. Where armourstone is being sought the secondary product may be aggregate. This process will be repeated until the deposit has been assessed for all the potential products.

The quantity and distribution of any stone which is unsuitable for any commercial product, and which will therefore either have to be avoided during quarrying or excavated and then returned to a worked-out part of the quarry, will be of considerable importance in determining the quantity of potentially usable stone which can be economically extracted. Areas of unsuitable stone, around which the quarry has to be worked, can result in the loss of large quantities of raw material which has to remain in the inclined walls of the quarry required for stability reasons (see §5.3.2.5). The extraction, transport and re-deposition of waste stone can be expensive. However, where there is a planning requirement to restore worked-out parts of the quarry to a new landform, such a material can be of value (see §5.2.3.10).

4.2.1. The use of sample data

Stone, whether it is worked as rock-fill, armourstone or dimension stone, is a bulk material and will be worked as such. However, the analytical and test results upon which the commercial operation to produce the stone product will be based are from point samples within the deposit; this aspect of sampling is discussed in §3.4. The analysis of a sample only provides information about the sample itself. Without further information on the population from which that sample was taken, the sample analysis is relatively meaningless in the context of the rock or mineral deposit. However, if a number of samples are taken, the required information on the whole deposit can be estimated. The accuracy of this estimate is dependent upon the number and spacing of the samples. If for example, a deposit is completely uniform, all samples will produce relatively similar results; variations being due mainly to errors in sample preparation and analysis. On the other hand, if variation occurs in the deposit, each sample will be different. If the samples are taken on a truly random basis the manner in which the deposit varies can be estimated; the more samples which are taken, the better the estimate of the variation.

4.2.2. Sampling errors

Although the main variation in sample test results will probably come from natural geological variation within the deposit, there will also be variation due to errors introduced whilst obtaining the sample data. These can be divided into:

- Sampling errors
  - Incorrect sample size (mass)
  - Incorrect sample method
- Sample reduction errors
  - Incorrect method
  - Incorrect sample size (mass)
  - Incorrect particle size
- Sample preparation errors
  - Contamination
  - Loss during processing
  - Alteration of the chemical or physical composition during processing
- Analytical errors
  - Incorrect sample preparation method
  - Unsuitable analytical method

The sum of the first three of these possible causes of error constitutes the 'Total sampling error' (Gy 1979), the errors during analysis have been discussed by Sides (1992). The problems associated with sampling block material such as armourstone and dimension stone have been discussed in §3.4.4.

In order to determine the quality and therefore quantity of a deposit as a whole, it is necessary to translate the point sample data, obtained during the exploration and testing of the deposit, into estimates of the grade of blocks of stone of a given size.

4.2.3. Variation in the stone

Being a natural material, all rock will vary. Often this variation is a feature which can add value to the stone for building or decorative purposes. Marbles, such as the Ledmore Marble from the North-West Highlands of Scotland, are sold on the basis of the variation in mineralogy, which produces a range of textures and colours as shown in Fig. 4.2. In other instances, variations such as the changes in bed thickness experienced in many limestone deposits can cause problems both in evaluation and in extraction; a typical situation is illustrated in Fig. 4.3. Table 4.1 lists the main types of variation that can occur.

Variation in stone, which is discussed in detail in Chapter 2 can be caused in the case of sedimentary rocks by a variation in the original sediments from which the rock was formed, or by later diagenetic changes. In the case of igneous rocks, original mineral segregation or rates of cooling across an intruded or extruded magma can produce variations in both the mineralogy and the texture of the stone (see §2.6.1). Metamorphism and metasomatism, imposed upon igneous or sedimentary rocks, can add a further variable to stone being investigated for structural use (see §2.6.3).

It is important that the distribution of the different lithologies within a rock is accurately determined and also that any variation within an individual lithology is also identified, since variation in the properties of the stone may be associated with such changes. This is especially true in the case of dimension or ornamental stone, where architects and builders will wish to know exactly how much variation will occur in the stone to be supplied. Moreover, where large orders are involved, the quarry must be in a position to schedule the extraction of stone with a known variability, without having to be concerned about unexpected variations occurring in the quarry faces.

4.2.3.1. Variation in petrography

The petrography of a stone not only controls its appearance, but also its durability and strength. Changes in the nature of the constituents of coarse-grained rocks are often visible to the naked eye. However, subtle changes in the type of mineral present, or in the nature of the natural cement in the case of sedimentary rocks, can often only be observed using thin sections and a petrographic microscope. Changes in fine-grained stone can only be seen using a microscope. A typical example is shown in Fig. 4.4, where a limestone, normally consisting almost entirely of calcium carbonate, has become packed with secondary quartz due to mineralization associated with a fault. In hand specimen, the mineralized limestone appears identical to the unaltered rock. The presence of the silica would not only cause enhanced wear on the saws used to cut it, but may also introduce quantities of respirable silica dust into the air of the processing plant, unless precautionary measures are taken.

It has been suggested by Hugman & Friedman (1979) that limestones containing more than 50% micrite are stronger than those with a preponderance of sparite. Although generalizations are best avoided, it would appear likely that in an essentially mono-mineralic rock such as limestone, the physical characteristics of the stone would be influenced by the size and shape of the constituent grains. There is certainly some evidence from the Jurassic limestones of England that the finer-grained micritic stone is more durable than the coarser-grained oöidal or shelly stone.

In sandstones, the nature of the cement appears to be a major factor in determining the characteristics of the stone. When assessing a stone to be used for construction purposes it is therefore necessary to identify such changes and, if necessary, classify and plot the distribution of the stone on the basis of the petrography. Although changes in the petrography of the stone may eventually prove to have little or no effect on its properties, the different variants of the stone should be treated, for sampling and testing purposes, as separate rock types until the results of the relevant tests are known.

4.2.3.2. Variation in discontinuities

Although the presence of a large number of discontinuities, in the form of joints and bedding planes, may be a great advantage when the stone is to be used for rock-fill, since they may reduce the extraction and processing costs, the potential of a rock as a source of dimension stone or armourstone could be seriously reduced by a high frequency of discontinuities. Variations in the spacing and orientation of all forms of discontinuity must be identified and quantified during the assessment process.

Although a reduction in the spacing of bedding planes could preclude a stone from being used as armourstone, the effect on building stone may only be to alter the product for which the stone is suitable. A block-stone capable of producing high-value sawn cladding or ashlar may be changed by an increase in the frequency of the bedding planes to a material only suitable for building or walling stone, with an accompanying reduction in value. There is a bed thickness, normally about 100 mm, below which the stone would be of little value for walling and cladding. However, should the bedding planes be relatively smooth and parallel, and should the

Fig. 4.3. Lateral changes in sedimentary rocks can cause thinning of the strata. Such changes affect every bed of sandstone in this small quarry, used to produce stone for buildings at Whitby Abbey in North Yorkshire. This results in variable course heights in buildings constructed from the stone. In the Abbey, individual courses of stone range from about 150 mm to 400 mm in height. The scale on the photograph is 500 mm long.

other properties of the stone such as porosity and hardness be acceptable, thinly bedded stone may have a value as paving or roofing tiles.

The angle at which sets of joints intersect is also of importance, especially in block dimension stone. Most stone products, whether they are quoins, lintels or fireplaces, are single orthogonal pieces, or are made up of such pieces. If wastage is to be kept to a minimum during processing, these are best cut from quarry blocks where the sides are approximately at right angles to each other (Fig. 4.5). If the joint pattern in the quarry is such that the discontinuities intersect at, for example, 45° to each other, there will be considerable wastage at the ends of the block when it is sawn into the required products. The same is true if the bedding planes or joint surfaces are highly irregular.

Table 4.1. *The effect of variation in stone for use in construction*

Variable	*Effect on the stone*	*Effect on the resource*
Petrography	Change in the mineral content, crystal size or distribution. This can affect the durability, strength, hardness and colour of the stone.	Stone used as armourstone or rock fill could fall outside specification, especially if the variation involved an increase in clay mineral content. Building stone could become less durable, and changes in colour or texture could make it aesthetically unacceptable.
Lateral facies change in sedimentary strata	Change in the thickness of beds. Change in rock type.	If the strata became thinner without a change in rock type, this could be an advantage if rock fill was being ripped. In the case of armourstone or building stone, the material could become unsuitable if the beds became too thin. Changes in rock type or petrography would affect the resource as above.
Porosity and microporosity	Increase or decrease in the absorption of water.	The durability of building stone and armourstone could be seriously affected. The performance of rock fill could also be affected.
Concentration of joints	Change in block size	If the frequency of the joints decreased, this may produce larger block sizes, a possible advantage in the case of building stone or armourstone. However, such an increase in size may result in blocks having to be split before extraction, involving additional cost. Large blocks may be a disadvantage for rock fill. An increase in frequency could result in smaller blocks, a disadvantage for armourstone and building stone; possibly an advantage for fill.
Orientation of joints	Change in block shape	Could make the blocks unsuitable for armourstone. May increase the wastage factor when processing block building stone.
Chemistry	Normally related to petrography, but could indicate variation in contained salts.	Could affect the durability of armourstone and building stone.

If the surface irregularities require that 25 mm of stone is cut off each of the six sides of a one metre block of ex-quarry stone in order to obtain a six-sided sawn piece, the wastage is of the order of 13%. If, due to greater irregularity of the block extracted from the quarry, the thickness of the off-cut has to be increased to 50 mm, the loss of material amounts to about 25% of the quarried stone. Although the off-cuts can sometimes be utilized for crazy-paving or some other purpose, they would normally be waste, which has not only to be removed for disposal, but has often been transported to the cutting facility at considerable cost.

If joints are inclined rather than being vertical, the shape of the resulting blocks is even less orthogonal than is the case where vertical joints intersect at some other angle than 90°. The wastage of stone which occurs during processing is therefore even greater.

Inclined joining, or steeply dipping bedding, can have a major impact on the development of the quarry and therefore its ability to supply the different products required by the market. Even vertical jointing will have an effect on the stability of the quarry face and bench heights will have to take this into account. Inclined joints or steep dips will affect the direction in which the quarry is to be developed. These potential stability problems must be identified and taken into account during the assessment procedures. Quarry stability is discussed in detail in §5.3.2.5.

During the exploration stage of the investigation, data on the bedding and jointing will have been collected from field exposures, pits and, possibly, boreholes. This will be analysed during the assessment. If variation occurs which could affect either the quality of the stone, the type of product to be produced, or the method of quarry development, the discontinuity data will have to be summarized and displayed in a manner that will make it meaningful to those responsible for the extraction of the stone.

Sections 5.3.2 and 5.3.9 discuss the effect of discontinuities on the extraction of stone in detail, and only those aspects which are pertinent to the assessment of the raw materials will be considered here.

The problem of estimating block size from borehole core is compounded by the fact that it is impossible to measure the persistence of the discontinuities encountered. Although bedding planes and other horizontal features may be intersected by more than one borehole, it is unlikely that a joint, or any other type of discontinuity

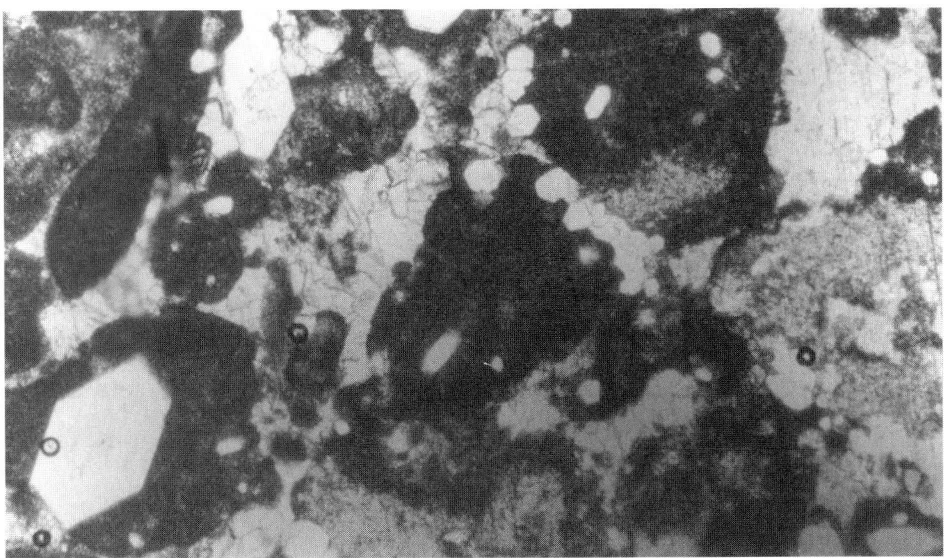

Fig. 4.4. This Carboniferous limestone, composed largely of crinoid fragments and rounded masses of filamentous algae set in a partly re-crystallized micritic matrix, is normally composed almost entirely of calcium carbonate. However, patches of stone can occur which are packed with diagentically formed euhedral crystals of quartz. These clear bi-pyramidal grains can be seen randomly scattered throughout the photo-micrograph of the stone. The largest crystal, in the bottom left-hand corner of the photograph, is 500 μm in length. Such siliceous developments, which cannot be seen in hand sample, can cause unexpected wear on stone saws, and could introduce relatively high concentrations of silica dust into the working environment.

that dips at a high angle, will be encountered more than once. In fact, a very major problem, especially in vertical boreholes, is that only those discontinuities that are close to the borehole and have a dip sufficiently great to take them across the line of the borehole will be intersected. The use of angled boreholes, discussed in §3.4.7.7, drilled in various directions, would be required to provide adequate information on the discontinuity pattern.

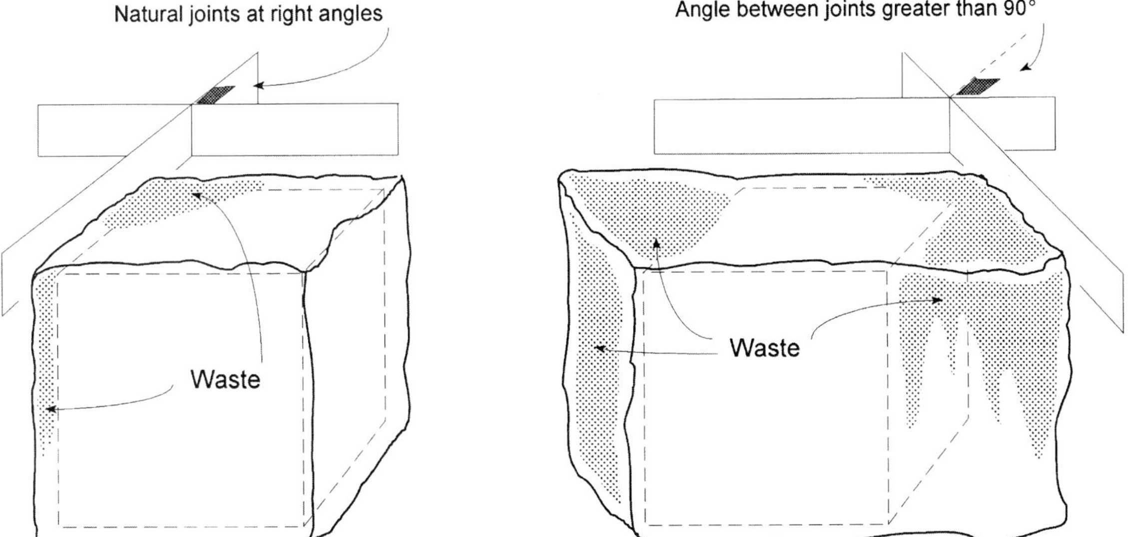

Fig. 4.5. Effect of the natural joint pattern on the potential wastage when processing sawn block stone.

The orientation of discontinuities can be assessed in various ways. Where single planes are being considered, be they bedding or structural features such as joints, a two-dimensional plot using dip/strike symbols, together with the value of the dip, will normally suffice. Areas with significantly different strike directions or dip values can then be easily identified and delineated; this is illustrated in Fig. 4.6.

Where more than one set of joints are to be plotted, the 'rose diagram' or 'joint rosette' (ISRM 1978) can be used. An example is given in Fig. 4.7. The diagram is essentially a circular histogram, the class intervals normal being 10. The strike directions of the discontinuities are grouped into the various classes and plotted on the compass rose. The length of the 'petals' represents the number of readings in that class. The range of dip values for the discontinuities cannot be represented on the diagram and would normally be written adjacent to the relevant class interval.

The traditional method of representing the data is to use solid radial sectors as indicated on the left-hand side of the rosette in Fig. 4.7. These would normally have mirror images about the centre of the diagram. It is also possible to average the strike values for each set of discontinuities and plot the results as a pointed 'petal', as shown on the right-hand side of the diagram.

The value of the rose diagram lies in the fact that it clearly indicates not only the direction of the joints but also the amount of variation in that direction. It can be included on maps and quarry development plans in order to give an immediate indication of the direction of the discontinuities in a specific area. This is particularly important where the directions vary throughout the deposit. Different joint rosettes drawn at the relevant parts of the planned development provide an immediate indication of the changes that will take place as the extraction progresses through the stone.

Where an area is structurally complex it may be preferable to use stereographic projection to classify and evaluate the data collected in the field. This procedure enables the three-dimensional aspect of a joint, fault, bedding plane or other structural feature or discontinuity, to be accurately represented in two dimensions. In order to represent both the strike and the dip of a planar surface, a lower hemispherical stereographic projection can be used. Both *polar* and *cyclographic* projections can be used.

The method of plotting discontinuities using a Schmidt contour diagram on a polar equal-area net (ISRM 1978), is illustrated in the text box. In principle, the method involves plotting the normal to the discontinuity surface onto the surface of a sphere and then projecting that position onto the equatorial plane of the sphere. A typical example is shown in Fig. 4.8. The projection of the poles will form clusters on the diagram. The size of these clusters will be a measure of the variation in the strike direction and dip of the members of the discontinuity set. These clusters can then be

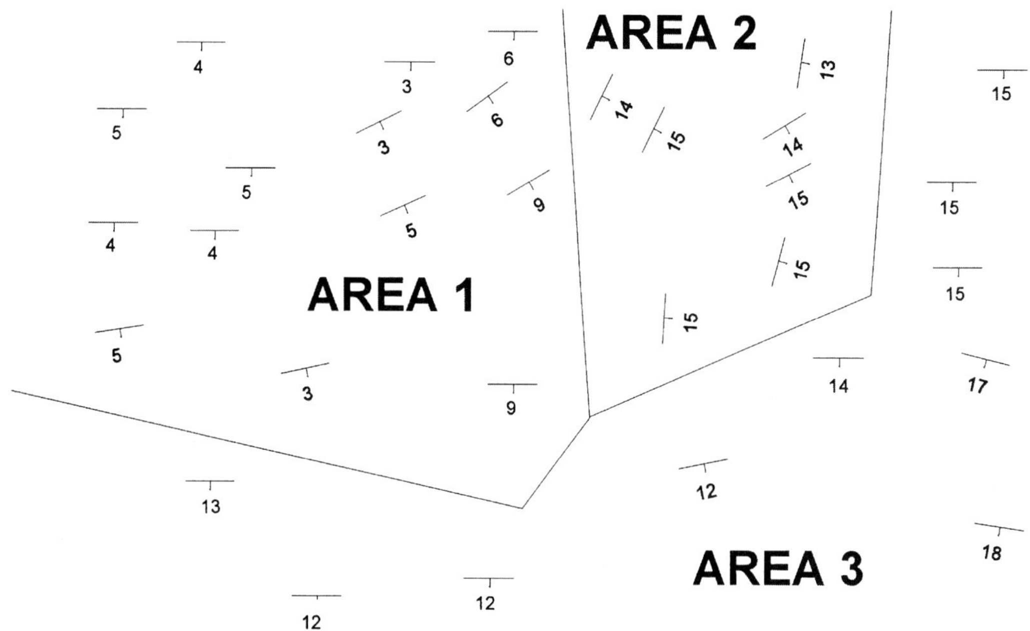

Fig. 4.6. Division of a deposit into separate areas for assessment purposes based upon the direction and inclination of the jointing.

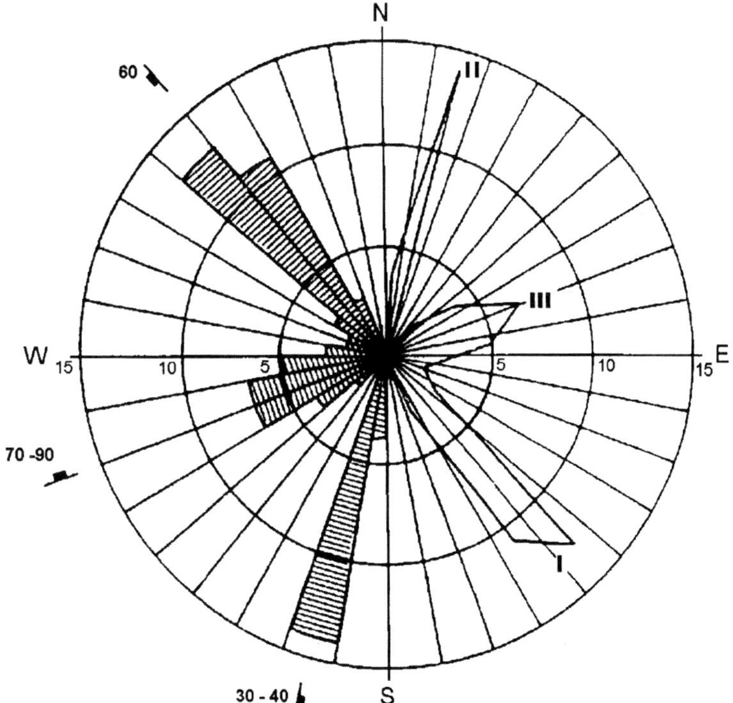

Fig. 4.7. Two methods of representing the orientation of discontinuities on a rose diagram. On the left the observations are grouped into sectors, the length of the bar being determined by the number of readings in that sector. Alternatively, the strike values can be averaged, resulting in the sharp 'petals' as on the right hand side (based on ISRM 1978).

contoured, as indicated in the diagram. The Schmidt contouring method involves superimposing a square grid onto the equal area net. A circle representing 1% of the total area of the net as indicated at the top of Fig. 4.8 is then placed over an intersection on the square grid, and the number of poles falling within the circle counted. This is repeated for each intersection in turn.

For cyclographic projection the plane is represented by its great circular trace with the discontinuity plane passing diametrically through the equatorial surface. This is illustrated in the text box. When cyclographic projection is used, discontinuities are represented by great circles, and poles are plotted as points, or clusters of points.

Once the different sets of discontinuities have been identified, mathematical analysis of each set will allow not only the direction and spacing of the specific feature to be determined, but also the variation of these factors. In this manner the probable range of block sizes, and the relative quantities of each size, can be estimated.

Details of the different types of stereographic nets which are available, and of how to use these techniques, is outside the scope of this discussion and works such as McClay (1987), Ragan (1985) and Priest (1985, 1993) should be consulted for details. Examples of the use of stereographic projection of discontinuities in slope stability studies are provided in §5.3.2.2 and illustrated in Fig. 5.11. Two types of net are illustrated in these diagrams. In Fig. 5.11 the data have been plotted on a Wulff equal angle net, which helps solve angular relationships whereas, in Fig. 4.8, a Schmidt equal area net has been used as this form of net is better for statistically evaluating orientation data.

It should be noted that, although stereographic projection may be used to classify and measure the discontinuity data, it is only an assessment tool and, being a potentially complex concept, care should be used when incorporating them in technical reports. As an example, in Fig. 4.8, the cluster of points marked as set I although occurring in the north-east quadrant of the rosette, actually represents a series of discontinuities which dip to the south-west at about 60°, the strike being to the north-west. Unlike the rose diagram, spherical projections are probably best avoided when communicating the results of the assessment to those responsible for the extraction of the stone, unless they are fully conversant with the techniques of stereographic projection.

Polar stereographic projection

In order to represent both the strike and the dip of the surface **D** on a planar surface, it is transposed to a position, **d**, where it passes through the centre of a sphere. A normal to the surface, is taken from the centre of the sphere to its surface, where it intersects it at **P**. From pole **P**, a line to the zenith of the sphere is taken to intersect the horizontal equatorial surface at point **p**.

The lower diagram indicates how points on the equatorial surface relate to the structural features such as joints and bedding plotted in this way. The compass points round the outside of the compass rose relate to the direction of the strike and of the maximum dip of the feature plotted. The inner concentric circles indicate the dip of the feature. Hence, surface D has a dip of about 65°. The strike of the surface is about (250°+90°), that is 340°, the azimuth or direction of maximum dip being about (250°+180°), or 70°. Note how, when determining the azimuth, 180° has to be added to the value read off the diagram. This is due to the pole **P** being a projection onto the lower hemisphere of the sphere. A direct reading of the azimuth would be given by using an upper hemispherical stereographic projection, rather than the lower hemisphere.

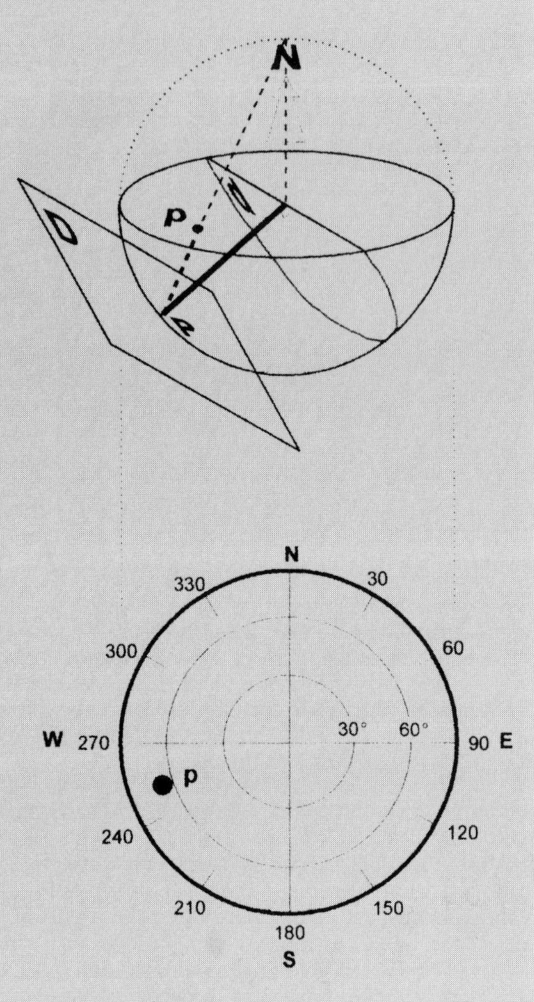

4.2.3.3. Colour and fabric variations
Although normally of little interest in the case of rockfill or armourstone, the colour and bulk texture of a stone can be of considerable importance in the evaluation of dimension stone (Fig. 4.2). What is often encountered when stone is used in construction is a lack of appreciation that, being a natural material, stone will vary in both colour and texture. Furthermore, the colour of a stone can change when wet, and can also vary with the type of finish applied to the stone during processing (Fig. 9.29).

Any assessment of a building stone should, therefore, take account of any changes which may occur in the colour, or texture, of the various finished products. If the variation occurs randomly throughout the deposit, the total variation should be reported, preferably with the aid of accurate colour reproductions of the average and extreme colour and textural variations, the colour variation being recorded using a standard colour code such as that developed by Munsell Color, described in §3.3.2.5.

4.2.4. Estimation of grade

4.2.4.1. The relationship between samples and blocks
Having divided the deposit into a series of areas on the basis of petrography, structure or potential product type, it is necessary to assess the quality of the stone within

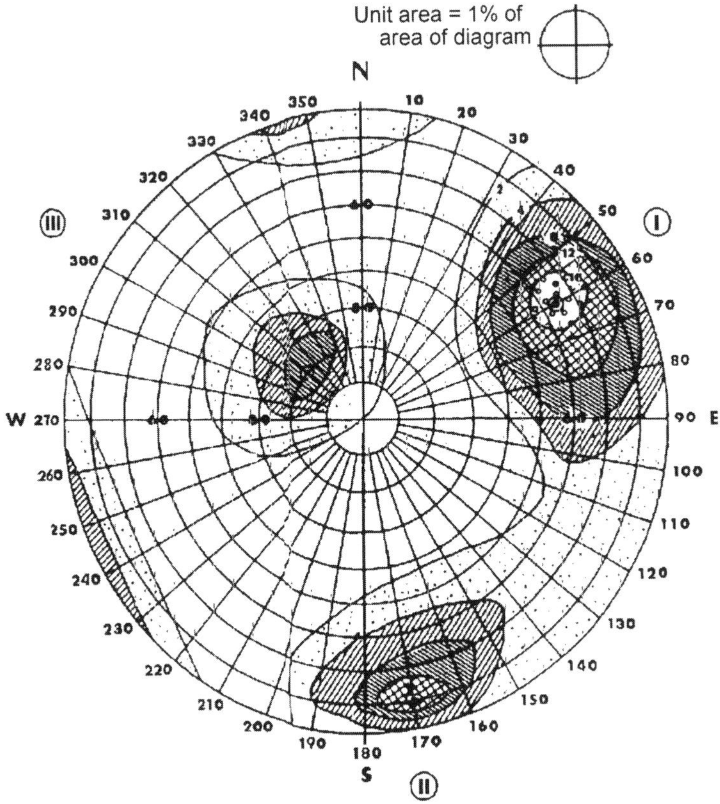

Fig. 4.8. Schmidt contour diagram representing the orientation of three sets of discontinuities. Set 1 strikes at about 330° and dips to the west at about 60°. Set II is almost vertical and strikes at about 80°. The third set is at a very low angle and probably represents the dip of the strata, being at about 20° and dipping to the southeast (based upon ISRM 1978).

these areas. For many industrial minerals, this will be the grade of the rock in terms of chemical composition. In the case of rock for construction purposes, criteria such as porosity, frost resistance or flexural strength are more likely to predominate, although the chemical composition, especially in the context of inherent soluble salts, can also be important.

From the point sample values for the property being evaluated, an overall average value for the grade can be calculated. However, in practical terms this is relatively meaningless since it is individual blocks of stone from the deposit that will be extracted and used. The standard deviation about the mean will provide valuable information on the range of sample values which may be encountered from that part of the deposit which has been assessed. The standard deviation of data sets is described in a little more detail in the text box. If this value is not too large, it may be adequate for many purposes, especially if the overall quality of the stone is high, despite its inherent variation. However, the simple arithmetic average and standard deviation will not provide any spatial information on the variation within the stone and will be of no assistance in helping to predict the quality of the stone in any specific part of the deposit. Nor will this method of assessment indicate whether or not the variation is uniform throughout the deposit, or whether there are differences in the manner in which the stone varies in different parts of the resource. Trends in the variation can also be obscured by such a simplistic approach. Furthermore, the values being used relate, not to blocks of stone or to loads of rock fill, but to pieces of stone the size of the small samples which were taken for analysis.

In order to provide practical information on the grade of a deposit of rock or mineral, it is necessary to use the point sample data to estimate the grade of blocks of material in the ground. The size of these blocks of ground will vary depending upon the nature of the raw material. In the case of stone which may be used for rock fill, or as raw material for a high-volume process with blending facilities such as lime or cement, it may be adequate to estimate the grade of stone in blocks as large

Cyclographic stereographic projection

If the surface **D** is transposed into a position **d**, where it passes through the centre of a sphere, the intersection of the surface with the sphere will take to form of a great circle. A perpendicular from the surface to the centre of the sphere will intersect it at the pole **P**. The stereographic projection can be visualized as the view of the lower hemisphere from above.

The lower diagram indicates how trace of the surface and the position of the pole are located on the projection. Two great circles are shown, one at 65° to the equatorial plane is the trace of planar surface **d**, the other is the 25° circle and passes through the pole **P**. Being on a perpendicular to the plane, the **P** is at an angle of (90° – dip). As a horizontal surface would coincide with the equatorial surface, the perimeter of the stereographic net has a dip value of 0°. A vertical surface, dip 90°, is represented by a straight line passing through the centre of the circular diagram.

The straight line joining the ends of a great circle trace on the diagram, will also pass through the centre of the net, and indicates the direction of strike of the surface. This value can be read directly from the compass points on the perimeter of the diagram. In the example shown, this is about 340°.

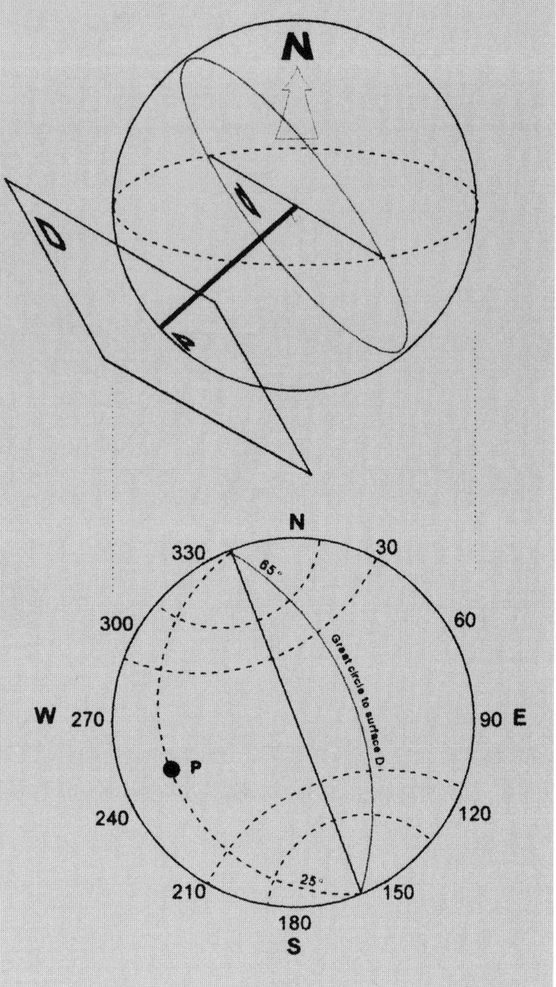

as 10 000 tonnes or more. Where high-quality dimension stone is to be extracted, an estimate of the quality of the stone in blocks as small as 1000 tonnes may be preferable.

There are a number of mathematical procedures which can be used to estimate the quality of blocks of rock from point sample data, some of which are illustrated in Figs 4.9A and B. The methods are:

- Area of influence around a sample point
- Use of isolines joining sample points of equal value
- Trend Surface Analysis
- Moving average
- Geostatistics

4.2.4.2. Area of influence of a sample

In a set of scattered points, such as the sandstone porosity data shown in diagram A in Fig. 4.9, there is an area around each point, within which all locations are closer to that point than to any other point in the set. A series of polygons can therefore be drawn round each point delineating these 'areas of influence'. In the case of a rectangular grid these polygons will be rectangles, whereas in the case of randomly distributed points they will be irregular. The set of polygons for the data in Fig. 4.9 is shown in diagram B of the figure. These Thiessen polygons can be used, for example, in preparing contour maps where the data involved are the elevations of survey points (Davis 1986).

Sample distribution and standard deviation

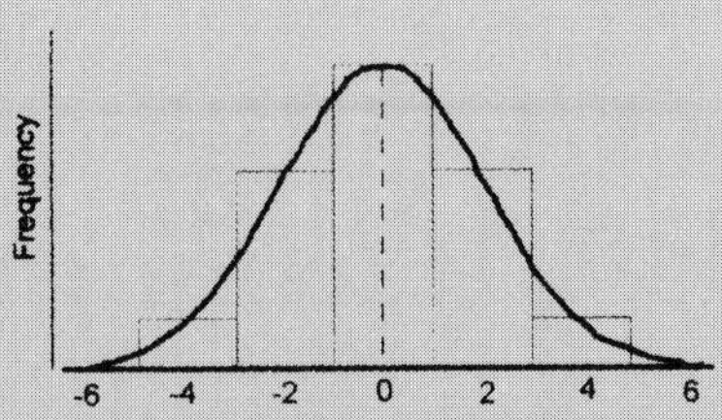

If sample data are plotted in the form of a histogram (left), and the centre points at the top of each box are joined, the resulting frequency distribution curve, or probability distribution function (pdf), provides a pictorial representation of the amount of variation present in the samples. The width of the curve is a measure of the spread of the sample data.

The mathematical function which represents this spread is the *standard deviation (s)*.

The standard deviation of a set of values $\{x_1, x_2, \ldots, x_n\}$ is given by

$$s = \sqrt{\frac{\sum_{i=1}^{n} (x_i - \bar{x})^2}{n}}$$

The lower the value, the narrower the curve, and the less the variation about the mean (right).

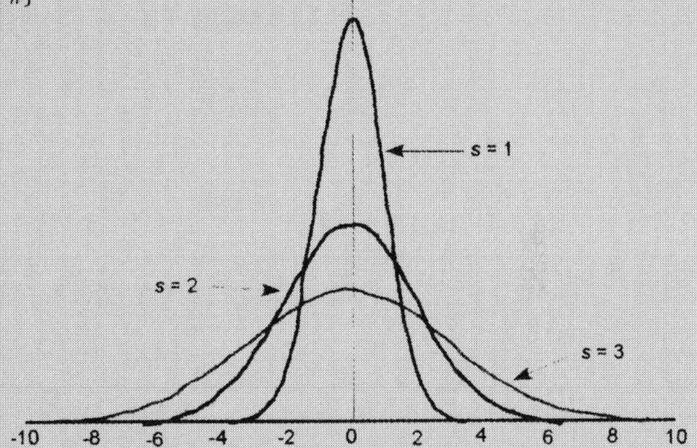

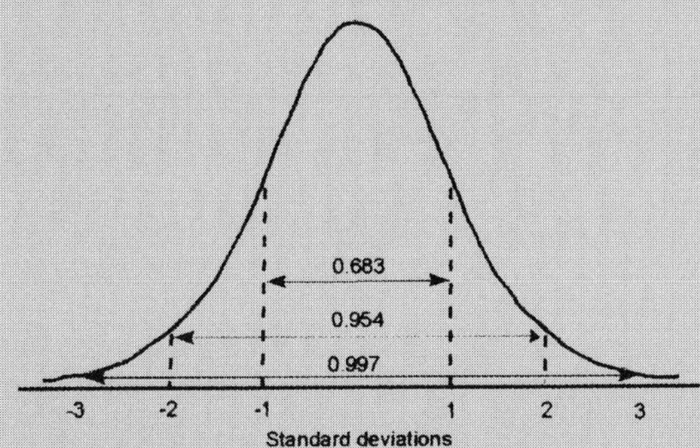

It is possible to use the standard deviation to estimate the approximate number of samples which are likely to fall within a certain distance from the arithmetic mean. Slightly over two thirds (68.3%) of observations will fall within one standard deviation on either side of the mean, approximately 95% within the interval −2 to +2 standard deviations, and more than 99% will fall between −3 and +3 standard deviations (left).

It should be noted that these estimates relate to samples. As blocks of rock are effectively composed of large numbers of sample-sized pieces, the standard deviation of such blocks will probably be less than the sample standard deviation.

The normal frequency distribution discussed above is symmetrical about the sample mean. Sample data from stone often have a skew distribution such as that shown below. For example. the distribution of calcium carbonate in samples of limestone would typically produce this type of curve. The formula for deermining standard deviation which is given above, cannot be used for this type of data unless it is first transformed. A textbook on the use of statistics should be consulted for further details (for example Davis, 1986).

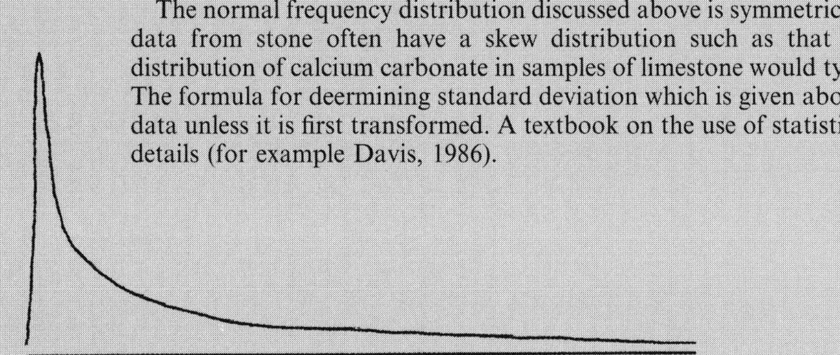

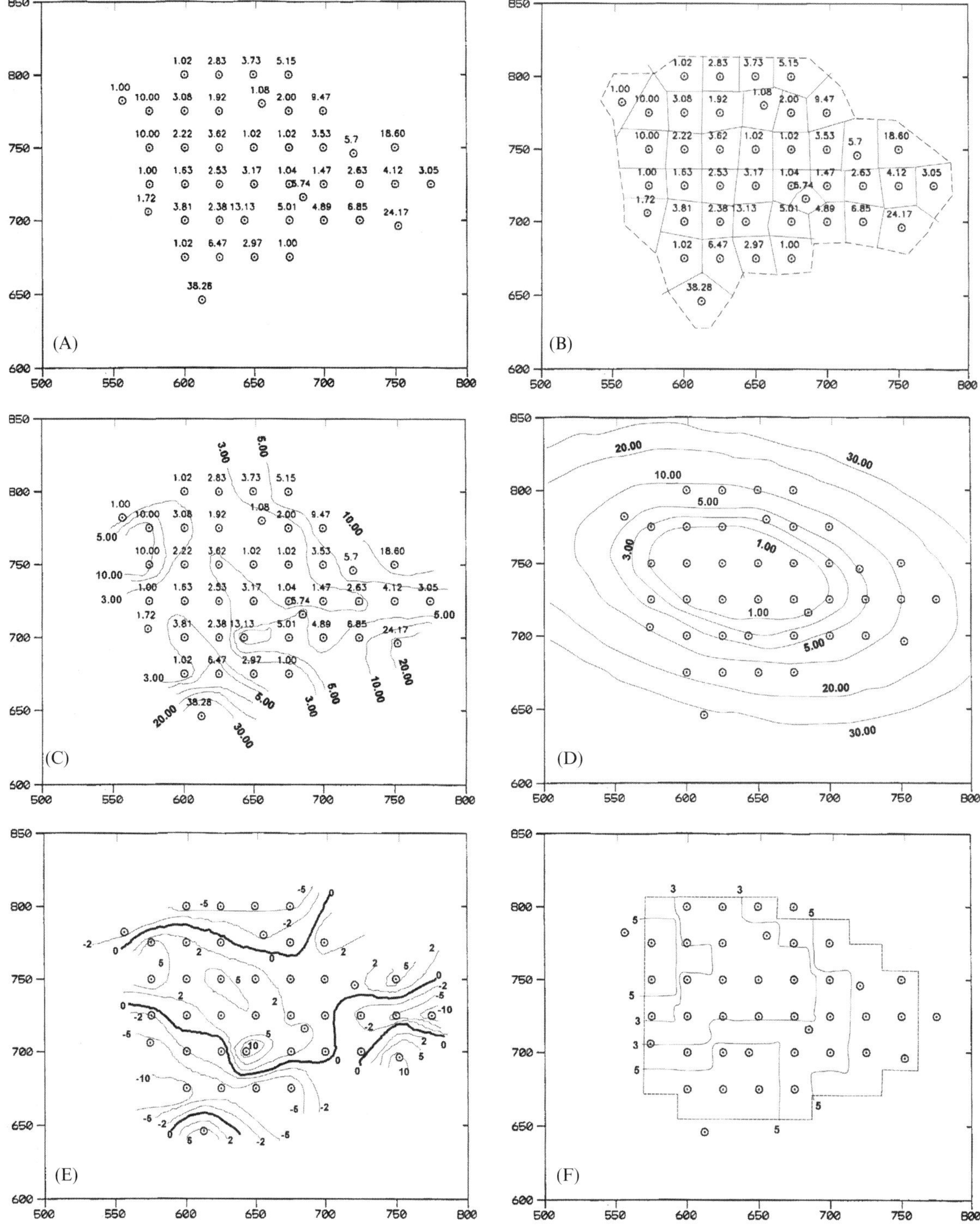

(A)
(B)
(C)
(D)
(E)
(F)
850
800
750
700
650
600
500
550
600
650
700
750
800
1.02 2.83 3.73 5.15
1.00 10.00 3.08 1.92 1.08 2.00 9.47
10.00 2.22 3.62 1.02 1.02 3.53 5.7 18.60
1.00 1.63 2.53 3.17 1.04 5.74 1.47 2.63 4.12 3.05
1.72 3.81 2.38 13.13 5.01 4.89 6.85 24.17
1.02 6.47 2.97 1.00
38.28

Unlike survey spot heights, which are carefully measured data points, the accuracy of test data from a rock sample, is subject to a large number of variables. The value of the measured parameter is, therefore, unlikely to be accurate, even at the sample point. To extend this value to the surrounding area could compound the problem. The method has been traditionally used for producing an overall average of a deposit, a weighting factor being applied which is a function of the 'area of influence' of the sample point. Although it can be argued that errors will tend to cancel out when this method is used, since there are probably a similar number of positive and negative errors, this will not be the case if the polygons are not all approximately the same size. Furthermore, there is still a problem in using the polygons to model the deposit as a whole, since where they join there will be a sudden unnatural step change in grade.

4.2.4.3. Modelling using isolines

A line joining points of equal value is termed an isoline. A contour line is, therefore, an isoline joining points of equal surface elevation. Just as surfaces can be modelled using contours, measured properties in a rock mass can be represented using isograds, or lines joining points of equal grade. Termed contouring, due its similarity to preparing topographic contours, the method produces a variable 'surface', which although being faithful at the individual data points, is estimated for all points between them. It has been shown (Dahlberg 1975) that, depending upon the experience and background of the person preparing the isograd plan, the surface produced by contouring will vary from person to person. Computer generated isograd plots, based upon purely mathematical algorithms, tend to be an average of those prepared by hand.

As well as indicating areas with high and low values for the parameter being studied, contouring will also emphasize the rate of change of value. Thus, in the sandstone porosity example shown in Fig. 4.9A, the isograds of porosity shown in diagram C suggest that, although porosity within the central part of the deposit varies only gradually, the rate of change around the edge of the sampled area, especially on the western and southern sides is much higher.

The possibility of erroneous results from the sampling and testing is also brought out by contouring. For example, the high rate of change in porosity on the southern side of the sandstone, in the example in Fig. 4.9A, could be due to the value of the southernmost sample being in error. The assessment by contouring suggests that further sampling and analysis is required in this area.

Fig. 4.9. (A) Porosity data from a sandstone is based on samples taken approximately every 25 metres on an essentially rectangular grid. The porosity values are in percent. The grid coordinates of the deposit are in metres, based on a local datum. (B) The polygonal 'area of influence' around the sample point can be attributed with the value of the sample. This however takes no account of sampling error, which will be extended to the area around the sample point. The method also results in sudden jumps in grade as boundaries between 'areas of influence' are crossed. Such sudden changes in porosity will not occur in practice. (C) Contouring the data points will enable areas of different grades to be identified, although no precise mathematical probability of a certain grade falling within a given area can be calculated. However if, for example, porosity values up to 5% are considered acceptable, those areas likely to provide such grades can be easily identified, although the chance of locating pockets of stone with a porosity in excess of 5% cannot be ruled out, especially at the edge of the selected area. Contouring will also identify samples which may, for some reason, have anomalous values, and therefore require further investigation. The southernmost sample in the example is such a case. (D) Trend Surface Analysis attempts to fit a series of polynomial functions to the data. In the case of this porosity information, the 'best fit' was a second-order polynomial. This results in an ellipse, the long axis of which is orientated a little north of west. This is a 'best fit' surface and is not a perfect fit, there being residual values between the actual and calculated values; these are shown in diagram E. What is suggested by the trend surface is that the deposit consists essentially of a sandstone, the central core of the outcrop of which is of low porosity, this parameter increasing away from the central core, especially in a northerly and southerly direction. However this relatively simple variation has been complicated by other factors. (E) When the differences between the actual recorded porosities, and the values predicted from the second order polynomial surface, shown in D, are compared, there are differences. If these 'residuals' are plotted and contoured as shown, a relatively simple surface varying between −5% and +5% results. However this is punctuated by a number of extreme anomalies. These should be investigated further, as they may result from sampling or analytical error, or from some feature actually present in the deposit. The extreme anomalies can be removed from the residuals and the surface added to that of the trend shown in D. This will give a final 'best fit' surface. Moreover, since a pure mathematical approach has been made, an estimate of the reliability of the surface can be made, thereby providing some guidance as to the possible variation which may be encountered in the porosity of the stone as extracted from the deposit. (F) The application of geostatistics to the data can allow estimates to be made of individual quarryable blocks of stone to be made. Moreover, because of the nature of the procedure, the variance of these estimates can also be calculated. A simple 'block kriging' procedure has been applied to the sandstone porosity data in order to estimate the porosity of quarry blocks approximately 24 metres square. The dashed line indicates the area assessed by the procedure, those samples not included were automatically removed since, being a method which takes into account the surrounding data points, those with less than a certain number of neighbours within a given radius can be excluded. This comparison with surrounding data will smooth any very high or low values, a valuable attribute if the anomalous value is due to poor sampling or analysis, but potentially a problem if it is truly an extreme value.

4.2.4.4. Trend Surface Analysis

Assessment procedures such as simple averaging of the data, calculation of the area of influence of a sample, and contouring, all take the sample test results at their face value. The various errors due to sampling and analysis are not only ignored, they are transmitted to the total deposit. It is clearly preferable to take the sample data, and from it attempt to model the population from which it was taken, allowing for the fact that the errors in the information relate to the processing of the sample, rather than to the deposit as a whole. In this way it should be possible to obtain a better estimate of the quality and variation in the stone which would be encountered, should extraction be undertaken. Trend Surface Analysis is one method that allows this approach to be made.

Trend Surface Analysis attempts to fit the point data to a series of mathematical surfaces known as polynomial functions. The 'first-order surface' is a plane, and is the three-dimensional equivalent of the straight line; the 'second-order surface' the equivalent of the parabola; the third-order surface is the 3-D equivalent of a cubic curve. Normally surfaces no higher than the sixth order are used, as at this level the number of variables is so high that the surface can be made to fit almost any data and is the equivalent of merely contouring the data points.

Although the results of the procedure are frequently represented by contoured plans, such as that shown in diagram D of Fig. 4.9, it must be emphasized that the surface represented by the isolines when using this method is not a contoured plan of the data but is purely a mathematical surface.

When such a mathematical surface if fitted to the data, it is unlikely to fit exactly. There will be differences, or 'residuals', between the actual point values and the value of the mathematical curve at that point. The smaller the 'residual', the better the 'goodness of fit'. A number of mathematical functions are therefore tested against the data and the one with the best fit accepted for further analysis.

The value of any property which is measured in a rock, is the result of a number of factors, such as mode of deposition, diagenetic history, structural history and weathering. The collection and analysis of the sample will also affect the value. It is likely that one feature will be the cause of the major variation in the stone. The other factors will affect the stone to a lesser, and probably variable, degree. In a multi-variate deposit, Trend Surface Analysis will probably fit a polynomial surface to the main variation. The secondary variable features will account for the residuals. If one of these secondary effects, for example weathering, is predominant, it is possible that the effect can be identified by contouring the residuals. In the case of the sandstone porosity example, this has been undertaken in Fig. 4.9, diagram E.

If the secondary variations are complex, it may be necessary to analyse the residual data as if it were primary data. This could also be undertaken by Trend Surface Analysis, or by one of the other techniques being described.

The main Trend Surface in the example data, shown as diagram D in Fig. 4.9, is a second-order polynomial producing a lensoid feature, orientated slightly north of west, with low porosities in the centre which increase outwards. The residual in diagram E can be seen to form an east–west 'ridge' containing a number of anomalous values. These latter sample sites would be studied further in order to determine if the anomalous values were due to sampling, or to an actual variation in the deposit that could affect the quality of the stone in that area.

4.2.4.5. Moving average

Contouring, using either the raw data, or by means of Trend Surface Analysis, provides an estimate of the value of point samples at any location within the deposit by producing a 'surface' connecting the points of known value. Any intervening point can then be estimated from this surface. Errors in the values attributed to each sample point, such as those due to poor sampling, can affect the estimated surface over a wide area. This will result in poor estimates of grade over this area. As the changes in the properties of a rock are normally gradational, the values of neighbouring samples should be related, to a greater or lesser extent, to each other. This property can be used to improve the grade estimate for an area.

When assessing the grade of a block from point samples, the values of neighbouring sample points can be taken into consideration. As they are likely to be some distance from the block being studied, the effect of these samples will be less than those in the block itself. Their influence will, therefore, have to be modified by some factor. This is normally undertaken on the basis of distance. Common weighting factors used are the inverse of the distance to the sample, or the inverse squared. This is explained in detail in the text box. Other inverse functions can be used, and the choice of the formula used tends to be based upon the experience of the person carrying out the assessment, and can therefore be rather subjective.

Where a complete deposit is to be assessed, the averaging procedure will be used for each of the blocks. This results in each sample point being used a number of times, once when it is the main sample within its own block, and with varying weighting factors when being utilized in the assessment of neighbouring blocks. This is also illustrated in the text box. Normally the averaging procedure will be undertaken progressively round the deposit, each sample point being used in turn as the centre of a block. This procedure is known as a 'moving average' or a 'rolling mean'.

4.2.4.6. Geostatistics

The estimation of block values using the moving average technique depends upon the assessor's choice of the

Estimation of grade by moving average

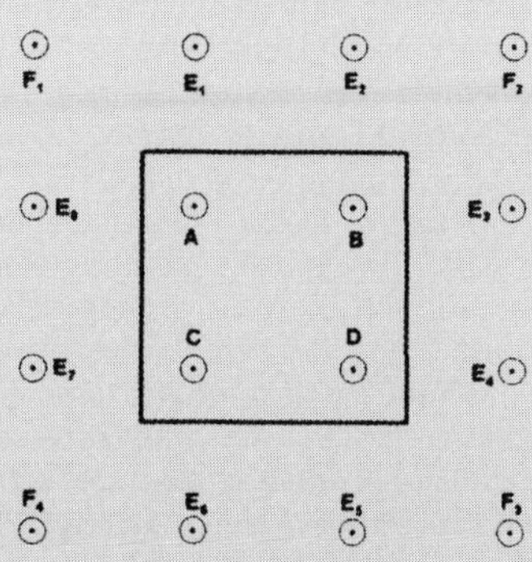

The grade of the block enclosing sample points A, B, C and D can be estimated by averaging the grades of these samples. However the samples taken outside the block will also supply some information as to the grade of the block itself. As they are outside the area being estimated, the same weighting cannot be applied to these samples as to the internal samples. If the inverse of the distance from the centre of the block is used as the weighting criteria, and the distance from the centre of the block to samples A, B, C or D is taken as unity, the weighting factor for E_{1-8} becomes 0.45, and that for F_{1-4} is 0.33. If it is considered that such weightings over-emphasize the external samples, the inverse distance squared $(1/d^2)$ could be applied. This would reduce the weighting factor for E_{1-8} to 0.20 and that for F_{1-4} to 0.11.

Progressive application of the method outlined above for estimating block grades, using both the internal and neighbouring samples, to a series of blocks, will allow block estimates for the total deposit to be built up. This method is known as the 'moving average' or 'rolling mean'.

Considering the series of blocks shown on the left, the block enclosing sample A will be evaluated in the following manner. If the distance from the sample to the edge of the block is taken as unity, the distances to the other sample points can be expressed as:

E_n: 2.00
F_n: 2.83
G_n: 4.00
H_n: 4.47
K_n: 5.66

Using either inverse or inverse squared weightings, these become:

	$1/d$	$1/d^2$
E_n	0.50	0.25
F_n	0.35	0.12
G_n	0.25	0.06
H_n	0.22	0.05
K_n	0.18	0.03

The average is then calculated by summing the sample values multiplied by their factors (f) and dividing by the sum of the factors.

$$\frac{Af_A + \sum E_{1-n'} f_E + \sum F_{1-n'} f_F + \dots}{\sum f_A + f_{E_{1-n}} + f_{F_{1-n}} + \dots}$$

When the value for block A has been calculated, the procedure is repeated for the next block, labelled B in the lowest diagram. It will be noted that the value of the sample in block A is also used in this calculation. However rather than have a weighting factor of 1, this is now reduced to 0.5 or 0.25 if inverse squared values are used).

Each block is treated in exactly the same manner until all the blocks have been evaluated.

weightings used for neighbouring sample values. If it is too low, individual sample errors can still have a major effect on block grade values. If the weighting applied is too high, the incorporation of too many neighbouring samples at large distances from the block can result in over-smoothing and the loss of important variations in the deposit. A mathematical procedure, known as the theory of regionalized variables can be used to overcome this problem. This is the basis of geostatistics. It should be noted that the term 'geostatistics' is used here in the European sense. North American usage has, at least in the past, tended to use the term in a general sense for traditional statistics applied to geology (e.g. McCammon 1975).

Since de Wijs (1952, 1953) first drew attention to the importance of the spatial relationships of mineral samples, geostatistics has developed into a universally accepted tool for modelling natural systems based on point samples (Matheron 1971). As well as ore deposit estimation, the technique can be used for the assessment of any data set where there are spatial relationships between sample values, for example in environmental assessment (Englund & Sparks 1988) and water resources (Delhomme & Delfiner 1973). Since geostatistical methods have been discussed in detail elsewhere, for example by Clark (1979), Journel & Huijbreghts (1978) and Isaaks & Srivastava (1989), only those points pertinent to the assessment of rock masses will be discussed here.

The application of geostatistics involves two stages. First, the nature of the spatial relationship between samples is identified, and secondly, this relationship is applied to the data points to give a best estimate model of the deposit as a whole. Unlike conventional statistics, this model can result in the generation of modified values for the data points, these values being considered as better estimates of the true values for those points. This situation arises since, as has been stressed previously, the recorded values include sampling and other errors, or may be the result of a random atypical features such as a cavity or an unusual mineral occurrence. Geostatistical techniques can be considered as estimating the size of this error and removing it.

The first part of the geostatistical procedure, the identification of the spatial relationship, is the most vital in the assessment (Royle 1992). An error at this stage could completely invalidate the assessment, and can lead to major financial losses. The model of the spatial relationship between samples is known as the semi-variogram because the sum of differences between assay values is divided by *twice* the number of sample pairs. This is a plot of the variation between samples, located at different distances apart. An outline description of the semi-variogram is given in the text box. Unlike the moving average discussed in §4.2.4.5, the calculation of semi-variograms can provide a precise mathematical model for the area around a sample point where there is likely to be a relationship between neighbouring samples. The arbitrary selection of an inverse distance or other factor is, therefore, avoided.

Once the model that best fits the pattern of variation in the grade of the stone has been determined it is possible to use the sample data to predict the grade of blocks of stone in the ground. This is normally accomplished by using the procedure known as 'kriging'. Essentially a form of weighted averaging, kriging has been the subject of much development in recent years and there are now a number of variations of the method (Royle 1992). Many of these are mathematically complex and should only be used with care. Just as it is possible to produce apparently valid models of random data using high-order polynomial equations in Trend Surface Analysis, it could be possible to produce similar artifacts by incautious use of kriging routines. This is especially true where the procedures are supplied in commercial computer software that is designed for mineral data assessment, but complete details of the mathematical procedures used are not given. An example of block kriging is given in Diagram F of Fig. 4.9.

One major advantage of using geostatistics to provide an estimate of the quality of volumes of stone is that a value for the variance of the error of the estimate can be calculated. This can be used to assist in estimating the financial risk associated with the development of the deposit and to design the further exploration of the deposit to reduce the uncertainty.

The techniques of weighted moving averages and geostatistics only have an advantage over normal statistical techniques if some form of model that describes the spatial relationship between the grades of neighbouring samples can be applied to that area immediately around each sample. In the case of geostatistics, where the model is derived from an analysis of the data itself, the calculation can only be undertaken if the sample spacing is less than the radius of what may be termed the 'area of influence'. As this distance is often relatively small, perhaps only a few tens of metres, samples are often too far apart for the technique to be used. This is especially true where boreholes are providing the samples, as they tend to be widely spaced. One method of overcoming this difficulty is to take a series of additional closely spaced surface or pit samples to provide information on short-range variations. However, great care must be used when combining data obtained with differing sampling techniques, which produce samples of different mass or volume, and with different spatial distributions.

4.2.5. The size of the grade block

4.2.5.1. Practical quarrying requirements

The aim of the assessment, irrespective of the method used, is to determine the grades of the rock in the ground together with the distribution of those grades. This will not only indicate whether or not suitable stone exists

The semi-variogram

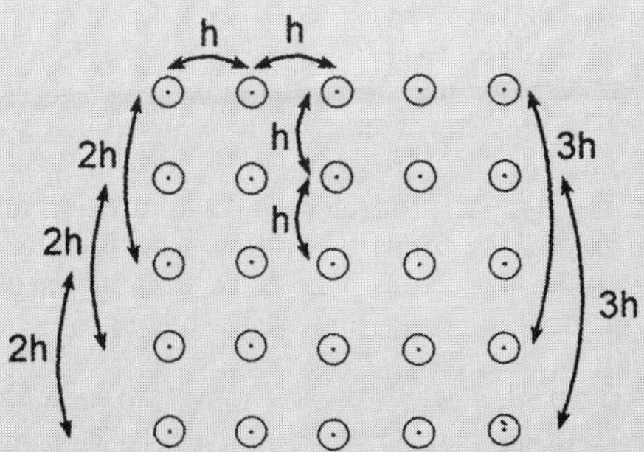

The differences between all possible pairs of samples are measured. This can be done as an actual length, or where there is a uniform sampling interval, as a 'lag', that is the number of sample intervals between the samples. In the diagram on the left, lag 1 is equal to h, lag 2 to $2h$, and so on. Since the variation between samples can vary with direction, the differences can be measured in a number of orientations. In the diagram, east-west and north-south orientations are shown. The two sets of data which would result from these two different data sets would be assessed separately.

The semi-variogram, $\gamma(h)$, is then calculated for each lag, or sample interval, using the formula:

$$\gamma(h) = \frac{1}{2n}\sum [g(x) - g(x+h)]^2$$

where $g(x)$ is the grade of one sample in a pair, and $g(x+h)$ the grade of the other. h is the lag and n the number of pairs of samples at this lag.

The semi-variograms which have been calculated for each lag, or sample interval, are plotted against the lag in the manner shown on the right. The resulting curve is the model which can be used to relate the samples to each other and to the deposit as a whole. A number of different models have been shown to be valid for geological data. Three common ones are shown below. The most likely to be encountered is the 'spherical' model shown on the right. The plot of semi-variogram data against sample distance rarely produces a perfect curve, and a certain amount of experience and judgement is normally required to fit the best model to the data. This procedure is extremely important since an incorrect choice of model, can invalidate all the later estimates of deposit grade.

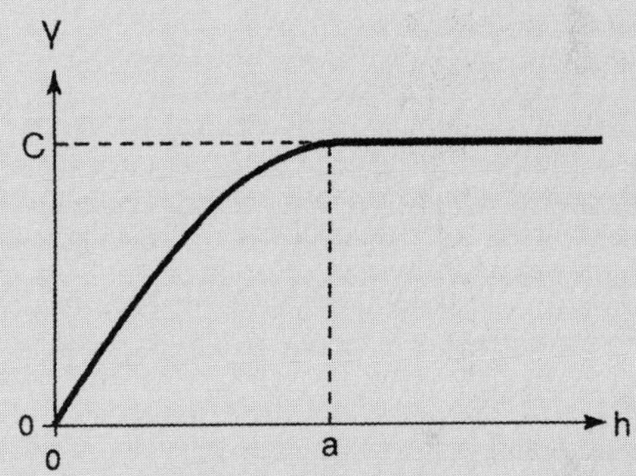

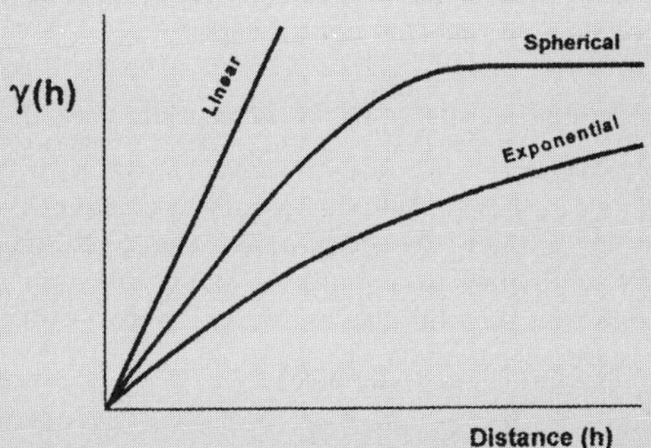

In the spherical model shown above, it can be seen that closely spaced samples have a smaller variation than widely spaced samples. In fact a point is reached where, at a certain distance a, known as the 'range' of influence of the sample, the variation becomes constant. This value of γ marked as C above, is known as the 'sill' and is equivalent to the ordinary sample variance of the grades.

For a more complete discussion on the semi-variogram, specialist works such as Clark (1979) should be consulted.

but also enable the viability of its extraction to be investigated. The size of the blocks of stone, for which the average grade and variance is calculated, must ideally be as small as possible. Dimension stone quarries tend to have faces which are measured in tens of metres rather than hundreds, and may advance only a few metres each year. To estimate the variation in a dimension stone deposit on the basis of the average grade of 100 metre square blocks is therefore of little value. Since the minimum size of the grade block is largely determined by the original sample spacing, this should be borne in mind when the initial exploration is being planned.

The assessment methods discussed in §4.2.4 are essentially two-dimensional. However, if the sample values represent, for example, the average porosity of a two metre thick bed of sandstone that is being studied as a potential source of dimension stone, the resulting grade assessment will represent the variation in grade throughout the bed. However, if the deposit consists of a number of individual beds, a similar assessment will be required for each.

4.2.5.2. Grade estimation with limited data

Despite the availability of mathematical techniques to assist in estimating the grade of rock and mineral in the ground, successful implementation of these techniques is dependent upon the availability of sufficient sample data. Unfortunately the cost of drilling, sampling and testing is often considered prohibitive by those financing the investigation. This is especially true in some situations in developing countries, where even the extraction and processing may have to be undertaken using simple methods, due to the limited finance available (Shadmon 1989).

It was noted in §4.2.4.1 that the use of conventional statistics with point sample data was of little use when investigating the variation of a deposit that was to be used to supply blocks of stone. Normally the variation between large pieces of stone will be less than between small hand samples or pieces of borehole core taken from the same deposit. If only a limited number of samples can be taken from a deposit, every effort should be made to ensure that the size of each sample is as close to the intended product size as possible. A number of test samples should then be taken from each large sample. This technique will not only allow an average grade to be determined for each of the block-sized pieces of stone but also give an indication of the variation likely to occur between blocks of product size. Conventional statistics can then be used to determine the overall grade of the deposit and the variation that may be expected in the grade of product-sized blocks.

Although all the blocks may have an acceptable average grade, this type of assessment may indicate that some blocks will not be sufficiently uniform for use as dimension stone or as armourstone. The predicted percentage of acceptable stone, based on the average analysis of block-sized samples, will therefore have to be modified.

This type of assessment can only provide an indication of the variation to be expected in the stone over the life of the deposit, and the percentage of product-sized blocks extracted from it that will be unsuitable for use. It cannot provide information on the location of poorer quality stone. Quarry development cannot therefore be planned to take account of known areas of low-grade material and must be designed to accommodate periods of high stone wastage as and when they occur.

A method that can be used to investigate the likely frequency of encountering poor quality material is the Monte Carlo simulation. This involves using a mathematical model with identical statistical parameters to the real deposit to simulate the output from the quarry. The variation in quality of the simulated output produced by the model will not be identical to that which will occur in practice. However, the pattern and rate of variation will be generally the same. For example, the length of periods when only poor quality, or extremely high quality, blocks of stone are available from the mathematical model will give an indication of what may occur in practice. The actual extraction can therefore be planned to cope with those periods when extremes of quality are likely to occur.

4.3. Determination of the quantity of stone available

Having divided the deposit up into a series of blocks of different grades of material, it is necessary to calculate the quantity of each grade that is available. At this stage of the assessment it is not necessary to consider the practicality of extracting the material. Economics is a major consideration in determining which parts of the deposit can be extracted, but until the quantity and distribution of the different potential stone products have been assessed, it would be premature to omit any parts of the deposit from consideration.

4.3.1. Estimation of the size of the deposit

4.3.1.1. Volume

Where the assessment involves strata of constant thickness, such as might be encountered when investigating massive sandstones as a source of dimension stone or a bulk source of rock fill, the volume of different grades of stone is simply calculated by multiplying the area occupied by the relevant grade by the bed thickness. Where the beds are steeply dipping, care must be taken to ensure that the area of the top of the strata is taken rather than the projection of the bed onto the horizontal plane of the map. This is illustrated in the accompanying text box.

Determination of rock volume

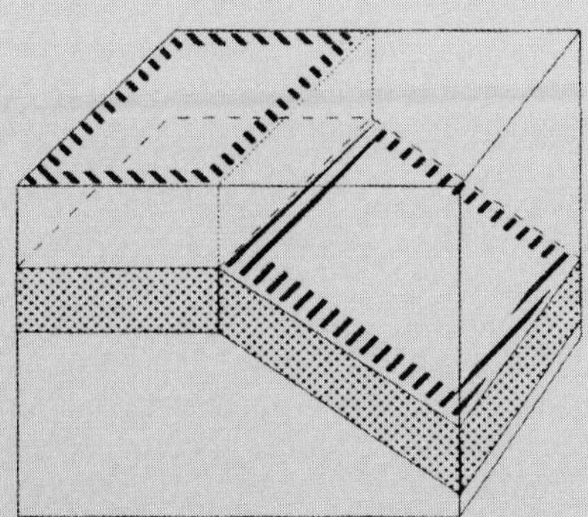

Although when calculating volumes of uniform horizontal beds, the area underlain by the stone can be multiplied by bed thickness, in the case of inclined strata it is necessary to calculate the area of the bed itself. Alternatively the projection of the inclined bed onto a horizontal surface can be multiplied by the *apparent* thickness of the bed measured vertically.

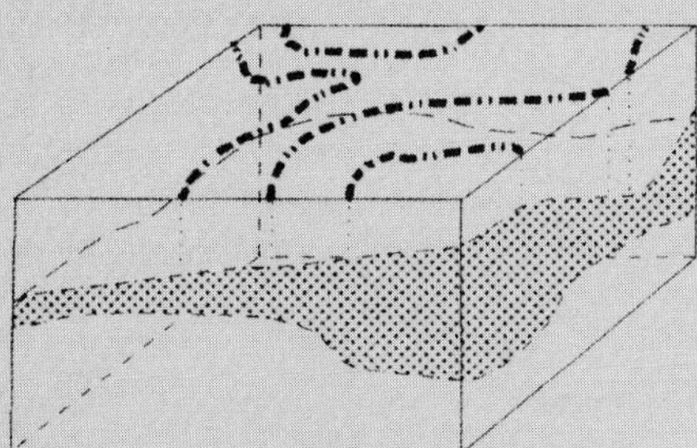

Isopachytes are lines joining points of equal thickness. They can be calculated in a similar fashion to surface contours or to isograds. If geostatistics is used to determine and contour the thickness variations, it is possible to determine the variance associated with the estimated thickness. This in turn allows an estimate of the error associated with the volume calculation to be made.

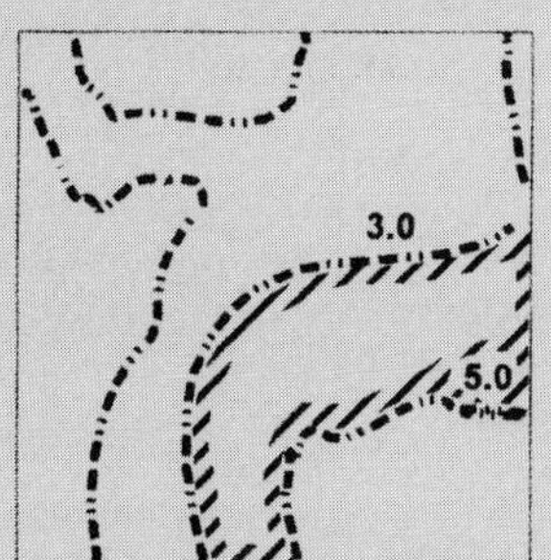

When using isopachytes for volume calculation, the area between two isopachytes is multiplied by the average value of the two thicknesses. In the example on the left, the area indicated would be multiplied by 4.0.

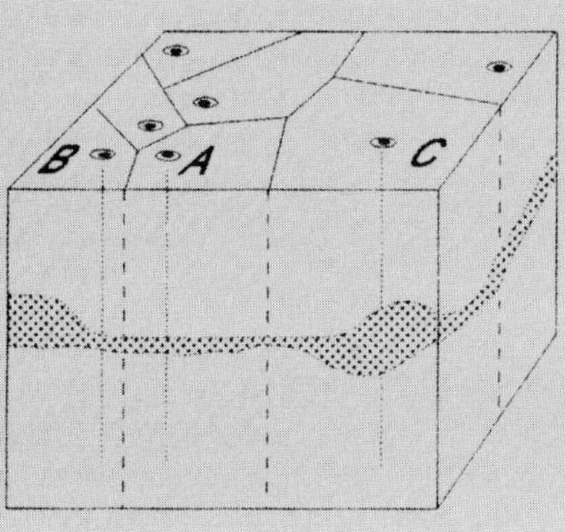

Thiessen polygons can be used to determine volume. The area of the polygon is multiplied by the thickness of the rock at the central borehole or sample point. However if the rock being assessed is variable in thickness, this can result in an erroneous volume estimate. Uneven spacing of the sample points can also result in errors. In the example on the left, the volume of mineral beneath polygon A will be correctly estimated by multiplying the area of the polygon by the thickness. However in blocks B and C, the result will be inaccurate. B will be underestimated, whereas C will be overestimated, the borehole passing through a thick portion of the stone. Furthermore, the area of C being much greater than the other polygons, the error will be much more significant than that associated with B.

Due to variation in the thickness of strata, or due to grade variation within a bed, the thickness of a particular material may vary within the deposit. Although the area of the bed could be multiplied by the average thickness in order to determine the volume, the errors which this procedure could introduce may have serious implications, especially if the deposit was marginally economically viable. Furthermore, the variation in thickness could have important consequences for the extraction of the stone. In a mineral or rock deposit of variable thickness, the distribution of thickness can be as important as the distribution of the various grades.

The thickness of a bed of stone, or of a grade of material within a bed, can be considered in exactly the same manner as the chemical and physical properties of the material. Hence it is possible to use the individual sample points to construct a detailed model of the variation in thickness throughout the deposit. This can be carried out using similar techniques to those described for grade determination in §4.2.4. Once this has been accomplished, the model can be contoured. The resulting lines, which join points of equal thickness, are known as 'isopachytes' (in the UK) or 'isopachs' (US terminology). By measuring the area between two isopachytes, the volume of stone within this area can be calculated; this is shown in the text box. If the estimates of the thickness throughout the deposit have been made by geostatistical means, the accuracy of the estimate will be known, and this can be extended to give an estimate of the accuracy of the volume calculation.

It is common for volume estimates to be made using Thiessen polygons (e.g. Nathanail 1994). However, as is shown in the text box, there is the possibility of over- or under-estimating thickness, and therefore volume, when using this method.

Variable sample spacing giving undue weighting to certain samples could also adversely effect the volume estimate.

4.3.1.2. Density and tonnage

The density of stone can be defined in a number ways, see Appendix B. In the context of assessing the commercial potential of a stone deposit, the dry bulk density is required. This is defined as the mass of dry rock per unit volume of ground.

In porous stone, where 5% or more of the mass of a block as sold can be moisture, care must be taken when comparing predicted or actual production requirements, and the quantity of stone in the ground. A quarry selling 3000 tonnes each year of moist ex-quarry stone may, over a period of 20 years, have sold around 3000 tonnes of water, equivalent to one year's sales of stone, worth perhaps £0.5M. It will also have extended the predicted life of the reserve by one year. However, if the stone is drier than usual for a period of time, perhaps because the climate is drier or the stone has been stored under cover, this will not apply. In order to ensure that estimates of reserves are not affected by the moisture factor, the dry density should always be used for the calculations.

4.3.1.3. Specialized quantity considerations for building stone

Although rock-fill, armourstone, rockery and rubble walling are sold by the tonne, both ex-quarry and sawn block-stone is sold by the cubic metre. Dressed and semi-dressed walling stone, ashlar and paving are sold by the square metre. Quoins can be sold by the metre rise and coping stones by the linear metre. Because of this traditional manner of trading in stone, many building stone quarries do not have weighbridges, and the conversion between tonnes and, for example, square metres of walling, is not known. Moreover, in order to translate tonnes in the ground into square metres of walling, the thickness of the stone needs to be known as do the quarrying and dressing losses (see §4.3.3). If the resource assessment is to be placed in the context of a building stone operation in order that its financial viability can be determined, the various processing factors need to be considered in order that the quantity of stone present can be quoted in terms that are meaningful to the industry.

4.3.2. Overburden

One of the most important factors affecting the extraction of stone and minerals is the cost of removing unusable material or overburden. Although it is often only considered in the context of the soil and other materials which overlie the rock to be quarried, overburden actually refers to all that material which has to be discarded, whether it be above the mineral or rock deposit or included in the deposit as beds of unsuitable material; the latter material sometimes being referred to as interburden.

The volume and tonnage of all the waste material is calculated in exactly the same manner as the different grades of stone. If physically different types of overburden are present, these should be estimated separately, since it may be necessary to remove them by significantly different means, resulting in potentially different costs, see §5.3.5. It is also possible that a potential economic use has been identified for some of the waste stone during the exploration and assessment of the data. Any material to which this applies should also be treated as a separate unit from the point of view of estimating the quantity present.

4.3.3. Calculation of the quantity of stone product

The calculations of volumes and tonnages discussed in §4.3.1 are theoretical in that they assume a 100% yield of product of the grade being assessed. However, in the case of armourstone and building stone, only stone that can be removed from the ground in lump form is of value. Even in the case of rock-fill, it cannot be assumed that the total volume of stone extracted for use will be the same as the measured volume of the ground.

There are a number of factors to be taken into account when translating the theoretical volume of stone into the actual quantity of saleable material which will be won from that volume. These are:

- Natural voids
- Extraction losses
- Processing losses

4.3.3.1. Losses due to cavities
An inspection of any quarry face will indicate that, except in the case of some igneous rocks, natural cavities are a common feature in the ground. In sedimentary rocks bedding planes and joints are rarely tightly closed and, although they may contain clay, sand or other loose material, should be counted as cavity. Limestones can contain solution cavities, as can some sandstones. Careful measurement of borehole core, natural exposures, and any existing quarry faces during the exploration stage should have provided sufficient information for a realistic factor to be applied to the volume measurements.

4.3.3.2. Extraction losses
Although most building stone is extracted without the use of explosives, there will always be stone lost during extraction. This may be very small, as in the case of the limestones on Malta which are cut directly from the bed using circular saws. The only loss in this case is the dust cut out by the saw-blade. At the other extreme are many of the British Jurassic limestones which are traditionally used as building materials. Many beds, although classified as good quality block-stone, can be found to have both structural and lithological discontinuities in them, which result in breakage during the extraction process. Sometimes the stone can be re-classified, block-stone being used for walling for example. An estimate for this potential downgrading must be included in any resource estimate and is not, therefore, an extraction loss although, being of lesser value, it will have financial implications. As with the case of natural cavities, an estimate of the percentage of stone likely to be affected by factors such as soft bands, which may affect its grade, will have become apparent during the exploration stage of the project.

Armourstone, which is extracted using the natural discontinuities in the stone, will suffer from similar wastage problems to building stone, undersized material or stone containing patches of unsuitable material having to be discarded. If the rock is also to be used for aggregate, much of the waste could probably be utilized and this would be reflected in the factors applied when estimating the quantities available.

Where armourstone is to be extracted using blasting techniques, the wastage will be dependent upon a number of factors (Wang *et al.* 1991*b*). Of these, the spacing of discontinuities, density, tensile strength and other physical features will have been determined during the exploration. Blasting factors such as burden, spacing, charge, initiation sequence and other controllable factors will have to be considered before an estimate of the yield of suitably sized blocks can be made.

The quantity of waste generated is an important factor in assessing a stone deposit. It may not only affect the viability of the scheme but also have a major influence on the quarry development plan. As well as waste stone generated during the extraction process, there will also be the overburden and processing waste discussed in §§4.3.2 and 4.3.3.3 respectively. All waste stone will invariably be disposed of on-site as backfill. Clearly, the rate at which the worked-out quarry void is infilled must not exceed the rate at which the working faces progress. With high waste factors, coupled with the bulking factor associated with tipping loose stone into the void, this can be a potential major problem. Some waste factors are quite remarkable. For example, in some quarries working Welsh slate or Norwegian larvikite, the waste stone can amount to 95% of the material extracted.

4.3.3.3. Processing losses
Armourstone and rock-fill is used in its ex-quarry state and no further losses will be experienced due to processing. Building stone, on the other hand, can be subject to further losses depending upon the amount of dressing which it undergoes prior to being sold. Such items as rubble walling and some forms of paving will require little or no processing and there will be no additional wastage of the stone. Dressed and semi-dressed building stone will be guillotined or sawn to shape and, if dressed, trimmed by hand. All these processes will result in some loss of stone.

Although some block-stone is sold as-dug, much is now sold as sawn six-sided block. Preparing stone in this manner can result in large processing losses, especially if the ex-quarry block is irregular. This has been discussed in §4.2.3.2 and is illustrated in Fig. 4.5. If the off-cuts from the processing are to be utilized for some other purpose, for example for paving, the yield of such material would have to be estimated and included in the assessment of the quantities of stone. The geologist must, therefore, work closely with the stonemasons and management of the stone company and must thoroughly understand the nature of the actual and potential products if he is to assess the size of the reserve correctly.

4.4. Resource or reserve?

The important distinction between a resource and a reserve has been discussed in §3.1.1. Having divided the deposit into a series of blocks of known quality and yield, the size of the *resource* has been determined. It is now necessary to calculate how much of this material can be extracted within the constraints of the economic climate which is prevailing at the time of the assessment, or which is predicted for the future. This calculation will determine the proportion of the *resource* which can be considered as a mineral *reserve*.

4.4.1. Economic aspects

4.4.1.1. Markets
Unlike fuels or metals, the economics of which tend to be related to global changes, the construction industry is largely controlled by the national economy. In fact, there can even be major differences between regions in the same country. Local variations in the economy can be important in the context of rock and stone used for construction as, being a bulk mineral, transport costs tend to be high and local sources are therefore often sought for projects. An exception would be high-quality armourstone for coastal defence work which can be transported large distances by sea, if the source is close to the coast. Furthermore, it can often be off-loaded from the barge in which it was transported, immediately adjacent to the project for which it is being used, see §8.4.3.

Rock-fill on the other hand will be sought as close as possible to the project for which it is required. The process of 'cut and fill', which is common where roads or railways are being constructed in undulating terrain, often results in relatively short haulage distances.

Whereas armourstone and rock-fill are normally required for major construction projects, building stone tends to be used for commercial and residential construction purposes. Here it is competing against man-made products such as bricks or ornamental pre-cast concrete panels. Only in areas such as restoration is there little competition. Unlike other uses for rock and stone in construction, building stone has the added factor of 'fashion' and, as a result, the market can be volatile. For example, during the period 1985 to 1994, an initial rapid increase in demand in the UK for stone to decorate and clad prestigious office developments incorporating 'atria' and shopping 'plazas', was followed by a severe recession in the requirement for materials for such projects.

Fashion is a variable which is difficult to assess, and many dimension stone quarries have had to close down because, for example, pink granite became fashionable at the expense of the white granite which was being produced by the quarry. In the early part of the 1990s, architects in the UK appeared to favour lighter colours, especially white and grey, and featureless, bland textures without veining, visible crystallinity or fossil content. There is evidence in the second part of the decade of a swing towards more textured and coloured stone such as red and dark-coloured granites. Fashion may also result in intense competition between the producers of the more common colours, textures and types, once again resulting in commercial failure if the marketing of the stone is not undertaken in a very professional manner and the extraction costs not carefully controlled (see §4.4.1.2). However, a quarry producing a stone with an unusual colour or texture, for example a green or blue stone, or one with unusual marbling, can benefit from a specialist niche that is largely free from the vagaries of fashion.

In addition to being used in the fabric of buildings and in flooring, stone is becoming popular as a component of fittings within the building. Kitchen work tops and bathroom fittings often utilize polished stone. Lightweight stone panels, made by bonding a stone veneer onto an aluminium honeycomb have been used in the liner Queen Elizabeth II, as well as on Boeing aircraft (see Fig. 9.18). Fashion will, once again, play an important role in the choice of stone for these markets.

4.4.1.2 Extraction costs
The market for stone is extremely cost-conscious, competitive and international and, unless a stone is in demand because of its special appearance or unusually high durability, the market-place will tend to dictate the price at which building stone can be sold. Extraction and processing costs are, therefore, subject to very tight constraints. Processing costs tend to be fixed. Assuming that the equipment is designed for the size of block being produced by the quarry, the amount of work required to prepare a sawn six-sided block of stone is relatively constant. This would not be the case if, due to an inadequate raw material assessment, saws capable of taking 2.5 metre long block were having to be used to cut 1 metre block, because the equipment had been sized on incorrect data. It is within the quarry that the economics of the operation are largely determined. Typical quarry costs, compared to a crushed stone quarry, are indicated in Table 4.2.

The most noticeable difference between building stone and aggregate quarries is the fact that the extraction cost of building stone can be ten times that of aggregate. The high production figures are offset by the fact that building stone can sell for £150 per tonne or more. A limited amount of simple processing, for example trimming and drilling stone roofing tiles, can increase this figure up to £1000 per tonne or more. The large proportion of the production costs which is contributed by the items related to plant is a reflection of the inefficient use of mobile plant in low-capacity operations. Table 4.2 also illustrates the labour-intensive nature of building stone extraction. An output of 1000 tonnes of stone per man per year would be typical of a building stone quarry; a crushed stone aggregate quarry may well expect 25 times this output for each employee (Jefferson 1993).

Table 4.2. *Comparison of quarrying costs for crushed and building stone*

	Crushed stone quarry 500 000 t.p.a.		*Building stone quarry 3000 t.p.a.*	
	Cost/ tonne £	*% of total cost*	*Cost/ tonne £*	*% of total cost*
Variable costs				
Materials incl. fuel	0.20	6	3.50	11
Explosives	0.20	6		
Royalties	0.40	13	2.30	7
Overburden	0.04	1		
Plant hire	0.02	1	0.50	2
Fixed costs				
Labour	0.50	16	12.70	40
Repair and maintenance	0.60	19	3.40	11
Power	0.18	6	0.85	3
Overheads	0.20	6	4.00	13
Depreciation	0.60	19	3.40	11
Sales and administration	0.18	6	0.70	2
Total	3.12		31.35	

The figures do not represent any particular quarrying operations and are intended to illustrate the differences between the two types of quarry. Blasting is not normally undertaken in building stone extraction, and overburden removal is frequently integral in winning the building material (from Jefferson 1993).

The cost of labour is an important factor in the international trade in building stone. As with many other mineral commodities, developing countries view the export of stone as a means to earn valuable foreign exchange and establish indigenous industry. The low labour rates and lack of high capital investment compensate for the cost of lengthy transport. This is especially true when transport is by sea and producers in countries such as India and Brazil compete strongly for markets in Europe, USA and Japan, all traditionally supplied by local quarries. Similar factors are also resulting in the introduction of cheap, high-quality stone from Eastern Europe into the world markets.

Since overburden removal is normally undertaken by the quarry personnel who extract the building stone, using the same mobile plant, this aspect of the quarrying operation does not appear as a separate item in Table 4.2. It is, however, a major consideration when assessing the reserves of the quarry. Since quarry faces tend to move slowly in building stone quarries due to the relatively low output, thick overburden on top of the deposit could be moved every two or three years, by contractors if necessary. Where waste occurs interbedded with the stone, its removal would have to be continuous. This could involve the purchase of additional plant and the employment of extra personnel, resulting in an increased cost of extraction.

The 'stripping ratio', i.e. the ratio of overburden and waste rock to useable stone, is determined by the economics of the quarrying operation. This can be complicated by the fact that the size of the reserve of stone is often increased considerably by accepting a higher stripping ratio. This is illustrated in Fig. 4.10, which can also be used to illustrate the problem of attempting to phase quarry working due to financial constraints. For example, should a stripping ratio of 1.5 be accepted initially, and the deposit represented in Fig. 4.10 be worked down to level *B*, the strata beneath this level will have an overburden to stone ratio of 2.29. Working the lower stone as a later phase would result in an overburden ratio almost 15% more than if a ratio of 2.0 had been accepted as the initial limit and the two horizons worked together. When carrying out an assessment of the stone in order to determine the

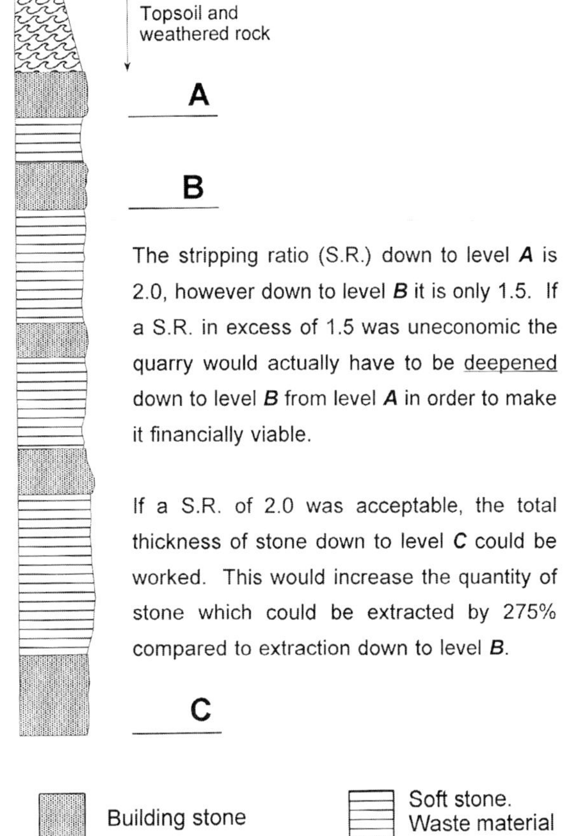

Fig. 4.10. The effect of stripping ratio on the size of a mineral reserve.

The effect of the distribution of the different grades of stone in a quarry can have a major effect on the economics of the quarrying operation. As an example, market analysis has indicated that tilestone, walling stone and block-stone can be sold in the ratio of 2:3:1.

The geological sequence and the thickness of the different beds will result in a number of different situations.

The thicknesses of the tilestone, walling stone and block-stone are 2 metres, 3 metres and 1 metre respectively. All products can be worked in the required quantity and the faces progress at the same rate.

The thicknesses of the tilestone, walling stone and block-stone are 1 metre, 3 metres and 4 metres respectively. All products can be worked in the required quantity. However, the faces progress at considerably different rates, the tilestone face advancing eight times faster than the block-stone face. It is likely that both the tilestone and walling stone will be exhausted before the block-stone. The economics of the project could be jeopardized. The size of the quarry, and the related environmental problems, will be greater than the previous case.

The thicknesses of all the beds is 2 metres. Although the tilestone and the block-stone can be worked in the required quantities, the walling stone cannot, since the face would catch up on the tilestone bench. However, the tilestone face is progressing twice as fast as the block-stone face. A financial decision is required whether or not to utilize half the high quality block-stone for walling, or whether to leave the walling stone market unsatisfied. If block-stone is used for lower grade purposes, the faces will all advance at the same rate.

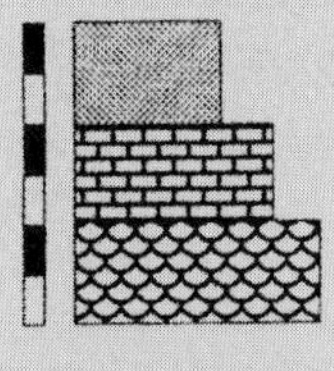

The thicknesses of all the beds is 2 metres. However the sequence is inverted. The low demand for block-stone will now limit the production of both walling stone and tilestone. It is likely that, unless half the block-stone is used for walling, the project will not be financially viable.

 Tilestone  Walling stone  Block-stone

The scale bars are marked in 1 metre intervals.

exact quantity available and the economic life of the deposit, factors such as these must be given careful consideration.

A further economic consideration can affect both dimension stone and armourstone deposits. This is the possible necessity of having to use some of the higher grade stone for lower-value products. Although a deposit may contain stone suitable for a range of products, it is the size of the market that determines the quantities of the products produced. A failure to judge the market correctly is often a source of investment error. A potential source of building stone may have been shown to contain many millions of tonnes of stone suitable for producing potentially high-value block-stone. However, if the market only requires low-value semi-dressed walling stone, the deposit must be assessed using the economics of walling stone production and not block production. The connection between stratigraphy and the market place is illustrated in the text box.

The relationship between the grade of the stone and the market place also affects the production of armourstone. If a quarry is producing both aggregate and armourstone, its economics will be a result of a balance between the two products. If, however, the armourstone horizon overlies that which is used for aggregate production, there is always the possibility that aggregate demand could outstrip block-stone production. During the assessment of the reserves it therefore, should be noted that it may be necessary either to stockpile the armourstone, which would involve the cost of double handling, or use some of the high-grade stone for aggregate production.

Certain other factors associated with the extraction of the stone have economic implications and need to be assessed before the reserve can finally be delineated. Principal amongst these are:

- Environmental factors
- Surface and sub-surface water

Protection of neighbouring properties from visual intrusion, noise, dust and other factors associated with mineral extraction will involve both capital and operating expenditure. Removal of water from the workings and its treatment before discharge is another operating cost which may arise. All these aspects of stone extraction are discussed in detail in §5.2.3. However, they all have to be researched in depth at the assessment stage. For example, the requirement to maintain both the level and quality of water in a wetland area on the edge of a quarry could have major financial implications for a building stone quarry, especially if there is going to be a long-term requirement for maintaining the quality of that wetland, even after the quarry is exhausted.

4.4.1.3. By-products

One method by which the financial risk associated with the production of both dimension stone and armourstone can be reduced is to diversify the product range. As was indicated in §3.2.2.5, all possible products must be investigated when assessing a deposit in order to determine its economic potential. Only that material for which no economic use can be found will be used for backfilling the quarry void. Soils will, of course, be preserved in storage for use in the ultimate restoration of the workings. Although the primary product from a dimension stone quarry may be block stone, any strong, durable consolidated rock overlying the massive beds used to produce the blocks can often be processed by splitting, cutting or sawing, to produce walling or building stone. Thinly bedded stone, or material of a slab-like or flaggy nature, may yield paving stone or even stone roofing tiles. In the case of quarries designed to produce armourstone, the production of aggregate for road construction or for concrete is an obvious secondary use for material which is not of sufficient size, or of appropriate shape, for use as armourstone. The overburden from armourstone quarries, which may be weathered granite or thinly bedded limestones, could be considered as general construction fill, or even low-quality aggregate such as road base.

Waste stone that is generated in quarries producing building stone, both from the quarrying and dressing operations, may be suitable for other forms of construction use. It may be suitable for crushing to produce a good quality aggregate, or used in an as-dug state for general construction fill, or low-quality aggregate such as road base. However, in the UK, such uses are not normally permitted by the Mineral Planning Authorities. Sufficient reserves of aggregate materials are known in the UK, and the large quantity of traffic that is associated with aggregate production, when compared to building stone production, is normally an unacceptable factor when planning permission for dimension stone quarries is being considered. Moreover, complete restoration of quarry voids is now a common condition of the extraction consent for stone quarries. The waste stone is therefore normally required for this purpose. There are known instances where, due to the bulking factor of the broken stone, the volume of waste exceeds the volume of the void. However, this is can normally be avoided by careful quarry planning and also by using more stone for secondary products such as walling or paving, rather than tipping all the waste into the worked-out quarry.

Exceptions to the restriction on aggregate or fill production from UK building stone quarries can occur. Where, for example, the overburden may be a superficial deposit of sand and gravel suitable for aggregate production, permission would normally be granted to sell this, as and when overburden stripping was taking place. In these circumstances the increase in road traffic would be restricted to a very short period of time at infrequent intervals. Where considerable quantities of waste are generated, as in slate quarrying, special circumstances may prevail and it may be acceptable to sell non-cleavable slate for non-building purposes. However, at the present time, the Department of Transport specification does not permit the use of slate waste as sub-base for roads. The production, by crushing and milling, of a material suitable for the manufacture of cast stone, which is made by bonding powdered stone with cement or resin, is another potential use for slate and other stone waste.

Where the waste stone has a special property, such as colour or mineral content, it may be of value, even in small quantities as a filler or a pigment, or as agricultural lime for local use. When assessing the financial potential of waste materials from a stone quarry, the overriding factors tend to be the cost of processing, for example crushing and milling, and the number of vehicle movements which the non-building stone activities of the site would generate.

One activity which is normally acceptable to the planning authorities is the production of powdered stone for addition to mortars. The colouring effect is used both in normal construction for aesthetic reasons, and also in stone restoration work for ensuring that repairs are as close in colour and texture to the original stone as possible (Ashhurst & Dimes 1990).

Just as it may be possible, in certain circumstances to produce secondary products from dimension stone and armourstone extraction sites, the opposite may also be possible. Dimension stone, armourstone and rip-rap may be produced as profitable by-products of an operation established to produce aggregates, or the raw materials for cement or other mineral-based product. However, in the case of building stone, the use of explosives which are used to free the stone from the quarry face and to ensure that it is suitably fragmented for its primary purpose, can potentially create micro-fracturing in the stone, which may seriously reduce its durability as a building material.

4.4.2. Financial evaluation

The financial evaluation of projects as part of the investment decision making process is a very large and complex subject and sufficient space is not available in this report to provide anything more than a very simple introduction and references to sources of further information. Comprehensive texts upon financial evaluation and investment decision making in general have been provided by several authors including Lumby (1994), Bierman & Smidt (1990), Barish & Kaplan (1978), Weston & Copeland (1992) and Stermole & Stermole (1993). A simpler introduction has been provided by Oldcon (1993). Financial evaluation of mining projects, in particular, has been described by Annels (1991), Hoskins & Green (1978) and Gentry & O'Neill (1984).

In developing countries, mining projects, including quarries for dimension stone, are often undertaken for the purpose of earning foreign exchange and promoting development of the nation through creation of associated infrastructure, training and acquisition of skills and technology. However, in this chapter, no account will be taken of any national and social benefits and the mine or quarry development will be considered only as a business opportunity which should produce a monetary benefit (profit) for the owners. Although several methods are available to evaluate the economic viability of a project, the most usual methods employed in the mineral industry are based upon the analysis of cash flow, the concept of discounting future earnings and the parameters of Net Present Value (NPV), Internal Rate of Return (IRR) and Pay Back Period (PBP).

Investment in the mineral industry has two unusual characteristics when compared to investment in more conventional manufacturing industry:

- A finite life of the project determined by the reserves and rate of working,
- An additional risk incurred by the uncertainties concerning the nature and quantity of the reserves.

The first aspect has created certain specialized tax allowances which permit the mineral operator to recover the costs of exploration in order that he may identify new reserves to replace those that have been consumed. Depletion is one such form of tax allowance. Furthermore, mining investment decisions are usually also supported by consideration of risk using techniques such as sensitivity analysis and Monte Carlo simulation.

4.4.2.1. Cash flow and discounted cash flow

The cash flow for a period, usually one year, is essentially the net profit after operating costs and taxes have been deducted from the income or revenue. However, the calculation is complicated by the inclusion of allowances against taxable income permitted by the taxation authorities for capital expenditure. A simple example of the projected cash flow for a small dimension stone quarry is presented in Table 4.3 but these figures do not represent any actual operation and are only for illustration. The capital investment is low because it is assumed that second-hand equipment will be used. The selling price is a weighted average of the prices of the various products including sawn slab, building stone and walling stone. The operating cost is simply the total annual cost divided by the output expressed in cubic metres.

In the financial evaluation of projects the practice of discounting the predicted cash flows in later years takes account of the perception of most people that a sum of money received today has a greater value than the same sum of money received in the future. Indeed, a given sum of money received today and deposited in a interest bearing account would be expected to increase in value. However, the selection of an appropriate discount rate is not straightforward although a starting point could be taken to be the prevailing interest rate or Bank base rate. In the example a discount rate of 15% has been used for the base case.

4.4.2.2. Present Value

The discounted value of the cash flow for a particular year is described as the Present Value and the sum of the predicted discounted cash flows over the life of the project is known as the Net Present Value (NPV). In the example presented in Table 4.3 the NPV is about £93 000 over a period of 20 years at a discount rate of 15%. It can be seen that the discounted cash flow in later years does not contribute so significantly to the NPV so the precise definition of the life is often not important.

Table 4.3. *Cash flow for a small dimension stone quarry*

	Year 1	2	3	4	5	6	7	8	9	10	11	12	13	14	15	16	17	18	19	20
Revenue	0	0	210 000	210 000	210 000	210 000	210 000	210 000	210 000	210 000	210 000	210 000	210 000	210 000	210 000	210 000	210 000	210 000	210 000	210 000
Capital expenditure																				
Exploration, drilling, planning	30 000		0	0	0	0	0	0	0	0	0	0	0	0	0	0	0	0	0	0
Fixed and mobile plant		100 000	0	0	0	0	0	0	0	0	0	0	0	0	0	0	0	0	0	0
Operating cost																				
Extraction cost			150 000	150 000	150 000	150 000	150 000	150 000	150 000	150 000	150 000	150 000	150 000	150 000	150 000	150 000	150 000	150 000	150 000	150 000
Profit before tax			60 000	60 000	60 000	60 000	60 000	60 000	60 000	60 000	60 000	60 000	60 000	60 000	60 000	60 000	60 000	60 000	60 000	60 000
Depreciation straight-line			6 500	6 500	6 500	6 500	6 500	6 500	6 500	6 500	6 500	6 500	6 500	6 500	6 500	6 500	6 500	6 500	6 500	6 500
Taxable income			53 500	53 500	53 500	53 500	53 500	53 500	53 500	53 500	53 500	53 500	53 500	53 500	53 500	53 500	53 500	53 500	53 500	53 500
Tax 35%			18 725	18 725	18 725	18 725	18 725	18 725	18 725	18 725	18 725	18 725	18 725	18 725	18 725	18 725	18 725	18 725	18 725	18 725
Cash flow	−30 000	−100 000	41 275	41 275	41 275	41 275	41 275	41 275	41 275	41 275	41 275	41 275	41 275	41 275	41 275	41 275	41 275	41 275	41 275	41 275
Discounted cash flow	−26 086	−98 298	27 138	23 599	20 520	17 844	15 516	13 492	11 732	10 202	8 871	7 714	6 708	5 833	5 072	4 410	3 835	3 335	2 900	2 521
Cumulative DCF	−26 086	−124 384	−71 160	−47 561	−27 041	−9 197	6 319	19 811	31 543	41 745	50 616	58 330	65 038	70 871	75 943	80 353	84 188	87 523	90 423	92 944
Cumulative cashflow	−30 000	−130 000	−88 725	−47 450	−6 175	35 100	76 375	117 650	158 925	200 200	241 475	282 750	324 025	365 300	406 575	447 850	489 125	530 400	571 675	612 950

Operational data		Financial data	
Output m^3/annum	1500	Selling price £/m^3	140
Life years	20		
		Extraction cost £/m^3	100
		Discount rate %	15%

Footnote: These costs do not relate to any particular operation and the table should be read together with §4.4.2.1.

Cash flow

The basic cash flow for a given period is the difference between the revenue and the operating costs and is called the net profit. However, to obtain the net cash flow any taxes due must be deducted and the calculation of the tax liability involves consideration of capital expenditure as well as operating costs.

$$\text{Net Profit} = \text{Revenue} - \text{Operating costs}$$

In most countries the owner of a company, including a mine or quarry, is allowed by the taxation authorities to recover the capital cost of equipment used by the business over a period of time. This is called depreciation or amortization and the taxation authority may have certain rules concerning the means of calculating this allowance. Common methods are known as straight-line, sum of years and declining balance.

$$\text{Taxable income} = \text{Net profit} - \text{Depreciation allowance}$$

$$\text{Tax liability} = (\text{Taxable income}) \times (\text{Tax rate, \%})$$

Then

NET CASH FLOW = Revenue – Operating costs – Tax – Capital expenditure

The latter term is only included when further capital expenditure takes place within the relevant period.

Depreciation and capital allowances

The method chosen or permitted by the taxation authorities for depreciation of capital expenditure can be very important to the cash flow and profitability of the business and this matter should be thoroughly investigated.

Straight-line. In this method the allowance is calculated by dividing the initial capital cost by the life of the project. Thus:

$$\text{Depreciation} = (C - S)/L$$

where C is capital cost, S is the salvage value of equipment and the project life is L years.

Unit of production. In this method the capital cost is recovered at the rate at which the reserve is exploited.

$$\text{Depreciation} = P(C - S)/R$$

where P is the production for the period and R is the total reserve.

Sum of years, Declining balance. These are known as accelerated methods of depreciation and, where permitted, the early ‘write-off’ of capital equipment is usually beneficial to the profitability of the project.

Depletion. This form of tax allowance is unique to the mineral industry where the business is based upon a wasting asset, the mineral reserve. It may allow the owner to recover the costs of exploration and acquisition of a property and minerals by capitalizing these costs and treating them as part of the initial capital investment. Furthermore, depletion allowances may take the form of a portion (%) of the taxable income which is exempt from tax which is intended as an incentive for mineral exploration and production.

Although a positive value of NPV is required for the project to be financially viable and a higher value would indicate a more profitable project, this parameter is not generally employed to determine the investment decision because it does not indicate the initial capital investment required or the risk. However, it is a useful means of valuing an established operation for purposes of sale or acquisition.

4.4.2.3. *Internal Rate of Return*

The internal rate of return is the converse of the discount rate and is defined as the discount rate at which the Net Present Value becomes zero. The calculation of IRR avoids the criticism of selecting an arbitrary discount rate and assessing the meaning of NPV. The IRR can be compared to the prevailing interest rates that might be enjoyed by depositing the funds in an interest bearing

Discounted cash flow

The discounted cash flow (DCF) for a year, *i*, in the future is calculated as follows:

$$DCF_i = CF_i/(1+r)^i$$

where CF_i is the cash flow for the *i*th year and *r* is the discount rate.

The *Net Present Value* of the project is the sum of all the discounted cash flows over the life of the project, *L* years.

$$NPV = S\,CF_i/(1+r)^i \quad i=L \quad i=0$$

A very simplified example of cash flow analysis and discounting to estimate the NPV of a proposed dimension stone quarry is presented in Table 4.3. It can be seen that NPV is a function of the assumed life of the project but that the cash flows of the later years contribute relatively little to the NPV

The *Internal Rate of Return* is the value of the discount rate, *r*, such that the NPV is zero. A simple method of estimating IRR, employed in the case of the example described in Table 4.3, is to calculate the NPV for a range of values of *r* using a computer and 'spreadsheet' software such as Excel or Lotus 123, ensuring that both negative and positive values of NPV are obtained. The value of *r* corresponding to zero NPV can be interpolated from the results.

In practice, financial evaluation is very much more complex than the example owing to the need to consider different possible taxation regimes, methods of depreciation, continuing capital investment, changes in costs and prices, inflation and other factors. Professional advice should be sought.

bank account rather than investing in the project or to the cost of borrowing money. The cost of borrowing can be estimated as a weighted average of bank interest rates and shareholders expectations in terms of dividends. A 'hurdle rate', which is several percentage points above the cost of borrowing, is often set for projects which will receive funding. In the example the IRR is about 31% which would indicate that the project is viable and attractive in the present economic climate of the UK (1997).

The IRR can also be used to compare and rank alternative projects which are competing for the same funds.

4.4.2.4. Pay-back period

The pay-back period is simply the period of time after production commences, usually a number of years, required for the non-discounted cash flow to repay the initial capital investment. Table 4.3 shows a PBP of between 4 and 5 years for this quarry. A shorter pay-back period indicates a more profitable project but, more importantly, the risk of financial loss caused by unforeseen events in the future is also reduced.

4.4.2.5. Sensitivity analysis

Sensitivity analysis is a simple method of assessing the risk associated with investment in a mine or other project. Changes to an indicator of financial viability, usually the IRR, are computed as a function of percentage changes in the individual elements of the cash flow calculation such as selling price, labour rates, fuel price etc. This rapidly identifies the most significant factors that experience shows are commonly selling price and the major operating costs of electrical power, fuel, consumables such as tyres and explosives and labour. In the simple example of Table 4.3, an analysis has been con-ducted and the results are presented in Table 4.4.

It is notable that the project is much more sensitive to a decrease of selling price (or increase in operating cost since both directly affect the revenue) than capital cost. It is then a matter of subjective judgement to assess the risk of the project failing owing to unexpected increases in costs or reduction of selling price.

Since the dominant use of building stone in modern construction is in the form of an aesthetic cladding material, the market and price can suffer from the vagaries of fashion. Forecasting the future market for a stone, especially one that has no history of use, in terms of volume and price is extremely difficult and great care must be taken to ensure that unrealistic and optimistic forecasts are not incorporated in the financial evaluation.

Table 4.4. *Sensitivity analysis for small dimension stone quarry (see Table 4.3)*

Change of element	*NPV*	*IRR*	*PBP*
Base case	£93 000	31%	4–5 years
10% fall of price	£30 000	21%	8–9 years
10% fall of output/ market	£75 000	29%	5–6 years
15% fall of price.	£~0	15%	19–20 years
20% increase of capital costs	£80 000	28%	5–6 years

4.4.2.6. Monte Carlo simulation

In this technique the financial performance of the business is simulated with the objective of quantifying the risk in terms of the probability that the IRR will exceed a certain minimum or 'hurdle' rate or, in other terms, the risk that it might fall below a critical value. The cash flow analysis is conducted many times using different values for the elements of the cash flow to permit the computation of frequency or probability as a function of internal rate of return. The values of the individual elements are selected randomly from a database of possible values using a random number generator, hence the name of the technique. However, it is necessary to develop the database for the important elements of the cash flow, such as selling price and principal operating costs, which must contain information on the probability that a particular element will assume a certain value. It is almost certainly too expensive and sophisticated for the evaluation of dimension stone and armourstone quarries.

4.4.3. Surface or underground extraction

Once the reserve of stone has been identified, an extraction plan will be developed based upon the distribution of the grades and the market requirement for the product or products. In the case of rock-fill, this is likely to be relatively simple. Armourstone workings may have to be integrated with aggregate production. Although the rate of building stone extraction is normally low, the large range of products produced, frequently using different strata within the same quarry can, as was indicated in §4.4.1, be complex and the need for flexibility in the operation of the site may be a major consideration when deciding the best extraction route.

As has been indicated in §4.4.1.2, one of the most important economic parameters in quarrying is the 'stripping ratio'. Obviously a deposit outcropping at the surface and having a zero stripping ratio, that is no overburden, is especially attractive provided that no detrimental alteration of the rock has occurred due to weathering, as described in §2.4. However, as the depth of overburden increases, so does the stripping ratio, and consequently the cost of extracting each tonne of useful stone.

As was explained in §4.4.1.2, the calculation of the stripping ratio is not necessarily a simple matter. The excavation may pass through several types of consolidated and unconsolidated rock, each of which may vary in strength and be affected by structural features such as the dip and strike of the bedding, folding and jointing. Some may even be permeable and act as aquifers. These features will determine the stability of the eventual quarry face, a subject discussed in detail in §5.3.2. It is rarely the case that a vertical face in the overburden will be stable, and more likely that, in order to produce stability, a face will have to be inclined at an angle of between 45° and 80° to the horizontal. This results in the quarry area becoming less as the depth of the excavation increases. Where the thickness of overburden is large, the area of overburden to be removed, and therefore the area occupied by the quarry, can be much greater than the area being worked for stone. This is illustrated in Fig. 4.11.

The maximum acceptable stripping ratio, at which the cost becomes either prohibitive or comparable to the cost of mining the stone, is a function of a number of, mostly local, factors such as:

- structural geology,
- the physical nature of the overburden, especially its strength, since this can have a major effect on the cost of removal. Hard material may possibly require drilling and blasting, whereas it may be possible to remove soft materials with an excavator,
- the depth of the overburden,
- the cost of labour, fuel, parts and repair.

In addition to considering the stripping ratio, when comparing the choice between surface and underground working it is also necessary to consider the space required for tipping the overburden, at least in the initial stages of development before the quarry void is available for the disposal of such material. Waste stone tips are just one of the environmental factors which can have an effect on the decision of whether to mine or quarry stone. These are discussed in detail in §§5.2.2, 5.2.3 and 5.2.12.

The advantages of quarrying include the opportunity to recover all the rock mass and the facility of using powered mobile equipment capable of extracting different types of stone from a number of locations throughout the deposit.

Although most stone for construction purposes will be obtained from surface workings, situations may arise when underground extraction is preferable. The cost of overburden removal and environmental constraints are the two main reasons why mining stone may be considered. Although a bulk material such as rock-fill could never be economically obtained by underground extraction unless it is waste material from a coal or mineral

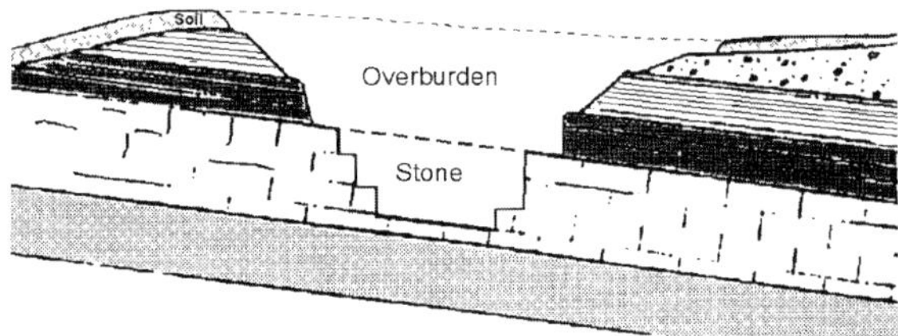

Fig. 4.11. Diagram of a stone quarry indicating overburden.

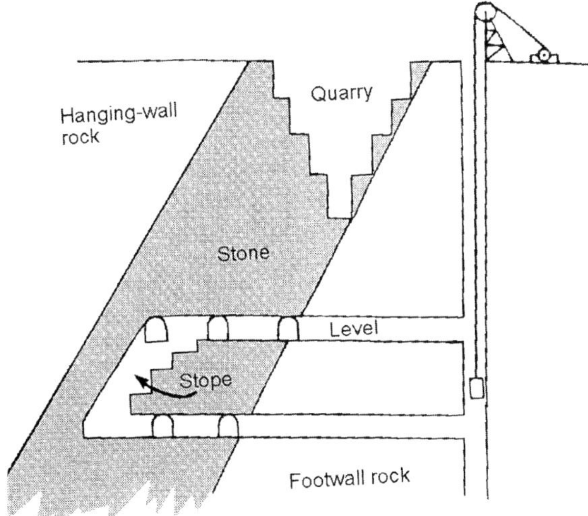

Fig. 4.12. Diagram of a mine with access by a shaft and levels.

mine, building stone has been obtained from underground workings for many centuries. Some of the stone for the medieval Lincoln Cathedral was obtained from a mine immediately adjacent to the cathedral. Limestone roofing tiles were obtained from underground workings at Stonesfield in the Cotswolds and Collyweston in Lincolnshire from the 18th century onwards. Weldon stone from Northamptonshire, clunch (a form of hard chalk) from Totternhoe in Bedfordshire, have all been worked underground. Chilmark limestone and Bath stone are both still being obtained in this manner today (see §6.6.2). There are underground marble workings in Tuscany, in northern Portugal and in Vermont in the USA, where a bed of marble that dips at between 30° and 45° is worked underground (Power 1983).

Although termed mining, the extraction of stone from underground is perhaps better termed 'underground quarrying'. The techniques used for the extraction of the stone, which are described in §5.3.10, are similar to those used in surface quarries. The main prerequisites for underground extraction is a suitable roof-rock and pillar design.

However, access to a mine is expensive, requiring the construction of a shaft or an inclined adit and possibly the installation of winding engines to raise the rock (Figs 4.12 and 4.13) (Hartman 1987). Indeed, in the UK two separate means of ingress and egress are required by law, although two would usually be required in any case in order to ensure adequate ventilation.

Costs are further increased if pumps are necessary to de-water the mine. However, an obvious exception exists if access to the rock can be made from an exposure in an escarpment, an existing quarry face or an exposure that has been created for another purpose, such as a railway or road cutting. It is then possible to drain the working relatively simply through the adit or by means of a drainage level, often known as a sough; this is shown in Fig. 4.13. In this manner, some quarries have been extended as mines, with the advantage of minimal environmental impact.

The mining of rock to produce dimension stone usually requires the use of the 'room and pillar' method of working, where rock is extracted from stopes called rooms and the roof is supported by rock left *in situ* as pillars. This is described in detail in §5.3.10.4. This system results in the loss of the stone that forms the supporting pillars. These roof supports normally require between 30% and 50% of the deposit. However, exceptions do occur where, due to a very strong roof-rock, huge cavernous stopes can be created. In dipping strata it is reported that the recovery of stone can be greater, Power (1983) noting that recoveries as high as 85% are not uncommon.

Underground extraction is potentially more expensive than surface working, due to the need to provide an underground infrastructure, including statutory supervision of a level higher than would normally be required in an open-cast working, ventilation and possible roof support. However, there are a number of advantages in this method of extraction. The most important of these are firstly, the absence of a requirement for overburden removal, transport and back-filling, and secondly the

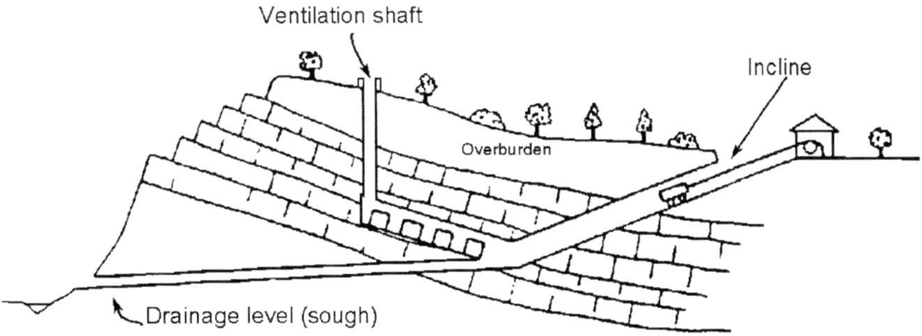

Fig. 4.13. Diagram of a mine with access by means of an incline.

fact that underground workings are potentially much more environmentally acceptable than surface workings. The financial pressures on quarry owners to landscape their sites, carry out complete restoration after stone extraction, and even undertake expensive archaeological surveys prior to disturbing the ground, could well result in underground working of stone becoming more common. The potential operating costs associated with the mitigation of noise, dust and water pollution which were noted in §4.4.1.2, and are discussed in detail in §5.2, could also be reduced by underground extraction of stone. Moreover, mining produces a minimal environmental impact on closure, especially if the roof-rock is sufficiently strong enough to prevent subsidence after mining. In addition, it is not necessary to purchase a large area of land surface, in order to extract the underlying minerals, although a lease will be required over the area to be mined.

It is unlikely that it would be economic to extract armourstone underground, since the rate of production is considerably higher than for block building stone. However, if there was a requirement for a large quantity of material in an area of high landscape value where any alternative source would involve high transport costs, the possibility of extracting block stone underground by drilling and blasting may be worthy of consideration.

4.5. The assessment report

Rock-fill and armourstone are used in major civil engineering works. Any report on reserves and their extraction is therefore likely to be aimed at an engineering audience. Technical discussions and the use of complex plans will therefore be acceptable. However, care must be taken when producing reports on the reserves of building stone and the development of those reserves. As well as being operated by major quarrying companies, building stone extraction and processing is often carried out by small rural companies or local entrepreneurs. This is especially true in developing countries, where the extraction of stone for construction use can be one of the first industries to be introduced into an area.

Although any report will contain all the necessary information for the successful implementation of the project, the emphasis will vary according to its purpose. In a report prepared for a civil engineering project, the rock properties, their variation and the details of extraction procedures will be highlighted. However, in preparing a bankable document for a financing organization such as one of the Development Banks, the financial implications of the reserves, their extraction, processing and marketing, together with details of the quantifiable risks, should be explained in detail (Farah 1995). The information required from a mining company wishing to be listed on the London Stock Exchange have been set out in the 'Listing rules', commonly called the 'Yellow book' (Stock Exchange 1993). Moreover, the terminology used in such a document to describe resources and reserves will have to conform strictly to one of the standard classifications such as those listed in the text box in §3.1.1 (Armitage & Potts 1994). In the United Kingdom, assessment reports are frequently used as supporting documentation for planning applications (see §5.2.2). In this case the emphasis will be on a step-by-step description of the extraction process coupled with a detailed assessment of the environmental implications of the extraction process.

References

ANNELS, A. E. 1991. *Mineral Deposit Evaluation*. Chapman & Hall, London.

——1992. *Case Histories and Methods in Mineral Resource Evaluation*. Geological Society, London, Special Publications, **63**.

ARMITAGE, M. G. & POTTS, M. F. A. 1994. Some comments on the classification of resources and reserves. *In*: WHATELEY, M. K. G. & HARVEY, P. K. (eds) *Mineral Resource Evaluation II: Methods and Case Histories*. Geological Society, London, Special Publications, **79**, 11–16.

ASHURST, J. & DIMES, F. G. 1990. *Conservation of Building and Decorative Stone*. (Volumes 1. & 2). Butterworth-Heinemann, London.

BARISH, N. & KAPLAN, S. 1978. *Economic Analysis for Engineering and Managerial Decision Making*. McGraw-Hill, New York.

BIERMAN, H. & SMIDT, S. 1990. *The Capital Budgeting Decision-Economic Analysis of Investment Projects*. 7th edition. Macmillan, New York.

CLARK, I. 1979. *Practical Geostatistics*. Elsevier, London.

DAHLBERG, E. C. 1975. Relative effectiveness of geologists and computers in mapping potential hydrocarbon exploration targets. *Journal of the International Association of Mathematical Geology*, **7**, 373–394.

DAVIS, J. C. 1986. *Statistics and Data Analysis in Geology*. 2nd edition. Wiley, New York.

DE WIJS, H. J. 1952, 1953. Statistics of ore distribution. *Journal of the Royal Geological and Mining Society of the Netherlands*. Part, 1. November 1952, Part, 2. January 1953.

DELHOMME, J. P. & DELFINER, P. 1973. *Application du krigeage, a. l'optimisation d'une campagne pluviometrique en zone aride*. Symposium on the design of water resources projects with inadequate data. UNESCO-WHO-IAHS. Madrid, Spain, 191–210.

ENGLUND, E. & SPARKS, A. 1988. *GEO-EAS. (Geostatistical environmental assessment software). User's guide*. Report EPA/600/4-88/033a. Environmental monitoring systems laboratory. Office of Research and Development. United States Environmental Protection Agency. Las Vegas, Nevada.

FARAH, H. H. 1995. Evaluation of private sector mining projects in Africa by the African Development Bank. *African Mining '95*. Institution of Mining and Metallurgy, London, 193–204.

GENTRY, D. W. & O'NEILL, T. J. 1984. *Mine Investment Analysis*. Society of Mining Engineers (AIME), New York.
GEOLOGICAL SOCIETY OF AMERICA 1991. *Rock Color Chart*. Prepared by the Rock-Color Chart Committee, published by The Geological Society of America, Boulder.
GY, P. M. 1979. *Sampling of particulate materials, theory and practice*. Developments in Geomathematics, 4. Elsevier Scientific Publishing Company, Amsterdam.
HARTMAN, H. 1987. *Introductory Mining Engineering*. Wiley, New York.
HOSKINS, J. R. & GREEN, W. R. 1987. *Mineral Industry Costs*, Northwest Mining Association, Spokane.
HUGMAN, R. H. H. & FRIEDMAN, M. 1979. Effects of texture and composition on mechanical behaviour of experimentally deformed carbonate nodes. *AAPG Bulletin*, **63**, 1478–1489
ISAAKS, E. H. & SRIVASTAVA, R. M. 1989. *Applied Geostatistics*. Oxford University Press. London.
ISRM 1978. Suggested methods for the quantitative description of discontinuities in rock masses. International Society for Rock Mechanics Commission on Standardisation of Laboratory and Field Tests. *International Journal of Rock Mechanics and Mining Sciences & Geomechanics Abstracts*, **15**, No. 6. 319–368.
JEFFERSON, D. P. 1993. Building stone: the geological dimension. *Quarterly Journal of Engineering Geology*, **26**, 305–319.
JOURNEL, A. G. & HUIJBREGHTS, CH. J. 1978. *Mining Geostatistics*. Academic, London.
LUMBY, S. 1994. *Investment Appraisal and Financial Decisions*. Chapman & Hall, London.
MATHERON, G. 1971. *The Theory of Regionalised Variables and its Applications*. Cahier No. 5. Centre de Morphologie Mathématique de Fontainebleau. France.
MCCAMMON, R. B. (ed.) 1975. *Concepts in Geostatistics*. Springer, New York.
MCCLAY, K. 1987. *The Mapping of Geological Structures*. Wiley, Chichester.
NATHANAIL, C. P. 1994. Reserve assessment of, a. stratified deposit with special reference to opencast coal mining in Great Britain. *In*: WHATELEY, M. K. G. & HARVEY, P. K. (eds) *Mineral Resource Evaluation II: Methods and Case Histories*. Geological Society, London, Special Publications, **79**, 45–52.
OLDCON, R. 1993. *Accounting for Managers*, Routledge, London.
POWER, W. R. 1983. Dimension and cut stone. *In*: LEFOND, S. J. (ed.) *Industrial Minerals and Rocks*. 5th Edition. Society of Mining Engineers, New York, 161–181.
PRIEST, S. D. 1985. *Hemispherical Projection Methods in Rock Mechanics*. George Allen & Unwin, London.
——1993. *Discontinuity Analysis for Rock Engineering*. Chapman & Hall, London.
RAGAN, D. M. 1985. *Structural Geology: an introduction to Geometric Techniques*. 3rd edition. John Wiley, New York.
ROYLE, A. G. 1992. A. personal overview of geostatistics. *In*: ANNELS, A. E. (ed.) *Case Histories and Methods in Mineral Resource Evaluation*. Geological Society, London, Special Publications, **63**, 233–241.
SHADMON, A. 1989. *Stone. An Introduction*. Intermediate Technology, London.
SIDES, E. J. 1992. Reconciliation studies and reserve estimation. *In*: ANNELS, A. E. (ed.) *Case Histories and Methods in Minerals Resource Evaluation*. Geological Society, London, Special Publications, **63**, 197–218.
STERMOLE, F. & STERMOLE, J. 1993. *Economic evaluation and investment decision methods*. 8th edition. Investment Evaluation Corporation, Golden.
STOCK EXCHANGE 1993. Chapter 19, Mining companies in *The Listing rules/London Stock Exchange*, London Stock Exchange.
WANG, H., LATHAM, J.-P. & POOLE, A. 1991*a*. Predictions of block size distributions for quarrying. *Quarterly Journal of Engineering Geology*, **24**, 91–99.
——, —— & ——1991*b*. Blast design for armour stone production. *Quarry Management*, Part, 1, July 1991, 17–21, Part, 2, August 1991, 19–22.
WESTON, J. F. & COPELAND, T. E. 1992. *Managerial Finance*. Dryden Press, Fort Worth.
WHATELEY, M. K. G. & HARVEY, P. K. 1994. *Mineral Resource Evaluation II, Methods and Case Histories*. Geological Society, London, Special Publications, **79**.

5. Extraction

5.1. Aims and content

The aim of this chapter is to describe and explain the extraction of rock to create material suitable for processing into rock fill, armourstone and dimension stone. Processing is described in Chapter 6 although little additional processing may be carried out in the production of rock fill and armourstone. Unfortunately there are few modern textbooks devoted to this subject to which the reader can be referred and several of these are intended for general reading, tourism and amateur industrial archaeologists (Ashurst & Dimes 1984; Stanier 1985; Greenwell & Elsden 1913).

Before detailed descriptions of the production of particular materials are given there are matters of general relevance to be discussed. In particular, after the choice of the primary method of extraction, mining or quarrying has been made, consideration must be given to obtaining the necessary permits from the regulatory authorities. Thus, the first section of this chapter

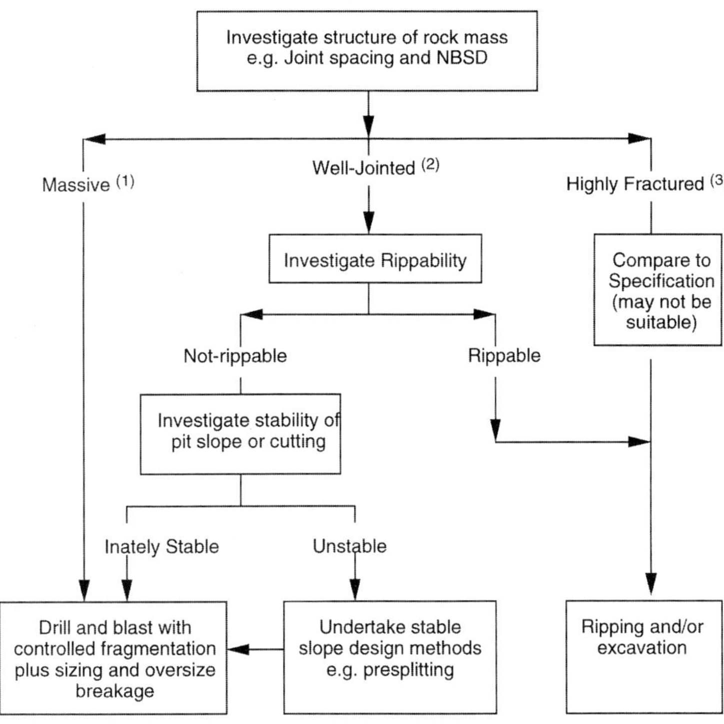

(1) Widely spaced joints, NBSD >> specification

(2) Joint spacings and NBSD ≥ specification

(3) Joint spacings and NBSD << specification

Fig. 5.1. Rock fill flowsheet for selection of extraction method.

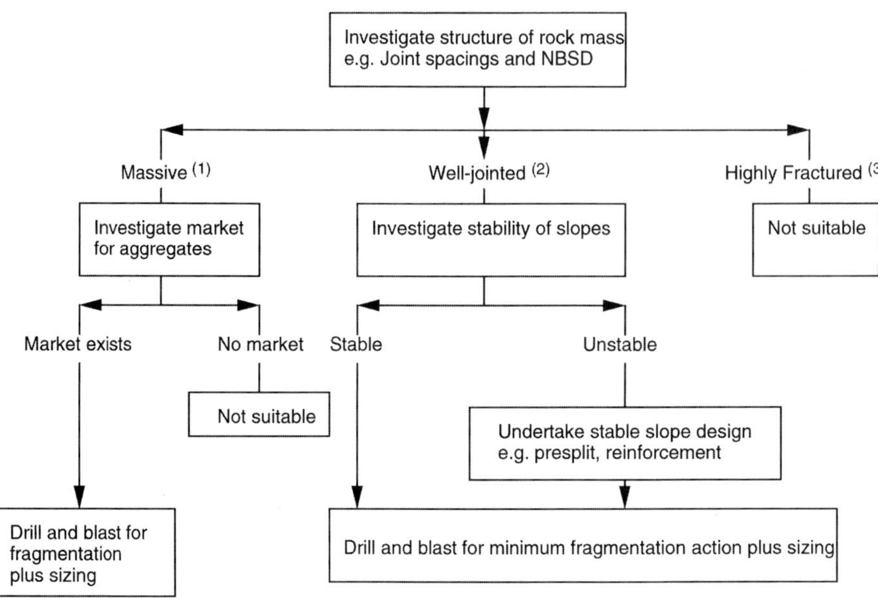

Fig. 5.2. Armourstone flowsheet for selection of extraction method.

discusses the design and planning of quarries and mines with particular emphasis given to the environmental impact of these activities.

The second part, extraction, comprises a discussion of the extraction of rock from a mine or quarry. In Figs 5.1, 5.2 and 5.3 advice is given, in the form of flowsheets, on the selection of an appropriate method of extraction depending on the desired product and the properties of the rock mass. It has been assumed that previous exploration and evaluation (see Chapters 3 and 4) has identified adequate potential volumes or tonnages of rock and that the mineralogy and petrography of this rock mass (see Chapter 2) are generally favourable. Several disciplines and sciences within geology and engineering (e.g. rock mechanics) are of general importance irrespective of the desired product as are several technologies (e.g. drilling and blasting). Thus, these subjects are discussed in the first part of the section on extraction. In the latter part detailed descriptions of the extraction of rock fill, armourstone and dimension stone are given.

5.2. Design and planning

5.2.1. Extraction methods

5.2.1.1. Introduction

In the UK, underground mineral workings are classified by law as a 'mine' and surface workings having no roof of rock as a 'quarry'. Historically, the name quarry tended to be associated with the extraction of non-metalliferous minerals, whereas metals and coal were mined. The name quarry is thought to derive from the Latin word 'quadraria', a place where rectangular stones were produced. Quarries may also be known as 'open pits' or 'surface mines' and 'open cast mines' with particular reference to surface working of coal.

5.2.1.2. Mining and quarrying

In general, mining incurs higher costs than quarrying and, in the absence of other considerations, the decision is based on economic analysis as discussed in §4.4.

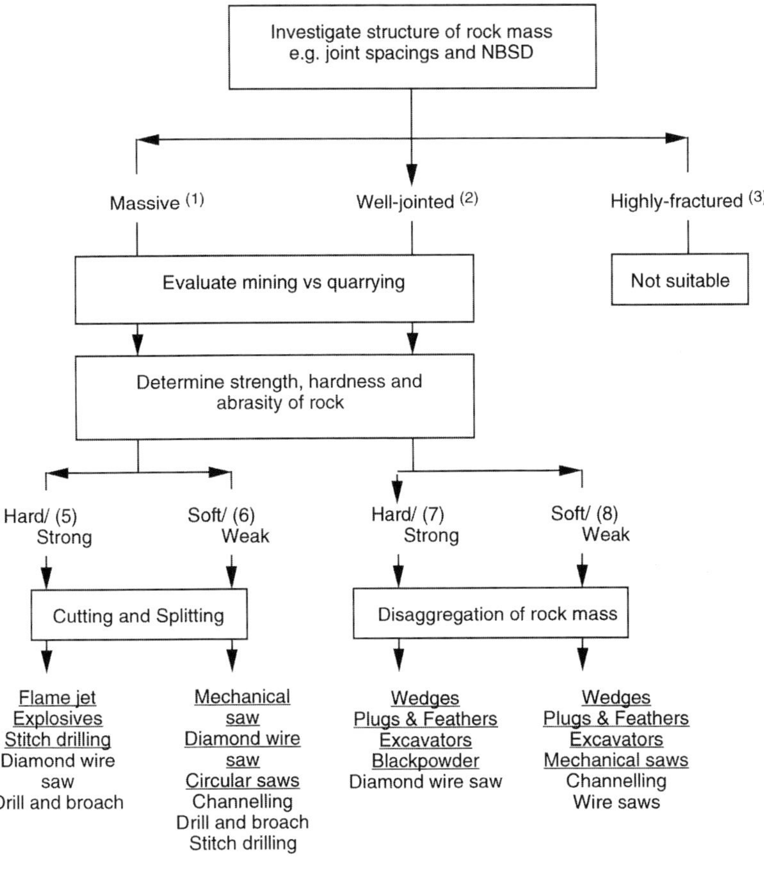

Fig. 5.3. Dimension stone flowsheet for selection of extraction method.

In surface mining the overlying rock of little or no value, the overburden, is completely removed to gain access to the valuable stone. Therefore, one of the most important economic parameters is the 'stripping ratio'; the quantity (tonnes) of valueless overburden that must be removed or stripped per tonne of valuable rock (ore) exposed (Kennedy 1990) as discussed further in §4.4.2 (see Fig. 4.13).

5.2.2. Planning considerations

In most parts of the world it is necessary to obtain a permit or licence to extract minerals from the regional or national government in addition, of course, to making an agreement with the land and mineral owner(s). The procedure to obtain 'planning permission' (i.e. permission to develop land for the production of minerals) that must be followed by the applicant in England and Wales is a relevant example (DoE 1988*a*). As in many countries, the authority to grant permissions is delegated to regional authorities although the central government retains the ultimate authority to make decisions in the national interest. A principal concern is always the environmental impact of the proposed development which must be balanced against economic and social gains.

The operator must establish ownership of both the surface and the mineral rights either by purchase or through negotiation of a lease with the actual owners. The latter may involve the payment of rent for surface rights and payment of royalty on the mineral extracted. In other countries, mineral rights may belong to the nation but in the UK this applies only to coal, oil and gas. Gold and sea-bed minerals are vested in the Crown and there may be other local exceptions, for example, lead ores in Derbyshire.

The operator submits the application to the Mineral Planning Authority, together with evidence that the proposal has been brought to the attention of the public. The application should contain the following:

- a description of the proposed development
- geological information including calculation of reserves
- description of the method of working
- discussion of all the potential environmental impacts of the operation
- a justification of the market or 'need' for the mineral

In fact, the wise operator and the MPA will have held informal meetings upon the proposal in an attempt to resolve any potential objections (see §5.2.3) before this stage is reached. The MPA is usually the relevant County Council but the National Parks, Unitary Authorities and Metropolitan Boroughs have also assumed this authority by delegation from the Secretary of State.

If the applicant and the MPA are unable to agree a mutually acceptable plan for extracting the mineral, the applicant may appeal to the Secretary of State for the Environment against a refusal of permission. The Minister then decides upon the application in the interests of the nation, often through the use of a public inquiry. However, it is unlikely that this situation would occur with respect to a small dimension stone quarry although it is becoming more common for much larger quarries producing aggregates and open cast coal mines.

Whereas there is a presumption in favour of working minerals and it is recognized that minerals are essential to the economy, it is considered essential that the environmental impact must be minimized. The MPA will consider very seriously the potential environmental impacts before granting permission and expects the operator to minimize these. Therefore, it is most likely that the MPA will impose conditions upon working as discussed in §5.2.3 (DoE 1988*b*).

For the benefit of Planning Authorities and operators alike, the Secretary of State publishes guidelines for the provision of mineral commodities including aggregates (DoE, 1994), coal and cement raw materials. There are no specific guidelines for dimension stone, armourstone and rockfill but, given the close association between the production of many rock products, maybe as by-products, the guidelines can be relevant. The guidelines consider the supply and demand for the mineral commodity and it is incumbent upon the operator to demonstrate the need or market for the proposed output. It is also expected that the Local Authority should publish Local Structure Plans indicating areas designated for development of housing, recreation sites, transport routes and mineral production. The MPA must take these plans into account when reaching a decision upon need.

5.2.3. Environmental and safety considerations

The environmental issues concerning the extraction of minerals generally include the following (Waller 1992):

- vehicle traffic
- noise
- visual intrusion
- blasting vibration
- dust
- hydrogeology
- loss of wild-life habitat
- loss of amenity
- archaeology
- restoration

The extraction of stone is unlikely to involve the use of toxic or noxious substances. In addition, legislation protecting the health of employees in the workplace imposes limits upon emissions and ambient conditions. Therefore, the environmental impacts of a stone quarry upon neighbours should constitute at worst a nuisance and not a direct hazard to health. Nevertheless, in affluent developed countries one should not underestimate the extent of concern for the environment and 'quality of life'. The safety of employees engaged in the quarrying and mining of stone within the UK is generally ensured by adherence to the provisions of the Health and Safety at Work etc. Act, 1974, the Mines and Quarries Act, 1954 and the subsequent regulations of those acts (King 1991). Primary considerations, discussed further below, are protection of employees from harmful exposures to dust and noise and the safe use and storage of explosives.

5.2.3.1. Vehicle traffic

The production of bulk mineral commodities, such as aggregates and coal, can create numerous movements of heavy goods vehicles as products are transported away from the mine. The location of most quarries in rural, often scenic areas can generate traffic upon unsuitable, narrow roads passing through small towns and villages which can cause conflict between the quarry operator, local residents and visitors such as tourists.

Traffic, especially heavy goods vehicles, produces both noise and vibration which can be a nuisance to residents. BS 6472 (BSI 1992) provides guidance to evaluate human exposure to vibration in buildings and traffic noise is discussed in detail by Nelson (1987). Roads not designed to carry heavy goods vehicles will deteriorate more rapidly under regular use and the uneven or damaged road surfaces will then generate higher levels of vibration and possibly airborne dust. Whereas the production of dimension stone itself is unlikely to generate excessive traffic, it has been shown in Chapter 4 that the financial viability of the operation may depend upon by-products such as aggregates. The ultimate solution to this problem is the use of an alternative means of transport such as by sea, by canal or by rail but this is usually either unavailable or uneconomic. In order to mitigate the nuisance the MPA may impose conditions upon the consent such as limited working hours, limited output, weight limits upon vehicles and obligatory routes for heavy lorries (DoE 1988*b*). A dimension stone quarry may be restricted to the sale of certain 'building products' only in order to ensure a low volume of output and limit movements of heavy goods vehicles.

Particular attention is paid to the design of the junction between the public road and access road to ensure safety. The operator may agree to make improvements to the road, for example, straightening and strengthening certain sections, creation of passing places, construction of a new access road to intersect a major highway (DoE 1994*b*) and constructing a by-pass.

Within quarries, mobile equipment has been a major cause of accidents and deaths because unseen employees have been struck by reversing vehicles such as dump trucks. The Quarry (Vehicles) Regulations, 1970 requires that vehicles be fitted with audible reversing alarms but these have been the cause of many complaints concerning noise nuisance and alternative detectors of the presence of persons behind reversing vehicles are being investigated.

5.2.3.2. Noise

Noise is often defined as unwanted sound and can be both a hazard to health and a nuisance as discussed below.

Since noise is received as energy transmitted through air it can be measured as energy transmittted per unit area or as peak pressure. However, owing to the fact that such values would range over many orders of magnitude, it is normally expressed in terms of a logarithmic scale, the decibel (dB) scale. This scale compares noise level to the reference pressure of $20\,\mu$Pa. Since the reference pressure is approximately equal to the minimum audible sound at 1 KHz, 0 dB corresponds closely to the threshold of hearing at 1 KHz. The noise level is also adjusted to take account of the response of the human ear (which is most sensitive to human speech in the frequency range 0.5 to 5 kHz) to sounds of differing frequencies giving the dBA scale. Illustrative sound levels on this scale are: whispering (30 dBA), rural background noise (40 dBA), normal speech (60 dBA), blast-hole drill (90–100 dBA) and the threshold of pain in the ears (120 dBA). However, it should be noted that noise is attenuated by distance according to an inverse square law and that the measurement of noise generated by equipment must state the distance between the source and meter.

The hazard to health is the potential damage to hearing called noise induced hearing loss or NIHL. Both the sound level and the duration of exposure must be considered when assessing the potential harm. For this purpose the parameter $L_{\mathrm{Aeq,T}}$, called the 'equivalent continuous noise level', is calculated

Regulations within the EC require that the exposure of employees should not exceed 85 dBA(8 h), the equivalent of 8 hours continuous exposure to a sound level of 85 dBA (Gregory 1987). In addition, the sound level should never exceed 130 dBA. Exposure to intermediate sound levels is acceptable provided that the duration is reduced proportionally. In situations where the exposure will exceed 85 dBA(8 h), warning notices, training and advice and ear protectors must be provided. Most modern equipment is provided with a soundproofed cabin for the operator and developments are continuing to assemble quieter machines employing such techniques as silenced exhausts, reduced rotational speeds, dampened surfaces etc.

Noise nuisance can also be defined in terms of an increase above the background noise level, measured as $L_{\mathrm{A90,T}}$ of between 5 and 10 dBA (BSI 1990). In this case the time period, T is commonly 1 or 2 hours. Equipment manufacturers are now required to provide imformation upon the noise generated by each machine termed the sound power level, L_{WA}, with units of dB. Using this value and the methods of calculation contained in BS 5228: 1984 (BSI 1984) it is possible to predict the sound levels at the perimeter of the workings or at a nearby property. The MPA is now likely to require such a prediction as part of the planning application document plus a measurement of the background noise level. There is also guidance for the MPA upon the maximum sound levels which would be considered acceptable. For example, at residential properties this level will vary from 42 dBA at night to 55 dBA during the day (DoE 1993).

The operator can reduce or eliminate noise nuisance both during design and operation.

Selection of equipment can reduce noise at source and location of selected noisy items remotely from receivers can attenuate noise by distance. Static equipment can be encapsulated in soundproof enclosures and buildings clad with sound absorbent materials. Site haul roads for trucks can be routed away from the perimeter or especially sensitive neighbours. Bunds constructed from soil or overburden can be used to attenuate sound levels by 5 to 10 dBA and usefully store these materials prior to restoration. Analysis of sounds emitted may identify particularly intrusive, usually high, frequencies or intermittent noises that can be easily eliminated. If deemed

Noise

The intensity of noise or Sound Pressure Level is a function of the square of the pressure wave travelling through the air and is expressed in units of Bels. Because the human ear can detect such a wide range of intensity the scale is logarithmic and because the Bel is such a large unit values are most commonly quoted in deciBels, equal to one tenth of a Bel. A reference pressure of 20 μPa is used since this is close to the threshold of hearing at 1 kHz.

Sound Pressure Level, SPL. In units of deciBels the SPL is given by:

$$\text{SPL} = 20 \log(\text{Actual pressure}/\text{Reference pressure})\ \text{dB}$$

Attenuation by distance. Sound intensity diminishes with increasing distance from the source according to an inverse square law so that if the SPL_1 at distance d_1 is known then the SPL_2 at distance d_2 from a source is given by:

$$SPL_2 = SPL_1 - 20 \log(d_2/d_1)\ \text{dB}$$

For example, doubling the distance reduces the SPL by 6 dB.

Addition of SPL values. Since the scale is logarithmic, values cannot be added or subtracted directly. A simple rule of thumb permits rapid estimation of the summation of two sound pressure levels. For differences greater than 10 dB the lower value of SPL can be neglected.

Difference of values to be summed, dB	Addition to greater value of SPL, dB
0–1	3
1–2	3
2–3	2
3–4	2
4–5	1
5–6	1
6–7	1
7–8	1
8–9	1
9–10	1
>10	0

A scale. The human ear responds differently to sounds of differing frequency and is more sensitive to sound in the frequency range of speech, approximately 500 to 5000 Hz. In other words, the sound seems louder. The adjustment factors of the A scale are subtracted from the absolute values of SPL measured in dB to give the dBA scale as illustrated below:

Frequency, Hz	63	125	500	1000	2000	4000	8000
Weighting factor, dB	−26	−6	−3.2	0	+1.2	+1.0	−1.1

Average values of SPL. The averaging procedure for SPL varying with time integrates each value of SPL with respect to the duration of that value. The results are expressed as $L_{Aeq,T}$ which is the equivalent continuous SPL in dBA over the defined period T hours.

Background noise level. Several methods exist to define the background sound pressure level in dBA. One of the most popular is the SPL **not** exceeded 90% of the time as averaged over a time period of T and with the time of day specified. This is known as $L_{A90,T}$.

necessary, the nuisance can be abated by imposition of sound level limits by the MPA and restriction of working hours.

5.2.3.3. Visual intrusion

Visual intrusion is created primarily by the excavation itself, waste tips and the process plant.

Mitigation can take several forms. Some areas of land of particularly high landscape value, such as the National Parks and Areas of Outstanding Natural Beauty (AONB) of the UK, may enjoy special protection by national or local government and can be identified by consultation with, for example, English Nature in England. The local government may have designated areas of particular landscape value to be preserved for recreational purposes but which do not enjoy national protection. These areas are identified in the Local Structure Plans in England. Clearly, development of this land will be strongly opposed.

At the design stage it is advisable to make use of topographic maps and field reconnaissance to identify critical viewpoints from which an uninterrupted view, or sight-line, into the proposed workings would be possible (see Fig. 5.4). Such points could be public roads, footpaths and windows of private residences. It is then possible to consider alternative remedial actions. In some cases the topography may permit natural visual screening of the operations. For example, the fixed plant may be located in a natural or excavated depression. Other factors, such as geology, permitting, the orientation of faces with respect to viewing points and their direction of advance or working may also be selected to provide natural visual screening (Nicholson 1995). Elevated parts of the deposit can be preserved as the quarry rim to prevent direct line of sight (see Fig. 5.4), but this illustrates the fact that many remedies may result in loss of reserves. As a general rule the quarry workings should not 'break the sky-line'. Commonly, bunds or mounds of soil, overburden and waste are constructed along the perimeter of the workings and planted with grasses, shrubs and trees to provide visual screens or even to recreate the sky-line (see Fig. 5.4).

These bunds may also usefully store soils before restoration and attenuate noise. However, their construction can create temporary nuisance and sterilise reserves of rock. An alternative is the use of vegetative screens comprising trees and hedges but these must be planted several years in advance of the workings to be effective.

The fixed plant is often camouflaged by coloured sheeting and constructed so as not to exceed maximum roof heights. The visible surfaces of waste tips should be completed, stabilized and planted with grasses etc. as soon as possible.

5.2.3.4. Blasting vibration

The safety aspects of the use of explosives are discussed in §5.3.3.8. Although blasting operations generate both noise and dust, ground vibration and 'air-blast' or 'overpressure' nuisance from blasting constitute two of the major environmental problems facing quarry operators. Part of the energy released by the detonation of explosives (see §5.3.3.4) is transmitted through the rock as 'blast vibration' over considerable distances while some may also be transferred to the air as noise and 'air-blast' (see Fig. 5.5). Both of these undesirable impacts may be reduced and controlled by attention to blast design. Fortunately, in the context of this book and with the exception of the production of rock-fill, stone quarries tend to make little or no use of explosives, other than low power black powder, since the objective is to minimize fragmentation of the rock.

Blast vibration. The peak particle velocity of a vibration is considered to be the most reliable criterion for assessing the potential for damage or nuisance caused by a quarry explosive. Conditions imposed on quarry operators often seek to ensure that there is neither damage to structures nor nuisance to local residents. Whereas the US Bureau of Mines has shown that damage to property is very unlikely if the ppv is less than 50 mm/s, complaints of nuisance may be generated if the

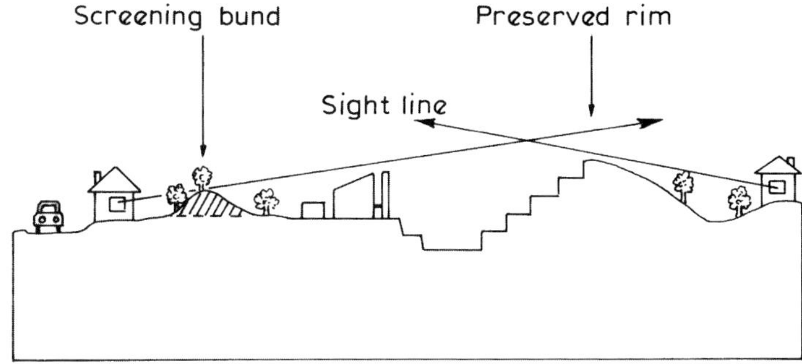

Fig. 5.4. Diagram of sight lines and visual screening methods.

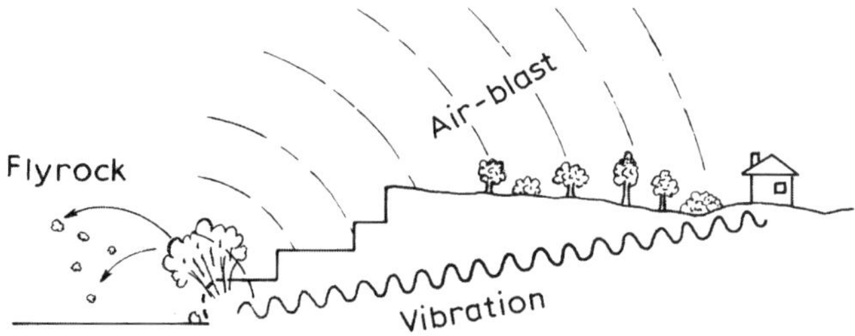

Fig. 5.5. Illustration of vibration and air-blast produced by blasting.

value exceeds 0.5 mm/s, especially when accompanied by air-blast. MPAs have imposed upper limits upon ppv of 10 mm/s and as low as 6 mm/s.

Minimizing the ppv and vibration is largely achieved by reduction of the instantaneous charge weight. The principal method is the use of delay detonators to separate the explosions in each blast hole and to use the minimum total weight of explosives commensurate with the desired fragmentation. Liaison with local residents and the agreement to the condition of restricted, notified blasting times can effectively reduce complaints but may be very inconvenient for a stone quarry (McKenzie 1990).

Air-blast. Air blast is of considerable importance because it can create noise and disturbance, for example, by the rattling of windows. This is often interpreted as vibration, giving rise to complaints (Wilton 1991).

To minimize air blast, the quarry operator should seek to design the blast so that the explosive energy is contained by the rock. The measures that might be employed include: (i) initiating the blast at the bottom of the blast hole; (ii) reducing or eliminating the use of surface detonating cord or burying the cord under a layer of waste material; (iii) ensuring that the blast hole is adequately stemmed and (iv) ensuring that a minimum burden exists in front of each blast hole and that the face

Blast vibration and air blast

It is generally agreed that the peak particle velocity, ppv, of blasting vibration is a good measure in terms of potential damage to structures and creation of nuisance. The ppv is related to the frequency, f in Hertz, and amplitude, A in millimetres, of the vibration, both of which can be readily measured by a seismograph or vibrometer, as follows:

$$\mathrm{ppv} = 2\pi f A \ \mathrm{mm/s}$$

One relationship between the ppv, distance in metres from the detonation, D and the charge weight, W, in kilograms is:

$$\mathrm{ppv} = K(D\sqrt{W})^{-n}$$

where K and n are site constants of typical values between 700 and 2000 and 1.5 and 2.0 respectively. The term $D\sqrt{W}$ is known as the scaled distance parameter.

The charge weight, W is, in fact, the weight of a given type of explosive detonated on a single delay. It is called the instantaneous charge weight and affords the principal means to control and reduce blast vibration. The total mass of explosive is divided into smaller individual masses contained in each blast hole which are separately detonated by different delay detonators. This effectively separates the explosions although the time separation may be only multiples of 25 milliseconds. If this procedure is not effective the total charge has to be distributed between a greater number of holes of smaller diameter which significantly increases the cost of drilling. The charge weight, W is assumed to comprise ANFO, an ammonium nitrate and fuel oil mixture, but can be scaled for other more powerful explosives by use of data given in §5.3.3.2.

Air-blast is energy from the explosion transmitted through the air at a frequency of less than 20 Hz so that it is essentially inaudible. It is unlikely that damage to even the most delicate parts of a building, the windows, will occur unless the blast is so great that vibration causes major structural damage. The air-blast is measured directly in deciBels. Limits are still evolving but are likely to be around 120 dB.

does not contain any fissures or planes of weakness through which the gases may vent explosively.

The operator needs to consider and avoid situations where explosives are unconfined such as the shallow blast holes used to split large blocks on the quarry floor or to release joint bounded blocks from the quarry face. For these reasons, non-explosive methods may be more attractive.

5.2.3.5. Dust

Dust, like noise, can be both a hazard to health and a nuisance. The former is covered in the UK by the provisions of the Control of Substances Hazardous to Health (COSHH) Regulations (1994), a regulation under the Health and Safety at Work Act. The latter is covered within the Environmental Protection Act, 1990. Dust can be considered to originate from two types of source: 'point sources' such as chimneys or screens and 'fugitive sources' such as roads and stockpiles. Dust is a hazard best prevented by elimination at the source, for example, by suppression using water sprays or by enclosure of equipment and preventing entrainment of dust in air through careful design and selection of operating procedures. The primary objective in the protection of the health of employees is to reduce the 'respirable dust', i.e. particles sized between about 5 and 1 μm, suspended in air to a very low concentration, e.g. less than 5 mg/m^3. Particles finer than 5 μm escape the filters of the human body within the respiratory tract and may enter and accumulate within the lungs. This is of particular concern if they contain a high free silica content (Tuck 1987).

The COSHH Regulations require that employees and the general public must not be exposed to any hazardous substance (Powley 1989). Exposure to hazardous substances must be controlled and any control measures must be regularly monitored and tested. Quarry dusts are considered to be potentially hazardous substances and standards and limitations to exposure, particularly of dusts containing silica and asbestiform minerals, are very stringent, often requiring considerable protective modification to plant and controlled operation and practice. In a masonry works, for example, where stone, especially siliceous stone, is being processed dry, the masons should work in cubicles connected to exhauster fans which draw off the dust laden air and pass it to

Fig. 5.6. Dolly pointing of a granite bollard by operator wearing an 'Airstream' helmet (Courtesy of Natural Stone Products Ltd).

filters. The individual masons may also wear helmets and visors which provide filtered air directly around the face and nostrils to prevent inhalation of dust e.g. 'Air stream' helmets, see Fig. 5.6.

Not all dusts are necessarily hazardous if they contain no harmful minerals but airborne dusts, whether hazardous or not, are always considered to be a nuisance and the quarry operator must ensure that emissions are minimized. The three principal sources of dust within a quarry are: (i) the drilling operation, (ii) the movement of traffic and (iii) the transferring of material between conveyors and dumping into hoppers, stockpiles, wagons and lorries etc..

In the case of drilling, the remedy is to fit dust collection cyclones and filters to the rigs, see Fig. 5.25.

Control of fugitive dust is usually carried out to prevent nuisance. For example, dust arising from roads can be suppressed by the preparation and maintenance of competent roads and watering by bowsers during dry weather. It may be possible to schedule or postpone some operations such as tipping or bund construction to avoid periods of exceedingly dry or windy weather. Atomising water sprays are effective in suppressing dust generated at material transfer points and from stockpiles and other open areas. It has also been recommended that open areas be surfaced to permit cleaning and washing. Furthermore, special consideration should be given to the handling of dry materials sized less than 3mm. Stockpiles should be enclosed, conveyors should be fitted with a cover and wind-board, transfer heights minimized and transfer points fully enclosed.

Dust nuisance can be further reduced by installing wheel washes for lorries at the quarry gate and by sheeting loads containing fine materials (DoE 1991). Early restoration and revegetation also mitigate dust problems by stabilizing waste and soil against erosion by wind and water.

5.2.3.6. *Hydrogeology*

The extraction of rock, especially limestones, sands and gravels, may have an effect upon ground water levels and flows particularly if the workings are dewatered by pumping. It is unusual for quarries or mines producing stone to operate below the water table so that this problem is not commonly encountered although the quarries near Rome producing travertine operate tens of metres below the water table. Indeed, the absence of significant ground water flows may be a prerequisite for mining stone. On the other hand it is a matter of increasing concern for crushed rock aggregate producers.

The problems that may be incurred include the following. The local depression of the water table can lead to drying-up of wells and surface water courses. Regional effects upon the water table can be caused by intersection of major aquifers or interference with catchments. Dewatering of permeable rocks underlying saturated rocks of low permeability such as clays could lead to drying shrinkage, consolidation of the rocks through reduction of pore pressure and subsidence.

The first may be resolved by compensation of the landowner, by purchase of properties adjacent to the quarry e.g farms or by recharging streams and rivers with the pumped water. The second is a major new and controversial issue applying, in particular, to limestone superquarries, that requires more research and is outside the scope of this chapter. The third is an unusual situation for which no proven case exists except the obvious shrinkage of peaty soils when drained for the purpose of farming. However, this factor should be considered when pumping water from flooded mine workings.

5.2.3.7. *Loss of wildlife habitat*

As discussed in §5.2.3.10, there is now less concern within the EU about the protection of agricultural land. However, there is increasing concern over the loss of wildlife habitat and disturbance to wild-life generally. In order to preserve the habitat of a particularly rare specie(s), the site of the proposed quarry may have been designated, in part or whole, as a site of especial ecological value, for example, by English Nature as a Site of Special Scientific Interest (SSSI). In this case either the entire development will be strongly opposed or parts of the reserve denied to extraction.

However, compared to the development of land for housing, industry or roads and transport which is usually permanent, use of the land for quarrying is temporary. Therefore, it is often possible to devise a restoration scheme which restores the land to its previous use and even to enhance the value of the site for wildlife. This applies particularly to the creation of open water and wet-land habitats. In some circumstances animals e.g. badgers may be moved to other prepared sites and sods of soil complete with rare flora and fauna transplanted to adjacent areas. Working might be suspended during the breeding season of birds that occupy nest sites in the quarry face and caves inhabited by bats may need to be preserved.

Sites of special scientific interest include geological exposures and it may be necessary to recreate, preserve or enhance such an exposure as a condition of working a quarry.

5.2.3.8. *Loss of amenity*

In the UK, footpath rights are strongly defended as is access to the countryside generally. Usually, at the expense of some loss of reserves of stone, footpaths can be diverted around the perimeter of the quarry workings. It may be possible to reinstate the footpath later after restoration. Occasionally, it may be necessary for the quarry developer to relocate or compensate a surface tenant of the land e.g. a farmer or members of a golf-club.

5.2.3.9. Archaeology
Hills and escarpments produced by outcrops of durable rock may have been inhabited by earlier civilisations or exploited as fortifications. It is thus advisable for the developer to consider and investigate the possibility of valuable archaeological remains existing on such a site. Objections to quarrying can be reduced if the operator meets the expenses of an archaeological excavation to make a record of the site which could not otherwise be afforded.

Exceptionally, the site may be designated as having national importance and protection, for example, a Scheduled Ancient Monument in the UK. These sites are likely to be very obvious and strong opposition to development is to be expected.

Furthermore, there is now a growing interest in industrial archaeology. Many stone quarries have been worked for a century or more and contain relics of past technology such as evidence of methods of extraction, workshops, enginehouses, water wheels and inclines and even remains of homes, hospitals and places of worship. Preservation of these sites may be required. Indeed, it may be possible to create a business based upon tourism.

5.2.3.10. Restoration
No application for permission is likely to be granted without submission of plans for restoration of the workings and it is a requirement of law in the UK by virtue of the Town and Country Planning Act. This also requires that the operator exercises aftercare of the restored site during a period of five years (DoE 1989; RMC 1986). For this reason the soils and, indeed, some overburden should be separately stored and preserved for use during restoration.

In the past, a major concern has been the preservation and restoration of agricultural land. Today, however, the accumulation of surpluses of agricultural products within the EU has led to farmers being paid to set land aside. Therefore, it is likely that opposition to the interruption of agriculture and the attachment of strict conditions to the restoration will only apply to the most fertile soils classified as grades 1 and 2 by the Ministry of Agriculture, Fisheries and Food (MAFF). Soils overlying reserves of hard rock are generally shallow and of low fertility so that they are rarely in these classes. Nevertheless, a viable and acceptable restoration scheme must be proposed. Some alternative uses for excavations are water reservoirs, water sports recreational areas, wildlife refuges and reserves, recreational areas, domestic housing, industrial parks and land-fill.

Deep hard rock excavations are not generally suitable for sailing and water sports, except possibly sub-aqua diving, since the quarry rims shelter the water from winds. Neither does deep water provide plant food for fish. The shallower excavations for sand and gravel are more usually restored to sailing, wind-surfing and fishing lakes. Generally, excavations in limestones are not suitable for disposal of domestic waste as landfill. This is because the rock tends to be fractured and permeable allowing leachate to contaminate groundwater. Although the site may be sealed to prevent pollution, this significantly increases costs (DoE 1986). For the same reason, unless they are very deep, limestone quarries are also unlikely to flood to produce reservoirs or wetland wildlife refuges. Excavations in impermeable igneous and metamorphic rocks are more likely to be amenable to restoration by flooding or landfill. However, earlier excavations in an area having a long history of stone production may provide for the local disposal of inert quarry waste which simultaneously solves two problems.

The problem of the restoration of exhausted, dry quarries, typically in limestone, remains largely unsolved. Many of these excavations will be in areas of scenic beauty often used for recreational purposes. Suggested uses include the development of small industrial estates, which will be naturally screened from view and provide employment in rural areas. Residential housing estates could also be contained in abandoned quarries or temporary accommodation provided for tourists in the form of a caravan park or holiday chalets. Both these schemes require the reduction of the slope of the faces or the elimination of sheer drops for obvious reasons of safety. Overburden can be pushed over the faces to achieve this. In the much larger dry quarries created by the extraction of chalk for cement manufacture, the sites have been successfully developed to contain housing, industry and shopping centres.

Some research has also been undertaken into the use of blasting to create a landform that replicates the form of dry limestone valleys in the immediate vicinity, a technique called 'restoration blasting' (Gunn 1992). Scree slopes are created by blasting using shallow blastholes and intervening sections of the quarry face are left intact to create rock buttresses. The disadvantages of the method are that it requires extensive planning during development of the quarry and usually extends the area of the excavation. Therefore, it is difficult to apply restrospectively to existing operations.

5.3. Extraction

5.3.1. Introduction

The reader is referred to Figs 5.1, 5.2 and 5.3 which are outlines of the selection procedures for an appropriate extraction method. These flowsheets will direct the reader to the most important aspects of design and to the most relevant sections within this chapter.

Although the methods employed for the production of fragmented rock for aggregates and rock fill are significantly different from those for the production of large, intact blocks for armour and dimension stone, as stated before, there are several common aspects of extraction methods, irrespective of desired product. These are discussed in the first part of this section as follows. The importance of the design of stable slopes and excavations is discussed under the title 'Rock mechanics' and the various uses of explosives in mines and quarries under 'Blasting and explosives'. Whereas 'Drilling' is an integral part of blasting it is also used alone for block production. 'Overburden removal' is as relevant to the production of rock fill as to that of dimension stone. The selection of equipment for extraction of rock is only briefly introduced in 'Quarry and mining machinery' and the reader is referred to Appendix A5.1 for more detail.

This section concludes with descriptions of the production of rock fill, armourstone and dimension stone. The particular techniques for the 'Cutting and splitting of rock', that are used almost exclusively in the dimension stone industry, are described under that heading.

5.3.2. Rock mechanics

5.3.2.1. Introduction

The stability of the sides or slopes bounding an excavation is clearly a subject of paramount importance to the workers and to the final abandonment of a quarry. Indeed, the excavation itself may form a cutting for road or railway. Stability is the subject of two disciplines in engineering geology: soil mechanics and rock mechanics. The former deals with soils and unconsolidated rocks such as alluvium, glacial tills, sands and gravels. It is assumed that such materials have been removed as they form the overburden above the useful stone and will not be considered further. Rock mechanics is the study of the behaviour of consolidated rocks (Hudson 1989; Goodman 1980). The consideration of the strength and deformation of the intact rock when subjected to high stress, through the use of properties such as uniaxial compressive strength and Young's modulus, together with the presence of discontinuities, is of importance in deep underground mining, tunnelling and other deep civil engineering projects. However, nearer the surface and in surface excavations such as quarries the strength of the intact rock is seldom of relevance since the rock is subject to low stresses only. The discontinuities assume greater importance since they represent planes of weakness within the rock mass which may cause instability of the slopes defining the excavation. This is discussed below.

5.3.2.2. Discontinuities

Discontinuities exist in essentially two forms: (a) joints or fissures, also called defects, produced by tensile forces and (b) faults, where relative movement has taken place between the two surfaces, see Chapter 2. They are generally assumed to be planar features exhibiting both dip inclination and strike, although use is commonly made of the orientation or azimuth of the line of maximum dip, called 'dip direction'. In most rock masses it will usually be possible to identify three or more 'sets' of discontinuities having the same general dip and dip direction.

The discontinuity may be in-filled with secondary minerals and the rock surfaces may be altered by weathering. The continuity of the feature is described as 'persistence' and the width, which, for example, determines permeability to water, is described as the 'aperture'.

Discontinuities are generally assumed to have negligible tensile strength but they may exhibit shear strength as a function of the normal stress, roughness, nature of in-filling material and presence of water.

The roughness of the surface can be described or measured in several ways. Empirically, it can be compared to standard profiles to give the value of the joint roughness coefficient, JRC, see Fig. 5.7 (Barton & Choubey 1977) which parameter has been used in the

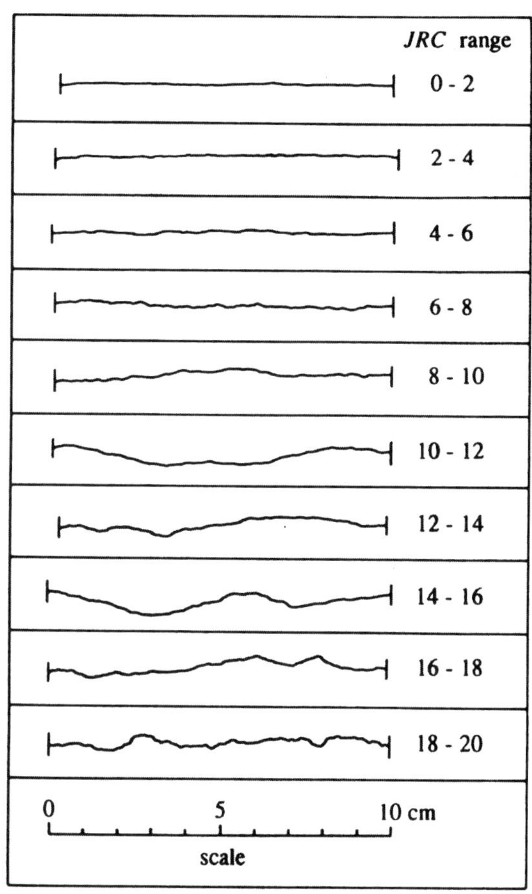

Fig. 5.7. Standard profiles to determine joint roughness coefficient, JRC (after Barton & Choubey 1977).

quantitative analysis of slope stability. The profile of the joint may also be represented approximately as a sine wave, with the roughness expressed as the ratio of amplitude divided by wavelength, or as a saw-tooth profile. Finally, the profiles of joints and joint surfaces have been analysed to determine whether they can be described by fractal mathematics. Some correlation has been shown between the fractal dimension and JRC but, to date, no quantitative use seems to be have been made of fractal dimensions or fractals to describe joints (Genske *et al.* 1992). In reported studies it has proved difficult to describe a joint surface by a single fractal dimension since this dimension does not prove to be a constant over a wide range of scales (Brown & Scholz 1985).

The greater the roughness of the joint surface and the normal stress the greater the shear strength and the greater the force opposing sliding movements. On the

Fractals

Fractal, derived from the word fracture, is the adjective given to an irregular curve, surface, object or pattern that can be described by fractal geometry. It is also often used as a noun to define such a curve or surface. Fractal geometry is not new having been conceived around 1900 but, as with many aspects of science and technology, its rapid advancement has only been only made possible by the computer and microprocessor which is able to carry out many iterative calculations in a very short time. Fractal geometry is attributed to Mandelbrot, who introduced the term in 1967, since which time several textbooks have been written on the subject, notably the general text of Feder (1988) and the more specialist text on applications in rock mechanics by Xie (1993). Space only permits the following highly simplified explanation of fractals and their applications.

Classical or Euclidean geometry has been found to be very useful to describe the shape and spatial relationship of man-made objects. It uses only three integer dimensions to describe lines, surfaces and solids which are made up of simple geometric elements that relate the orthogonal coordinates x, y and z by smooth mathematical functions or equations that can be differentiated at any point. Lines have only one dimension, surfaces have two and solid objects have three. However, Euclidean geometry has limited success in describing the shape and spatial relationships of natural objects.

Fractal geometry embraces the idea that some natural phenomena do not fully occupy the Euclidean dimensions and that they have a fractional dimension. Examples of application include Brownian motion, fracture surfaces, distribution of pore spaces and percolation of fluids through permeable rocks (known as sparse solids), fluid dynamics and boundaries between laminar and turbulent flow regimes, lightning and electrical discharges, cloud shapes and distribution of rainfall, dendritic growth of plants and crystals, natural drainage patterns, coastlines and weathering profiles.

There are two important concepts in fractal geometry:

(i) The fractal dimension of an irregular curve, surface or solid has a non-integer value; between 1 and 2 for irregular curves or profiles and between 2 and 3 for irregular, rough or rugous surfaces. The higher the value the more irregular the profile or surface and the functions relating the coordinates x, y and z are not differentiable.

(ii) Self-similarity, the property of an object to remain the same irrespective of the scale of magnification or measurement. Self-similarity is contained in two attempts to define fractals:
'A fractal is a shape made of parts similar to the whole in some way'
'A fractal is a set that is more irregular than the sets considered in classical geometry. No matter how much the set is magnified, smaller and smaller irregularities become visible'.

The important and useful aspects of these concepts are:

(i) the degree of irregularity of a line or surface may be essentially described by a single number, the fractal dimension, which simplifies descriptors

(ii) the fractal dimension may be determined by investigation at a convenient scale and then extrapolated to other larger or smaller scales. However, it should be noted that in practice objects do not always exhibit self-similarity over a wide range of scales, a fact that can limit the usefulness of fractals.

Self-affinity is the term used to describe the relationship between fractal curves and shapes that are clearly derived from one another by transformation or distortion but do not display self-similarity.

In all texts it seems to be accepted that the easiest means to gain some comprehension of fractals is through a worked example of the determination of the fractal dimension as presented below. Many texts have made use of maps of coastlines, such as that of Norway, but this example is a deliberately exaggerated profile drawn for the purpose. Figure 5.8 shows an irregular profile, part of which has been magnified, which could be a joint, trace of an electrical discharge, section of a fracture surface, a map of a coastline or even a profile of a mountain chain. To determine whether the curve is fractal its length is measured at several scales and the profile length, L, plotted against the scale, d, on logarithmic paper as shown in Fig. 5.9. If the curve is fractal the plot is a straight line of gradient $1 - D$, where D is the fractal dimension. In the example the length of the profile has been measured five times using calipers set at five values of d, equivalent to five scales of magnification, of 10, 5 2, 1 and 0.5 units. The relative lengths measured are 80, 85, 88, 92 and 97 units respectively. An alternative method is to overlay a grid of squares of side d and to count the number of squares, N required to cover the curve. N can be plotted against d to determine the fractal dimension, D. The graph of L against d should be examined over several orders of magnitude of values of L and d to determine if the plot is linear. The range of values in this case is insufficient since it is impractical to magnify the profile in the text but the plot of Fig. 5.9 has a negative gradient of about -0.07, i.e. $D = 1.07$.

In principle, the same method is used to measure the fractal dimension of surfaces except that the surface is imagined to be covered by balls of diameter d. Perhaps the simplest and most obvious use of fractals is to describe the roughness of joint surfaces and profiles. The use of fractal dimension removes the subjectivity of ascribing a value to JRC by comparison with standard profiles (see Fig. 5.7). Analysis of the standard profiles has shown a non-linear proportionality between JRC and D over the respective ranges 0 to 20 and 1.000 to 1.015 according to an equation of the form:

$$\mathrm{JRC} = A + B(D - 1) + C(D - 1)^2, \text{ where } A, B \text{ and } C \text{ are coefficients.}$$

Interestingly, it has also been shown that several well established relationships already used in geology and mining are fractal, notably those describing the distribution of particle size which have themselves been used to model fragmentation by blasting, natural block size distribution and size analysis of sediments. These include the Weibull, Gates–Gaudin–Schuhmann (G–G–S) and Rosin–Rammler (R–R) size distribution functions. In all cases these equations relate the number, N_x, or cumulative percentage weight, Y_x, of particles greater than size x to the particle size, x, raised to a given power denoted as n. These are known as power laws.

Weibull and Rosin-Rammler: $Y_x = \exp[-x/k]^n$

Gates-Gaudin-Schuhmann: $Y_x = 1 - [x/k]^n$

The term, k, is a size modulus or characteristic size depending upon the specific relationship. A mathematical expression of a geomtrical relationship which could be described as fractal is:

$$N_x = C.\, x^{-D}, \text{ where } C \text{ is a constant parameter or coefficient.}$$

Since the mass of a particles of size x is given by:

$$\text{Mass} = (\text{density})x^3$$

it can be shown that the exponent n of the power relationships is related to the fractal dimension D by:

$$D = 3 - n.$$

For disaggregated blocks generated from igneous rocks masses the value of D has been found to be around 2.2.

At present, the description of discontinuities in terms of their spacing distributions is the subject of investigation, research and academic interest. For example, it has been suggested that the fractal dimension may provide some insight into the tectonic movements and mechanisms that produced fault and joint patterns. However, for the engineering geologist the orientation, dip and persistence of discontinuities are also essential parameters for the evaluation of stability of slopes and excavations (see §5.3.2.5). Although realistic joint patterns have been produced by computer simulations, modelling of the distribution of joints by use of fractals requires that these parameters are separately determined or assumed for each joint set.

Finally, as stated at the beginning, it should also be remembered that although fractal geometry can be useful when proved to describe a set, it is not necessarily the case that a natural profile, surface or pattern is fractal. This has resulted in the development of multifractals which exhibit self-similarity only over a limited range of scales and is outside the scope of this text.

other hand, the presence of water is likely to lubricate the surfaces of the discontinuity and promote sliding. The presence of water under pressure, such as hydrostatic pressure, can, of course, reduce the normal force and also reduce the frictional resistance to sliding.

The principal discontinuity sets in a rock mass can be identified by field investigations, see §3.5. Using a geological compass, many measurements of dip and dip direction of the obviously more persistent discontinuities are made and recorded. The almost universally accepted method of presenting these data is the 'lower hemispherical projection' shown in Fig. 5.10 which illustrates the representation of a plane dipping at 60° to the southwest (225°) (Priest 1985). This graphical method of presenting data on a stereoplot can be used for the following purposes:

- Identification of sets of discontinuities
- Prediction of potential slope instability caused by intersection of the planes of discontinuities and sides of excavations. This use of the stereonet is explained below in the text box.

The frequency and spacing of discontinuities are obviously of great interest to the mineral operator as they determine both slope stability and the feasibilty of production of large blocks (Priest 1993). These

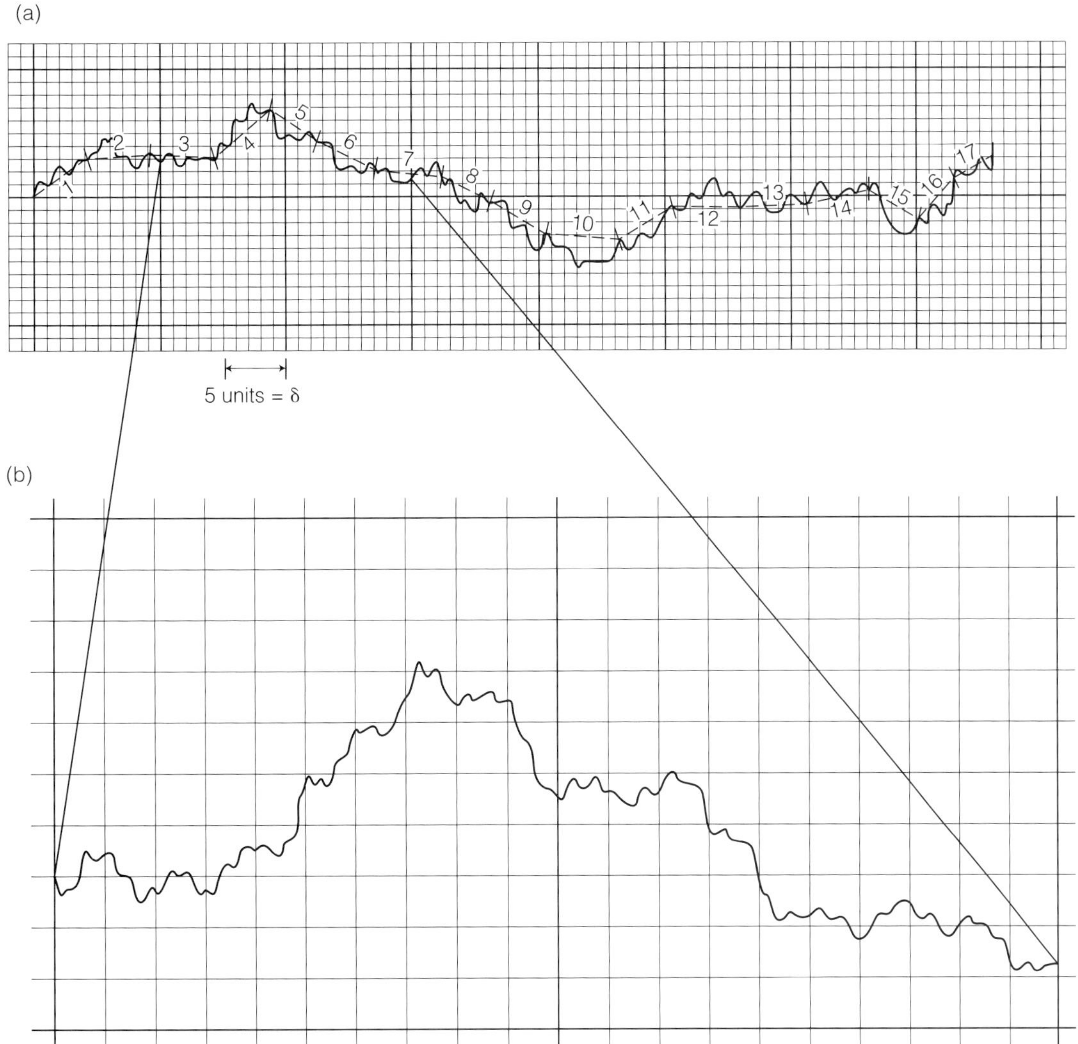

Fig. 5.8. Fractal profile with magnified section showing measurement of length, L at different scales, d.

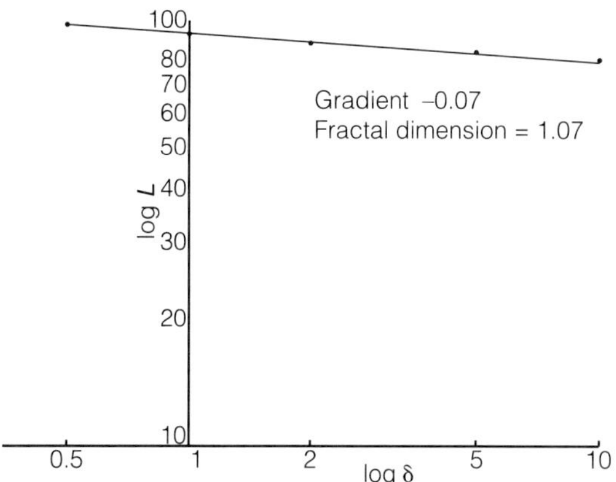

Fig. 5.9. Plot of $\log L$ versus $\log d$ for fractal profile Fig. 5.8.

parameters can be measured by recording the number, N and position of discontinuities upon a scan-line of length, L drawn on an exposed rock face or on a drill core. The frequency and mean spacing can then be calculated by:

Frequency, $h = N/L$
Mean spacing, $x = L/N = 1/h$

It can often be shown that the spacing, x, is related to the frequency, h, by a negative exponential function:

$$f(x) = h\,e^{-hx}$$

The Rock Quality Designation, RQD, is the proportion (%) of the scan line represented by spacings of more than 0.1m. (Deere 1963). Thus, assuming that the above relationship holds:

$$RQD = 100(0.1h + 1)\,e^{-0.1h}$$

Because the value of RQD is not very sensitive to spacings above 0.3m, other critical values of spacing, t, may be chosen so that

$$RQD = 100(ht + 1)\,e^{-ht}$$

However, the engineer should be wary of values of RQD since these will vary according to the orientation of the scan line and the experience of the surveyor. It is important that several scan lines or cores orientated in different directions should be studied but problems of access or cost can prevent this action.

It should also be noted that the frequency and mean spacing may not be constant. In particular, mean spacing may increase with depth and it is a common observation that larger blocks of dimension stone are won from the deeper benches of a quarry. Nevertheless, values of RQD simply determined from drill core or exposures can be a rapid and useful indication of the potential for block production.

5.3.2.3. Block size distribution

Given a mathematical relationship between frequency and spacing, as shown above in §5.3.2.2, and the orientation of the planes of the discontinuities, it is possible to calculate the distribution of areas or volumes of blocks produced by the intersection of these discontinuities in either two or three dimensions, see Fig. 5.13. This is called the natural block size distribution, NBSD, which is clearly of immense value to producers of armourstone and dimension stone. It is complicated, however, by the inexactness of computational techniques, errors in measurements, simplifying assumptions of the frequency distribution models and the fact that some discontinuities may be more or less persistent. Subjective judgement is needed to select those discontinuity sets having a persistence of the same order of

Analysis of slope stability using the hemispherical projection

The hemispherical projection is explained in §4.2.3.2.

There are two common forms of the projection, 'equal area' as depicted in Fig. 4.8, and 'equal angle' as shown in Figs 5.10–5.12.

The circular chart or stereoplot forming Fig. 5.10 shows the representation of a planar discontinuity having a compass direction or azimuth, $\beta = 225°$, and an angle of dip, $\alpha = 60°$ (Priest 1985). This representation is most useful for studying the intersection of more than one set of discontinuities to create wedges and, hence, potential instability of slopes, see §5.3.2.5.

An example of this analysis is presented with reference to Fig. 5.14b. Figure 5.11 shows two discontinuity sets, each dipping at about 60°, which intersect a pit slope inclined at 75° to the horizontal. The crest of the pit slope strikes north–south (0°) and the two joint sets have azimuths of 315° (northwest) and 225° (southwest) respectively. The shaded area indicates potential wedge failure with the azimuth of the valley formed by intersection of the two joint sets predicted as 270° or west.

Figure 5.12 shows clustering indicative of three sets of nearly orthogonal discontinuities as may be commonly encountered: (1) near vertical (85°), azimuth 210° (2) near vertical (80°), azimuth 130° and (3) near horizontal (10°), azimuth 0°. This use of the stereonet to identify joint sets is explained in §4.2.

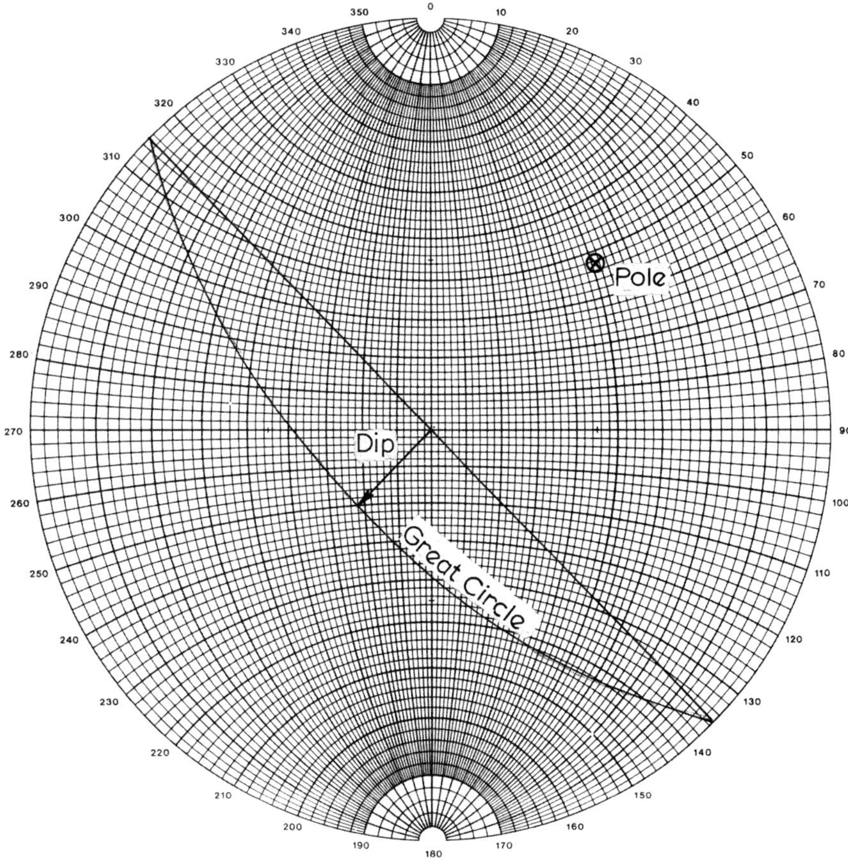

Fig. 5.10. Lower hemispherical projection showing the representation of a plane dipping at 60° to the south west (225°).

magnitude as the excavation, for example, the bench height or tunnel diameter. In many cases, smaller discontinuities will terminate at the boundary of blocks determined by other sets having wider spacings. In a quarry a persistence of greater than 4m might be selected as comparable to the typical values of burden and spacing, see §5.3.3.5.

5.3.2.4. Rock masses

Owing to the difficulty of describing exactly the rock structure and measuring the mechanical and physical properties of heterogeneous rock masses for engineering purposes, some simpler parameters have been developed to describe the rock mass. These parameters were not developed for the purpose of assessing the feasibility of the extraction of blocks for armourstone and dimension stone nor the stability of slopes. They have been proposed for the evaluation of the stability of underground excavations with time. In addition, it should be noted that the use of these parameters is no substitute for a detailed evaluation of potential failure mechanisms and an engineered design.

Nevertheless, if already available, they may be useful to obtain an appreciation of the general nature of the rock mass in terms of likely problems of instability (West 1991). The two principal systems are the Rock Mass Rating (RMR) (Bieniawski 1974) and the Q rating (Barton *et al.* 1974). RMR lies between 0 and 100 and Q rating between 0.001 and 1000. In general, the higher the value of the parameter, the more competent the rock and the more stable the excavation. With respect to armourstone and dimension stone, the higher the value the more likely it is that large blocks can be extracted.

It has been possible to correlate these two parameters empirically and to relate the values to the duration of stable excavations in rock. Specifically, the parameters may indicate whether reinforcement or support is required.

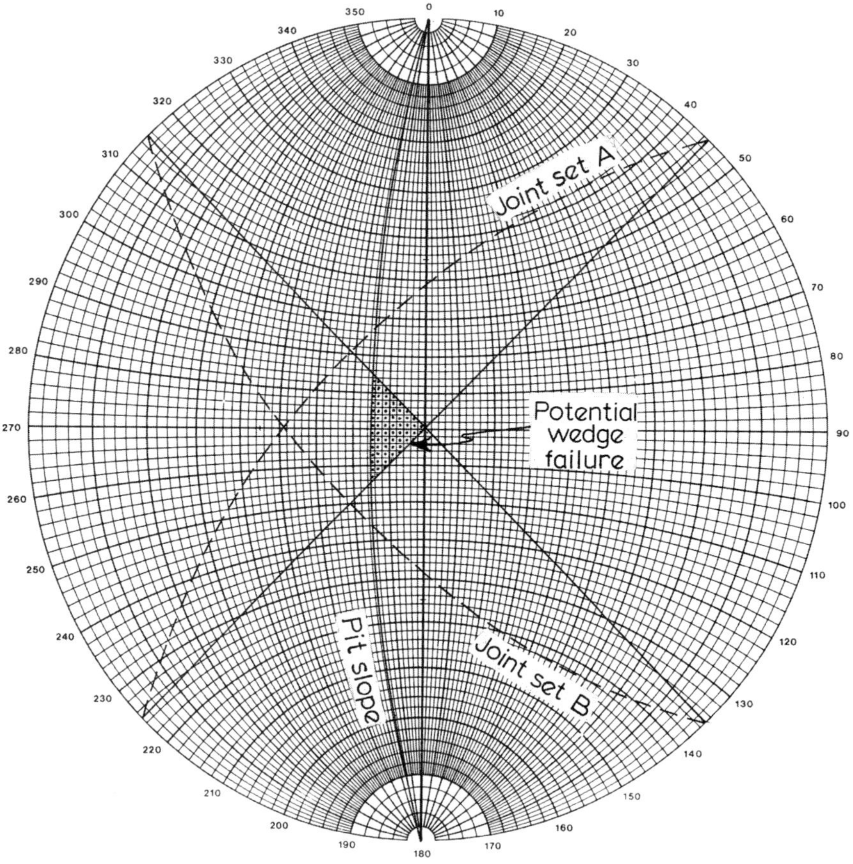

Fig. 5.11. Lower hemispherical projection showing the intersection of two sets of joints and the pit slope to create potential wedge failure.

5.3.2.5. Slope stability

It has been explained above that discontinuities divide the rock mass into discrete blocks, see Fig. 5.13. Moreover, the discontinuities may intersect the face of the excavation in such a manner as to release or potentially release blocks. There are a number of well understood situations as shown in Figs 5.14 and 4.6 which create unstable slopes known as 'plane failure' or 'sliding block', 'toppling' and 'wedge' failure. The geometry of the face and discontinuities alone will determine the potential for failure. Whether the slope actually fails usually depends upon the shear strengths of the discontinuities. Roughness of the surface will generate frictional resistance to sliding and asperities can obstruct movement. On the other hand, obviously slickensided faults will generate little frictional resistance. It is common for joint and fissure surfaces to have been altered by weathering and for the discontinuity to be filled with clays or other finely divided minerals. These alteration products may lubricate the surfaces contributing to slope instabilty especially when wet. Therefore, the consideration of water flows resulting from precipitation, surface run-off and ground water is important for the creation of stable slopes (Walton 1988). It is common practice, for example, to dig an interceptor ditch behind the crest of a slope to prevent surface water draining down from higher levels and entering the rock face.

The shear strength, τ is commonly expressed as a function of normal stress, z, and a coefficient of friction, $\tan\phi$, so that,

$$\tau = z \tan\phi.$$

This expression can be modified to incorporate roughness and asperities as follows:

$$\tau = z \tan(\phi + \mathrm{i})$$

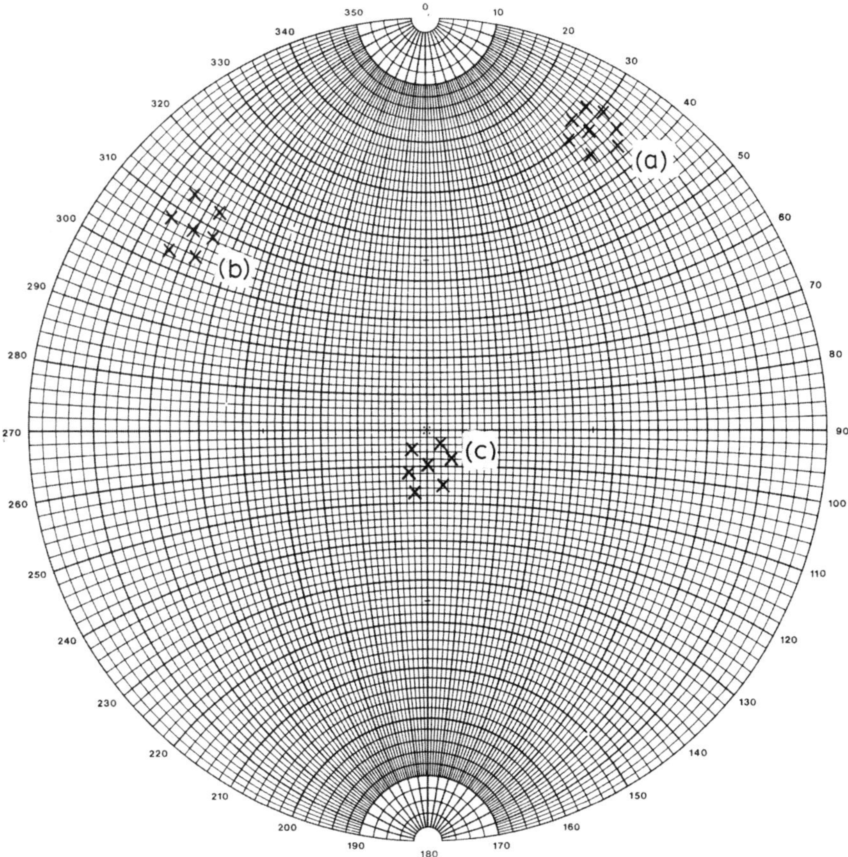

Fig. 5.12. Lower hemispherical projection showing clustering of poles indicating sets of discontinuities.

where i is related to the JRC and compressive strength of the rock. Values of the coefficient of friction can be determined by laboratory testing of samples containing discontinuities.

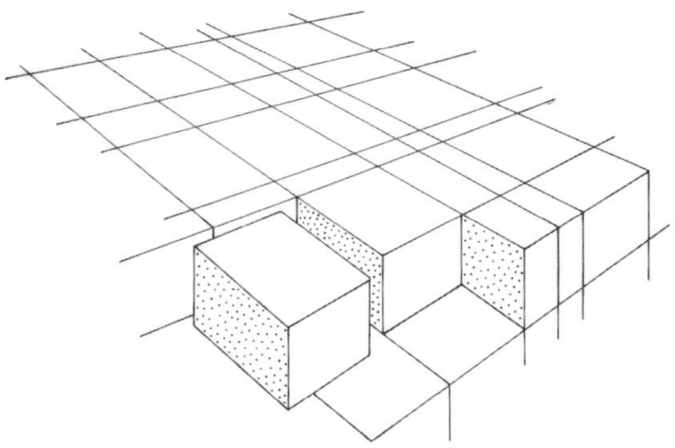

Fig. 5.13. Diagram of the intersection of discontinuities in three dimensions producing a natural distribution of block sizes.

Calculations can be carried out to determine the ratio, known as the factor of safety, between forces opposing motion, such as friction discussed above, and forces acting to move the block, such as gravity. An additional important force contributing to instability is the hydrostatic pressure exerted upon the faces of blocks by water contained in fissures.

A final consideration is the protection of persons at the toe of the final slope from occasional falling rocks. It is usual to leave the face in a stepped form having a catch bench of, say, width 5 m at selected vertical intervals. Thus, a final face in a totally competent rock will not be truly vertical. In summary, where a competent rock contains either no discontinuities or only horizontal bedding planes and vertical joints it may be possible to create stable, near vertical (85°) faces. However, where discontinuities of low shear strength are inclined to the horizontal, naturally stable faces will have low inclinations. Each face in each excavation must be considered and designed individually but, in a typical case, it is unlikely that the finished, stable, unsupported slope

Block size distribution

The calculation of the block size distribution can be accomplished in several ways, two of which are discussed below.

A simple calculation of block size distribution assumes that there are three principal, orthogonal discontinuity sets, which is a common situation, see Fig. 5.13. A random number generator is used to sample the frequency distributions of the spacings in each of the three dimensions. This procedure provides three dimensions of a random block, namely, x, y and z. The block volume is then given by the multiple xyz and iteration will compile a block volume frequency distribution.

In a second method, block size coefficients, C_p, which are independent of the actual values of mean spacings have been tabulated for various spacing frequency distributions, for example, negative exponential, uniform and log normal, see Table 5.1. C_p is the size or volume of a block such that p% of the model rock mass or volume exists as blocks smaller than C_p.

It is then possible to determine the block size distribution for a given case from the following equation:

$$V_p = C_p(\mathrm{PMS1} \cdot \mathrm{PMS2} \cdot \mathrm{PMS3})/(\cos\theta \cdot \cos\phi \cdot \cos\alpha)$$

where

V_p is the size (volume) of a block such that p% of the rock mass is smaller than V_p,

PMS1, PMS2, PMS3 are the mean spacings of the three principal sets of discontinuities.

θ, ϕ, α are the orientations of the discontinuities as defined by the angles formed by the intersection of the great circles representing the discontinuities on a stereoplot. More sophisticated methods require more complex software which creates a three dimensional model of the rock mass as an array of points with coordinates in three dimensions. It is assumed that the discontinuities are both planar and persistent. However, the discontinuities need not be orthogonal since data upon dip and azimuth can be entered. The initial, defined volume of rock is progressively dissected by the planes of the discontinuities. The coordinates of the points of intersection of planes, which define the individual blocks, can then be determined. Computing times are lengthy but the programs can provide both the block size distribution and information on block shape. For example, the program could be used calculate the ratios of dimensions (Da Gama 1977; Wang *et al.* 1991*a*, *b*; 1992).

Table 5.1. *Block size coefficients for various spacing frequency distributions*

% passing	*Exponential*	*Uniform*	*Lognormal*
100	38.9	17.8	38.2
90	15.3	6.6	13.4
80	8.9	4.5	8.5
70	5.9	3.3	5.9
60	4.0	2.5	4.3
50	2.7	1.9	3.1
40	1.9	1.5	2.2
30	1.2	1.1	1.5
20	0.7	0.7	0.9
10	0.3	0.4	0.5

will have an overall inclination greater than 70° with consequent implications upon reserves and quarrying costs, see Chapter 4.

A very similar analysis of the potential release of blocks from the roof of an underground excavation can be conducted to evaluate the stability of mines (Hoek & Brown 1980). However, the analysis is complicated by the significant stresses that may exist in the rock owing to the weight of overlying strata.

5.3.2.6. Reinforcement

Reinforcement of the rock structure is intended to prevent the release or movement of blocks and to exploit the inherent strength of the stabilised rock mass. The

Rock mass parameters

These systems were not developed to assess the rock mass in terms of the block size distribution or the ease of producing blocks. Rather they were proposed as indicators of the stability of underground excavations with time and the necessity of support and reinforcement. The value of the parameter is determined by summation or multiplication of scores given to the rock mass for six component attributes.

Rock Mass Rating (RMR)

The attributes considered and scores are:

(1) uniaxial compressive strength, 0 to 15 increasing with UCS,
(2) RQD, 3 to 20 increasing with RQD,
(3) spacing of discontinuities, 5 to 20 increasing with spacing,
(4) surface condition of discontinuity, 0 to 30 increasing with roughness,
(5) groundwater conditions, 15 to 0 decreasing with water flow and,
(6) orientation of discontinuity sets with respect to the engineering structure, 0 to −60 for slopes and 0 to −12 for tunnels. Note the negative values of this factor.

The parameter is calculated by summation of the scores and acquires values between 0 and 100 with the following classification according to actual value:

RMR	<20	21–40	41–60	61–80	81–100
Class	V	IV	III	II	I
	Very poor rock	Poor rock	Fair rock	Good rock	Very good rock
Span, metres	1	2.5	5	10	15
Stand-up time	30 min	10 hours	1 week	1 year	20 years

With respect to stability of slopes, the importance of the factors discontinuity spacing, joint roughness, alteration and presence of water is evident. In addition, the overwhelming influence of the orientation of discontinuities with respect to the slopes of an excavation is illustrated. Indeed, attempts have been made to extend this form of analysis to evaluate the stability of slopes through the Slope Mass Rating, SMR (Romana 1985, 1988).

Q-system

The attributes considered and the factors are:

(1) RQD, used directly as %,
(2) number of discontinuity sets, *Jn*, 0.5 to 20 increasing from massive rock to multiple joint sets,
(3) roughness of surface of discontinuity, *Jr*, 0.5 to 4 increasing from slickensides to very irregular joints,
(4) alteration of discontinuity surface, *Ja*, 0.75 to 20 increasing with degree of alteration and thickness of infilling material,
(5) water inflow, *Jw*, 1 to 0.05 decreasing with water inflow,
(6) stress, SRF, 0.5 to 20 increasing as a function of stress in competent rock.

The parameter is calculated by multiplication according to the formula:

$$Q = (\mathrm{RQD} \times Jr \times Jw)/(Jn \times Ja \times \mathrm{SRF})$$

Values of between 0.001 and 1000 can be obtained with 0.001 describing exceptionally poor rock.

principal means are rock bolts and shotcreting. Alternatively, support can be provided to the rock face in the form of buttresses, steel or concrete arches and steel or concrete ring segments as, for example, in tunnels and mines.

It is seldom economic to provide reinforcement or support to a quarry face especially in view of the fact that, eventually, the quarry will be abandoned and that the final faces must be inherently stable. However, in civil engineering works, such as road cuttings, it may be

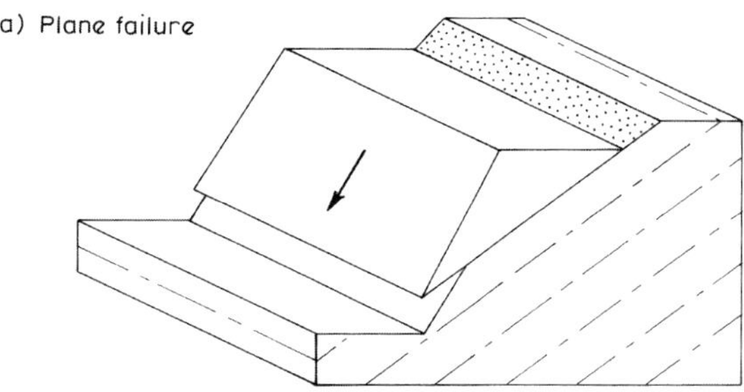

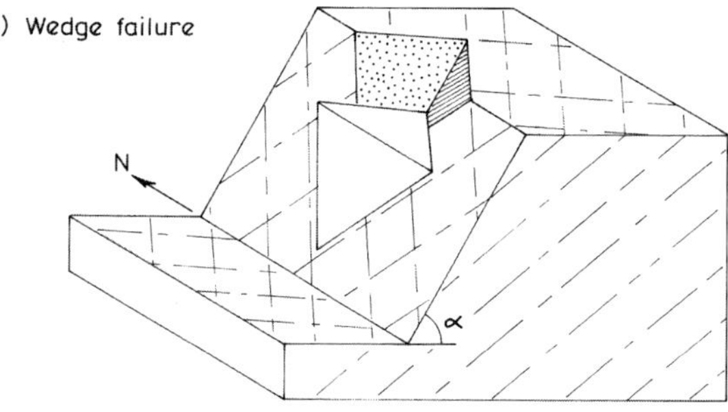

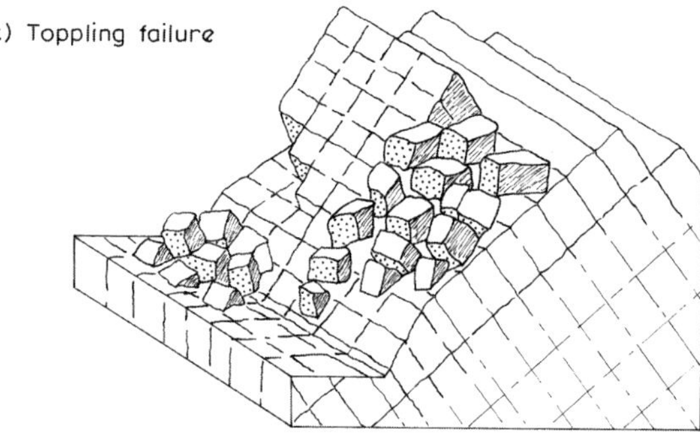

Fig. 5.14. Illustrations of slope instability caused by (a) plane failure (b) wedge failure and (c) toppling.

essential that the slope is reinforced and in mines it may be necessary to reinforce the roof or walls, at least temporarily.

On slopes where small rocks are likely to be released (ravelling), stabilization and protection of the road can be provided by steel mesh pinned to the surface and the use of a catch fence and ditch. The rock surface can also be shotcreted to prevent ravelling and weathering of the rock.

Major block failure can be prevented by locking the potentially free blocks into the slope, or the roof of a mine, using rock-bolts. A rock bolt or cable-bolt comprises a long steel bar or cable, threaded at one end, which is inserted into a hole drilled through the block and into the rock mass, see Fig. 5.15. The number and depth of these holes is determined by the frequency and spacing of the discontinuities. The bolt is anchored or

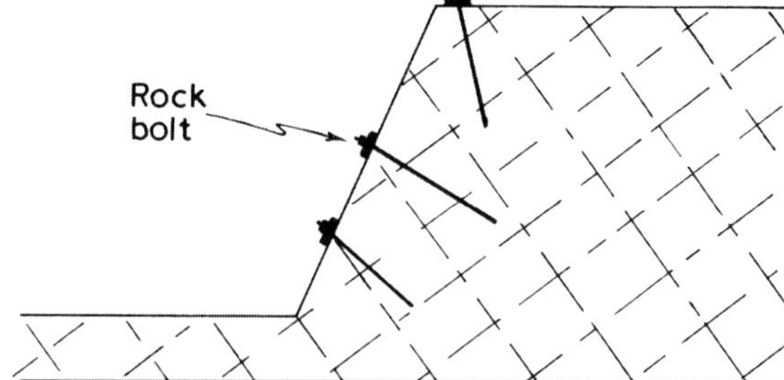

Fig. 5.15. Use of rock bolting to reinforce a rock mass.

fixed into the hole using a cement grout or resin. A plate is then placed over the projecting, threaded portion and tightened down using a nut (Hoek & Wood 1988).

Movement of rock blocks may also be prevented by inserting rock dowels into holes drilled through the block. Further discussion of the stabilization of slopes forming cuttings will be found in §7.4.

5.3.2.7. Presplitting

Finally, it should be noted (see §5.3.3) that the use of explosives to fragment rock in front of a blast hole often generates fractures in rock behind the blast hole, known as 'back-break'. These fractures can induce or exacerbate slope instability and a technique to avoid this problem, 'presplitting' is common in both quarries and civil engineering, see §7.4.3.

In the traditional method a series of parallel holes of small diameter, D (typically 50–75 mm), are drilled on closely spaced (600 to 1000 mm) centres, along the line of the final face or intended slope and behind the final row of primary blast holes. Accuracy in drilling is most important so a drill alignment tool may be used (Matheson 1984). In block production the presplit blastholes may be reamered to favour the intended line of the presplit, especially in granites and sandstones. A chisel is used to create a sharp pointed groove along each side of the hole (see Fig. 5.16), in line with the intended presplit. The primary blast holes will not be fired until after the presplit has been created but the minimum time interval between the two firings may be as short as 50 milliseconds. The presplit blast holes are charged with relatively small quantities of explosives often in the form of vertically separated charges connected together by detonating cord. Indeed, the only explosive employed may be detonating cord or specially manufactured cartridges containing spaced charges within a plastic tube can be used. The charges are

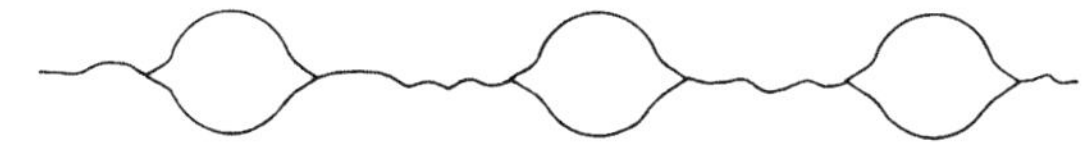

Fig. 5.16. Reamered drill holes as used in presplitting.

'uncoupled', that is, not in contact with the wall of the blast hole, in order to minimize pulverization of the rock, or each other, see Fig. 5.17. When the charges are detonated simultaneously in all of the presplit blast holes the expanding gases create a fracture linking the blast holes and forming the presplit. This fracture intercepts the shock wave created by the later primary blast preventing 'back-break' and producing a smooth, stable surface.

A recent alternative method makes use of larger diameter holes drilled with conventional blasthole drills. The small charges are separated vertically within the blasthole by self-inflating airbags. These balloons were originally developed for decking explosive charges, air-decking', and overcoming certain blasthole charging problems such as sealing water in the base of the hole to permit maximum use of ANFO (Cleeton 1997). Slowly

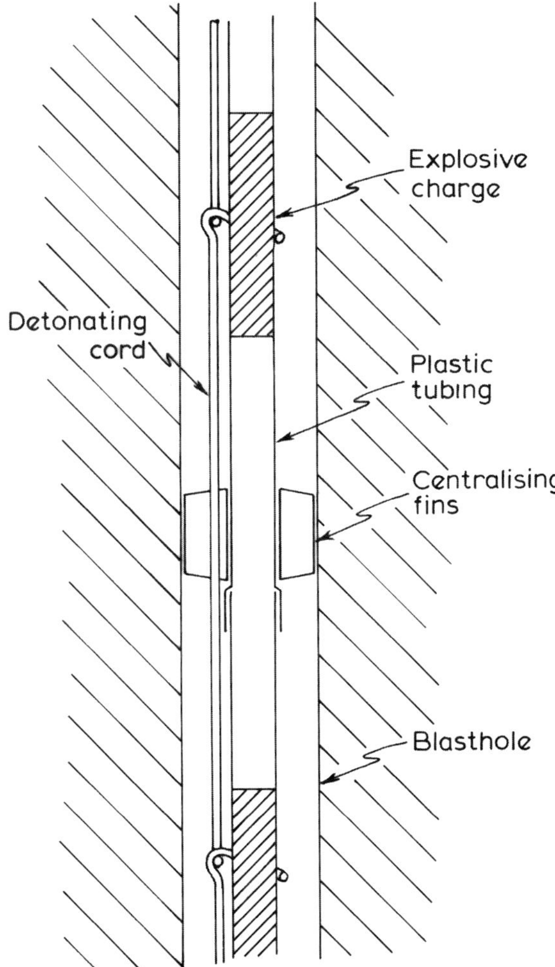

Fig. 5.17. Decoupled explosive charges for presplitting.

expanding 'splitting powders' can also be used to avoid the problems incurred by explosives, see §5.3.9.12.

A presplit rock surface is characterized by a smooth appearance showing one half of the presplit holes, known as half barrels, as a pattern upon the rock face, see Figs 5.18 and 7.5.

5.3.2.8. Cleavage

Discontinuities having no tensile strength have been discussed above, see §5.3.2.2. Moreover, many rocks exhibit planes of weakness, having significant tensile strength but along which preferential cleavage occurs as described in §§2.3.5 and 2.6.1.3. These planes of weakness are most useful in the production of dimension stone. Most obvious examples are bedding in flaggy micaceous sandstones and the cleavage of slate but some are invisible to the untrained eye. Indeed, thick slabs of some Cotswold limestones are allowed to weather in the open after quarrying so as to develop the inherent lamination and produce roofing tiles. Igneous rocks such as granite are said to exhibit 'grain', 'rift', 'hem' or 'way'. There are usually two planes of cleavage and they have been named, in descending order of preferential cleavage, as; (i) 'freeway' or 'cleaving way' or 'rift'; and (ii) 'second way' or 'quartering way' or 'grain'. Cleavage in the third vertical plane can be difficult and the plane is described as the 'toughway', see Fig. 5.19. In favourable circumstances the freeway is horizontal.

In the absence of convenient jointing, extraction of blocks may involve cutting faces on the toughway and splitting along the freeway and secondway. Basic igneous extrusive rocks e.g. basalt, are often devoid of these ways which limits their usefulness as dimension stone. Great importance is attached to the existence of these cleavage planes in the manual production of setts. Furthermore, it can be found easier to match the texture of the finished slab or ashlar if a certain cleavage surface, e.g. secondway, is consistently chosen for polishing.

Slate can exhibit three approximately orthogonal planes of weakness, see Fig. 5.20. The most prominent plane is universally referred to as the cleavage. It is generally believed to be created by the parallel lamination of platy minerals i.e. micas comprising the slate. The second plane, at right angle to the cleavage, is known as the pillaring plane in Wales and variously as the grain, sculp and scallop (Pennsylvannia) and the longrain (France) (Behre 1933). It is believed to be created by the parallel orientation of the long axes of the micas. Finally, there may be jointing planes. The ease with which the slate splits on the cleavage plane varies considerably and is very important to the production of roofing slates, see §6.4.13. The joints are usually in-filled with another mineral, for example, calcite or, more rarely, quartz.

5.3.2.9. Rippability

Ripping can be an inexpensive method of producing rock fill where the *in situ* material contains a large

Fig. 5.18. Presplit face showing half-barrels (Courtesy of RMC Roadstone Ltd).

number of discontinuities such as joints, is thinly bedded or relatively weak. The method involves the use of a crawler tractor fitted with one or more steel tines or rippers which break up the rock as the tractor moves forward, see Appendix A5.1.7. It also avoids the problems incurred by the use of explosives, see §5.2.3.4.

The choice of either ripping or blasting to break the rock will depend upon the relative costs of each method and the productivity of ripping, usually measured in cubic metres per hour. The feasibilty of ripping and the productivity achieved are obviously related to the intact rock strength, the presence and spacing of fractures and the power or weight of the tractor, amongst other factors. Several classification systems have been developed

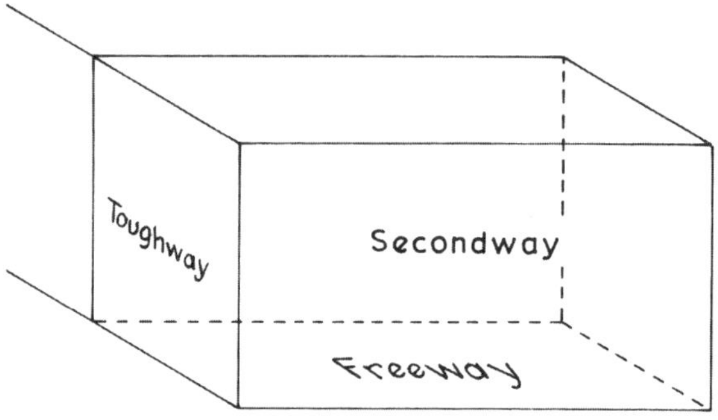

Fig. 5.19. Diagram of rift and ways in granite.

Fig. 5.20. Diagram of cleavage in slate.

to determine the rippability of rock (Franklin *et al.* 1971; Fookes *et al.* 1971; Caterpillar 1990; Macgregor *et al.* 1994).

As a single diagnostic property, seismic velocity has been suggested as the best indicator of rippability (Caterpillar 1990) since it will be influenced by rock strength, degree of weathering and the presence and condition of discontinuities. Rocks exhibiting a seismic velocity of less than 2000 m/s are typically rippable by tractors having power units of 250 kW or greater. This

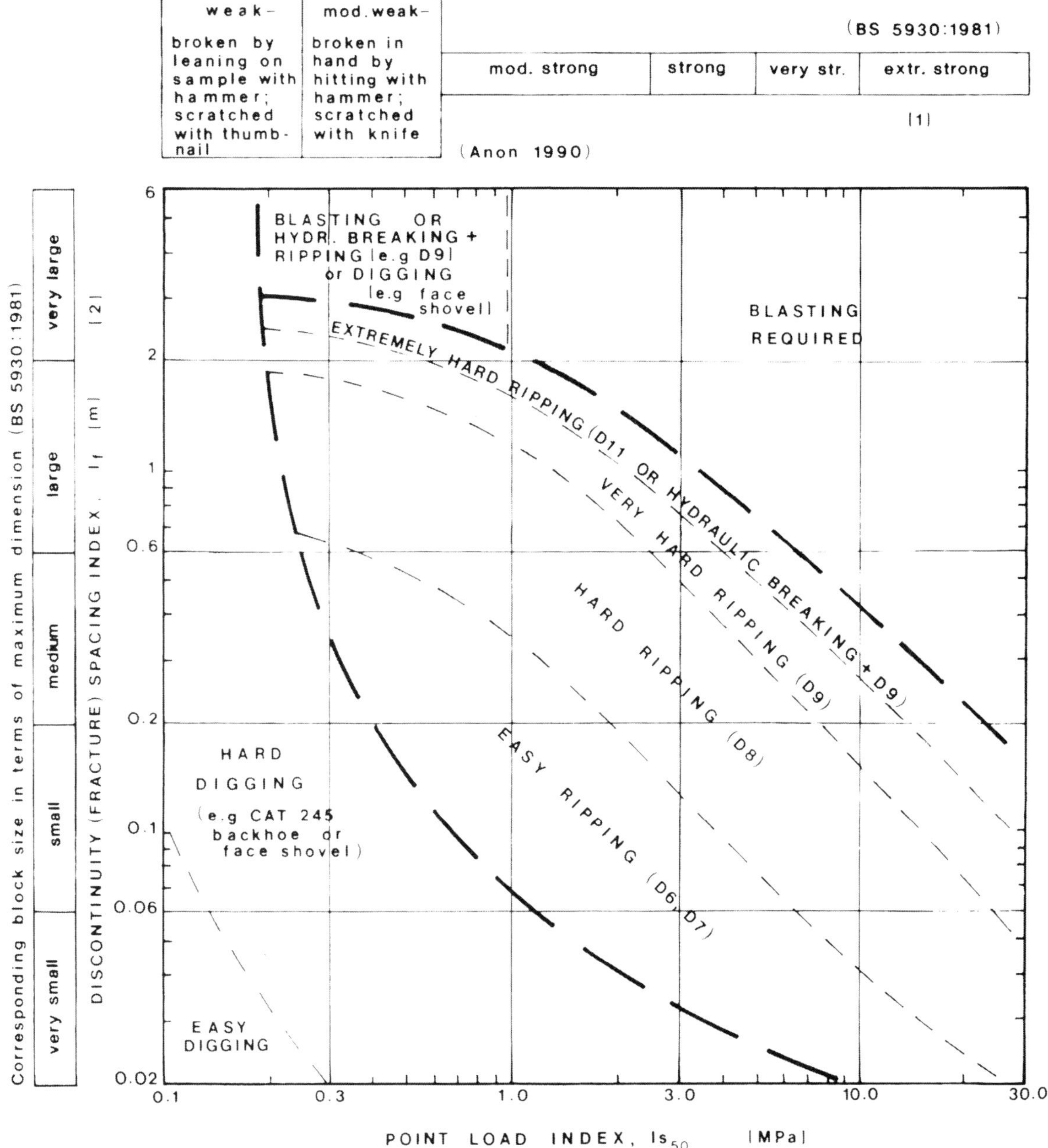

Fig. 5.21. Rippability of rock as a function of mean spacing of discontinuities and compressive strength (after Pettifer & Fookes 1994).

limit can be increased to 3000 m/s by using more powerful tractors (575 kW) or impact rippers. However, the use of this single parameter has not been found to be a reliable means of predicting rippability in every case.

A simple field approach considers both the spacing of discontinuities and intact rock strength (Franklin *et al.* 1971; Fookes *et al.* 1971) which are plotted on a graph as the y and x coordinates respectively. Spacing, I_f, is defined as the mean of the spacings of discontinuities in three orthogonal directions and the strength of the rock is measured in the field by the point load test. From practical experience, it is then possible to describe areas of the graph according to the ease of ripping or the necessity for blasting. This system has been recently up-dated and revised (Pettifer & Fookes 1994) see Fig. 5.21. The difficulty concerns the measurement of the parameter I_f for which relevant and convenient exposures may not be available. In practice, it may also be necessary to increase I_f by as much as 50% to take account of rock structure. For example, a horizontally bedded, flaggy sandstone might yield a low value of mean spacing but prove very difficult to rip since the tine cannot easily penetrate the rock.

A large data base containing 527 observations of ripper performance was gathered in New South Wales, Australia and subjected to regression analysis in an attempt to relate productivity to descriptions of the rock mass (MacGregor *et al.* 1994). The previous systems of rating rippability were also reviewed and evaluated against observations and found to be inadequate or unreliable. The various rock types were not equally represented, however, and separate equations were proposed for igneous and sedimentary rocks. Caveats were also expressed concerning the rippability of weathered igneous rocks, which can contain isolated remnant boulders which reduce productivity or which give deceptively low values of seismic velocity if they contain deeply weathered joints. The dependent variable was determined to be the square root of productivity (m^3/h) divided by the mass of the tractor (tonnes). (The mass of the tractor correlates strongly with power.) The significant parameters of the linear regression equations were found to be; unconfined compressive strength, weathering grade, seismic velocity, mean spacing of the dominant discontinuity set and joint roughness. Productivity could not be related to a single parameter. It was recommended that an initial evaluation should be made to determine productivity using the regression equations. If the values indicated low ($<750\,m^3/h$) or marginal rippability ($<250\,m^3/h$) then further investigation was necessary.

Overall, it could be concluded that the time and cost expended to survey a site for geotechnical parameters and measure seismic velocity might be more effectively expended upon trials in situations where hire plant is readily available. Trials will provide direct evidence of rippability and permit measurement of productivity.

5.3.3. Blasting and explosives

5.3.3.1. Introduction

The breakage of rock using explosives, called blasting, is generally a low cost method widely employed in the production of aggregates and mineral ores and in excavation of rock for civil engineering purposes. However, it should be noted that, with a few exceptions, explosives are not favoured for the production of dimension stone owing to the risk of introducing new fractures into otherwise competent blocks defined by natural discontinuities.

Blasting comprises the stages of drilling blastholes, charging explosives and detonation or firing of explosives. A diagram of a section through a typical blasthole is shown in Fig. 5.22 to explain the terms used. The hole may be drilled in any direction or orientation, notably inclined slightly to the vertical and horizontal. The hole is filled with a column charge of explosives above a primer charge into which are inserted the detonators. The hole is then plugged or stemmed to contain the expanding gases generated by the explosion. Sometimes, an additional, stronger base charge is loaded near the base of the hole to ensure fragmentation of the rock in front of the hole and a level quarry floor.

Loose explosives, such as ammonium nitrate-fuel oil mixtures (ANFO), are loaded by gravity or pneumatically. Cartridge type explosives are charged by gravity or tamping rod into the blastholes drilled by one of the techniques described below in §5.3.4. In the usual practice the column of explosive such as ANFO is loaded above the primer charge, into which have been inserted the detonators, placed at the base of the hole.

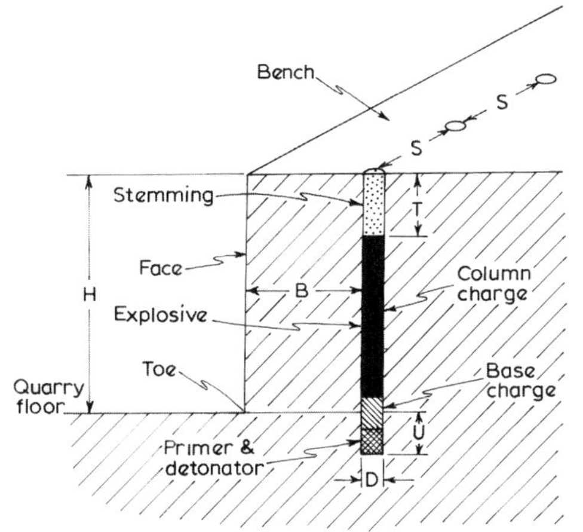

Fig. 5.22. Diagram of a blasthole.

The distance between holes is called the 'spacing' and the distance from the free face the 'burden'. The 'stemming' comprises chippings, clay or other material. This prevents wasteful and environmentally unacceptable release of pressurized gases, see §5.2.3.4. The successful use of explosives for excavation or extraction requires an understanding of the nature of explosives and the behaviour of rock masses (Hemphill 1981) as discussed below.

5.3.3.2. Explosives. Explosive materials used in quarrying are divided into two main groups: high explosives and blasting agents (Atlas 1987; Berta 1990). Use of the most appropriate explosive will depend upon the objectives of the blast and costs. High explosives include the gelatines and dynamites and are used in a wide range of civil engineering, mining and military applications. Being both extremely powerful and water resistant, they can be used in wet blast holes for demolition. They are, however, expensive when used exclusively in quarries. In addition, gelignites and other gelatine type explosives can be sensitive to accidental detonation, for example, by static electricity or even impact, and require the most rigorous safety precautions. Blasting agents, which include ANFO, are generally less powerful than high explosives but less expensive. In addition, because they contain raw materials which are not themselves explosives, they can be transported safely and they can be manufactured or mixed on site. (It should be noted, however, that in the UK and most other countries a licence is required for the handling, storage and preparation of explosive materials). They are also less sensitive to accidental detonation. Owing to these advantages ANFO or its derivatives are the most commonly used explosives employed in quarries. They do, however, require a high explosive primer to ensure reliable initiation and complete detonation. A distinct disadvantage of ANFO is that it cannot be used in wet blastholes. In such adverse conditions ANFO has to be pre-packaged or employed in a water resistant slurry or emulsion forms (ICI Explosives).

Black powder, 'blasting gun powder', is a low power explosive which can be initiated with a burning safety fuse or detonator. The free flowing granulated powder is formulated to release energy relatively slowly by deflagration rather than detonation. The use of this explosive minimizes fragmentation and damage to the surfaces of blocks but the pressure generated by rapidly expanding gases can be usefully employed. It is not water resistant either and will be fired promptly after charging.

5.3.3.3. Detonators

Most explosives, including ANFO, are initiated by a detonator with, in the case of ANFO, an additional primer charge of about 0.5 kg of high explosive. A detonator is essentially a small quantity of a sensitive explosive compound that can be relatively easily and reliably initiated (fired) by heat or shock thereby initiating the detonation of a larger mass of less sensitive explosive. The most common form of detonator contains a platinum fuse wire and is fired by an electrical current but other types are initiated by shock.

Detonators and the associated firing devices called 'exploders' can be constructed to incorporate time delays, usually measured in intervals of 25 to 30 milliseconds. Delay detonators and sequences of initiation are extremely useful, if not essential, for the achievement of good fragmentation, if this is desired, without unacceptable environmental impacts of blasting, see §5.2.3.4. The detonation of explosive within a single blasthole can also be sequenced if the column is divided vertically by packs of stemming, a procedure called 'decking'. For reasons of safety, it is advisable to include two detonators for each explosive charge in order to minimize misfires.

5.3.3.4. Blasting

Following the initial explosion, the rock may be pulverized to dust in the immediate vicinity of the blasthole. A shock wave set up by the explosion then travels at a velocity equivalent to the velocity of sound in the rock. As joints, bedding planes or the free surface of the quarry face are encountered, the compression wave will be reflected in part or transmitted depending upon the

Explosives

Explosives are chemical compounds or mixtures of reagents comprising oxidising agents, usually nitrates, and fuels. When initiated or fired the fuel is oxidised very rapidly or explosively. If the velocity of the reaction as it proceeds through the mass of explosive from the point of initiation exceeds the velocity of sound through the material the explosive is said to detonate.

Detonating velocity. The velocity of detonation, VOD, is a measure of the shattering effect of the explosive. This leads to the term 'high explosive' for those explosives having a very high VOD that are particularly suitable for demolition and destruction. Typical values are given below.

Strength. The strength of an explosive can be measured either directly in terms of energy released, for example, approximately 4500 J/g for dynamite, or relatively by comparison to TNT or ANFO. Some values are given below.

Nitroglycerine. NG is a highly explosive oily liquid which has to be handled with great care.

Dynamite. Dynamites, widely introduced by Nobel, were first manufactured by absorbing NG into kieselguhr or diatomaceous earth to produce a solid explosive much safer to handle. Modern dynamites contain various amounts of ammonium nitrate and carbonaceous fuels in addition to NG, nitroglycol and the inert substrate. This explosive is water resistant.

Blasting gelatines. A powerful gel explosive e.g. gelignite, can be prepared by mixing NG with nitrocellulose or nitrocotton (gun-cotton). The gel has excellent water resistance.

PETN. Pentaerythritoltetranitrate is a solid high explosive compound often used in primer charges and detonators. A 50/50 mix with TNT is called Pentolite.

TNT. Trinitrotoluene is a typical military explosive in that it is very difficult to initiate. It has little industrial use but other explosives may be compared to it in terms of power.

Pentolite. Pentolite is an explosive used in primers, see PETN.

Detonating cord. Detonating cord comprises a linear charge of between 4 and 12 g/m of PETN encased in a textile wrapping. It can be used as a connector between other explosive charges and to initiate ANFO.

ANFO. Prills, small spherical pellets, of ammonium nitrate when mixed with 5.5% to 6% by weight fuel oil form an explosive or blasting agent called ANFO. The ingredients are intrinsically safe but the blasting agent requires a high explosive primer charge to achieve detonation. Detonating velocity depends upon the diameter of the charge and degree of confinement. ANFO has no resistance to water since the salt is soluble.

Slurries. A water resistant form of explosive derived from ANFO in which solid carbonaceous fuels (not necessarily fuel oil) and finely divided aluminium are suspended in a solution of ammonium and other nitrate oxidizers. The gel is stabilised with thickening and cross linking compounds.

Emulsions. Water resistant forms of ANFO can be prepared by emulsifying a solution of ammonium nitrate in the fuel oil together with stabilisers and other fuels e.g. finely divided aluminium and waxes.

Black powder. Black powder, named after the inventor Bernhold Schwartz (circa 1250), is an intimate mixture of Chile saltpetre (sodium nitrate), carbon and sulphur. It deflagrates or burns very rapidly rather than detonates. It is not water resistant.

Safety fuse. A cable or string containing black powder will burn at a steady, controlled rate of about 0.6 m per minute. It can be used to initiate other explosives with a time delay determined by the length of fuse.

Explosive	VOD m/s	Strength rel. TNT	Strength rel. ANFO
PETN	8300	1.66	–
NG	–	–	1.5
TNT	6900	1	–
Detonating cord	6500	–	–
Dynamites	3–6000	0.7–0.9	150–200
Ammonium dynamites	–	0.4–0.5	–
ANFO	2–4500	–	100
Emulsions	3–6000	–	110–130
Black powder	2–400	0.5	–

acoustic impedances of the materials either side of the boundary. Reflected energy takes the form of a tensile or shear wave. When the tensile strength of the rock is exceeded new fractures develop, shattering the rock. New fractures form new reflective surfaces for the oncoming compression waves which are in turn reflected.

At this stage, the expanding gases produced from the explosion create pressure upon the fractured rock, pushing the material in the direction of least resistance and separating fragments along fracture lines.

Thus, breakage of the rock mass is determined by a combination of two factors: (i) explosive energy creating new fracture surfaces (fragmentation) and (ii) cleaving of the rock mass along pre-existing planes of weakness, such as joints, fissures, bedding planes etc.. Therefore, depending upon the objective of the blast namely either (a) fragmentation to produce aggregates and rock-fill or (b) disaggregation of blocks to produce armour and dimension stone, more or less explosive of greater or lesser power will be used. In this respect, the production of aggregates and rockfill is significantly different from the production of armour and dimension stone (Hemphill 1981; Langefors & Kilhstrom 1978; Persson *et al.* 1994).

5.3.3.5. Fragmentation blasting

With particular reference to the fragmentation of rock to produce rock fill and to excavate rock, it has been shown above that each blast requires the determination of a number of factors: (i) hole diameter; (ii) bench height and depth of hole; (iii) burden of holes; (iv) spacing of holes; (v) inclination and alignment; (vi) depth of subgrade drilling; (vii) length of stemming; (viii) charge weight and (ix) type of explosive and method of initiation. The complete description of the design of the blast is known as the 'blast specification'. The selection of hole diameter is discussed below, see §5.3.4.2. Modern blasting practice tends to favour blast holes inclined to the vertical at angles between 5° and 10° (Pass 1970). The depth of the hole is unlikely to exceed 20 metres, see §5.3.3.8. Obviously, the bench height may also be limited by geological factors such as stratum thickness, intrusions, interbedding and faulting.

With respect to Fig. 5.22, the burden, B is generally considered to be proportional to the hole diameter, D where $B = nD$. In strong rock formations n will be 30 and in weaker formations n equals 40 (Ball 1988). Ideally, the burden should equal the spacing distance, S but in good blasting conditions a $B:S$ ratio of 1:1.25 can often be used thus reducing the amount of drilling necessary to achieve the desired blast. Common burden/spacing patterns in UK quarries producing aggegates by fragmentation of rock are 3 metres by 3.75 metres or 4 metres by 4 metres and, occasionally, 4 metres by 5 metres depending upon the blasthole diameter and maximum permissible instantaneous charge weight.

Sub-grade drilling is often necessary to ensure that the rock face is blasted cleanly away from the quarry floor and to ensure that 'toes' are not left which would hamper digging and lead to uneven floors. Depending upon the rock formation, the depth of sub-grade is usually 0.3 times the burden distance up to a maximum of 1 metre. The length of stemming will usually equal that of the burden.

5.3.3.6. Block production

Blasting to produce blocks will generally have the objective of minimising fragmentation through the exploitation of existing discontinuities within the rock mass. An explosive of low power, generating a large volume of expanding gases, such as black powder, see §5.3.3.2., is most appropriate.

The blastholes will have been drilled so as to avoid the intersection of competent blocks thereby minimising the generation of new fractures. Indeed, the holes may actually be drilled along the line of joints or bedding

Fragmentation and disaggregation

The effects produced by the detonation of explosives within a blasthole have been described in §5.3.3.4. These can be illustrated by reference to Fig. 5.23.

Fig. 5.23a shows the rock pile produced by blasting limestone having a large number of very closely spaced discontinuities, namely joints and bedding planes. Despite the lower than normal explosive use the high degree of fragmentation/disaggregation is obvious which is advantageous to producers of aggregates but denies the opportunity to produce blocks.

Figure 5.23b shows the rock pile produced by blasting of limestone containing moderately spaced, well defined orthogonal joints. There is virtually no fragmentation evident and the rock pile comprises almost entirely disaggregated blocks.

Figure 5.23c shows the few, regularly and widely spaced joints in a mass of granite which is being exploited to produce blocks. In fact, flame jet cutting is employed in this case.

Figure 5.23d shows the fragmentation of granite achieved by blasting in the absence of closely spaced joints.

(a)

(b)

Fig. 5.23. Examples of discontinuities (a) limestone with closely spaced joints and bedding planes (b) limestone with regular, orthogonal and widely spaced joints (c) granite with few very widely spaced joints (d) blasted rock pile produced from rock with few joints.

planes, see Fig. 5.24. The black powder is often contained in simple paper wrappings or cardboard tubes and the holes stemmed with any conveniently available dilatant material such as clay, soil/sand mixes or drill cuttings. The specific charge is typically very low, see §5.3.9.11.

5.3.3.7. Blasting of overburden

Overburden may be fragmented by blasting, as described in §5.3.3.5 above, in order to facilitate excavation and removal. However, as the blasting approaches the horizon of a rock intended for extraction as dimension stone or armourstone, care must be exercized so as not to introduce additional fractures into this rock. It may be advisable to reduce or obviate sub-grade drilling and, indeed, blastholes may terminate above the base of the overburden. It may also be necessary to reduce the explosive charge weight to prevent damage to the underlying stone. Blastholes may be drilled on a regular grid rather than along a single line as in bench blasting and the blastholes may be loaded with small explosive charges designed to loosen rather than fragment the rock. This is called 'pattern blasting' and is commonly applied in open-cast coal mines to loosen overburden without disturbing the underlying seam of coal. A powerful hydraulic excavator is then used to dig the loosened overburden and load into dump trucks.

(c)

(d)

Fig. 5.23. *(continued).*

5.3.3.8. Safety and Regulations
In the UK the Quarries (Explosives) Regulations (1988) came into force in 1990 to ensure the safe and efficient use of explosives in quarries. In particular, the Regulations address the matters of safe handling and storage of explosives and safe use with particular emphasis upon minimizing the undesirable environmental impacts of their use, see §5.2.3.4. including the hazard of 'fly rock'. There are three principal requirements:

(a) all managers and shot-firers are required to have adequate practical experience and training including successful completion of an accredited course;

Prediction of fragmentation

A fundamental model of fragmentation has been proposed based upon the equation which was developed by Bond (Bond 1961) to relate energy consumption to the comminution of rocks and ores in crushers and grinding mills. In the case of fragmentation, of course, the energy is generated by explosives not electric motors. The equation employs a characteristic size to describe both the initial rock mass and the fragmented rock. This size is equal to the square aperture which would pass 80% by weight of the material. The equation is:

$$\text{Energy input} = 10W_i(1\sqrt{}P_{80} - 1\sqrt{}F_{80})\,\text{kWh/tonne}$$

where F_{80} and P_{80} characterize the natural block size distribution, see §5.3.2.3, and the fragmented rock respectively. The energy input can be estimated from the weight and type of explosive used and the 'work index', W_i, of the rock can be obtained from tables or determined by laboratory testwork. Having calculated the value of P_{80} the entire size distribution can be estimated by assuming that the particle size distribution conforms to, say, the Rosin Rammler or Gates–Gaudin-Schumann models.

Other models predicting the fragmentation produced by blasting have generally attempted to relate empirically the parameters of the blast design (the 'blast specification) to a characteristic size of fragment produced. Assumptions are then made concerning the size distribution of fragments in the blasted rock pile, such as it fitting the Rosin Rammler or Weibull distribution (Langerfors & Kihlstrom 1978; Persson *et al.* 1994). As an example, the model equations of 'Kuzram', named after Kuznetzov–Rosin Rammler, are as follows:

The mean particle size of the fragments, x_{50}, is given by:

$$x_{50} = A(K)^{-0.8}Q^{1/6}(115/E)^{19/30}\ \text{centimetres}$$

and the index of uniformity, n which is the gradient of the Rosin–Rammler plot of the particle size distribution is given by:

$$n = (2.2 - 14B/d)(1 + a)/2)^{0.5}(1 - W/B)L/H$$

where:

A is a factor describing the rock including discontinuities and usually varies between 8 and 11
K is the powder factor, kilograms of explosive per m^3 of rock
Q is the explosive charge per hole (kg),
E is the relative power of the explosive; ANFO = 100
B is burden in metres
H is bench height in metres
d is blasthole diameter (mm)
a is spacing/burden
L is the length of charge above grade
W is a measure of drilling accuracy

n may be expected to assume values between 0.75 and 2.0. The complete fragment size distribution can then be determined by graphical methods. Rosin–Rammler graph paper, having axes of log–log (reciprocal % weight passing a given size) and log(particle size), should be used since the 50% passing size, x_{50}, has been estimated above and the gradient of the plot is n (Wang *et al.* 1992).

$$\text{Cumulative \% wt passing size } x = 1 - \exp(x/k)^n$$

where k is a constant equal to the size passing 63.2% weight.

However, the calibration and testing of these models is not easy since it requires the determination of the size distributions of piles of blasted rock. In many cases photographic methods have been employed for this purpose. Recently more sophisticated software programs e.g. SABREX (ICI Explosives), have been written to predict fragmentation, rock pile shape and throw of material away from the face.

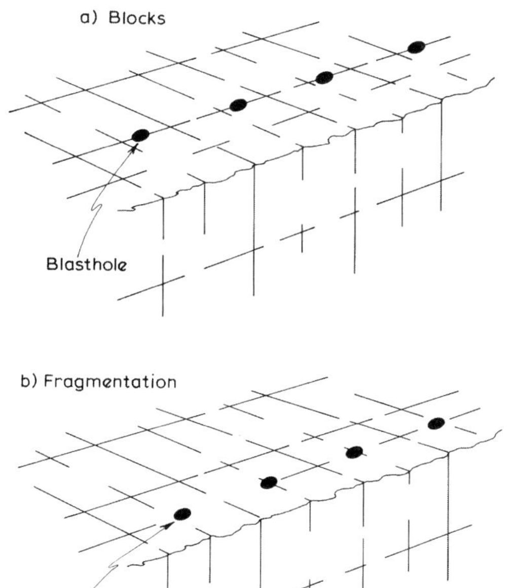

Fig. 5.24. Diagram showing the spacing and positioning of blast holes for (a) for block production and (b) for fragmentation.

(b) the manager must prepare or approve and record a specification for each blast to indicate a profile of the face in front of each blast hole, the angle, spacing and burden of each blast hole and the type and position of explosives, stemming and system of initiation.

(c) the manager is also required to formulate and publish rules concerning shot-firing procedures (Butler *et al.* 1988; Saunders 1987; HSC 1989).

A particularly important requirement is the estimation of the minimum burden in front of each blasthole to ensure that sufficient burden exists to prevent explosive release of gases, which gives rise to air blast, or the generation of 'fly rock'. Where undetected deviations in the direction or angle of deep blastholes occur overcharging or undercharging of the blast can result and the burden can be significantly reduced. A number of highly accurate and computerised in-borehole and quarry face profile survey techniques are now available. These face profiling techniques are laser-based survey systems which rapidly collect basic data. The data are then downloaded to desktop computers for analysis (Anon 1988). The designed burdens, spacings and alignment can be checked against the actual measured values and blasthole charges adjusted accordingly. The maintenance of records, together with monitoring of the effects of the blast, should lead to improvements in efficiency, safety and environmental performance (White 1989).

Reasonable surface plans of the drilling pattern can be produced by simple, traditional survey techniques used carefully by the quarry manager and driller. In the case of many dimension stone quarries the blast holes are relatively shallow giving little opportunity for deviation and the faces are low, permitting direct measurement by tape. Blast-hole alignment can be checked easily, for example, by visual inspection using torches. Adequate plans and the estimates of burden can then be made simply. Alternatively, a survey of the profile of the face(s) can be conducted in advance of, say, several months of production since output is typically low. It should be noted that no profile is required when the blastholes are horizontal as is often the case in dimension stone quarries.

In the UK, apart from the general requirement of the Health and Safety at Work Act (King 1991) to provide a safe system of work, there is no regulation that specifies a maximum bench height. However, for quarries it is generally agreed that 15 m provides a reasonable compromise between safety and productivity.

5.3.4. Drilling

5.3.4.1. Introduction

Holes may be required for use as blastholes, to permit introduction of wire saws and wedges and even to cut and define blocks. Several types of drill rig are available capable of drilling holes from 50 to 230 mm diameter. The smaller diameter holes, less than 100 mm, are usually associated with wire saws and wedges while the larger diameters are blastholes. An exception is the practice of presplitting, see §5.3.2.7.

5.3.4.2. Blastholes

In fragmentation blasting, the volume of a blasthole is determined by the blast ratio (also known as the powder factor in mining), the weight of explosive required to break one tonne or one cubic metre of rock, which usually ranges between 80 and 250 g/t. In principle the cost of drilling and blasting is minimized by the drilling of as few holes of as large diameter as possible. This practice also favours a greater production rate. However, in practice, the blast design is constrained by two conflicting considerations: (i) limitation of the instantaneous charge weight owing to environmental considerations, see §5.2.3.4., which reduces the hole diameter and increases the number of holes and (ii) the discontinuities within the rock mass. The discontinuities can determine the spacing and precise location of blastholes. With reference to the discussion in §5.3.3.4 and Fig. 5.24 it can be seen that should the spacing between blastholes be greater than that between discontinuities there is the potential to generate large blocks defined only by the discontinuities themselves. This may be highly desirable for the production of armourstone but a serious problem in the production of rock-fill and aggregates.

The corollary is that good fragmentation demands that the spacing of blastholes should be less than that of the discontinuities and that each large block should be intersected by at least one blasthole.

5.3.4.3. Drills

Essentially three drilling methods are common in quarries and mines:

(i) rotary drills for producing large-diameter holes in weak, non abrasive rocks or very deep holes such as oil wells and water wells. These would not normally have any application in the production of stone. Of course, there are also rotary core drills used extensively in exploration, see Chapter 3.

(ii) down-the-hole, pneumatic drive, rotary percussive drills for intermediate diameter holes, usually blast holes, in medium to strong rocks, see Fig. 5.25.

(iii) pneumatic, top-hammer, rotary percussive drills for small diameter holes in any rock type, see Fig. 5.26.

More recently, hydraulic drive, top-hammer, rotary percussive drills have been introduced (Tapaninaho 1987) with claimed advantages of increased fuel efficiency and penetration rates under suitable conditions, see Fig. 5.27.

Rotary percussive drills operate on the principle of delivering rapid blows to the rock through bits shaped as chisels or of circular section studded with buttons which are attached to a drill rod. Figure 5.28 shows several types of bit from the most simple drill steel that terminates in a chisel, a type usually employed with small hand-held drills, to the button bits used to drill holes of larger diameter. The diagrams show modern bits having silicon carbide inserts which can be re-sharpened by grinding. Historically, the drill steel itself was tempered and sharpened by grinding. The bit partially rotates between each blow and the chippings of spalled rock are removed or flushed from the hole by air. In most cases the hammer is pneumatic (driven by compressed air) and the exhaust air is conducted through the hollow drill rod to the bit. The names of different types relate to the means of imparting impact to the bit.

Top-hammers deliver the impact to the top (surface) end of the drill rod and are sometimes known as drifter drills. The hammer may be hydraulically or pneumatically driven and the system is suitable for any hole diameter although there is a greater tendency for a deep hole to deviate. It is the only practical system for drilling holes of small diameter i.e. less than 75mm and hand-held versions are commonly used to drill holes for wedges, see Fig. 5.26.

A down-the-hole drill comprises a pneumatically operated hammer located directly behind the drill bit and attached to the drill rod which also acts as the conduit for compressed air. The necessity for the hole to accommodate the hammer restricts this system to the drilling of larger diameters but it is claimed that better directional control can be obtained, i.e. less hole deviation.

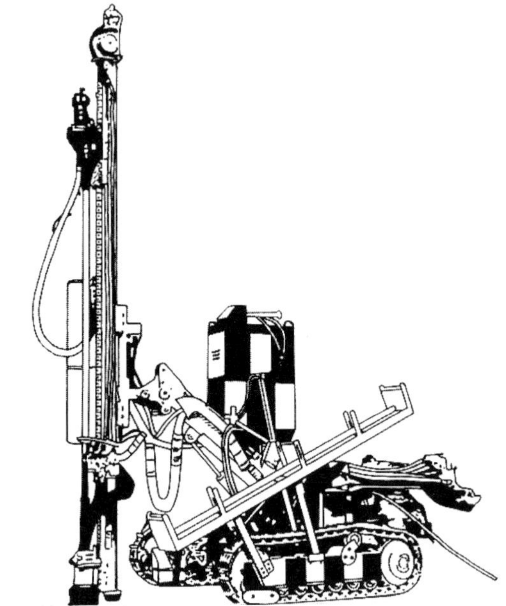

Fig. 5.25. Crawler mounted, pneumatic, DTH drill rig (Courtesy of Atlas Copco).

The drill can be mounted upon a vehicle or a self-propelled chassis which may also support an integral compressor and operator's cabin. Commonly, the drill is mounted on crawler tracks and tows a separate air compressor.

5.3.5. Overburden removal

Before the decision to extract stone by quarrying is taken consideration will have to be given to the overburden in terms of thickness, extent and properties. The thickness of the overburden material can vary from nil to tens of metres but it must be removed or stripped before extraction can commence.

The exploration and evaluation studies described in Chapters 3 and 4 will have determined the thickness and profile of overburden and weathered rock which can be either a simple constant thickness or highly variable and complex (Anon 1977). The overburden may comprise other indurated rocks or weaker, generally unconsolidated younger formations, for example, sands, gravels, marls or other superficial materials such as glacial till or weathered rock.

Fig. 5.26. Pneumatic top hammer drill being used to drill a hole for plug and feathers (Courtesy of Ffestiniog Slate Quarry Co. Ltd).

The physical nature, condition and volume of overburden will have a considerable influence on the method and type of equipment employed. In some cases, assuming that the conditions imposed for restoration of the site allow, the overburden will be wholly or partly saleable as a by-product, see Chapter 4. Figure 5.29 shows some examples of overburden cover.

For purposes of discussion, overburden will be taken to include soils and sub-soils. In cases where there is a requirement to restore the site after excavation by the use of the soils, it is often necessary to conduct a separate specialized survey to identify soil profiles and depths, soil types and volumes. The necessity to separately remove and store soils has a significant effect upon quarry planning (Corker 1987; Samuel 1990) more especially since soil movements may be restricted to the dry season of the year e.g. May to September in the UK.

In Europe and other temperate zones the depth of the weathered layer is generally not a severe problem although weathering of some slates in north Wales has extended to depths of between 30 and 50 metres below the outcrop. In tropical and subtropical climates it is frequently of considerable thickness and it is often necessary to remove large quantities before unaltered rock is uncovered. For example, quarries operating in the granites of West Africa will almost inevitably encounter weathered zones of depth between 15 and 25 metres. The proportion of weathered rock to payrock can be very high. In the granites of Hong Kong the ratio is frequently 1:1 so that as much attention needs to be given to the excavation of overburden as to the excavation of stone itself (Earle 1991). An added difficulty is that the weathered profiles are not always a simple function of the depth below surface but can be highly variable and influenced by such factors as joint frequency and persistence. Classification of the weathering grade of overburden cover can be of considerable assistance in assessing the most suitable method of excavation, see §2.4, Fig. 2.14, Table 2.4 and Table 5.2.

Assessing the ratio of the volume of overburden to be removed per unit volume of payrock extracted is a very important factor in the economic evaluation of the deposit, see Chapter 4. In the majority of quarries overburden removal is not a continuous exercise but is carried out occasionally so as to expose reserves of rock sufficient for one or more years of production. Furthermore, the removal will usually be undertaken by contractors.

Fig. 5.27. Hydraulic, top hammer drill rig (Courtesy of ARC Ltd).

Unconsolidated or weakly indurated overburden can be removed with a variety of excavators similar or even identical to those used for loading blasted, fragmented rock. Rope-operated face shovels or hydraulically operated shovels and backhoes are the most common digging and loading machines, see §§A5.1.2, A5.1.3 and A5.1.4. In suitable conditions the high break-out force of these types of excavator obviates the need for any preliminary loosening of the overburden and they can dig directly into the overburden face.

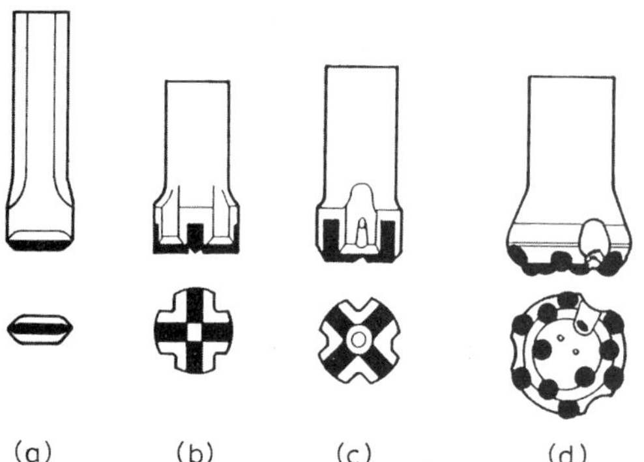

Fig. 5.28. Drill bits (a) simple chisel bit (b) and (c) cross point bits (d) button bit. Dark shading indicates silicon carbide inserts.

For stripping large volumes of weak, unconsolidated materials of considerable thickness, motorised scrapers, see §A5.1.8, assisted by crawler tractors (bulldozers), see §A5.1.7, are commonly employed, see Fig. 5.30. This method has the distinct advantage that the overburden is removed and transported to the dumping area in one operation and by one machine (Brewster 1987). It is thus rapid and of low cost.

In those overburden formations which are weakly cemented, thinly bedded or highly jointed, crawler tractors fitted with a rear-mounted tooth or tine are used to rip and loosen the rock, see Fig. 5.31. The overburden materials are pushed by the dozer into piles which can then be loaded by an excavator usually of the wheeled type. The conditions under which ripping might be considered are further discussed in §5.3.2.9.

Highly indurated overburden may require drilling and blasting as described in §5.3.3.5, prior to excavation and loading into dump trucks for transport to waste tips or by-product processing plant. The disposal of waste is considered in §5.3.12.

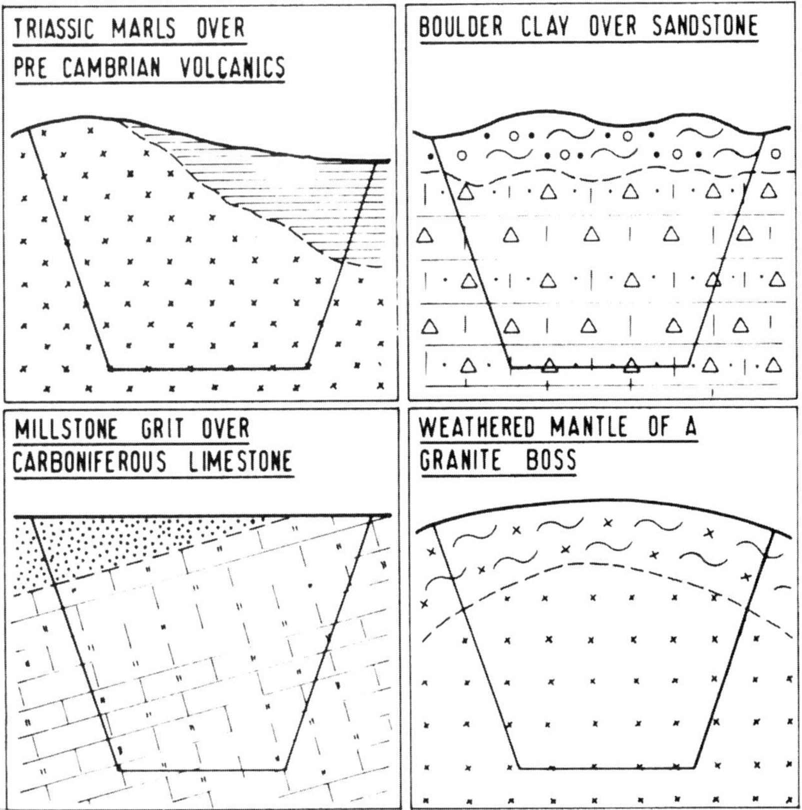

Fig. 5.29. Examples of overburden above stone.

5.3.6. Quarry and mining machinery

5.3.6.1. Equipment application and selection
The operator of a quarry or mine has the choice of a wide variety of mechanised equipment or mobile tools. Some are of very specialised design to accomplish a particular task with greatest efficiency. However, the operator of a small quarry in particular, with limited capital available for investment, must consider that each piece of equipment must be fully utilised and that some flexibilty of use may be necessary. In addition, used, refurbished or redundant equipment may be available at low cost from other operations. Therefore, equipment selection is based partly upon consideration of technical efficiency but ultimately upon cost efficiency. The descriptions of individual items of equipment given in Appendix 5.1 indicate their principal tasks but they may be observed operating in other roles. Finally, machines of short term utility, such as excavators and trucks to remove overburden, can be economically hired so that the purchase of a complete range of equipment is not necessary.

The machines most suitable for removing soils and unconsolidated overburden are the scraper and hydraulic backhoe. The rope excavator, see §A5.1.2, is almost obsolete in British quarries although popular in very large open pit mines elsewhere in the world. The dragline excavator is most unlikey to be observed in stone quarries and then only handling overburden. The application of machines is further discussed under the relevant sections describing production of rockfill, armourstone and dimension stone, see §§5.3.7, 5.3.8 and 5.3.9, and the removal of overburden, §5.3.5.

5.3.7. Production of rock fill

5.3.7.1. General. The specification and use of rock fill is thoroughly discussed in Chapter 7 and this section is concerned only with production aspects. Highway construction involves both the excavation of cuttings through rock and the filling of voids to create elevated sections of road. Obviously it is generally desirable that the rock produced from the excavated section should be

Table 5.2. *Weathering and alteration grades*

Term	*Grade**	*Description*	*Materials characteristics†*
Fresh	IA	No visible sign of rock weathering.	Aggregate properties not influenced by weathering. Mineral constituents of rock are fresh and sound.
Faintly weathered	IB	Discoloration on major discontinuity (e.g. joint) surfaces.	Aggregate properties not significantly influenced by weathering. Mineral constituents sound.
Slightly weathered (this grade is capable of further subdivision)	II	Discoloration indicates weathering of rock material and discontinuity surfaces. All the rock material may be discoloured by weathering and may be somewhat weaker than in its fresh condition.	Aggregate properties may be significantly influenced by weathering. Strength and abrasion characteristics show some weakening. Some alteration of mineral constituents with micro-cracking.
Moderately weathered	III	Less than half of the rock material is decomposed and/or disintegrated to a soil. Fresh or discoloured rock is present either as a continuous framework or as corestones.	Aggregate properties will be significantly influenced by weathering. Soundness characteristics markedly affected. Alternation of mineral constituents common and much micro-cracking.
Highly weathered	IV	More than half of the rock material is decomposed and/or disintegrated to a soil. Fresh or discoloured rock is present either as a discontinuous framework or as corestones.	Not generally suitable for aggregate but may be suitable for lower parts of road pavement and hardcore.
Completely weathered	V	All rock material is decomposed and/or disintegrated to soil. The original mass structure is still largely intact.	Not suitable for aggregate, or pavement but may be suitable for select fill.
Residual soil	VI	All rock material is converted to soil. The mass structure and material fabric are destroyed. There is a large change in volume, but the soil still has not been significantly transported.	May be suitable for random fill.

* After Geological Society (1977).
† After Fookes *et al.* (1971).

used as fill elsewhere on the route. Since the final face of the excavation producing rock fill may also form the sides of a cutting containing the road there is also concern for the stability of the slope, see §5.3.2.5.

Weak rock can be excavated directly by scrapers, hydraulic excavators and ripping, see §§A5.1.3, A5.1.7 and A5.1.8. The rippability of rock is considerd in §5.3.2.9.

However, at present, excavation of strong rocks in highway projects can only be accomplished economically by blasting, see §5.3.3. In this case, the broken rock will most likely be loaded into either rigid body or articulated dump trucks, see §§A5.1.9 and A5.1.10, by hydraulic face shovels, backhoes or large wheeled loaders. The use of explosives to excavate rock and produce rock fill has the disadvantage that the slope may be damaged by blasting and that instability is induced. This matter is discussed in detail in §7.4.2.

5.3.7.2. Fragmentation blasting

Fragmentation blasting is employed to break the blocks of rock naturally present in a rock mass to a size consistent with the intended use. For instance, in highway cuttings the resultant blocks must be of a size that can be readily loaded and transported by mechanical plant and, if required as fill, must be within the grading specified. This use of explosives is in complete contrast to the technique of presplitting, see §5.3.2.7. Discontinuities and the natural block size distribution are discussed in §§5.3.2.2. and 5.3.2.3. The design of blasts to achieve fragmentation is discussed in §5.3.3.5 and the breakage of any remaining oversize blocks in §5.4.2.2. Descriptions of the production of rock fill for specific projects will be found in Chapter 7.

5.3.8. Production of armourstone

5.3.8.1. Introduction

Armourstone is produced by several methods:

(i) Specialized blasting practice within rock masses of a suitable rock type containing a distribution of discontinuities so as to create a favourable natural block size distribution. In such rock masses a quarry may be developed primarily to produce armourstone with crushed rock aggregates or other by-products as a means to dispose of waste.

Fig. 5.30. Scraper assisted by tractor bulldozer removing soil (Courtesy of Caterpillar).

(ii) Selection of oversize blocks produced as a by-product of blasting a rock mass primarily with the objective of achieving fragmentation.
(iii) Utilization of superficial deposits of blocks may be possible, but the blocks are often too rounded.

5.3.8.2. Blasting to produce armourstone

It is most important to study the *in situ* block size distribution if the production of armourstone is being considered. Not only will the discontinuities determine the maximum yield of blocks of all sizes, especially the maximum block size, but the orientation of the discontinuities will determine block shape. In general, regular cubical blocks are most desirable, see Chapter 8. Within the constraints imposed by the in-situ block size distribution (see §5.3.2.3) the following design parameters of the blast specification can be controlled to increase production of large blocks (Wang *et al.* 1991). A low specific charge weight, say, less than 100 g/tonne, of an explosive having a relatively low velocity of detonation and producing a large volume of gas, e.g. ANFO, should be used. This will minimize fragmentation of the intact rock. The explosive charges may be decoupled to reduce pulverisation of the rock and separated vertically in the blast hole, that is decked. The decking can be achieved by introducing intervening columns of stemming material but an air space or void between charges can be more effective. Self-inflating gas bags can be inserted into the blasthole to produce platforms or decks for the individual small charges, see §5.3.3. A burden greater than the spacing and long stemming will favour block production. Indeed, in the fragmentation blasting of rock to produce aggregates the necessity for stemming the blasthole can cause problems in that most oversize blocks originate from the top of the face.

Ideally, the charges should detonate simultaneously but this may not be acceptable for environmental reasons, see §5.2.3.4. Therefore, as many charges as

Fig. 5.31. Crawler tractor fitted with ripper (Courtesy of Caterpillar).

possible should detonate on the same delay. The primer charge, comprising high explosive, should be as light as possible commensurate with adequate initiation of the column of explosive and prevention of toes. Single row blasting is preferred to multi-row blasting.

A description of a practice at a Norwegian quarry producing armourstone has been given by Rayson (1993) and a further example can be found in Chapter 8.

5.3.9. Quarrying of dimension stone

5.3.9.1. Introduction

The production of dimension stone usually begins with the extraction of blocks from the quarry face and requires that the block is freed on the basal, rear and two lateral surfaces (see Fig. 5.13) since the upper surface will have been freed by the removal of overburden or overlying beds of stone. In the absence of other constraints the face height can be decided at the convenience of the operator in rock having widely spaced discontinuities such as some marbles and granites.

Otherwise, it will be determined by the vertical spacing between horizontal joints or by the strata or bed thicknesses of sedimentary rocks. In this respect the maximum size or volume of block that can be produced by an individual quarry, as determined by the equipment or structural geology, can be an important piece of information when sourcing dimension stone. For example, the maximum bed thickness of a sedimentary rock will affect the yield and will determine the maximum course height when sawing blocks into slab and ashlar. It is usually quoted in directories of quarries producing blocks.

At this point the reader is referred back to Chapter 4 for discussion of evaluation of deposits and factors other than bedding and jointing that may determine bench heights and dimensions of blocks. In particular these factors include variations in colour and texture of the rock since it is often a requirement to produce large areas of finished dimension stone, say, cladding that is uniform in appearance. Changes of texture can be caused by slight differences in the depositional environment of sedimentary rocks. This is not uncommon in sandstones which may exhibit colour banding or gradations owing to differences in the iron content of the cement. As another example, the stratum of the Portland limestone is divided into three distinct varieties owing to differences of depositional environment and fossil content and is worked on three separate benches for this reason. Veining, colour and crystallinity of marbles will probably vary within a single deposit thus defining discreet benches and working areas to produce stones of particular surface appearance which may be marketed under specific names. Changes of texture and colour may also occur with depth in igneous rocks owing to differences of crystal size. This may necessitate working on several levels to produce stone that matches'. In the case of slate consideration may need to be given to differences of colour, cleavage and presence of flaws such as banding and spots when setting out the benches. An interesting and comprehensive discussion of the effects of structural geology and distribution of imperfections upon the slate quarries of Pennsylvannia was given by Behre (Behre 1933).

In general the objective is to remove as large a block as possible from the face provided that it can be handled. The blocks are subsequently divided again on the floor of the quarry into sizes most useful to the masons and the processing works, usually up to 10 tonnes in weight or 3 to 4 cubic metres in volume.

An exception is slate which is sub-divided along the cleavage plane to generate smaller slabs weighing only a few tonnes. The critical dimension is the thickness, normal to the cleavage, which will usually be less than 1 metre to suit the primary saws. However, it should be noted that large blocks are not produced in every quarry or mine. Where the principal demand is for building blocks or 'bricks', in particular for use in local houses and buildings, and the deposit is massive (without well developed joints) blocks of the desired dimensions may be sawn or split directly from the face. Hand saws can be used in soft, weak rocks such as porous limestones and tufa. Powered saws are employed in some modern marble mines and quarries, where circular diamond saws are used to cut small blocks and slabs directly from the face, see Fig. 5.32.

In the past bedded limestones were worked by wedging and use of crow-bars to lever blocks from mine openings thereby creating 'cave' systems now used to ferment and mature wines and historically as dwellings (Forster & Forster 1996).

5.3.9.2. Superficial deposits

From the study of monuments it is obvious that man has made use of isolated boulders some of which were probably transported over long distances by ice and deposited as the ice melted. A well known example of the use of residual boulders are the sarsen stones of Stonehenge. Large quantities of scree have also been removed from hillside slopes for the construction of field walls and houses including roofing tiles. Many resources were identified and worked at outcrops such as escarpments and sea cliffs, long before planned quarries were developed. The large boulders released by weathering of these outcrops formed convenient sources of building materials. Examples are the sea cliffs of the Isle of Portland and Penmaenmawr in Wales (Bezzant 1980). Later, escarpments above the sea, rivers, canals and railway cuttings e.g Box Hill, near Bath, provided particularly attractive exposures close to means of transport before the advent of the motor vehicle. These factors established the use and popularity of readily accessible rocks such as Portland limestone, Bath and Cotswold Jurassic limestones, Penmaenmawr and Creetown granites, Welsh slate and Carrara marbles. The legacy still enhances the beauty of modern cities. It also, to some extent, determines the continuing demand for production of particular stones through the desire, and often the requirement, to match new buildings to existing structures. Similar superficial deposits may still be exploited in many parts of the World.

Finally, it should be recognized that later civilizations often reworked and re-used the stone contained in buildings constructed by earlier civilizations that were either derelict or considered to be no longer relevant. There is evidence of this even in the fate of some of the Seven Wonders of the World. For example, marble blocks from the tomb of King Mausolus now appear, mixed with other rock types, in the fort of Bodrum, Turkey.

5.3.9.3. Block production

In the most favourable situation in a quarry, the basal surface of a block will be a horizontal bedding plane or joint and the rear surface a persistent discontinuity known as a 'back'. Therefore, the face of the bench will often be orientated parallel to the plane of a set of major, vertical discontinuities, see Fig. 5.13.

In the absence of suitable joints, known as 'cutters' or cleavage, a lateral surface must then be cut to produce the block. The only problem arises during the removal of the first block from a new face when there is no access for a saw to cut the rear face or for a drill to produce a hole for a wire saw. Methods such as channelling, line-drilling or flame jet cutting described below can be used. An alternative, simple expedient is to fragment the first block by drilling and blasting and to accept the loss. The blasted rock can then be processed to aggregate or other by-product or sent to waste. Wire saws are more likely to be used to cut the faces in massive formations, for example, many marble deposits, where suitable discontinuities do not exist. Similarly, mechanical saws may also be employed.

In view of the legal regulations, the necessity to consider aspects of safety and security of storage of explosives and the risk of lower yields, there are considerable incentives to obviate the use of explosives in the relatively small quarries typical of dimension stone production. Therefore, mechanical or non-explosive methods of breakage of considerable antiquity are still common although quarries may have been modernised by the introduction of mechanical equipment to effect

Fig. 5.32. Circular diamond saw mounted upon crawler tracks (Courtesy of Nantlle Slate Co. Ltd).

the tasks traditionally carried out by hand. For example, large wheeled loaders fitted with forks or a single prong are now used to prise blocks out of the face of the quarry by exploiting existing joints and bedding planes, a task previously accomplished with hammer driven wedges. Powerful hydraulic excavators are also used for the same purpose in quarries where natural discontinuities define blocks.

In particular, pneumatic and hydraulically powered drills have replaced hammers and hand drills although the principle of percussive drilling is identical. Despite the high capital cost, the use of powered machines greatly increases the output of the quarry and often the profitability of the operation. Derrick cranes and mobile cranes, see §A5.1.1, which are often the most conspicuous features of dimension stone quarries, can also be used to manoeuvre the block away from the face prior to lifting and transport. For this purpose, a recess, called the 'dog-hole', is cut into a vertical side of the block, see Fig. 5.33 into which is inserted the 'dog' or hook attached to the crane. Blocks may be further divided, commonly with the use of plugs and feathers, whilst resting on the quarry floor.

The following descriptions of methods of cutting and splitting rock almost certainly include methods that are now obsolete in the UK and some methods that have never been employed. Various sources have been consulted for descriptions including the most informative textbook of Greenwell and Elsden (Greenwell & Elsden 1913). Descriptions of the extraction of blocks of limestone, granite and slate in selected examples of British quarries and mines, which illustrate the practical use of techniques discussed below, can be found in §6.6.

5.3.9.4. Wedges

Tapered, broad wedges are driven by hammer into bedding planes or joints to free the block or to manoeuvre the block to assist further handling. Damage to the face of the block may be avoided by driving the wedge between two flat metal plates, 'chips' or scales', that have been inserted into the joint aperture. The action of lifting the block from the bedding plane may also cause a fracture surface to be formed in another plane e.g. creating the rear face of a block, see Fig. 5.34. Hydraulic cylinders are now available to replace wedges when manoeuvring and toppling blocks away from the granite or marble face

Review of the dimension stone industry

Since 1930 there has been a huge increase in the output of dimension stone from an estimated 1.5 million tonnes per annum at that date to 23 million tonnes per annum in the middle of the 1980s. This expansion of output was not shared equally between the calcareous rocks, limestones and marbles, and the siliceous rocks, e.g. granites and slate. In fact, the output of limestones and marbles increased by a multiplier of twelve whereas that of granites increased even more rapidly by a factor of about thirty six. This in part reflects technical developments within the industry beginning with the introduction of wire saws which greatly increased the productivity of marble and limestone quarries at the turn of the century. This was followed by the development of frame saws using steel shot to cut granites during the 1960s and the later introduction, from 1970, of diamond tools which greatly benefitted the producers of siliceous rocks. On the other hand the production of slate, particularly roofing slate, has declined dramatically owing to the use of clay and concrete roofing tiles.

In 1930, production was dominated by only six countries: Italy, which alone accounted for 40% of world production, France, Belgium, USA, Germany and the UK. Sixty years later several new producers have gained significant shares in the world market including Spain, Greece, Japan, Brazil and India. Several of these countries, for example, Brazil, India and emerging producers such as Finland have particularly benefitted from technologies of cutting and processing granites. Spain has emerged as a major supplier of slates and Portugal of marbles. These countries together with Italy, which still accounts for 30% of world production, USA, France and Belgium produce 70% of world output. In the future it is expected that historically important producers such as the UK, Belgium, Germany and Sweden will continue to lose market share owing to exhaustion of reserves and constraints upon development (Anon 1993). Production in Italy, USA, Japan and Canada, where it is already at a high level, is predicted to stagnate whereas expansion is forecast for Spain, India, Brazil, Taiwan, Portugal, Finland and Turkey. Great potential for production also exists in countries of eastern Europe such as Bulgaria, Yugoslavia and the CIS (Commonwealth of Independent States within the former USSR) when economic and political stability have been restored. Finally, of course, there is the huge potential of China to consider. The unique position of Italy, which still dominates the industry, and is threatened only by Spain, deserves comment. It is attributed to two principal factors:

(i) large national reserves of limestones, marbles and granites but more importantly,
(ii) a large domestic market for dimension stone which consumes 20% of world production.

These factors have created a large indigenous industry comprising a huge capital investment in modern, precise and productive machinery, a wealth of experience and skills held by a large labour force and, in addition, an innovative industry designing and manufacturing stone working machinery. Italy now processes 30% of world production including substantial tonnages of blocks that are imported through ports such as Marina di Carrara and then re-exported as finished products. Indeed, the initial successful penetration of a new source of stone into the market may depend upon processing in Italy which has gained a reputation for being able to provide both quantity and quality (Conti 1986).

Today, slate takes only a small share, probably less than 5%, of the market for roofing materials in the United Kingdom. Indeed of this small share only about one quarter is taken by natural slate creating a demand for about 60 000 tonnes per year. It has been estimated that nearly half of this is supplied by imports from France and Spain and, more recently, by new quarries in Newfoundland, Canada.

in a quarry. After the concealed, rear vertical face of the block has been created by presplitting, line drilling or wire saw etc. and the block is free, two or more cylinders containing pistons are lowered into the fissure. Expression of the pistons causes the block to tilt forward away from the face and it is held in this position by props or packing inserted into the fissure, see Fig. 5.35. The pistons are now retracted and the cylinders are lowered to a deeper point in the fissure. Ultimately, the block topples forward onto a cushioning mass of quarry waste where it can be examined prior to sub-division by splitting, for example, by plugs and feathers.

In order to introduce hydraulic cylinders it may first be necessary to cut two or more box-shaped recesses along the line of the fracture. Pneumatic wedges or 'air bags' can also be used to topple blocks once a cut has been made. These consist of pillow-shaped bags fabricated from metal sheet which are lowered into the cut and then inflated by compressed air. In some cases the block has not been undercut and inflation of the air bag is also used to create a fracture at the base before the block is toppled. This appears to be a common method of progressively splitting slabs from the face of a massive rock e.g. marbles and granites.

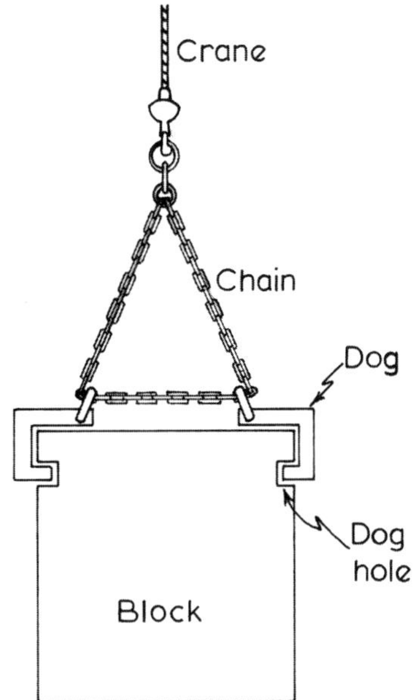

Fig. 5.33. Dogs and dog holes used for lifting a block by crane.

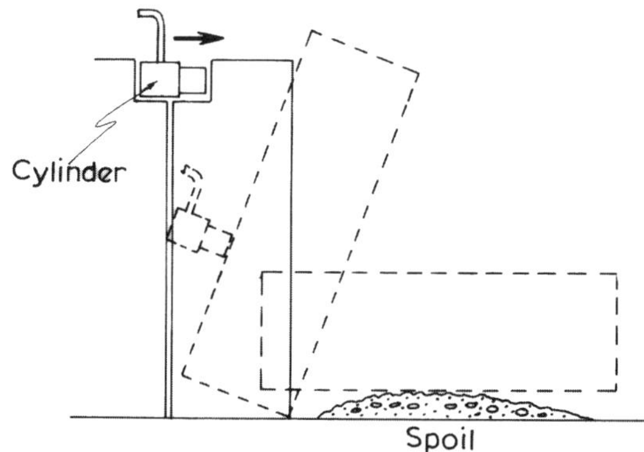

Fig. 5.35. Action of hydraulic cylinders to topple a block.

5.3.9.5. Plug and feathers

The rock is split by driving plugs, which are wedges, by hammer between pairs of tapered feathers inserted into a line of drill holes, see Fig. 5.36. Owing to the differing strengths and brittleness of rocks it may be found that deep (600 mm), widely spaced holes are successful in limestones whereas shallow (75 mm), closely spaced holes are drilled in granites. The cross section of the feather is that of a segment of a circle which tapers vertically having the largest section at the deepest point in the hole. The feathers are prevented from falling into the hole by ears. Several sets of plugs and feathers are inserted into holes drilled along a line and the plugs driven progressively and sequentially until the rock splits.

A modern development replaces the hammer with a hydraulic cylinder to drive the plug, see Fig. 5.37. In this case, the action is reversed and the wedge shaped 'plug' is drawn up into the cylinder between two tapered feathers.

This method is common for 'free cutting', thinly bedded sedimentary rocks since it avoids the problems incurred by use of explosives, see Fig. 5.38. Even granites exhibit cleavage along preferred planes called 'rift', see §5.3.2.8, so plugs and feathers are often used to subdivide blocks on the quarry floor. The method is also used to split slate along the cleavage plane.

5.3.9.6. Channelling

In channelling, a free surface was created using a chisel to excavate a slot and, although historically important, the method was labour intensive and slow. The technique was mechanized during the 1800s using steam power and multiple chisels to achieve rates of 1 to 2.5 m^2/h. The action was very similar to that of a modern rock drill without rotation of the bit. However, sharpening and tempering of chisels was a major activity and it does not seem to have been applied economically to granites. It is now obsolete in British quarries probably owing to the rapid technical evolution of fast, efficient,

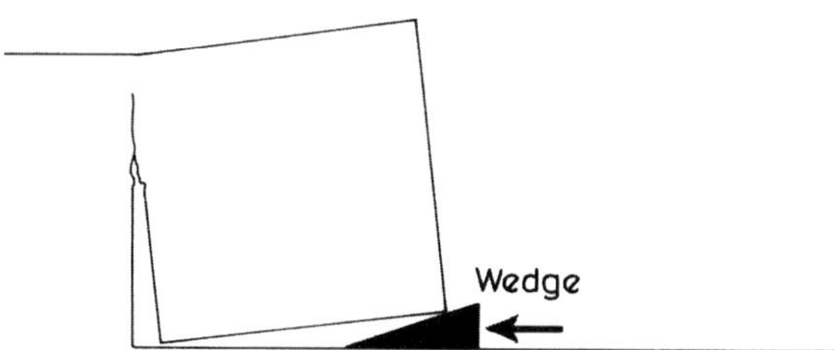

Fig. 5.34. Action of wedges to create a fracture.

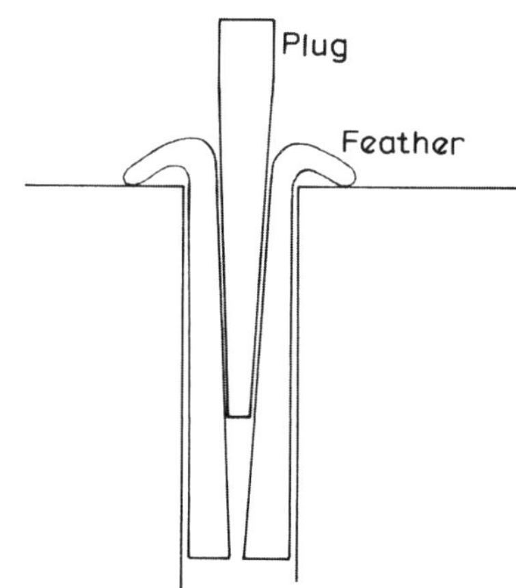

Fig. 5.36. Diagram of plug and feathers.

pneumatic rock drills. To illustrate this last point, the term 'channelling' seems to be used in Welsh slate quarries to describe 'drill and broach' (see next section).

5.3.9.7. Drilling
One method of generating blocks is to drill a series of closely spaced holes along a line. The intervening material is then broken out or broached using chisels. This method is called 'drill and broach'. Alternatively, a line of overlapping holes are drilled. This is called 'stitch drilling' or 'line drilling'. The close spacing or overlapping of parallel holes can be achieved by using a mandrel inserted into a previous hole to guide the drill. These methods are still commonly used to define very regular blocks in massive rock and result in little waste especially at the subsequent stage of primary sawing to trim the blocks, see Fig. 5.39.

5.3.9.8. Saws
Traditionally, long, thin hand-held saws have been used to create free faces in soft rocks such as limestones and marbles. Long, mechanically driven, hand-held chain saws are now available for the same duty. Recently, quarries exploiting rock not containing convenient discontinuities e.g. marble, have introduced circular diamond saws into the quarry to cut slab directly, see §§6.4.5 and 6.4.6. Moreover, track-mounted mechanical coal cutters, essentially large chain saws fitted with replaceable teeth or picks, capable of cutting soft rocks to a depth of about 4 m in any orientation, have been introduced from the coal mining industry, see Fig. 5.40. These are especially useful underground since they can cut directly into the floor or wall of an excavation. They are also useful to undercut a block in the face of a quarry and can achieve cutting rates of 4 to 5 m^2/h in marble. Originally the teeth were made of hardened steel but tungsten carbide now provides a longer life. Most recently, diamond, in the form of a polycrystalline coating (PCD) on tungsten carbide teeth, has been introduced here also.

Fig. 5.37. Hydraulic splitters (Courtesy of ARC Ltd).

5.3.9.9. Wire saws
A modern wire saw comprises a continuous loop of stainless steel wire rope running through the rock and driven by a single, large diameter, pulley wheel. The wire saw is lubricated with water supplied through jets, see Fig. 5.41. The tension is maintained by mounting the drive unit upon temporary rail tracks with the wheels of the unit driven to move the unit away from the face along the track, see Fig. 5.42. The drive to these wheels is controlled automatically according to the tension in the wire. Alternatively, a tensioning pulley can be introduced into the route taken by the wire. This is necessary when a fixed engine is used to drive the wire saw. Two types of wire saw are used. The original, helical wire saw, has a helix of wire wound onto the wire rope which carries the abrasive-water slurry which actually erodes the rock. An abrasive such as sharp sand for limestones and some slates, emery, corundum or carborundum (silicon carbide) for harder rocks, must be added separately into the cut as a slurry comprising about 70% solids. The selection of the abrasive is determined by consideration of cost but it must obviously be harder than the rock. The Mohs' scale provides a suitable measure of relative hardness. The wire travels at about 12 to 14 m/s and cuts calcareous rocks such as limestones and marbles at rates between 1 and 2.5 m^2/h. Wear of the wire can be severe reaching values of 10 to 30 metres of wire consumed per square metre of cut rock. Owing to wear, the wire also often breaks and much time can be lost in repairs. As a consequence, loops of very long length, extending to hundreds of metres, were employed to provide an acceptable life. In the late 1970s diamond wire saws were introduced with beads of 10 to 12mm diameter threaded onto the wire rope spaced by springs or plastic spacers. A bead comprises a short steel tube onto which has been sintered a mixture of diamond grit comprising diamonds of about 0.35 mm in size and a cobalt bronze alloy, see

Fig. 5.38. Fracture connecting drill holes produced by hydraulic splitters (Courtesy of ARC Ltd).

Fig. 5.43. The wire runs at a higher speed of between 20 and 40 m/s, the lower speeds being associated with cutting granites. No additional abrasive is required but lubrication by water is necessary. A substantial increase to cutting rate has been achieved with values of up to 15 m^2/h being quoted for calcareous rocks. The wear rate is dependent upon the rock type, feed rate and wire speed etc but for best utilization of the diamonds and longer life the wire must rotate as it travels.

Wire saws were introduced into the marble quarries of Belgium, and a little later into the Apuan district of Italy around Carrara, at the beginning of this century. This heralded a great increase in productivity and did much to establish the dominant position of the Carrara region in the market place and the popularity of white marbles. In the Italian quarries several loops of wire were directed around the quarry by pulleys and used to cut blocks directly from the face. The wires were driven by passing them around large diameter pulleys driven by a static engine at some central point in the quarry.

To commence the cut and introduce the wire saw, two narrow shafts to accommodate the pulley wheels had to be sunk, one at each end of the intended cut, either by excavation or using an annular, coring machine. The time and cost of sinking these shafts were major disadvantages to this method. The wire ran down one shaft, around a pulley and through the rock until it emerged into the second shaft where it passed around the return pulley towards the surface. A problem of this type of wire saw was fatigue failure of the wire caused by repeated flexing around pulleys of small diameter. In a later development, the necessity to sink two shafts was obviated by the development of the cutting or penetrating pulley in the quarries of Carrara. This is a unit comprising a pulley wheel with a shallow semi-circular groove around its perimeter attached to a long spindle. As a result of the shallow groove the wire stands proud of the pulley wheel and can cut the rock to create a slot in advance of the wheel as it is driven into the rock, see Fig. 5.44. In fact, a borehole of small diameter is drilled to accommodate the spindle and to guide the penetrating pulley. These devices are still in use today.

Introduction of a modern wire saw can also be effected by drilling two, perpendicular, intersecting holes from accessible faces, see Figs 5.41 and 5.45. This is not so difficult as it may seem since the distances are usually short and little deviation of the drill occurs. More than one attempt may be necessary and the vertical hole can

Fig. 5.39. Block defined on front face by stitch drilling and side by splitting (plug and feather) (Courtesy of Natural Stone Products Ltd).

be drilled at a greater diameter to provide a larger target. The wire is threaded through the hole by attaching a button or ball to the free end, inserting this button into the hole and introducing compressed air behind it. Usually the wire appears at the surface but 'fishing tools' are also available. In general, the advantages of wire saws are as follows:

- the ability to cut the rock independently of natural cleavage planes
- the narrow cut
- the production of a smooth, virtually finished face on the block

The latter two factors reduce wastage of rock and increase yield. Wire saws are generally best suited to massive rocks e.g. igneous and metamorphic rocks devoid of frequent joints or hard inclusions which might deflect the cut. They produce little benefit in thinly bedded and well jointed sedimentary formations of limestone or fractured slate. Diamond wires are significantly more expensive but offer simplicity of use and ability to cut any rock at substantially greater rates. Cutting rates of 4–7 m^2/h are quoted for marble and some 'granites' but the lives of the wire, measured as area of rock cut per metre of wire worn, are very different; typically 20–30 m^2/m for marble and 3–15 m^2/m for granite.

5.3.9.10. Flame jet cutting

In flame jet cutting a flame produced by the combustion of a fuel, e.g. propane, diesel oil or paraffin, in air or oxygen enriched air is directed at the surface of the rock. The heat causes local expansion of the rock generating stress which may be concentrated at a shallow flaw such as a grain boundary. The surface buckles and spalls but little damage is caused to the new surface. The combustion gases remove spalls from the cut. The method was developed to drill blastholes in the taconite iron ores of North America and transferred to the stone quarrying industry (Calaman & Roseth 1968; Rauenzahn & Tester 1989). A water cooled, hand-held lance is usually employed (see Fig. 5.46a) to create a channel of about 100 mm wide. The water is necessary to cool the jet assembly and the impingement of jets of water upon the heated rock surface assists spalling. This method is slow, about 0.5–1.0 m^2/h, and relatively expensive and cannot be used to cut limestones and marbles which would calcine. It is also very noisy. However, it is one method of cutting granites and other strong, abrasive,

Fig. 5.40. Pneumatically driven chain saw (Welsh Slate Museum, Dinorwig).

polycrystalline, rocks and produces little waste (Browning 1969). It thus competes with diamond wire saws and line-drilling in this application and is used in at least one granite quarry in the UK (see Fig. 5.46b and §6.6.3) and in the granite quarries of Sardinia.

5.3.9.11. Explosives

Explosives have been discussed in §5.3.3.2. Explosives are used in the production of blocks by splitting rocks along pronounced cleavage planes or bedding planes and to topple blocks away from the face. The blast is designed to minimize fragmentation, for which purpose black powder is most commonly employed. Small charges of black powder, wrapped in paper or card tubes, are loaded into horizontal or vertical holes stemmed with clay, sand, soil or other dilatant materials compounded on site (Anon 1989). The explosive can be initiated by electric detonator, detonating cord or slow burning safety fuse although some slate quarries do not use detonators as a precaution against damage to the blocks, see Fig. 5.47. The powder factor is specific to the application but generally small ranging from 10 to 50 g per cubic metre of rock. As an example, at one quarry blast holes of diameter 22 mm ($\frac{7}{8}$ inch) drilled on the pillaring plane of slate are fully charged with black powder whilst those on the weaker cleavage plane are charged only 8% ('one inch per foot') of their length.

In contrast, in quarries with plentiful reserves and ready markets for fragmented rock e.g. for aggregates and cement, blastholes may be charged with blasting agents such as ANFO and detonated so as to create a large pile of fragmented rock. Any suitable oversize blocks contained in the rock pile are then selected for dimension stone production. This method, known as 'varata' in Italy, is flexible in that production rate may be easily increased or reduced to meet orders and is less costly than the skilled, labour intensive methods described above. The disadvantages are that the yield of blocks is low and that blocks may contain hair-line or micro-fractures, introduced by the blasting. Therefore, wastage during later processing, for example sawing to make slabs, is increased.

In certain large quarries primarily dedicated to the production of aggregates or cement, certain benches or areas are designated specifically for the production of blocks and the blast designed appropriately.

To favour production of large blocks and minimize damage to the blocks, black powder may be used as the explosive. In a progressive blasting practice called 'springing', applied particularly to granite, the blast

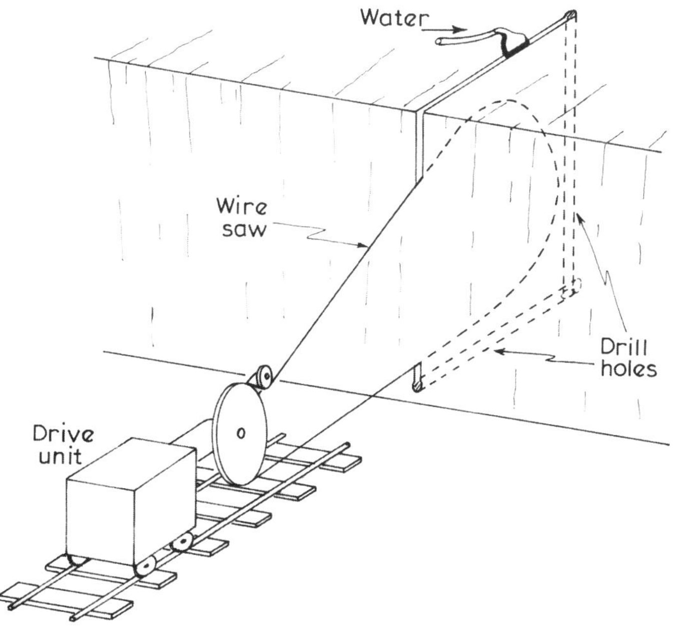

Fig. 5.41. Diagram of simple wire saw.

Fig. 5.42. Diamond wire saw in a Greek marble quarry.

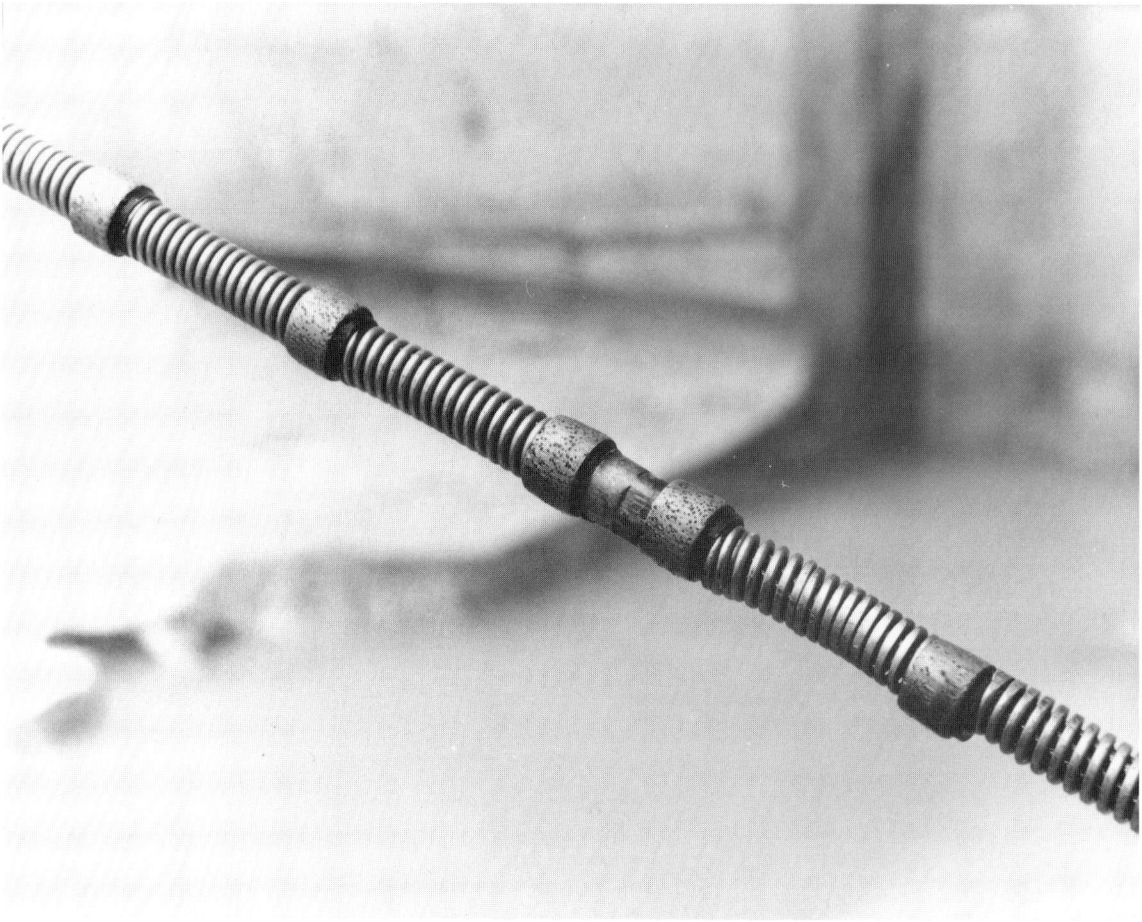

Fig. 5.43. Diamond wire saw showing beads (Courtesy of De Beers Industrial Diamonds).

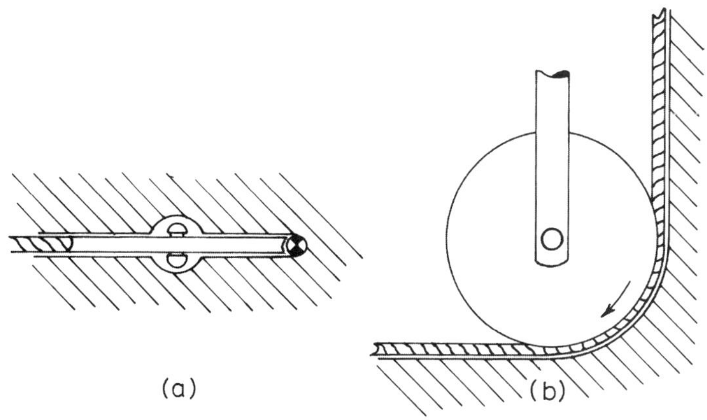

Fig. 5.44. Arrangement of a penetrating pulley.

Fig. 5.45. Drilling a vertical hole for a wire saw in marble.

holes are drilled and lightly charged with black powder. After detonation of the explosive the rock is examined for cracks and the blast hole recharged with an appropriate quantity of powder which is again detonated (O'Neill 1961). This procedure is repeated until a block is 'sprung' from the face but is now not permitted since it involves recharging a fired hole.

In some operations, notably granite and sandstone quarries, where alternative methods of cutting the rock are not attractive, use is made of the presplitting technique, also called smooth blasting by some, described in §5.3.2.7. Two faces, the rear vertical face and the lower horizontal face, can be split simultaneously. The blast is of the form of an L' defined by lines of vertical and horizontal blastholes charged with decoupled explosives. This practice has been used in South Africa and Finland(AECI 1987; Smith 1987).

In summary, not withstanding what has been said about the disadvantages of the use of explosives in dimension stone quarries, the structure of the rock and the scale of the operation can determine that this is the most suitable method. In highly fractured rock masses wire saws, circular saws and chain saws become jammed by loose blocks and have not been successful. More selective methods of block extraction can be labour intensive and not suited to maintaining a high output level although the yield of blocks might be greater. By careful attention to blast design fragmentation can be minimized and explosives used to disaggregate the naturally defined blocks.

5.3.9.12. Expanding powders

A wedging action can be created by other means such as the historical use of wooden wedges wetted by water and the expansion of lime through hydration, although these methods are very slow.

In coal mining, where the use of explosives incurs the risk of ignition of methane gas called 'firedamp', a patented non-explosive method of rock breakage called 'Cardox' was developed that employed liquefied carbon dioxide. Reuseable cartridges containing the liquid carbon dioxide are inserted into drill holes. These are activated by electrical heating which creates an increase in pressure which bursts a metal sealing disc. Expanding gas is thereby released into the coal seam and disaggregates the rock along pre-existing discontinuities. It is known that at least one dimension stone quarry in the UK employs this method to extract blocks of sandstone

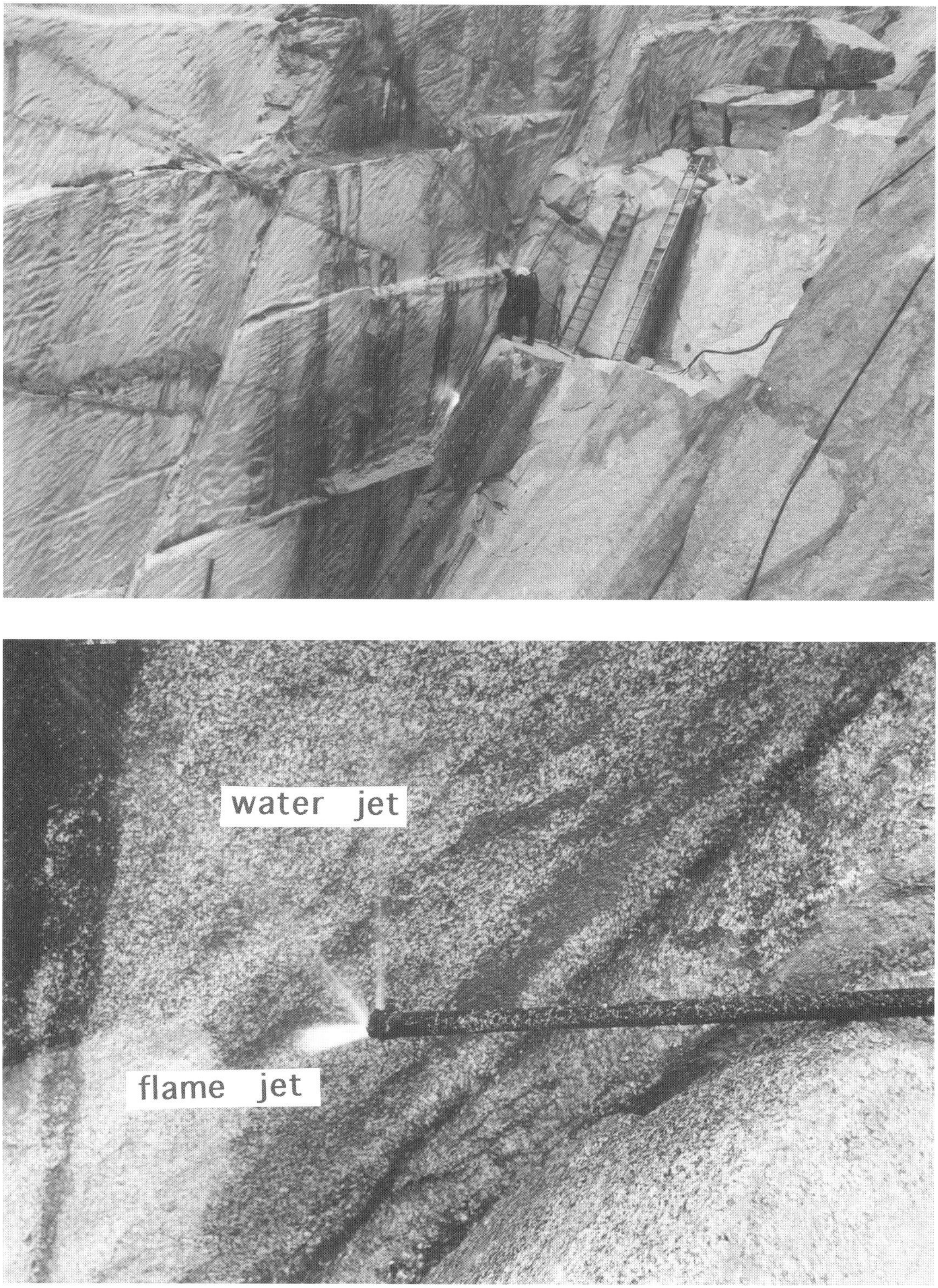

water jet

flame jet

Fig. 5.46. Flame jet cutting of granite (Courtesy of Natural Stone Products Ltd).

Fig. 5.47. Stemming being rammed into a blasthole loaded with black powder. The quarryman is lying on the cleavage plane of the slate and the hole is drilled on the pillaring plane. The safety fuse is clearly visible (Courtesy of Ffestiniog Slate Quarry Co.).

and the method may be about to enjoy a revival in opencast coal operations since it avoids all of the problems of vibration and safety incurred by explosives.

A modern expanding powder is 'Bristar' employed in civil engineering for excavation and demolition in situations where explosives could not be used (Anon 1991a). Essentially, it is a silicate compound similar to cement that hardens and expands when hydrated. It is used as a slurry comprising about 30% by weight water. Optimum hole diameter is usually between 30 and 50 mm at a spacing of 0.3 to 0.5 metres. The smaller the hole diameter and the closer the spacing the straighter is the split. Consumption of powder is about 5 kg/m^3 of broken rock. As with loose explosives, the drill hole can be lined with polythene if there is a danger of loss into fissures.

5.3.9.13. Mobile equipment

As stated above, powered machines have been adapted to the removal of blocks defined by natural joints and discontinuities from the quarry face. In the simplest case, unmodified hydraulic excavators can employ the bucket as a tool to remove blocks. In other cases, the excavator or wheeled loader is fitted with tools such as forks and prongs to assist the removal of blocks. Although the capital cost is high, these machines can greatly increase the output of a quarry and their purchase is often necessary for other duties such as overburden removal or loading.

5.3.9.14. Other methods

Research is being undertaken to develop methods employing high pressure water jets to cut rock both in quarries and mines. However, this technique is experimental at the present time.

5.3.9.15. Transport

The selection of the method of transport of the blocks to the processing plant depends to a great degree upon the topographical situation of the quarry and the land area available.

In hillside quarries, for example, in the Apuan district surrounding Carrara in Italy, blocks were lowered down the mountain sides on wooden sledges and trolleys running down inclined railways have been used in many localities, see §A5.1.12.

Blocks can be raised using the bucket of hydraulic excavators or wheeled loaders and loaded onto a flat-bed truck for transport, see Fig. 6.44. In many quarries the wheeled loader also carries the block in the bucket or forks attachment, see Fig. 5.48, (Anon 1991b). Alternatively, the block can be lifted by straps and chains and loaded onto a truck or the block can be drawn onto the truck by a winch.

Eye bolts can be inserted into holes drilled into the block to facilitate lifting by cranes. A particular lifting eye called a 'lewis' comprises a scissor-like assembly that is inserted into an undercut hole in the block. When the scissors open the lewis expands and interlocks with the hole. However, with both of these methods there is a risk that the rock or cement might fail allowing the block to fall. Therefore, considerations of the safety of operators may preclude their use.

The use of wheeled loaders or trucks to transport blocks out of the quarry to the processing plant requires the construction of haul roads of modest gradient. In a deep quarry, these haul roads or ramps may sterilise a large proportion of the reserves or necessitate the use of a much greater land area.

Therefore, stone quarries have traditionally made use of static derrick cranes and, more recently, mobile cranes, see §A5.1.1. When cranes are used for transport of blocks the quarry faces can be vertical if they are stable. This greatly reduces the land area occupied by the quarry and the volume of overburden to be removed. The block can be lifted by chains but this presents the problem of threading the chain under the block. One solution is the use of two 'dogs' attached to chains which locate into dog holes on opposite sides of the block, see Fig. 5.33. Another is the use of the 'lewis'. Until the introduction of large wheeled loaders the crane was one of the principal methods employed and has enjoyed a revival through the use of mobile, crawler mounted cranes, see Fig. 5.49. The crane also provides a means of carrying tools and equipment into the quarry although the men gain access by ladders.

The relatively low cost of transport compared to the value of dimension stone means that transport may represent less than 5% of the delivered price. Therefore, in many cases the blocks are not carried directly to the processing plant but are exported from the country of origin and transported over long distances before processing. Proximity to a sea-port is a great advantage to the establishment of foreign markets and important ports which handle significant quantities of blocks include: Marina di Carrara, Italy; Vigo, Spain; Madras and Mangalore, India; Larvik, Norway; Ahus, Sweden; Rio de Janeiro, Brazil and Durban, South Africa.

Fig. 5.48. Wheeled loader with fork attachment carrying a block (Courtesy of Realstone Ltd).

Containerization has further promoted the export of blocks and sawn slabs since it provides a secure, protective means of transport.

5.3.10. Underground mining of dimension stone

5.3.10.1. Introduction
The arguments for the selection of mining to extract stone have been presented in §4.5.2. It is most unlikely that the cost of mining rock for armourstone or rock fill can be justified. However, mining is not uncommon for dimension stone, especially stratiform deposits of limestones, deeply buried beds of slate and marble.

5.3.10.2. Access
Access to a stone mine is usually provided by a horizontal tunnel (an adit) or inclined shaft (an incline) see Fig. 4.15. The incline, usually of gradient between 1 in 2 and 1 in 4 must obviously be provided with a winch or hoisting system to raise the stone blocks that are carried upon trolleys or bogies. Stone mines are generally shallow to avoid high costs and the problems incurred by ground water. Shafts are seldom used in dimension stone mines because of the problem of raising large individual blocks but may be found in slate mines where blocks are smaller. In most countries it is a requirement of law that two shafts are sunk or, at least, that the mine has two means of ingress and egress. In metal and coal mining it is usual to equip one shaft with skips to raise the mineral (hoisting) and the other with cages for carrying men and materials.

Occasionally, access to deep rock may be provided fortuitously by other excavations such as railway cuttings, for example Box Hill, in the UK and abandoned tunnels, for example, Carrara, Italy. In many other cases, the mine is an extension to a quarry where extraction has continued into the face to produce blind excavations called *sotto tecchia* in Italy; translated as 'below the wall'.

Fig. 5.49. Crawler crane (Courtesy of ARC Ltd).

5.3.10.3. Ventilation
The objective of ventilation is obviously to provide breathing air for the mine workers but the volumetric flow of air is usually determined by the necessity to remove flammable gases e.g methane in coal mines, to cool the workings since the temperature of rock increases with depth and to remove exhaust gases produced by motorised equipment. In deep underground mines ventilation is achieved by positioning an exhauster fan at the top of one of the shafts known as the up-cast shaft. Air is then drawn down the other shaft and through the workings.

In shallower stone mines ventilation can often be achieved by natural circulation of air through the workings which may enter along the adit and exhaust up a ventilation shaft as shown in Fig. 4.15. Where this is inadequate, circulation of air can be directed by 'ventilation doors' within the workings and air movement can be assisted by fans suspended in the tunnels or 'driveways'.

There are several reasons that the ventilation of a stone mine can be simple including the small number of men working underground, the use of electrically powered equipment rather than diesel engines, the absence of methane, the shallow depth and the short length of the air circuit which generates only a low resistance to air circulation. However, recently, there has been concern about the accumulation of radioactive gases, e.g. radon, and methane in shallow underground workings. These gases usually derive from deeper strata, coal seams in the case of methane, and may necessitate the installation of fan assisted ventilation as in the Bathstone mines.

5.3.10.4. 'Room and pillar' method
The most common method of extracting bedded deposits of stone underground is called 'room and pillar' or 'pillar and stall'. Stopes, the name given to the chamber or room created by active mineral extraction underground, are excavated whilst 'pillars' or walls of rock remain intact to provide support for the roof. The

pillars also prevent surface subsidence which is an important consideration in view of the shallow nature of the mine, see Fig. 5.50.

Typically, between half and two thirds of the rock is extracted. A greater proportion may be recovered if the strata are particularly strong and self-supporting. The roof may be supported by rock-bolts, see §5.3.2.6.

Back-filling the rooms with cemented waste to permit removal of the pillars is usually uneconomic in non-metalliferous mining. In this respect, it is interesting to note that abandoned limestone mines in the West Midlands of the UK are presently being back-filled with pumped waste to prevent further collapse and subsidence. Owing to the regular layout of haulage roads and the use of rail or trackless (wheeled vehicles) haulage, the room and pillar extraction technique is best suited to continuous, undisturbed, horizontal or gently dipping strata without significant faulting.

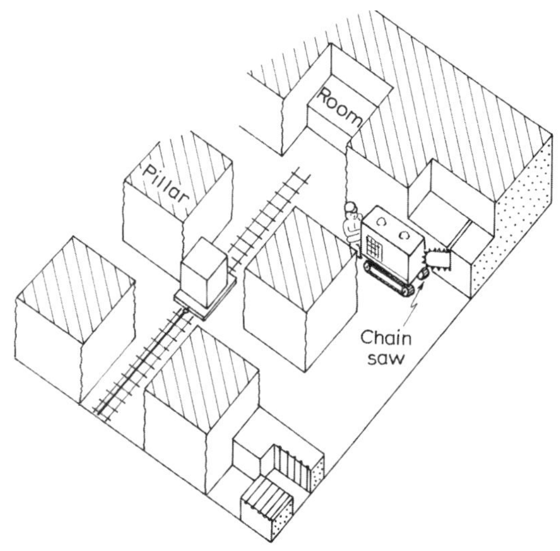

Fig. 5.50. Room and pillar working.

5.3.10.5. Mining of gently dipping strata

Tunnels or driveways to give access to the reserves are constructed from the bottom of the incline or shaft into the rock mass. Parallel cross-cuts or galleries are then driven from the driveways to divide the rock in a rectangular pattern. Extraction then commences with the miners facing a wall or face of rock exposed in the gallery. The height of this face will be determined by the stratum thickness although some rock may be left deliberately to create a competent roof and a clean floor.

The width of the room is determined by the strength of the roof-rock, referred to as the 'hanging wall', which must span the eventual room. In this respect, a favourable geological situation will be where the stratum immediately above the stone is strong and self-supporting, for example the Ragstone above the oolitic limestone in the Bathstone mines and igneous intrusions, that is sills and dykes, above beds of slate. The width of the intervening pillars should be determined by the compressive strength of the rock and the stresses imposed by overlying strata although a common practice is to have equal rooms and pillars.

The room may be divided horizontally into benches, steps or 'lifts'. In sedimentary formations these lifts are likely to correspond to the major beds within the stratum. If the rock is not bedded the lifts can be arranged at the convenience of the miners to produce readily handleable or saleable blocks of, say, one metre in thickness. The orientation of the face may also be determined by the structural geology. Where possible, joints will be used to define blocks such that in one direction the galleries must run parallel to a major, vertical joint set. If possible, the galleries used for haulage should be on the strike so that haulage roads or rail tracks can be level and not up or down dip.

The typical procedures for the extraction of a block are described below with reference to Fig. 5.51. In principle, the methods are the same as those of quarrying described in §5.3.9. Indeed, it should also be noted here that not all mines produce blocks and that hand-held or mechanical saws can sometimes be used to cut building stone directly from underground faces.

Historically, in soft, weak rocks such as limestones, many of the following actions were carried out using hand tools including long heavy saws and picks but are now accomplished using mechanical saws, see Fig. 5.40. The following description is based upon the methods employed at a Bathstone mine.

The first action is to create a deep, narrow slot above the top lift to permit the introduction of saws and the raising of the top block, see Fig. 5.51.

The second stage is the creation of a recess or chamber in the top lift, traditionally on the left-hand side, since most miners are right-handed. For this purpose two vertical cuts are made at the left side of the top bed to define a narrow block with a trapezoidal or wedge shape to facilitate its withdrawal from the face. This 'wrist' block is now free on four sides. In ideal circumstances the fifth, invisible rear face is also free as a joint surface. Nevertheless, wedges are now driven into the bedding plane under the top bed. The action of the wedges lifts the block from the bedding plane and creates a rear face by fracture if no joint exists. The wrist block can now be manoeuvred away from the face.

With the recess created, a thin saw, either mechanical or hand-held, can be introduced to cut the rear face of the adjacent block and the process is repeated. After each block has been removed from the face it is examined to discover any faults or false bedding planes. The quarryman taps the block with a piece of iron or a stone; a distinct ring should be heard if the block is good. If a dull thud is heard the block will be split along the fault with

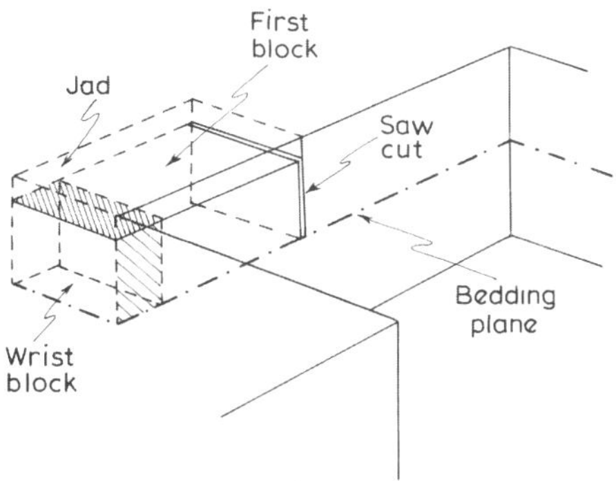

Fig. 5.51. Diagram of the extraction of a block in a mine.

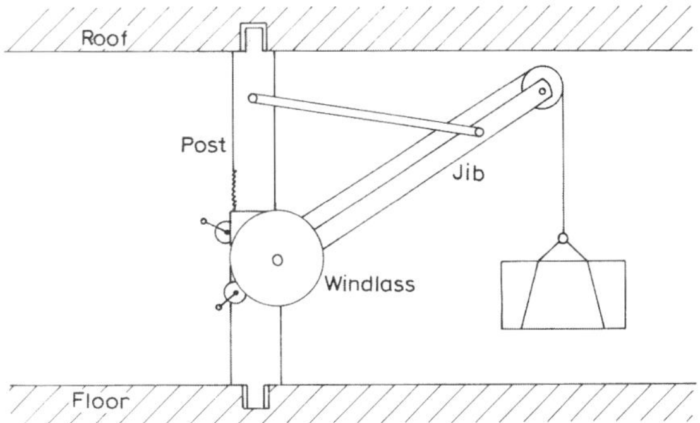

Fig. 5.52. Diagram of a jib crane.

wedges until no further defects remain. The block is then measured and marked both with its volume and the orientation of the bedding planes. The blocks are transported upon bogies running on temporary rail track to the bottom of the incline to await raising to the surface. However, a crane is required to lift the blocks onto the carriages and the blocks may be moved slowly along the galleries using the same cranes.

The crane comprises a column of adjustable height fitted with a jib and a windlass, see Fig. 5.52. The column is fixed rigidly between the roof and floor of the mine by means of the pegs that extend from either end of the column and which locate in recesses cut into the rock for this purpose. A wire rope connected to the windlass and running over a sheave wheel at the end of the jib is used to raise the block. Rotation of the column to slew the jib then affords translocation of the block before it is lowered. The crane is then dismantled and fixed at a further point within reach of the block to move it further along the gallery. A more detailed description of the extraction of Bathstone from Monks Park Mine is given in §6.6.2.

5.3.10.6. Mining of steeply dipping strata

These rocks, most commonly slates, usually outcropped at surface where they were quarried until increasing depth of overburden forced mining to commence. Again, access is usually by incline to permit raising the blocks carried upon four wheel bogies running on rails. Shafts may also be constructed to accommodate ladders for the miners and to provide ventilation. Occasionally shafts are constructed for hoisting blocks.

Historically, huge vaulted caverns have been excavated around the base of vertical shafts which were sunk directly into the slate. These excavations were not always safe and stable and little space will be devoted to their description. Excavation proceeded in a downwards direction, called underhand sloping, until the slate was exhausted. However, the method provided no support for the roof and little opportunity to inspect the state of the roof. There were collapses incurring loss of life and machinery and, sometimes, surface subsidence.

Another method was to sink a deep shaft to the base of the slate and extract the slate in an upwards direction, called overhand stoping, with miners standing on waste or wooden platforms to reach the roof of slate. Nevertheless, danger still existed since the roof was being brought down continuously during production.

A safer, but more costly, method, akin to the mining of steeply inclined ore bodies containing metals, is to sink the shaft in the footwall rocks and to drive horizontal galleries or levels at vertical intervals to intersect the slate, see Fig. 4.14. In this situation the shaft is contained and protected in competent rock isolated from the slopes. Once the slate has been intersected, cross cuts can be driven horizontally from the levels along the strike. The stopes can then be developed along the crosscuts in a variety of ways. A particular consideration in steeply dipping strata is that, once a block is freed on a basal inclined joint surface, bedding plane or cleavage plane, unless it is restrained, the block of stone will tend to slide under the influence of gravity towards the lowest point in the stope. Therefore, attention must be paid to the safety of mine workers usually by evacuation to a safe area when the block is freed.

A mining method for steeply dipping beds is a form of room and pillar working. This was applied in many of the slate mines, now abandoned, of north Wales and is described below, see Fig. 5.53.

An incline, rather than a shaft, is driven from the base of the exhausted quarry following the dip of the strata just below the hanging wall which provides a competent roof. At vertical intervals, say 15 m, levels are driven along the strike across the strata just below the hanging wall. These levels accommodate the transport system e.g. narrow gauge railway, which connects to the incline.

The length of this level is divided into chambers (rooms) and walls (pillars), often of approximately equal length, in such a manner that walls and chambers extend in a continuous line down dip. At the extreme edge of each chamber an inclined shaft, called a 'raise' or 'roofing shaft', is driven upwards in the line of pillaring to intersect with the level above and complete a ventilation circuit. A small chamber is then created above the lower level and under the hanging wall by excavation (blasting) of rock. This permits access by rockmen and subsequent removal of blocks. Miner was a name given only to those men who excavated rock to create inclines, raises and levels. In the case of slate, the blocks may be defined by cleavage, pillaring and veins (joints), see §5.3.2.8. In favourable situations the cleavage plane is close to that of the dip plane of the strata, the pillaring plane is normal to both the dip and the strike and the joint plane is parallel to the strike. The block is freed first on the cleavage plane by a small explosive charge loaded into a blast hole and then on the joint plane in a similar manner. If no joint exists a cut is created by 'drill and broach'. Finally, the block is freed on the pillaring plane by explosives and slides down dip towards the lower level. In order to gain access for drilling the miners required ladders and platforms to be erected. Traditionally, suspended chains and harnesses were also used by the miners to facilitate movement over the steeply inclined surfaces. Inspection of the roof required the use of very long ladders steadied by guy ropes.

After suitable splitting and trimming, block was lifted by a rope running through a pulley wheel suspended from a four-leg tressle onto a bogie running upon temporary rail track and drawn away from the room by locomotive.

Descriptions of modern methods of extracting and processing slate in north Wales can be found in §§6.6.6, 6.6.7 and 6.6.8 and a method of mining a very steeply dipping slate vein is illustrated in Fig. 5.54.

5.3.11. Storage

Slate intended for splitting to roofing slates is an exception to what follows in that large quantities of blocks are not stored ahead of the processing plant. Furthermore, slabs are wetted with water by spray systems or even immersed in tanks of water since this

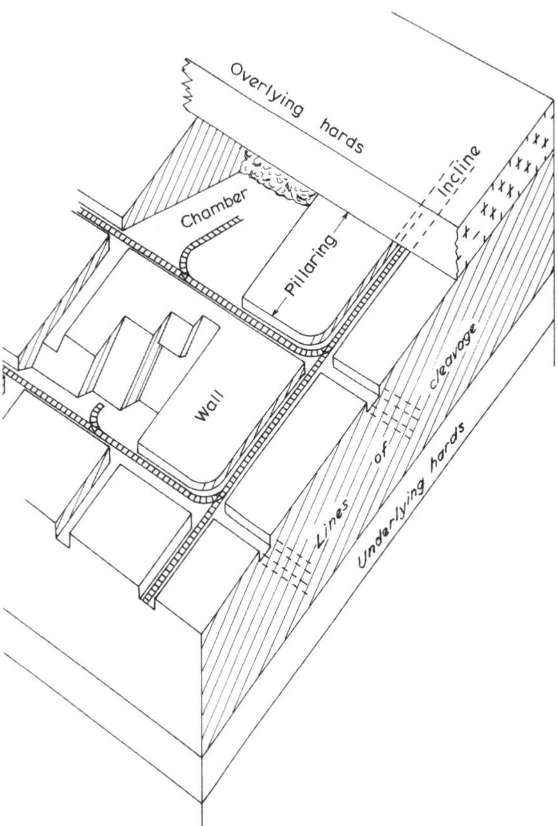

Fig. 5.53. Diagram of the room-and pillar mining of slate in steeply dipping strata.

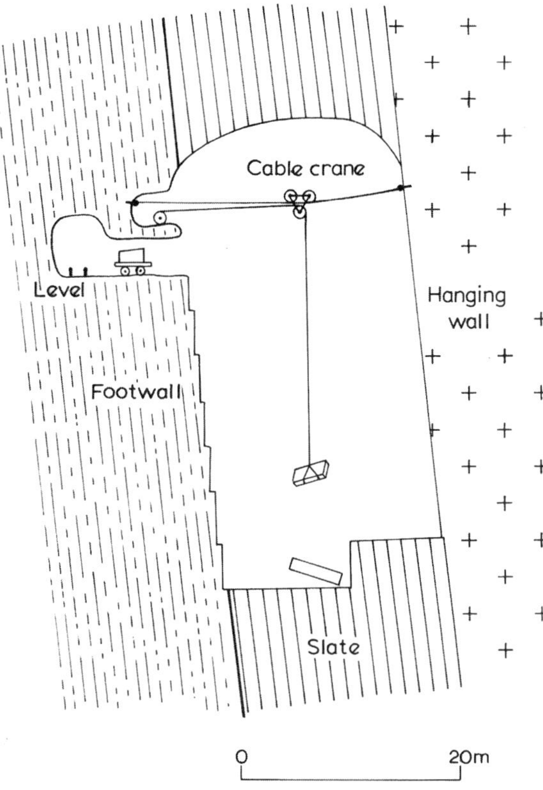

Fig. 5.54. Modern method of mining very steeply dipping beds of slate (Courtesy of Wincilate Ltd).

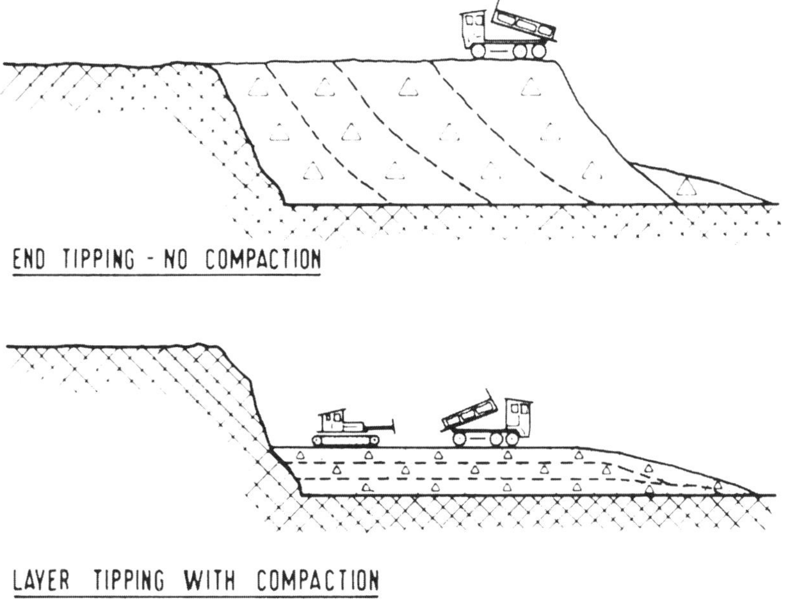

Fig. 5.55. Methods of creating tips.

promotes good cleavage. All other blocks will be marked with a code number and the weight or volume of the block before storage or shipment.

Certain porous stones e.g. some Jurassic limestones and the Namurian sandstones of the 'Millstone Grit Series', contain water, also known as 'quarry sap', when extracted from the mine or quarry and must be protected from frost damage until they have dried or partially drained. Failure to do so results in the spalling of the surface or spectacular explosion of the block if the surface freezes. Abandoned underground slopes are convenient drying and storage areas or sheds may be constructed for this purpose on the surface. Many operators of dimension stone quarries producing porous rock, for example, oolitic limestones, also report that the saturated stone is so soft that it can be sculpted when first extracted. This property may be exploited to shape the block crudely using the bucket of an hydraulic excavator, for example. It is further claimed that the stone hardens or increases in strength as it dries and develops a hard shell. The strengthening of drying rock was investigated by TRRL who confirmed that suction can significantly increase the strength of partially saturated porous rocks (West 1994). It is also claimed that a hardened shell is formed around the block by the crystallization of salts dissolved in the pore water.

In the case of stone other than slate, it is important to maintain a substantial stock of blocks ahead of the masonry works in order to cater for the typically irregular pattern of orders received. It is also wise to allow for interuptions to quarry operations caused by the weather, equipment failure, etc. It is seldom possible to increase significantly the output of blocks from a single quarry in a short time period and the ability to respond immediately to large orders can determine commercial success. For this reason directories and data files will usually include information upon the volumetric output of each quarry (Stone Industries 1994).

5.3.12. Waste disposal

The economic importance of minimising waste has been discussed above in Chapter 4. When waste generation cannot be wholly avoided the material must be tipped on a site away from the quarry or mine to prevent interference with extractive operations and sterilisation of reserves As an extreme example of the need to fully consider waste disposal, it has been estimated that the production of 1 tonne of roofing slate creates up to 20 tonnes of various forms of waste (DoE 1995). Planning consents must also be obtained for tips.

The selection of tipping sites to minimise haul distances and environmental impacts such as visual intrusion can be a major exercise. It may involve additional land purchase for the purpose of tipping. Alternatively, wherever possible, overburden and waste are used to backfill the active or previous excavations as part of the restoration programme.

All tipping and refuse disposal operations within quarries in the UK are subject to the Mines and

Quarries (Tips) Act and Regulations, 1969, which demand regular inspection and monitoring of the tips and, in the case of 'classified tips', detailed design and reporting by competent engineers. A tip is defined as 'classified' if it exceeds certain criteria of height, volume or area. Tips must be designed to be inherently stable and adequately drained (Walton 1990; Garrard & Walton 1990).

Waste will usually be delivered to the tip by dump truck or motor scraper or, in some major operations, by conveyor. Whichever is the method of transport, it is the method of emplacement and compaction that will ensure the permanent security of the tip. Layer tipping as opposed to end-tipping, see Fig. 5.55, is considered the preferred method but requires, in addition to the transport equipment, dozers to place the material in the correct position and to achieve the necessary compaction.

References

AECI, 1987. Dimensional stone blasting. *Explosives Today*, No. 45, March, AECI, Johannesburg, RSA.

ANON 1977. The description of rock masses for engineering purposes: Working Party Report. *Quarterly Journal of Engineering Geology*, **10**, 355–388.

——1988. Laser profiling at Moorcroft quarry. *Mine & Quarry*. February.

——1989. Scottish stone quarry invests for the future. *Quarry Management*. May, 27–31.

——1991*a*. Rock cracking agent at Shropshire quarry. *Quarry Management*. January, 43.

——1991*b*. Caterpillar loaders get to grips with Norwegian granite. *Quarry Management*. August, 33.

——1993. Trade in stone. *Stone Industries*. July, 14–16.

ASHURST, J. & DIMES, F. G. 1984. *Stone in Building*. Stone Federation, London.

ATLAS POWDER CO. 1987. *Explosives and Rock Blasting*. Dallas.

BALL, M. 1988. A review of blast design considerations in quarrying and opencast mining. *Quarry Management*, June, 35–43 and July, 23–27.

BARTON, N. & CHOUBEY, V. 1977. The shear strength of rock joints in theory and practice. *Rock Mechanics*, **10**, 1–54

——, LIEN, R. & LUNDE, J. 1974. Engineering classification of rock masses for the design of tunnel support. *Rock Mechanics*, **6**, 189–236.

BEHRE, C. H. 1933. *Slate in Pennsylvannia*. Pennsylvannia Geological Survey, Department of Internal Affairs, Commonwealth of Pennsylvannia.

BERTA, G. 1990. *Explosives*, Italesplosivi, Milan.

BEZZANT, N. 1980. *Out of the Rock*. Heinemann, London.

BIENIAWSKI, Z. T. 1974. Geomechanics classification of rock masses and its application in tunnelling. *Proceedings of 3rd International Symposium on Rock Mechanics*. Denver, **2**, 27.

BOND, F. C. 1961. Crushing and grinding calculations, *British Chemical Engineering*, **6**, 378–391 & **6**, 543–548.

BREWSTER, P. 1987. The use of motor graders, dozers and tractors in quarrying applications. *Quarry Management*, September, 27–28.

BRITISH STANDARDS INSTITUTION 1984. BS 5228. *Noise Control on Construction and Open Sites*, BSI, London.

——1990. BS 4142. *Rating industrial noise affecting mixed residentail and industrial areas*, BSI, London.

——1992. BS 6472. *Guide to evaluation of human exposure to vibration in buildings*, BSI, London.

BROWN, S. R. & SCHOLZ, C. H. 1985. Broad band width study of the topology of natural rock surface, *Journal of Geophysical Research*, **90**, 12 575–12 582.

BROWNING, J. A. 1969. *Flame Jet Drilling*. U.S. Patent 3476194.

BUTLER, A., CROOK, R. & SHROVE, G. 1988. Training and the Explosives Regulations, *Quarry Management*, June, 41–43.

CALAMAN, J. J. & ROSETH, H. C. 1968. *Jet Piercing* in *Surface Mining*. *In*: PFLEIDER, E. (ed.) Seely Mudd Series, AIME, New York, 325–337.

CATERPILLAR TRACTOR CO. 1990. *Caterpillar Performance Handbook*. 21st edition, Peoria, Illinois.

CLEETON, J. 1997. Air-deck techniques, *Quarry Management*, April, 23–27.

CONTI, G., *et al.* 1986. *Marble in the World*, Societa Editrice Apuana, Cascara, Italy.

CORKER, S. 1987. Bulk soil handling techniques. *Mine & Quarry Environment*, **1**, 15–17.

DA GAMA, 1977. Computer model for block size analysis of jointed rock masses, *15th APCOM*, Brisbane, Australia, 305–315.

DEERE, D. U. 1963. Technical description of rock cores for engineering purposes, *Rock Mechanics and Engineering Geology*, **1**, 18.

DEPARTMENT OF THE ENVIRONMENT 1986. *Landfilling Wastes*. Waste management paper No. 26, HMSO, London.

——1988*a*. *Mineral Planning Guidance: General Considerations and the Development Plan System*, MPG1, HMSO, London.

——1988*b*. *Minerals Planning Guidance: Applications. Permissions and Conditions*, MPG2, HMSO, London.

——1989. *Minerals Planning Guidance: The Reclamation of Minerals Workings*, MPG7, HMSO, London.

——1990. *Planning Policy Guidance: Archaeology and Planning*, PPG16, HMSO, London.

——1991. *Quarry Processes Including Roadstone Plants and the Size Reduction of Bricks, Tiles and Concrete*, Planning Guidance, PG3/8(91), HMSO, London.

——1992. *Planning Policy Guidance: The Countryside and the Rural Economy*, PPG7, HMSO, London.

——1993. *Minerals Planning Guidance: The Control of Noise at Surface Mineral Workings*, MPG11, HMSO, London.

——1994*a*. *Minerals Planning Guidance: Guidelines for Aggregates Provision in England*, MPG6, HMSO, London.

——1994*b*. *Planning Policy Guidance: Transport*, PPG13, HMSO, London.

EARLE, Q. 1991. The quarrying industry in Hong Kong. *Quarry Management*, February, 19–24.

FEDER, J. 1988. *Fractals*, Plenum, New York.

FOOKES, P. G., DEARMAN, W. R. & FRANKLIN, J. A. 1971. Engineering aspects of rock weathering, *Quarterly Journal of Engineering Geology*, **4**, 139–185.

FORSTER, A. & FORSTER, S. C. 1996. Troglodyte dwellings of the Loire Valley, France, *Quarterly Journal of Engineering Geology*, **29**, 193–197.

FRANKLIN, J. A., BROCK, E. & WALTON, G. 1971. Logging the mechanical character of rock. *Transactions of IMM*, Vol. 80, A1–A9.

GARRARD, G. & WALTON, G. 1990. Guidance in the design and inspection of tips and related structures, *Transactions of IMM*, A115–A124.

GENSKE, D. D., HERDA, W. & OHNISHI, Y. 1992. Fractures and fractals, *Proceedings of Eurock '92*, ISRM, British Geotechnical Society, London, 19–24.

GOODMAN, R. E. 1980. *Introduction to Rock Mechanics*. Wiley, New York.

GREENWELL, A. & ELSDEN, J. V. 1913. *Practical Stone Quarrying*. Crosby Lockwood, London.

GREGORY, J. 1987. The measurement and control of industrial noise, *Quarry Management*, January, 25–33.

GUNN, J. 1992. *Landform Replication as a Technique for Reclamation of Limestone Quarries*. Department of the Environment, HMSO, London.

HEMPHILL, G. 1981. *Blasting Operations*, McGraw-Hill, New York.

HOEK, E. & BRAY, J. W. 1981. *Rock Slope Engineering*. Institution of Mining and Metallurgy, London.

—— & BROWN, E. 1980. Underground excavations in rock, Institution of mining and Metallurgy, London.

—— & WOOD, D. F. 1988. Rock support, *Mining Magazine*, October.

HSC, 1989. *Explosives at Quarries*, Approved Code of Practice, HMSO, London.

HUDSON, J. A. 1989. *Rock Mechanics Principles in Engineering Practice*, CIRIA, Butterworths, Borough Green.

ICI EXPLOSIVES *Explosives at Quarries*, Information leaflets.

KENNEDY, B. 1990. *Surface Mining*. Seely Mudd series, (Society of Mining Engineers) AIME, New York.

KING, T. 1991. *Safety and Legislation*, Institute of Quarrying, Nottingham.

LANGEFORS, U. & KIHLSTROM, B. 1978. *The Modern Technique of Rock Blasting*. Wiley, New York.

MACGREGOR, F., FELL, R., MOSTYN, G. R., HOCKING, G. & MCNALLY, G. 1994. The estimation of rock rippability, *Quarterly Journal of Engineering Geology*, **27**, 123–144.

MATHESON, G. D. 1984. A device for measuring drill rod and drill hole orientations, Departments of Transport and Environment, TRL report SR817, Transport Research Laboratory, Crowthorne.

MCKENZIE, C. 1990. Quarry blast monitoring, *Quarry Management*, December, 23–29.

NELSON, P. 1987. *Transportation Noise*, Butterworths, Borough Green.

NICHOLSON, D. T. 1995. The visual impact of quarrying, *Quarry Management*, July, 39–42.

O'NEILL, H. 1961. The working of the Aberdeen granites, *Quarry Manager's Journal*, Dec., 479–490.

PASS, R. 1970. Planning for production, *Quarry Manager's Journal*, **54**, 163–176.

PERSSON, P. A., HOLMBERG, R. & LEE, J. 1994. *Rock Blasting and Explosives Engineering*. CRC Press, Boca Raton.

PETTIFER, G. S. & FOOKES, P. G. 1994. A revision of the graphical method for asessing the excavatabllity of rock, *Quarterly Journal of Engineering Geology*, **27**, 145–164.

POWLEY, D. 1989. The new COSHH regulations, 1988. *Quarry Management*, October, 32.

PRIEST, S. D. 1985. *Hemispherical Projection Methods in Rock Mechanics*. George Allen & Unwin, London.

——1993. *Discontinuity Analysis for Rock Engineering*, Chapman Hall, London.

RAUENZAHN, M. & TESTER, W. 1989. Rock failure mechanisms of flame jet spallation drilling. *International Journal of Rock Mechanics, Min. Sci. and Geomechanics*.

RAYSON, S. 1993. Quarrying for armourstone in Norway, *Quarry Management*, January, 11–15.

RMC 1986. *A Practical Guide to Restoration*. RMC Group Ltd., Feltham.

ROMANA, M. 1985. New adjustment ratings for application of Bienawski classification to slopes, *Proceedings of International Symposium on the Role of Rock Mechanics*, Zacatecas, 49–53.

——1988. Practice of SMR classification for slope appraisal. *Proceedings of 5th International Symposium on Landslides, Lausanne*. Balkema, Rotterdam.

SAMUEL, P. 1990. Land restoration to agriculture. *Quarry Management*, October, 25–33.

SAUNDERS, E. 1987. The safe use of explosives in quarries, *Quarry Management*, February, 31–37.

SMITH, M. 1987. Dimensional stone blasting in Finland, *Mining Magazine*, October, 312–317.

STANIER, P. H. 1985. *Quarries and Quarrying*, Shire Album 134, Shire Publications, Princes Risborough.

STONE INDUSTRIES 1994. *Natural Stone Directory*, No. 9, 1994–1995, Herald House Ltd., Worthing.

TAPANINAHO, T. 1987. Development in hydraulic drifter drilling, *Quarry Management*, March, 29–32.

TUCK, G. 1987. The control of airborne dusts in quarries, *Quarry Management*, April 23–31.

WALLER, R. 1992. *Environmental Effects of Surface Mineral Workings*. Department of the Environment, HMSO, London.

WALTON, G. 1988. *Handbook on the Hydrogeology and Stability of Excavated Slopes in Quarries*. HMSO, London.

——1990. *Handbook on the Design of Tips and Related Structures*. Department of the Environment, HMSO, London.

WANG, G., LATHAM, J.-P. & MATHESON, G. D. 1992. Design of fragmentation blasting in surface rock excavation, *'Euroc '92 Rock Characterization'* ISRM, Thomas Telford, London, 233–238.

——, —— & POOLE, A. 1991*a*. Predictions of block size distributions for quarrying, *Quarterly Journal of Engineering Geology*, 91–99.

——, —— & ——1991*b*. Blast design for armour stone production, *Quarry Management*, July, 17–21.

WEST, G. 1991. *The Field Description of Engineering Soils and Rocks*. Wiley, Chichester.

——1994. Effect of suction on the strength of rock. *Quarterly Journal of Engineering Geology*, **27**, 51–56.

WHITE, T. 1989. Blasting to specification. *Quarry Management*, December, 27–34.

WILTON, T. 1991. The air overpressure problem. *Quarry Management*, July, 25–27.

XIE, HEPING 1993. *Fractals in Rock Mechanics*. Balkema, Rotterdam.

Appendix 5.1

Quarry and mining machinery

A5.1.1. Derrick crane

The derrick crane is often the most obvious visual feature and characteristic of a dimension stone quarry.

Fig. 5.56. Derrick crane with stiff-legs (Courtesy of Natural Stone Products Ltd).

In many quarries derrick cranes provide the only means of removing blocks from the quarry or introducing machinery and tools. A derrick crane comprises a luffing jib pivoted at the base of a vertical mast that rotates to permit stewing of the crane jib. The top of the mast is braced by two beams in the form of an 'A' frame, see Fig. 5.56 to form a 'derrick on stifflegs'. The braces may be bolted to the rock or held down by counterweights often comprising blocks of quarried stone. The stifflegs restrict the rotation of the jib to about 200°. Alternatively, the mast may be braced by wire ropes to form a 'guy derrick' which offers the advantage of full rotation of the jib through 360°, see Fig. 5.57. The first steam powered derrick crane was developed by Mr Andrew Barclay and installed at the Kemnay granite quarry by Mr John Fyfe. Derrick cranes offer the distinct advantages that the quarry can be developed with steep, even vertical, sides to maximise the extraction, minimise surface area and stripping of overburden and avoid the costly and wasteful construction of roads. However, the crane cannot be rapidly repositioned so the deposit must extend to depth. Cranage also limits the output capacity of the quarry so is not attractive to producers of aggregates.

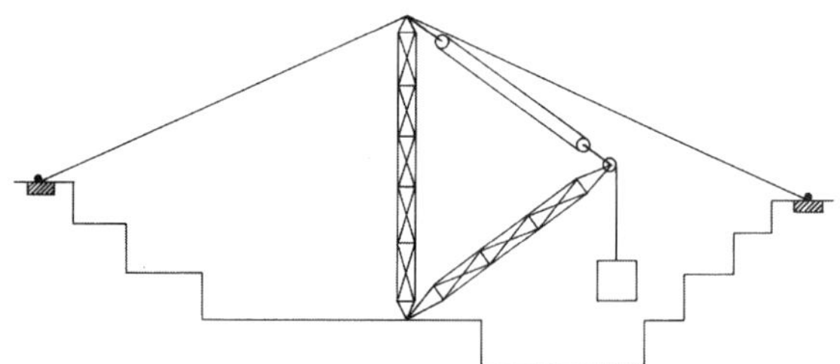

Fig. 5.57. Derrick crane with guy ropes.

A5.1.2. Rope excavator

The excavator has a base plate, usually crawler mounted, upon which rotates the superstructure comprising the power unit (diesel or electric), cable winches, control cabin, boom and bucket arm (stick), see Figs 5.58. The boom has a saddle attachment at about half of its length to which the bucket arm is pivoted; the boom and bucket are controlled by cables (ropes) from the cab. This type of excavator has been used traditionally to load blasted rock of any type into dump trucks. It may also dig directly into weakly consolidated materials. It is most likely to be seen associated with overburden removal.

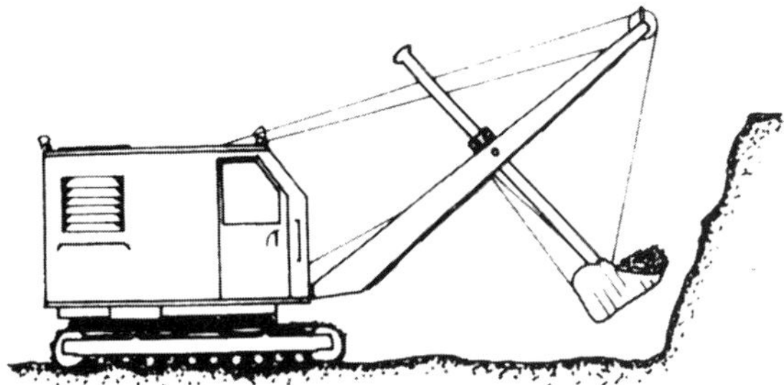

Fig. 5.58. Rope excavator.

A5.1.3. Hydraulic face excavators

The hydraulic shovel is very similar in construction and application to the rope shovel which it is steadily replacing in many quarry applications, see Fig. 5.59. The rigid, cable operated boom and stick are replaced by a jointed boom actuated by several hydraulic cylinders. The bucket can be precisely positioned and directed normally towards the face/rock pile rather than constrained to travel in an arc. The main advantages are their excavating power through the especially high break-out forces exerted upon the rock, reduced cycle times and lower maintenance costs. In some quarries hydraulic excavators are used to break blocks away from the face exploiting natural joints.

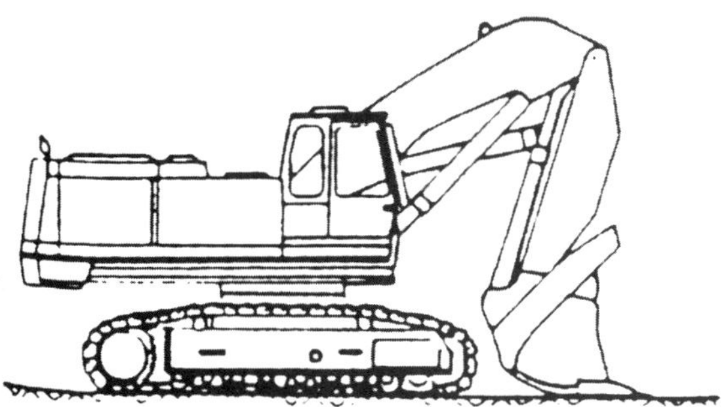

Fig. 5.59. Hydraulic face excavator.

A5.1.4. Hydraulic backhoes

Also known as a 'back acter' this excavator is extremely accurate and rapid and has become very common both loading blasted rock into dump trucks and digging soils and overburden. It is usually mounted upon driven crawler tracks and can slew through 360°, see Fig. 5.60. The versatility of the backhoe is a distinct advantage in quarry operations where different bucket sizes and types can be fitted to the excavator arm. In addition, the bucket can be replaced with a variety of other tools including hydraulic impact hammers to break oversize rocks and cactus grabs to handle such rocks.

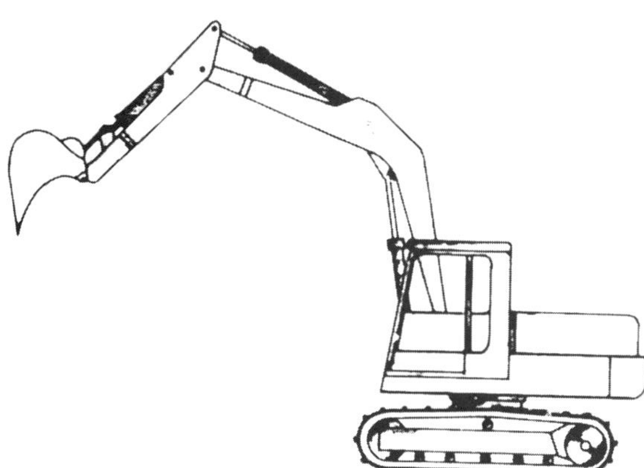

Fig. 5.60. Hydraulic back-hoe excavator.

A5.1.5. Wheeled loaders

Also known as a 'front-end loader', FEL, this machine is mounted upon rubber tyres and normally steered by the front wheels. Even greater manoeuvrability has been achieved in recent years by articulation, see Fig. 5.61. Whereas smaller units are commonly employed to load lorries and rail wagons, larger units are becoming common for loading blasted rock into dumptrucks. It can also be used to carry material in the bucket over limited distances to obviate the need for dump trucks; a 'load and carry' operation. Wheel loaders do require blasted rock to be well fragmented and the width of the bucket prevents selective work. Tyre wear is a major consideration and protective chains are fitted to tyres in some operations. The running surface should also be free of loose sharp rocks, dry and firm to provide good traction otherwise a track mounted excavator may be the better choice. However, this machine is highly versatile in application since various types of bucket may be fitted or the bucket replaced by a variety of tools such as lifting beams, single and multi-tine forks, dozer blades and hydraulic grabs.

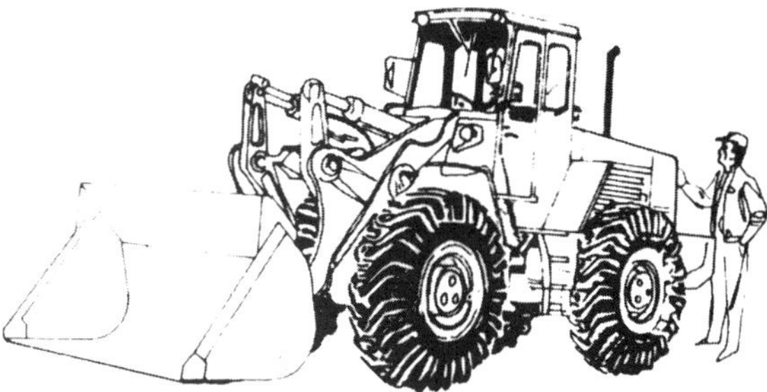

Fig. 5.61. Wheeled loader.

A5.1.6. Dragline excavator

The dragline is usually mounted upon crawler tracks since the long side tracks reduce bearing pressure and increase stability, see Fig. 5.62. The superstructure comprising power unit, winch, cabin and boom rotate on this base. The machine is usually situated on a bank

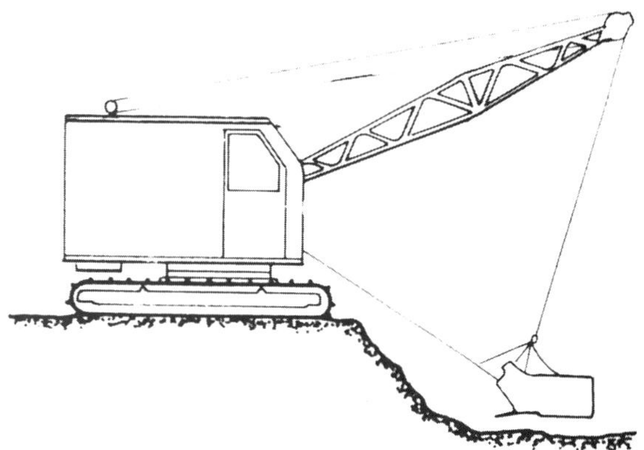

Fig. 5.62. Dragline excavator.

and is able to excavate material to a considerable depth below the bank depending upon boom length. The dragline can excavate unconsolidated rocks e.g. sands, gravels and alluvium and well fragmented blasted rock. However, it is not suited to the selective extraction of thinly bedded materials e.g. soils. It can operate 'wet' by extracting minerals from under water which is very useful for sands and gravels but unlikely to be seen in a stone quarry. A major application in surface mining is in 'strip mining' where the overburden is fragmented by blasting before being excavated by the dragline bucket. Having slewed the boom through 90° to 180° the overburden is then dumped behind the dragline to fill the previous void. Drag-lines modified as cranes are common in dimension stone quarries since they offer mobility.

A5.1.7. Crawler tractors
The tractor consists of a power unit fitted with crawler or caterpillar tracks that reduce the bearing pressure on the ground and enable the machine to move across most types of surface. A blade may be attached across the front of the machine (bulldozer) to move and spread materials over short distances, see Fig. 5.63. The tractor can draw a scraper bowl or assist the loading of motorised scrapers by pushing, see Fig. 5.30. A tyne or ripper may also be attached to the drawbar of a crawler tractor which is used to loosen unconsolidated, friable and thinly bedded rocks, see also §5.3.2. A recent development is the impact ripper utilising an hydraulic hammer action to break even more competent rock such as thinly bedded limestones and weathered overburden. The crawler tractor (bulldozer/ripper) can be employed in the removal of overburden and tipping of waste.

Fig. 5.63. Crawler tractor.

A5.1.8. Motor scraper
The scraper (box) is usually associated with the rapid, low cost excavation soils and unconsolidated overburden. It is not suitable for excavation of hard rock, blasted rock or gravels containing large boulders. It comprises a box or bowl mounted on pneumatic tyres which is either towed by a tractor or articulated and motorised, see Fig. 5.30. The front of the box is open and the leading edge is fitted with a blade which scrapes the surface of the material when the edge is lowered. The box is discharged by a ram acting upon a pusher plate.

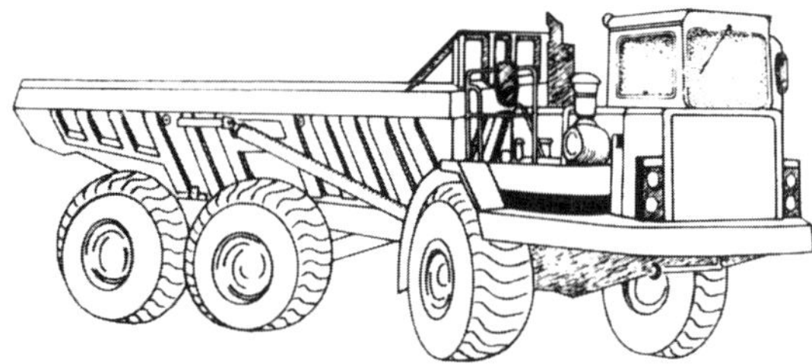

Fig. 5.64. Articulated dump truck.

A5.1.9. Articulated dump truck
The articulation of the body and the multiple wheel drive create a dump truck that can operate successfully on very poor and constricted haul roads as often found when moving overburden and soils, see Fig. 5.64. However, the ADT is generally not suitable to the loading and carrying of blasted rock owing to the shock loads and wear upon the body.

A5.1.10. Rigid body dump truck
On well maintained haul roads the rigid body dump truck can achieve higher speeds and be expected to return lower operating costs than the ADT. It is usually employed to haul blasted rock which has been loaded by an hydraulic or rope excavator, see Fig. 5.65, either to the process plant or waste tips.

Fig. 5.65. Rigid body, rear-dump truck.

A5.1.11. Trolleys and scows
Mechanically propelled trolleys with jacking devices are available to lift blocks off the floor of the quarry and move them about the quarry workings. The scow is a modified road vehicle employing the chassis of a truck fitted with a robust, flat-bed body that is often covered

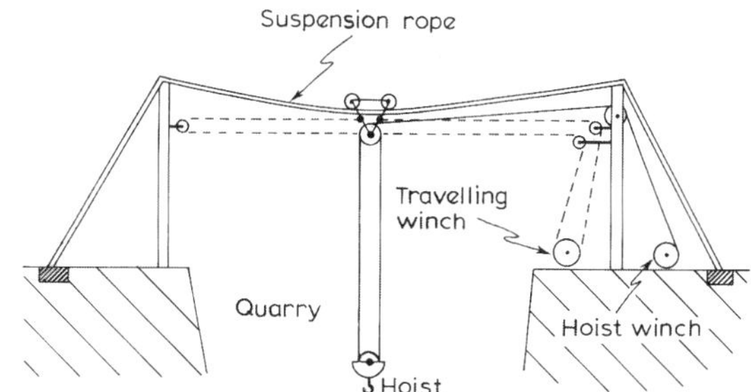

Fig. 5.66. Cable crane.

with a layer of scalpings or waste. It is used to transport large blocks within the quarry workings.

A5.1.12. Ropeways, cableways and inclines

Although unusual in modern quarries, aerial ropeways have been and are used to transport blasted rock and especially waste. Buckets are suspended from the rope which is itself supported by isolated pylons. It is particulary suitable for traversing very rugged, mountainous terrain, rivers, snowfields, marsh and bog where roads for trucks are difficult to construct and maintain. Ropeways were used, for example, to carry waste clear of the quarries at Carrara. To obtain a longer reach than that possible with a derrick crane a static cable can be strung across an excavation to support a pulley wheel suspended from a trolley or 'horse'. A lifting rope connected to a fixed winch runs over the pulley to produce a cable-crane as was used in the granite quarries near Aberdeen and many slate quarries of Wales, see Fig. 5.66. This device is sometimes named a 'Blondin', after the famous tight-rope walker, and was first introduced into stone quarries by Mr John Fyfe.

On inclines, the use of rail mounted bogies controlled by ropes have been a historical feature of many quarries. The incline had at least two parallel tracks and was described as 'powered' in that the winch drum was driven by electric motor or steam engine or as 'self-acting'. On a self-acting incline the weight of a descending bogie together with load of stone block(s) was sufficient to raise the empty bogie. Each bogie was connected to the winding drum by a rope but one rope was wound over the drum and the other under the drum. The speed of ascent or descent was controlled by brakes applied to the drum.

Fig. 5.67. Quarry bar supporting two top-hammer drills (Courtesy of ARC Ltd).

Another application of the self-acting incline was the water balance which was used to raise a load against the gradient of an incline. Each bogie was fitted with a tank which was filled with water at the top of the incline to act as the counterbalance and then drained at the bottom where the bogie was loaded with block(s) or waste. It was popular in slate mines and was adapted to operate in vertical shafts also.

A5.1.13. Quarry bar

As the name implies, this is a term used traditionally to describe a bar or scaffold erected within the quarry and used to support equipment such as drills or channelling machines. It is useful when a series of holes are to be drilled along a line or for guiding the channelling machine, see Fig. 5.67.

6. Processing

6.1. Introduction

This chapter describes the processing of the blocks or fragmented stone after removal of the rock from the mine or quarry face. The processing of armourstone and rock fill have much in common and armourstone will be taken to include material intended for coastal protection as well as other forms of 'hydraulic stone' and 'rip-rap' used to prevent erosion of water courses. In the most part processing will have the following objectives:

- ensuring the quality of the stone in terms of fitness for purpose including, strength, competency and durability in service
- Defining the required physical dimensions and shape of the stone
- conferring the desired surface finish, where appropriate

6.2. Rock fill

6.2.1. Introduction

Processing of fragmented rock to produce rock fill is relatively simple comprising breakage of oversize and sizing or grading of the material using grids and screens. Crushing of rock should not be necessary to meet the specification but may be carried out to reduce blasted rock to a size suitable for other construction uses within the same project, for example, road sub-base.

6.2.2. Secondary breaking

Oversize blocks of stone produced by quarry blasting may be sorted as armourstone by the face excavator or set aside for secondary breakage. In highway cuttings, oversize blocks may be used for landscaping purposes but would normally be set aside for secondary breakage. In most cases, however, the design of the blast should provide material substantially within the grading specified without the need for further breakage.

Traditional methods of secondary breakage are 'popping' and 'plaster blasting' both involving the use of explosives. They are not currently favoured owing to the adverse environmental impact (see §5.2.3.4). and are too hazardous for use in construction sites. Popping consists of drilling a blasthole in the block and using a small, relatively unconfined explosive charge to break the block. 'Plaster shooting' consists of packing a charge against the surface of the block using clay or other suitable material. A drop-ball machine usually comprises a redundant crane or dragline which raises and then drops a heavy steel weight onto oversize blocks. The method is slow but effective. Many modern quarries now make use of hydraulic impact hammers mounted upon the chassis of an excavator to break oversize, see Fig. 6.1.

6.2.3. Sizing

The fragmented rock is excavated from the rock-pile either by hydraulic excavator or front-end loader (FEL). Depending upon the distance over which the rock must be carried, dump trucks may be used to transport the blasted rock to a static grid. The static grid, often referred to as a grizzly, is a very robustly constructed screen comprising parallel steel bars or rails, sometimes of trapezoidal cross-section to prevent pegging of lumps between the bars, see Fig. 6.2. The grid may be inclined, to induce oversize to flow across the grid, or horizontal and the aperture will typically exceed 200 mm.

Horizontal grids although static, are not usually fixed. One edge is located by a hinge so that the grid can be inclined when required. Typically, the blasted rock is tipped over the grid by a wheeled loader climbing a ramp constructed from quarry waste or by a back-hoe excavator working from a stockpile. Undersize passes through directly into a dump truck or onto the ground or onto further vibrating screens. Any oversize resting on the grid is removed by raising one edge of the grid with the bucket of the loader. Thus, both feeding the grid and removal of oversize and undersize can be accomplished by a single wheeled loader or back-hoe excavator. The undersize product from the grid can be further separated into sized fractions by vibrating or rotary screens, see Figs 6.3 and 6.5.

6.3. Armourstone

6.3.1. Introduction

The processing of armourstone has much in common with rock fill. Large blocks are selected individually and further sizing is carried out by grids and screens (Hartley & Bjerkan 1994; CIRIA 1991).

6.3.2. Selection

Large blocks weighing over 1000kg (750mm cube) are sorted individually using the excavator bucket or an attachment such as a 'cactus grab' (swivel-peel type grab) or power forks, see Fig. 6.4. The blocks should be individually numbered and marked with the weight. This is facilitated by the incorporation into the excavator of a means of weighing the block. One method is to monitor the pressure in the hydraulic system and to calibrate this against known weights carried in the bucket.

Fig. 6.1. Hydraulic hammer attached to an hydraulic excavator.

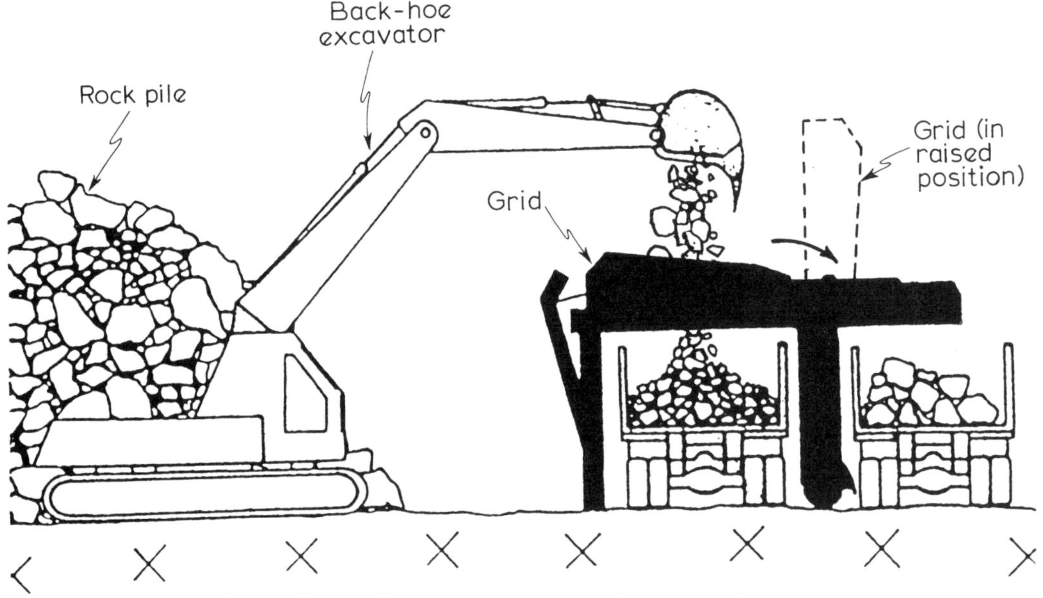

Fig. 6.2. Static grid for sizing armourstone (Courtesy Simbas Ltd).

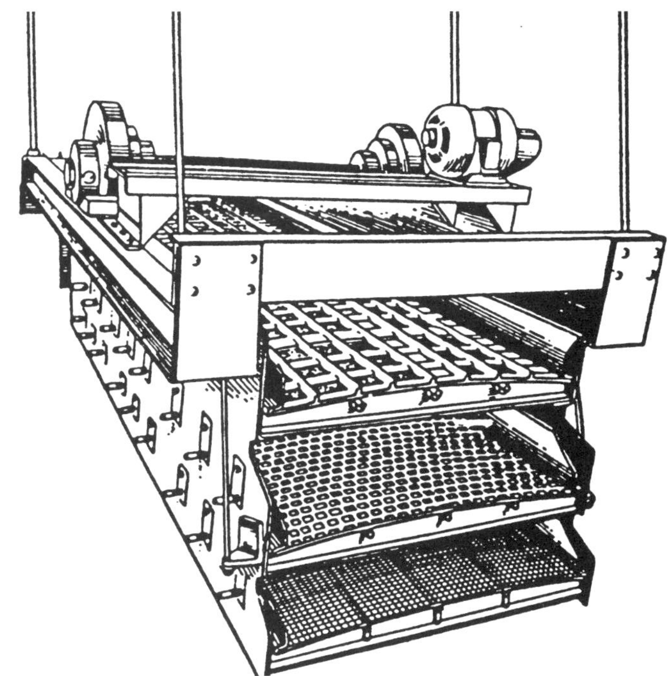

Fig. 6.3. Vibrating screen.

Fig. 6.4. Handling armourstone by mechanical tongs fitted to a hydraulic excavator.

Fig. 6.5. Screening coarse rock by (a) vibrating grizzly and (b) trommel screen.

6.3.3. Sizing

Static grids (see Fig. 6.2) can be used to size lumps greater than about 150 mm (up to 8 kg). Provision should be made for adjustment of the aperture between 100 and 600 mm. Vibrating grizzly screens, having the same form of screening surface as grids, can be used to size lumps below 300 mm, see Fig. 6.5(a). Robust rotary trommel screens are also available for producing several sized fractions simultaneously, see Fig. 6.5(b).

For finer material, conventional inclined vibrating screens can be used, see Fig. 6.3. Sizing of finer material arising during the production of armourstone can provide rock fill for gabions and aggregates etc. At this point it should be noted that the production of finer material is unavoidable and is often a critical aspect of an operation to produce armourstone. In a remote area space for waste tips must be found. In an area nearer to urbanization, markets for aggregates must be proved or space identified for waste. The armourstone must bear the full cost of extraction if no markets for finer materials exist.

6.3.4. Picking rip-rap

A device for selecting rip-rap can be installed above a conveyor belt carrying crushed or blasted rock. The device, trade name 'Side-kick', comprises several radial assemblies of spokes freely mounted upon shafts supported by a simple beam fixed diagonally across the line of the conveyor, see Fig. 6.6. The device relies upon the fact that material on the conveyor belt naturally segregates under the influence of mild agitation during transport so that larger pieces rest upon fines. The spokes rotate through contact with the larger particles that protrude above the bed of material travelling upon the belt. A sideways force is applied to such particles and they are eventually pushed over the edge of the belt.

6.3.5. Handling

Large individual stones can be handled directly in several ways which include 'cactus grabs', power grapples, fork-lifts and buckets. They may also be lifted by chains and straps. However, in order to secure the chain(s) eye bolts

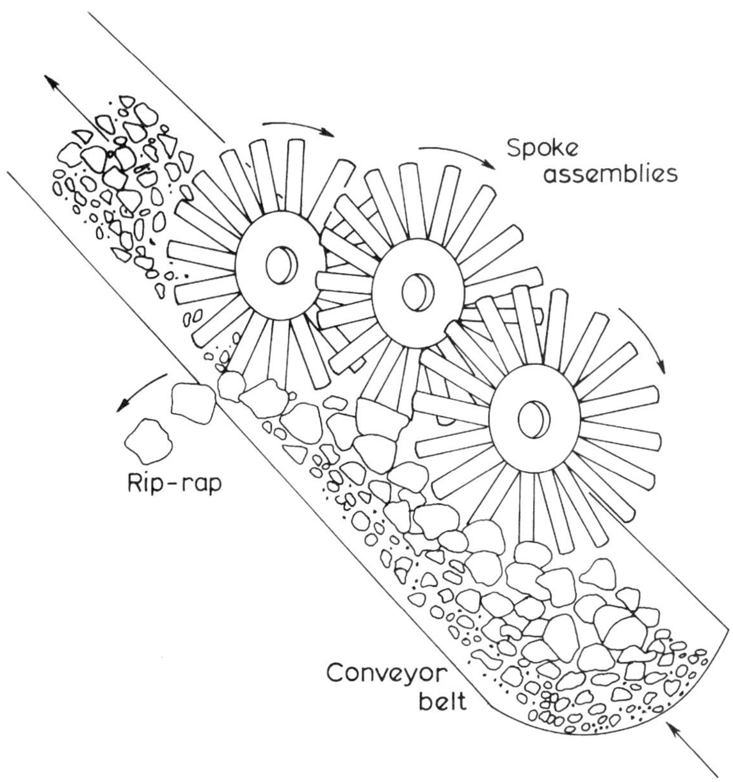

Fig. 6.6. Diagram of 'Side-kick' separator for rip-rap.

Fig. 6.7. Barge loaded with armourstone (Courtesy of Tarmac plc).

or lugs must be inserted into holes drilled into the stone. Smaller sizes can be handled by any type of excavator, principally the wheeled loader.

6.3.6. Transport

Armourstone is in most demand for the construction of sea defences and, therefore, has to be delivered to the very margin of the sea. Although armourstone is transported by road, the individual stones are heavy and there is some danger attached to road transport. This method is also relatively expensive and the delivery point may still be remote from the construction site. The ideal method of transport is by the sea itself permitting the carriage of large loads and delivery directly to the point of use. For this reason, exploration for deposits suitable for armourstone production is particularly directed to coastal areas with easy access to the sea. Purpose-built barges that can be unloaded by beaching on the shore at low tide are commonly employed for transport, see Fig. 6.7.

6.4. Dimension stone

6.4.1. Introduction

Owing to the high capital investment incurred there is a general trend for masonry works to become centralised and to serve several quarries rather than be dedicated to each individual quarry as in the past (Bruce 1989). Indeed, in some cases, quarries or mines are worked only sporadically or in campaigns to establish a stock of blocks in store or at the masonry works. This is certainly the case for quarries at high altitude or in high latitudes where snowfall determines a seasonal operation.

There is also a substantial international trade in blocks and roughly sawn slabs, called scants, since these centralised masonry works contain machinery capable of processing a wide variety of rock types. Thus, to satisfy the demands of large contracts, for example provision of cladding for a major building, it is common for the principal contractor to share work between subcontractors.

Modern stone working machinery often resembles metal working machine tools and has, indeed, been adopted from that industry. In recent years much of the traditionally labour intensive work of masons has been transformed by the introduction of powered machine tools, automated production lines, stone handling equipment and diamond tools. Many repetitive, routine operations are now carried out by machines controlled by computer software and supervised by only a few operators. For example, machines such as saws that can be programmed to work 24 hours per day greatly increase the output and productivity of masonry works. Fully integrated, automated production lines for common items such as tiles are now readily available from equipment manufacturers. Handling of stones is facilitated by trolleys and the extensive use of roller tracks to transfer workpieces between units of a production line. Fork-lift trucks are also available to carry large work pieces and machines for working stone can be located in aisles under travelling gantry cranes. Rapidly acting vacuum-cups are now used to attach slabs to electric hoists and gantry cranes instead of chains, see Fig. 6.8. Similar vacuum devices are also used to hold workpieces during machining. Evidence of this change is provided, for example, by the number of persons employed in the marble quarries of the Apuan district of Italy which in 1984 had decreased to one fifth of its value in 1961.

Despite the obvious expense, diamond tools are being introduced into the industry since the cost can often be justified owing to the much greater speed of machining. Indeed the greater productivity brought about by the introduction of diamond tools is largely responsible for the present day popularity and availability of dimension stone and the fact that it can still compete with alternative materials of construction. However, caution should be exercised when comparing quoted values of the wear life of diamond and other tools. Obviously, the wear life will depend to some extent upon the abrasiveness or hardness of the rock type but it will also depend upon other factors such as the skill of the machine operator, the application and the operating conditions. For example, the clarity of the process water can have a significant affect upon wear life of tools. Poorly trained or unskilled operators may damage tools causing them to be prematurely scrapped thereby incurring higher operating costs.

Although this section describes a variety of machines for working stone, it should be noted that the largest use of dimension stone is in the relatively simple form of sawn rectangular slabs used to clad external walls and as tiles and paving.

6.4.2. Masonry design and detailing

The masonry works receives the drawings produced by architects and engineers. These vary in the amount of detail shown but generally depict the desired elevations of the structure. The architect's drawings will

Fig. 6.8. Vacuum cup device handling a stone slab (Courtesy of Vacustonelift).

Diamond tools

Diamond tools are of several types, including (i) a sintered mixture of diamond grit and bronze alloy as used to make segments for drill bits, saw tips and beads for wire saws, and (ii) diamond grit bonded to a metal substrate such as woven wire mesh by the electrolytic deposition of a nickel matrix used, for example, to produce sanding discs. The original circular diamond saws employed individual diamonds set into cups on the perimeter of the disc but, later, replaceable segments were brazed onto the teeth. Most recently, laser welding has been introduced to fix segments to the disc or centre, and this has enabled even faster cutting speeds to be achieved.

thus show the desired course heights and dimensions of visible stones on the facade, the openings for doors and windows and the detail of interfaces between these and the facade.

Using these drawings, the masonry draughtsman proposes the design and detail of the fixing system of the cladding for approval by the architect and engineer. He will also identify any necessary modifications to the course heights or individual stones that are required by the availability of blocks. In addition, and most importantly, he determines the size, shape and profile of each individual stone and creates detailed drawings. The masonry draughtsman may also act as the co-ordinator for the design of the detail of the external envelope by repeatedly exchanging drawings with window and door frame manufacturers, architects, structural engineers and construction contractors as the detail is brought to a final state.

Although drawings may be produced manually on a drawing board, it is normal for these to be generated by a computer-aided design (CAD) drawing system with transfer of information by disk or modem. The use of CAD and multi-discipline co-ordination meetings can greatly reduce the time required to complete the design detailing stage. Following the finalisation and approval of the drawings they are passed to the mould cutting section of the masonry works for the preparation of production cards (see Fig. 6.9) which may relate to a single or several stones. Each stone is given a unique number corresponding to the drawing number, stone number and number of the pallet on which it will be delivered to the construction site. For example, stone number 56 on drawing GA9 which will be delivered on pallet 37 will be identified as 9/56/37. These cards also carry a three-dimensional drawing of the stone and all the information necessary for the production of that stone. This card can also be printed directly by the CAD system. Templates (moulds) of the bed profiles of each stone for use by the masons in the works can also be printed directly onto flexible plastic sheet by the CAD system and cut out by hand. When the profile is complex or to be used repeatedly, moulds may be cut from zinc metal sheet.

The production cards and templates are then passed to the production control department. Ideally, the production and the batching of the stones on pallets for delivery should anticipate the order of use in construction so that no delays are incurred nor excessive storage required. Very importantly, batching must result in the best utilization of blocks available at any given time without unecessary waste generation. Good management at this stage is important to an efficient and profitable operation.

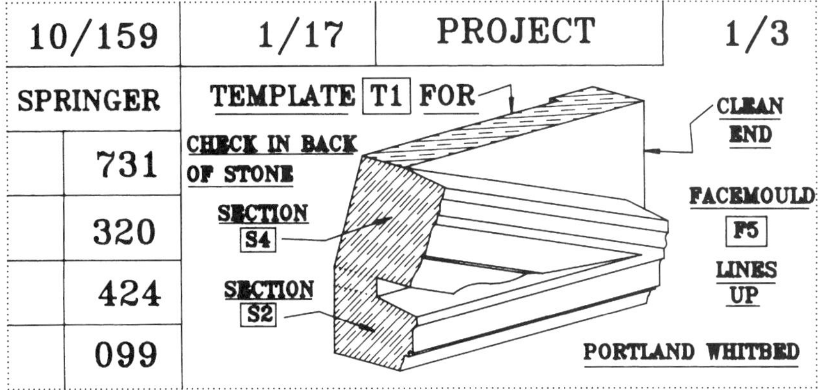

Fig. 6.9. Production cards for stones (Courtesy of Bath & Portland Stone Ltd and Rattee and Kent).

MOWLEM	Rattee And Kett Purbeck Road Cambridge	Contract Ely Cathedral -South Choir	Chart No 3 PC No MI498/03

Location	Gablet on Pinnacles	Stone Type	CLIPSHAM	Date Required 31/03/94	Date Charted 23/03/94

No off	Stone No	Length	Thickness	Height	Saw	Work	Del	26.3 Diagram	Ft3	Bonus Masons	Bonus Saws
1	A65	416	205	370				Gablet Finiale	1.114	10	7HRS
1	A66	322	256	277				Gablet	0.806	4	TOTAL
1	A67	322	276	277				Gablet	0.869	4	
1	A68	350	348	277				Gablet	1.191	5	
1	A69	300	390	277				Gablet	1.145	5	
1	A70	294	256	277				Gablet	0.736	4	
1	A71	336	256	277				Gablet	0.841	4	
1									0.000		
1									0.000		
1									0.000		
1									0.000		
1									0.000		
1									0.000		
1								Note*Total Of Charted Stones Is 1.8FC.Larger Than In The BQ	0.000		
1								Carving*Stones A65 . 10HRS&StoneA66-A71. 5HRS.Each	0.000		

Drawn By		Circulation	Q.C.	C.Manager	Production	Q.C. Check	Total F3	6.70
Material Used:			W.Surveyor		Site	Date 23/3/94	176.3057	

Fig. 6.9. (*continued*).

6.4.3. Stone selection

Where stone blocks are of a uniform texture and colour and relatively free from faults such as vents, clay pockets, ferrous nodules and fractures, they can be selected with some confidence at the quarry by size to suit production requirements. Stone which is prone to colour or textural changes and likely to contain faults is more problematic in that a block selected for size may not produce the expected yield and its nature may not be evident until it has been cut. The worst examples of stones in current use may yield less than 20% of the volume of the raw block. Further discussion and illustrations of flaws can be found under the subject of quality systems (§6.5).

Historically, masonry producers tended to work only their local stone and, therefore, had an intimate knowledge of the quarry and its stone. In more recent years, with the increasing use of machinery designed primarily for the granite and marble industries, producers have found that they have tools capable of working any stone. Consequently they have broadened their base to include not only the various colours and textures within their own type of stone but also all types. This, of course, means that the local intimate knowledge regarding the stone and its characteristics is absent. Thus, greater reliance is now put upon either the quarry owner to provide blocks of good quality or on an intermediary, a stockholder, who may act for many quarries, around the world.

6.4.4. Splitting

Blocks removed from the face can be sub-divided on the quarry floor or in the masonry works by the methods described in §5.3.9, especially by plugs and feathers.

6.4.5. Primary saws

Large blocks are first prepared by primary saws comprising either wire saws, circular saws or frame saws. The first stage is often the trimming of an irregular block to obtain a rectangular prism.

It should be noted at this stage that the choice of the plane for the cut is not arbitrary. Many sedimentary rocks such as sandstones and limestones will exhibit marked textural differences on cut surfaces depending upon the orientation with respect to original bedding planes and features such as current bedding. Furthermore, stones cut from sedimentary rocks must generally be laid so that the original bedding plane is horizontal in the structure to retard delamination, see Chapter 9. On the other hand, non-structural cladding may be sawn vertically with respect to the bedding plane to obtain greater flexural strength. Blocks of slate to be split to make roofing tiles must first be cut perpendicularly to the cleavage and pillaring planes and then in the plane of pillaring. If this is not done it will be impossible to produce rectangular slates.

The wire saw described in §5.3.9.9 is simple and portable such that it can be operated on the quarry floor as an alternative to splitting. In this case the wire can be wrapped around the block, which is raised up and supported by rock scrap or wooden blocks, without the need to drill holes. Fixed wire saws are used in masonry works as primary saws and offer the advantage over all other types that they can cut the block in any profile like a fret saw or jig saw (see Fig. 6.10). Thus, they are called contouring wire saws.

A primary circular saw is a vertical, steel disc of large diameter, called the 'centre', having diamond impregnated segments brazed to the teeth around the perimeter,

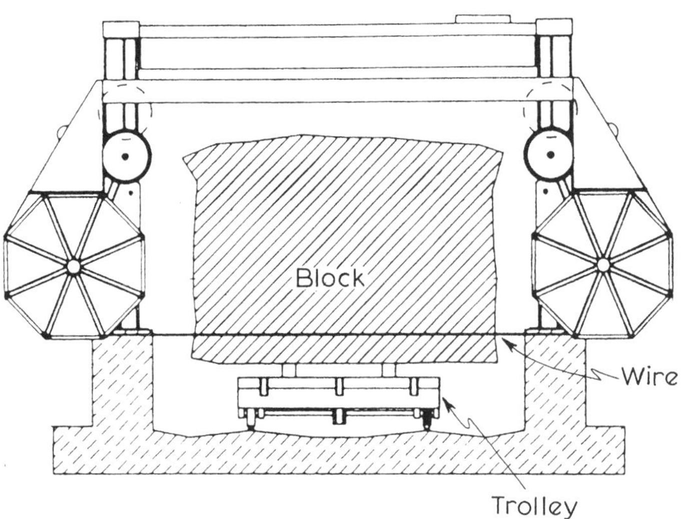

Fig. 6.10. Arrangement of a fixed (monofilament) wire saw.

see Fig. 6.11. The segments can be replaced several times, maybe four, before erosion of the teeth requires that the centre is renewed or recut. The disc is driven by a central shaft powered by a motor travelling across a gantry or bridge spanning the work table so that the saw may move both transversely and vertically. In the most modern works the bridge itself may also travel longitudinally along rails running either side of an aisle. Several blocks positioned along the length of the aisle are cut sequentially into slabs by the automatic saw working continuously without further supervision. The circular saw is most economically used to 'square' irregular blocks, to cut thick slabs (>100 mm) and to produce blocks of a given course height that will be converted into ashlar.

The circular saw cuts faster than the frame saw but can make only a single cut. The depth of cut is limited to

Fig. 6.11. Primary circular saw (Courtesy of Bath & Portland Stone Ltd).

between 25% and 33% of the diameter of the disc, increasing with disc diameter to a maximum of about 2.2 m with the largest available blade of diameter 5 m. Thus, prior to the development of circular saws of large diameter, highly tensioned, single bladed frame saws were used and are still used to trim blocks, see Fig. 6.12. Circular saws produce high noise levels in contrast to the relatively quiet frame saws and wire saws. Therefore, special blades with laminated centres comprising copper sandwiched between steel have been developed to reduce noise levels by 12–15 dB.

Frame saws are capable of simultaneously dividing a block into many slabs (see Fig. 6.13), although the rate of cutting is slow, say, 8 mm/hour in granite. The principal application is the production of slab of thickness less than 50mm. The saw is a blade of steel, which is tensioned within the frame by wedges, screws or hydraulic cylinders, and which reciprocates through the block being lubricated and cooled by water. The frame may contain many parallel blades (up to 60 or more) and the spacing between them can be adjusted according to the desired thickness of slab. The blade has corrugations or vertical grooves in the surface to accommodate the separate cutting media which are fed into the cut, for example, sharp sand for limestones and marbles and steel shot for granite. The introduction during the 1960s of cast iron and steel shot as cutting media for granites was a very significant development resulting in substantial increases to productivity and the availabilty of sawn granite (O'Neill 1961). Frame saws employing steel shot are still considered to be the most economic method of cutting granite slabs. The steel shot is partially crushed to generate sharp edges on the particles of size about 1 mm. The shot is contained in a recirculating, viscous cutting medium comprising water, shot and cuttings. The saw blade describes an arc as it moves through the cut raising at the extremity of each swing to permit medium to flow beneath the blade. When using steel shot as a cutting medium care should be taken that all media is removed from the slab by washing to prevent iron staining.

Most modern frame saws for marble have diamond impregnated tips brazed onto the teeth of a notched blade. Initially, with the introduction of diamond tools, the existing frame saws were fitted with diamond impregnated blades but the full potential of increased cutting rate was not realised owing to the oscillating action of the frame. Modern, purpose-built, diamond frame saws use a rectilinear or reciprocating action and gain additional speed. However, these have not been applied to granite owing to the excessively high tension

Fig. 6.12. Single blade frame saw cutting a marble block.

Fig. 6.13. Multi-blade frame saw cutting a marble block.

in the blade that is required. Application to granites has required rearrangement of the saw to reciprocate through the block in a vertical direction in order to reduce the length of cut to less than 1 m and, thereby, the tension in the blade.

The surface finish of the sawn slabs is good, offering the advantage over some other methods of splitting that little material needs to removed by later polishing. However, in all sawing stages there is a significant loss of yield caused by the cut or kerf. It is claimed that diamond saws produce a smoother finish to compensate for the greater cost.

Not all masonry works need to contain a primary saw(s) since there is now an extensive international trade in roughly sawn slabs called scants which can enter the process at the stage of secondary sawing.

6.4.6. Secondary saws

Secondary saws are circular saws of smaller diameter (see Fig. 6.14 which shows a secondary saw on a fixed bridge). In the past, the teeth have been impregnated with silicon carbide (carborundum) but most are now diamond saws. Approximate cutting rates are 0.1–0.5 m^2/min in marble and 0.01–0.1 m^2/min in granite with an expected life of 3000–4000 m^2 in marble. Saws with a diameter greater than 0.5m are usually retipped when worn.

The saw is mounted on a head that can traverse a bridge which itself spans a travelling table for the workpiece. In this case the block rests upon timber or scrap rock slabs. Commonly, the table is replaced by a travel-ling belt that can move a block into the path of the saw and then remove sawn pieces. The saw is set to cut through the block and partly into the rubberized belt beneath.

Angled cuts can be made by the use of a universal head or a rotating bridge piece, see Fig. 6.15. The table can be supported so that it can be raised, lowered or rotated. Thus, it is possible to create chamfers, steps, slots and rebates and even do much of the traditional work of a mason. In this respect, a series of parallel cuts of varying depth can be made to define the profile of an object within a block after which the intervening webs are broken out by the mason, see Fig. 6.16.

In the particular case of the production of tiles and ashlar, automated bridge saws, known as block cutting or slabbing saws, equipped with both a vertical and a horizontal circular saw blade can divide trimmed block directly into slabs in a number of descending passes, see Fig. 6.17, thus replacing the traditional frame saw.

Fig. 6.14. Photograph of secondary, circular diamond saw supported by a fixed bridge.

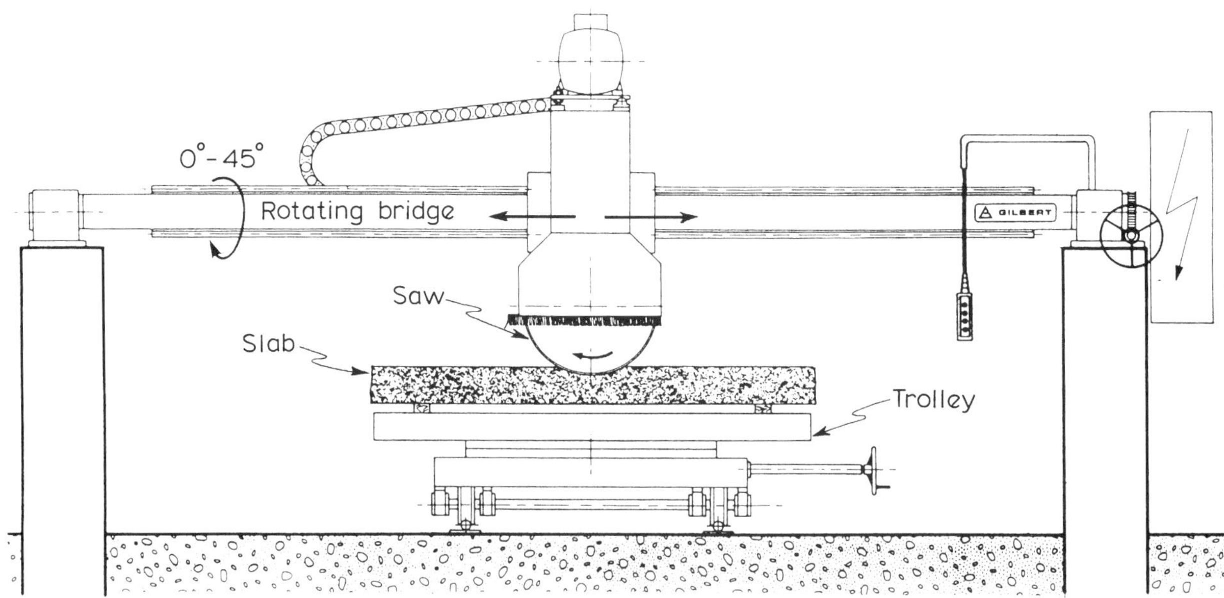

Fig. 6.15. Diagram of a secondary circular saw supported on a rotating bridge.

Fig. 6.16. Block sawn by circular saw to rough outline of half column (Courtesy of Dimensional Stone Ltd).

Variants having multiple, parallel vertical circular saws and a single horizontal circular blade have been developed to cut granites in order to compensate for the slow speed of cutting, see Fig. 6.18.

The ability to cut slab precisely to small tolerances and to produce thin slab has contributed significantly to the success of stone as a cladding material. Thin slab reduces the weight of cladding and thereby the cost of the supporting structures. In addition, thin slab reduces the cost of the stone since a greater area is created from a given volume of block. Precise, reproducible thickness allows the use of modern, rapid techiques for installation of cladding. In an attempt to reduce weight even further, diamond saws have been developed to cut marble into slab as thin as 6 mm and granites to 10 mm.

The technique for cutting marble into such thin slab is as follows. The block is cut into 20 mm slabs but the saw does not cut completely through to the base of the block. The cuts or kerfs are now filled with polystyrene foam to hold the slabs in position. The saw is then run through the centre of each slab to produce two slabs of thickness 6 mm when allowance is made for the kerf itself. These very thin slabs are bonded to metal panels or plaster boards by adhesives. Thin slabs of granite are cut by frame saw and milled to the exact thickness.

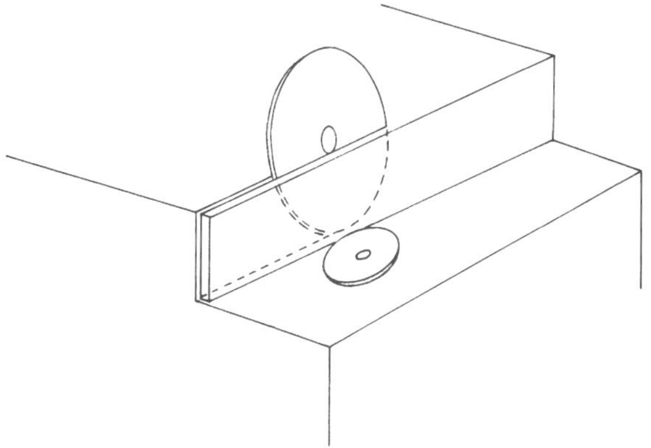

Fig. 6.17. Diagram of the action of a block cutting or slabbing saw.

6.4.7. Planers

In a planer, the workpiece is mounted upon a horizontal bed plate which is driven linearly against a fixed tool that cuts the stone, see Fig. 6.19. The machine is used to

Fig. 6.18. Block cutting or stabbing saw (Courtesy of SEA Diamond Tools).

produce masonry items such as mullions, sills and copings or any long piece of fixed profile e.g. stone for string courses. The stone is worked dry.

6.4.8. Lathes

A roughly sawn block, usually hexagonal or octagonal in shape, is clamped into the chuck or head of the lathe and rotated against a cutting tool. For smaller diameters the workpiece rotates on a horizontal axis; for larger diameters the axis is vertical. The tool may also be moved in a controlled manner to produce spiral or twisted columns in a process similar to thread cutting. The lathe is used to turn items such as column sections and balusters. In place of a fixed tool a small diameter circular, diamond saw or a grinding wheel is now often used to cut the stone, see Fig. 6.20.

6.4.9. Routers

The router is adapted from the wood-working industry and comprises a rotating, conical or cylindrical tool covered with diamond or cutting compound. It can work in any direction to produce complex surface forms. It can be guided in several ways including (i) by a stylus moving over a three-dimensional pattern (ii) by an light detector moving over a tracing or drawing and (iii) by digitized data describing coordinates upon a surface. The differences between routers and mills no longer appears to be distinct especially with the introduction of CNC machines. Usage sometimes implies small hand held machines and generally implies the production of a complex three-dimensional surface.

6.4.10. Milling

The mill is very similar to a metal working machine in that the rotating tool is generally cylindrical although it is commonly profiled, see Fig. 6.21. The axis of rotation is usually vertical and the surface produced has simple curvature. An important use is the creation of profiled edges to slabs. These edge profiles are given recognized names such as (a) bull nose-half round or semicircular and ogee- smooth S shaped curve. In addition, the mill is used in the production of curved pieces such as arch sections and curved risers for stone stair cases and steps. It can also cut rebates and apertures in slabs, for example, bath and sink tops, see Fig. 6.22.

6.4.11. Work centres

A work centre comprises a motor driven, universal head or chuck travelling on a bridge spanning an elevating work table, see Fig. 6.23. The chuck can accept a variety of tools from a magazine which contains such items as; circular diamond saw, mills of various profiles, routers, power chisels and polishing heads. The chuck will select and load the appropriate tool automatically as directed by the computer (numerical) control system. The motion of the head and tool is controlled automatically by either (i) a stylus travelling over a pattern or (ii) digitized coordinates taken directly from drawings, or (iii) software programmes containing electronic data files created by a CAD system. These machines are known by the acronym CNC (computerised numerical control) or NC (numerical control) or CN as in the metal working industry. They are ideally suited to the repetitive production of such items as bas-relief plaques, stone marquetry table tops and tiles, mouldings and engravings.

6.4.12. Surface finishes

There are many types of finish available often described by traditional terms. The natural state of the face of a stone produced by splitting rock is described as riven or rock faced. This may be entirely appropriate for some uses including paving, walling, roofing, kerb stones and some cladding. Certainly, if the face is not to be exposed

Fig. 6.19. Planer (Courtesy of Bath & Portland Stone Ltd).

there is often no need for further processing. Some methods of surface finishing may cause a change to the appearance of the stone and to the durability of the surface. Schaffer (1972) states that methods employing blunt tools and chisel points can 'bruise' the surface of the rock causing fracturing of mineral grains or the cement of a sedimentary rock. Therefore, the surface may initially exhibit less durability as loosely bonded material is rapidly removed by weathering. For this reason it would not be expected that flame texturing, broaching or dolly pointing would be used as finishing processes for cladding on the upper elevations of buildings.

6.4.12.1. Sawn

Sawing permits better control of the dimensions of a stone but may leave striations on the sawn surface. In many cases the rough sawn finish will be adequate for the application or the sawn surface will be concealed by mortar in a joint. In other cases the sawn surface is subjected to further treatment. Blocks cut by saws are often described by the number of sawn surfaces for example 'sawn six sides'. It should be noted that it may be necessary to clean the surface of stones cut by frame saws employing steel shot to ensure that all shot has been removed and to prevent any future risk of staining due to rust formation.

6.4.12.2. Rubbed

Rubbing with an abrasive block or sanding with a power tool to remove saw marks can create a satisfactory finish for, say, cladding, paving and ashlar.

6.4.12.3. Dolly pointed

This may also be called 'bush hammered' and is currently very popular. The term is a corruption of a French word describing a multi-pointed chisel. A pneumatic, multi-pointed chisel or pick (6 to 24 points) is moved over the surface to produce a flat but roughened, non reflective surface (see Fig. 5.6). It eradicates marks left by working the stone by sawing and imparts a slip resistant surface to the stone. It is popular for granites and used as a finish for paving and street furniture such as kerbs and bollards. In the past stone slabs were trimmed by a chop axe and then dressed by axe so the term 'fine axed' may also be used to describe a bush hammered surface.

6.4.12.4. Grit blasted

Grit blasting using sand for softer rocks or carbide for granite, is used to produce a smooth but dull finish. This is also very popular for cladding. Grit blasting may also be used for engraving memorials and slab, see Fig. 6.33.

Fig. 6.20. Lathe with diamond saw in place of fixed tool turning a column from a hexagonal sawn work piece (Courtesy of Bath & Portland Stone Ltd).

6.4.12.5. Flame textured

A flame is moved across the surface to induce spalling and create a particular rippled effect which is popular for paving slabs and cladding, see Fig. 6.24. Rates of 25 to 30 m^2/h can be achieved. Consideration may need to be given to possible adverse effects of flame texturing with respect to surface durability and change of colour with some rock types. It is obviously inappropriate for limestones and marbles but applied to granites and sandstones.

6.4.12.6. Honed

This term is used to describe the roughly polished but non-reflective, surface of sandstone and slate in particular.

6.4.12.7. Polished

The process is also sometimes referred to as 'glossing'. It is important to realise that not all rocks can be polished to a high gloss and that other finishes, such as rubbed, flame textured or bush-hammered, are more

Fig. 6.21. Various mills and diamond tools.

Fig. 6.22. Milling machine (Courtesy of Dimensional Stone Ltd).

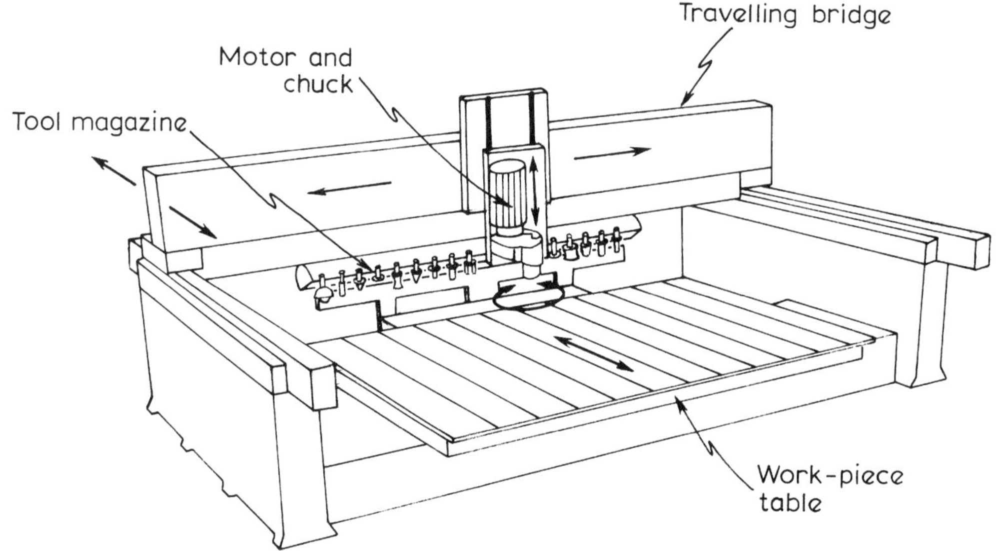

Fig. 6.23. Arrangement of an CNC machine.

Fig. 6.24. Flame texturing of sandstone paving (Courtesy of Dimensional Stone Ltd).

Polish

The quality of the polish has been assessed traditionally by visual inspection or touch. It is now possible to measure the polish directly. A stylus can be drawn across the surface to measure the surface profile from which average values of the height or depth of irregularities can be calculated. Reflection of a light beam incident at an angle to the normal can be used to calculate reflectivity, known as 'gloss value'. Sawn slabs may exhibit roughness values of 15 to 20 μm and gloss values of less than 10%. Highly polished surfaces may exhibit gloss values greater than 90% and roughness of less than 0.5 μm. However, care should be taken during the interpretation of values of gloss and roughness since some highly polished surfaces of coarsely grained rocks, e.g. granite, can exhibit significant roughness values owing to the grain boundaries exposed on the surface.

appropriate. These rocks would include sandstones, porous limestones and some dolerites. Indeed, the ability to take a polish has been used in the trade to define a marble as 'any limestone that can be polished'.

Traditionally, the surface was polished using a single, motor driven, disc rotating about a vertical axis that could be traversed across the stationary sawn slab, which was laid upon a horizontal table, in sweeping circular motions by the operator. This is the Jenny Lind which was named after the popular songstress, also known as the Swedish Nightingale, because the humming sound of the machine was likened to her voice, see Fig. 6.25.

Large slabs were laid horizontally over a trough which collected the polish comprising an abrasive, e.g. corundum or carborundum powder, suspended in water. The polishing disc was a wheel composed of several concentric rings of cast iron (coarse polish) or wood (fine polish). The wooden wheel was covered in cloth or felt and the highest gloss on granite was achieved using tin oxide as the abrasive. High polishing rates can be obtained with modern polishing machines. These have many driven polishing discs mounted in a frame which describes the circular motion so that no operator is required, see Fig. 6.26. The slabs lie on a flat concrete surface or pass under the polishing heads upon a horizontal, moving belt. The polishing discs are lubricated

Fig. 6.25. Jenny Lind polisher (Courtesy of Zattoni SPA).

Fig. 6.26. Multi-head polisher.

and cooled by water but separate abrasive is generally not used in modern practice. The entire discs are replaceable or made up from a number of replaceable sectors comprising the abrasive, aluminium oxide (corundum and emery), silicon carbide (carborundum), or diamond, bonded with resin or magnesite. Diamonds, which are being introduced only slowly, are much more expensive than other abrasives (×10) but offer longer life and higher polishing rates. This may be of particular advantage to producers of granite and other hard stones. The polishing process proceeds in stages and may be terminated before a high gloss is achieved according to the specification of the customer. Polishing rates of 15 to 20 m^2/h can be achieved on tiles and cut slabs with belt polishers. Higher polishing rates of up to 40 m^2/h can be obtained, even on granites, when employing multiple head machines working upon large pieces of untrimmmed sawn slab carried on a conveyor belt because less attention has to be paid to preventing damage to cut edges. In this respect it may be more productive to polish untrimmed slab before it is sawn into tiles of exact dimensions and the edges are chamfered.

6.4.12.8. Ashlar

Quoins (corner stones) for walling may be decorated on the surface by finishes given recognised names in the trade. Common examples include: 'boasted', a raised central panel with chamfered margins, 'picked panel', a recessed panel and 'reticulated panel', see Fig. 6.27. A very rough texture, 'broached', is produced by the use of a single pointed pick or punch.

6.4.1. Roofing slate

The production of roofing slates from blocks comprises three stages:

(i) sawing of the blocks of slate into slabs
(ii) splitting
(iii) dressing

The process demands the application of skill and experience even when highly mechanised and only a basic description is given below. The process begins in the quarry where blocks are examined for faults, joints and other flaws. Flaws could also include curvature and inflection of the cleavage plane, banding and colour

Fig. 6.27. Reticulated pattern of quoins.

changes. The quarryman may actually split the block along the cleavage using hammer and chisel or plug and feathers to determine the quality of the slate. Similarly, the block may be tested for pillaring. In any case, the block extracted from the face will be split along the cleavage until it is of a thickness suitable for the primary saws which is generally less than 1 metre and maybe less than 0.5 metres.

The blocks of slate are repeatedly inspected at each stage of the process to identify any flaws that become exposed. When these are identified the flaws will be removed by sawing to remove the unsatisfactory stone or the block is rejected.

As the block is loaded onto the saw bed it is aligned so that the saw blade is perpendicular to both the pillaring and cleavage planes. In modern plants this is achieved by aligning evidence of the pillaring plane exhibited on the block with a laser light beam directed along the saw table. Typically, the sawn pieces now move over belts or rollers to the next saws set at right angles to the first where the slate is sawn in the plane of pillaring. The slate block has now been reduced to rectangular slabs defined by the planes of cleavage and pillaring and a third plane normal to both, the plane of joints or heads (if present). The cut surface in the jointing plane is sometimes called the 'end'. Historically, these slabs were produced by a combination of sawing and striking the block with a very large wooden mallet to pillar the slab.

The dimensions of the sawn slab are decided by the operator of the saws with the general objective of cutting the largest rectangular, fault free slabs from the block.

Table 6.1. *Standard or common sizes or roofing slates*

Length		*Widths inches*	*Traditional name*
Imperial inches	*Metric mm*		
+30	760	–	Queen
26	660	16	Empress
24	610	14, 12	Duchess
22	560	12, 11	Small Duchess, Marchioness
20	510	12, 10	Countess
18	460	12, 10, 9	Viscountess
16	405	12, 10, 9, 8	Lady
14	355	12, 10, 8, 7	Small lady
13	330	11, 10, 8, 7	
12	305	10, 8 6	
10	255	10, 8 6	

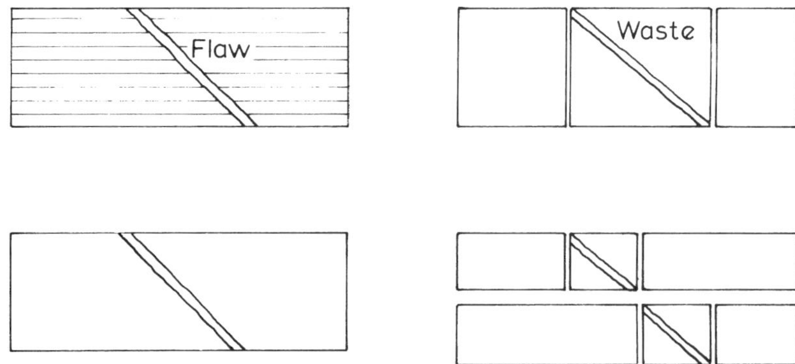

Fig. 6.28. Method of sawing a block to increase the yield of slates.

The exact dimensions should conform closely to those of the standard roof slates with an additional margin all round of between 25 and 35 mm to allow for losses during dressing. Traditionally and romantically, slates sizes in the UK have been given the names of female members of the aristocracy from the largest, queen, to the smallest, ladies although this information is not contained within the standards. The British Standard for roofing slates, BS 680; 1944, contained a listing of common sizes but has been withdrawn. The metric version, BS 680; 1971, contains a list of standard sizes which are effectively the metric equivalents (Table 6.1).

In this respect, a profitable operation must take notice of the price structure of roofing slates. Larger slates command a substantial price premium and the objective of the saw operators must be to cut as great a proportion of large slabs from the blocks as possible. For instance, a Duchess has twice the value per unit area of a Viscountess and all smaller slates. Indeed, it is likely that a profitable operation should be capable of producing a significant proportion, say 15%, of Duchesses and Countesses.

In this respect when eliminating flaws from blocks by sawing, the yield of large slates can be increased by splitting a given block into two thinner slabs as illustrated in Fig. 6.28. However, this incurs additional costs of splitting, inspection and handling and is at the expense of production. Therefore, the final decision is commercial. In the next step the slate slab is split or riven into roofing slates. There are several accepted thicknesses of roofing slates from the 'best' of thickness 4 mm to 'heavy' or 'strong' grades of thickness 6 mm or greater. There is a small price premium for thin slates but the real benefit is the increased number of slates that can be split from a given volume of slab. Therefore, the ambition is to split the slab into a number of 4 mm slates but this is determined by the quality of the cleavage and not solely by the skill of the workman, the 'river'.

In good slate the slab is split from end to end, see Fig. 6.29, and there is no need to attack the pillaring edge. One or two blows of the hammer or wooden mallet delivered to the broad chisel placed in the centre of the slab will begin the split. Leverage ('pressure') exerted upon the chisel will then cause the split to run cleanly

Fig. 6.29. River splitting a block of slate from end-to end (Courtesy of Nantlle Slate Quarry Co Ltd).

and exactly divide the original slab into two slabs of equal thickness. Therefore, the riving process begins with a slab of thickness equal to 8 slates, typically 32 to 50 mm depending upon the quality of the slate. A gauge is used to mark this thickness onto the end of the original sawn slab and an '8' is split away. Splitting then continues to produce '4's', '2's' and then single slates. Finally, the slate is dressed to the desired dimensions. This now employs a rotary guillotine patented by Greaves, owner of one of the famous slate quarries in Blaenau Ffestiniog, Wales. An experienced river can split and dress about 1000 slates per day.

In the past, dressing was carried out manually using a heavy knife and a chopping action with the slate resting on a sharp, steel edge. The essential feature of a dressed slate is that it now has a chamfered edge which has been found to be essential in the laying of a water-tight roof. Since it is possible for the cleavage surface to have a slight curvature it is important that the slate is dressed on the correct side so that the final roof is 'closed', that is, the chamfer is presented upon the upper convex surface of the slate when lying on the roof.

Splitting or riving has largely defeated attempts at mechanization although machines equipped with chisels are reportedly used in quarries in Spain and France. The slate must cleave very readily and the chisels must be positioned exactly in the centre of the slab for each split. Nail holes are driven by pneumatic punches and there is some loss at this stage owing to breakage. For this reason some suppliers do not provide this service or make an additional charge.

The yield of slates is obviously low and may be only 10% of the block delivered to the saws. Slate waste may find a use as tiles, paving or walling stone. Crushed slate waste can be used as a low specification aggregate and rock fill and granulated slate, especially green slate, is used to finish roofing felt. Powdered slate waste also has a market as a filler and parting agent to replace talc and mica.

6.4.14. Tiles

Polished tiles and slabs are two of the most important single products of the stone industry and many

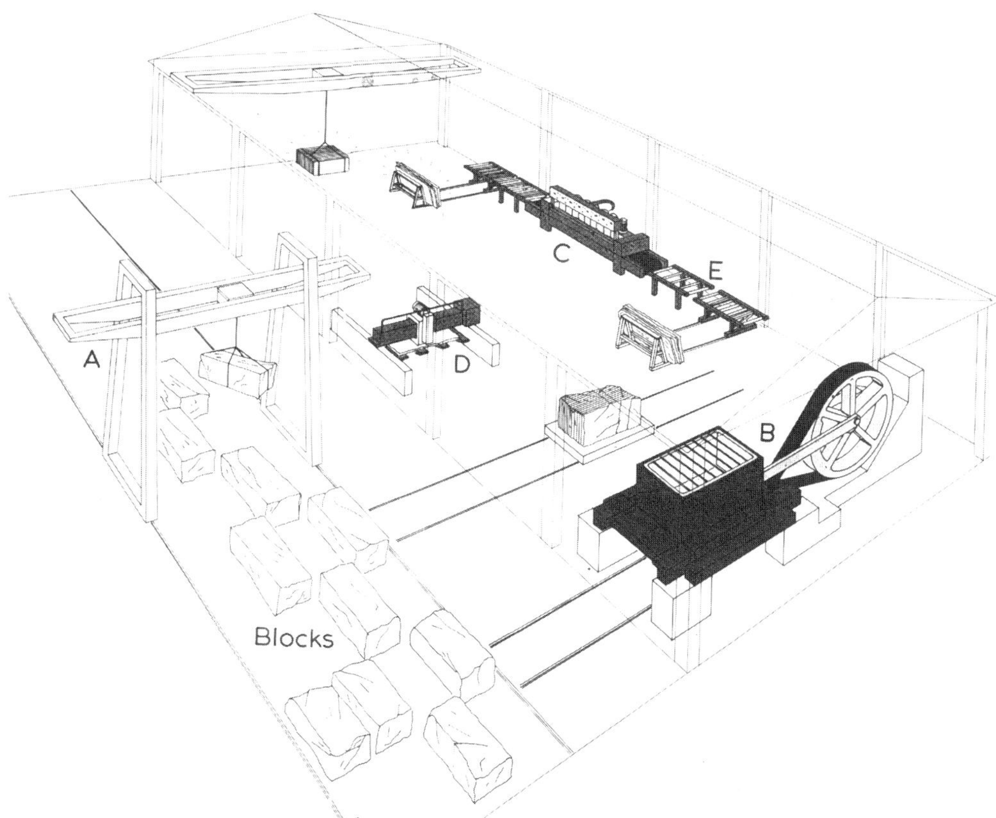

Fig. 6.30. Diagrammatic layout of tile production with frame saw (Courtesy of Terzago SPA).

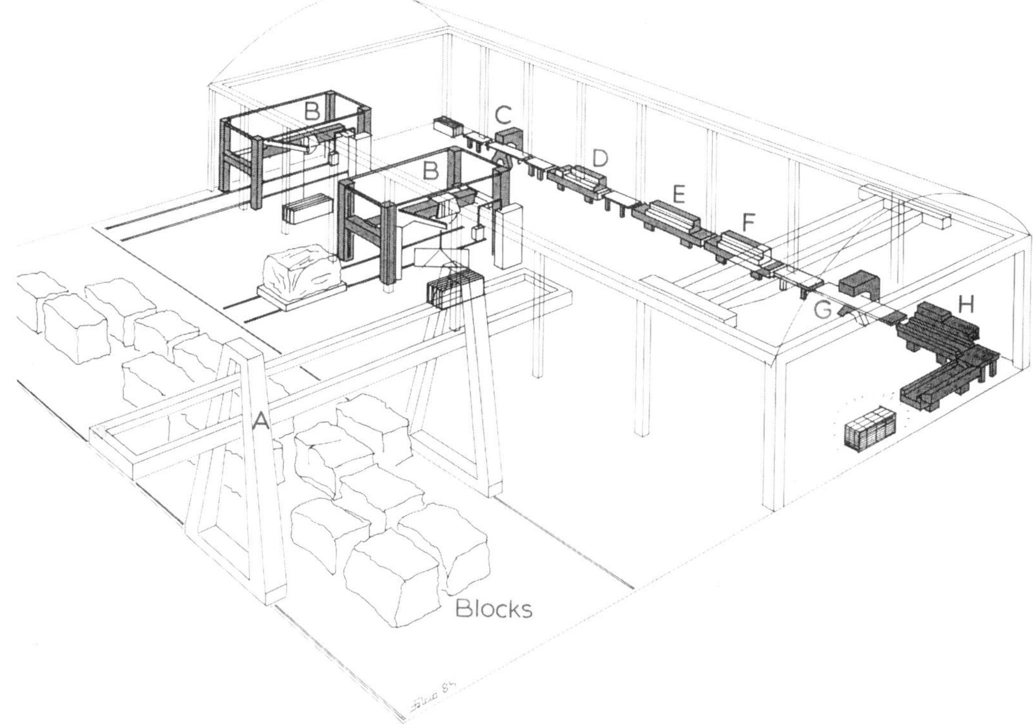

Fig. 6.31. Diagrammatic layout of tile production with block cutter. (Courtesy of Terzago SPA).

masonry works include semi-automated production lines. Figure 6.30 shows a production line commencing with a frame saw B. The sawn slabs from the frame saw pass to a continuous polishing machine C before the slab is sawn into tiles of the desired dimensions D.

Figure 6.31 shows slabs being cut direcly from blocks by slabbing saws B. Owing to the importance of tiles having uniform and standard dimensions, the first process is calibration C. Oversize sawn slab passes under a horizontal mill or roller, usually set with diamonds, to ensure a uniform thickness within tolerances of ±0.1 mm. The slabs are then progressively polished whilst travelling continuously upon a horizontal conveyor belt D–F, before being sawn into tiles G. The tiles are often chamfered on the edges to prevent chipping before being dried and inspected H. Remedial action such as buffing of blemishes and filling of surface indentations may then be carried out by hand. The overall yield of tiles from block entering the works at the primary saw is likely to be between only 30% and 50%.

6.4.15. Setts

Hydraulically actuated guillotines are used to prepare roughly surfaced, described as rock faced or riven, 'bricks' and setts, see Fig. 6.32. Knowledge of the rift or 'ways' was of great importance to the production of regularly shaped granite setts by hand but is less so with powered guillotines.

6.4.16. Carving and hand-dressing

Some 'hand-carving' is now conducted using pneumatic chisels and other powered hand tools, not mallet and chisel. However, the masons' fear of 'vibration white finger' ensures that much carving is still done by hand. Stone can also be carved by grit blasting to remove material and engraved using grit blasting and rubber stencils, see Fig. 6.33. Many forms which were previously carved can now be roughly produced by machines, especially the diamond saw, and finished by powered hand tools. Sealants and fillers may also be applied by hand to rectify surface flaws. A significant amount of stone is still worked by hand in small workshops around the world, and during the restoration of buildings where the cost of modern tooling cannot be justified for production of a single or few stones of any given shape. Excellent descriptions of the skills and techniques of the mason in carving stone by hand have been given by Warland (1953) and Clifton-Taylor & Ireson (1983).

Fig. 6.32. Guillotine to produce setts and bricks (Courtesy of ARC Ltd.).

Fig. 6.33. Engraving a monument by grit blasting (Courtesy of Natural Stone Products Ltd).

6.4.17. Artificial and reconstituted stone

It is not the purpose of this volume to describe in detail the production of synthetic stone materials, but they should be mentioned at this point since they may be confused with the real thing. Reconstituted stone represents one profitable use of finely sized rock that would otherwise be waste. For the customer buying a number of stones of identical profile or shape, the cost is usually significantly lower than that of real stone because moulding can replace expensive carving and machining. The similarity to real stone can be enhanced by manufacturing techniques that produce a coating of rock dust or chippings on the surface of reconstituted stone.

Nevertheless, some types of reconstituted material will exhibit a very uniform texture and the surface is likely to weather differently from the real stone that it is intended to simulate. Therefore, the appearance is likely to be less pleasing and reconstituted stone may not blend well with real stone. For example, for this reason, some planning authorities require that roofs be repaired or re-tiled with real slates and not reconstituted slates.

Many rock types can and have been reconstituted by bonding crushed and powdered rock with cement or lime and can be considered to be forms of concrete or mortar. For example, in the UK, crushed waste from quarries producing Cotswold stone (a popular yellow, Jurassic oolitic limestone) is mixed with cement and aggregates and then cast into slabs, bricks and moulded sections. In Italy, marble fragments are cast as concrete in large moulds to create synthetic blocks of 'brecciated marble' that are then sawn into tiles which are polished. This is often known as 'terrazo'. Historically, materials called 'scagliola' were synthesised from fragments of stone and coloured mortars for internal use and decoration (Ashurst & Dimes 1984). Fragments of crushed rock of most types, notably granites and marbles, can be bonded with resins to create slabs for internal flooring. The bonding of powdered slate waste with resins to produce synthetic roofing slates is another important example.

6.4.17.1. Coade stone

Coade stone is not a natural stone at all but a form of partially vitrified ceramic that was produced by the works of that name in London. It was moulded before firing to simulate carvings and was used extensively in the decoration of portals of houses, particularly as quoin stones and keystones of arches. The details of the manufacturing process now appear to be lost.

6.4.18. Process water

The processing of stone consumes significant quantities of water which may not be readily available locally. In any case, there are likely to be limits imposed upon the quality of water discharged from the masonry works usually in terms of flowrate and suspended solids content at least. Recirculation of water is common but the removal of suspended solids can increase the life of tools and permit discharge. Many works employ settling ponds but where space is not available, flocculant dosage systems and thickeners have been installed to clarify recirculated water.

6.5. Quality systems

Quality systems can be considered in two categories; quality control and the more recently introduced quality assurance. One problem common to both, however, is the definition or concept of quality. Today, this is usually interpreted to mean that the product or service is of adequate quality sometimes described as 'fitness for purpose'. This implies neither a high nor a low specification but that the product will perform satisfactorily in the given duty.

To some extent, quality may be measured by tests stipulated in the specification document but it may be impossible to identify a suitable test to predict performance under the particular conditions. In other cases, the interpretation of results from available laboratory tests can be highly controversial in terms of their relevance to the actual service conditions of the material. There is a temptation to over specify materials of construction in order to ensure high performance and minimize risk although this policy is likely to reject satisfactory materials and increase costs.

Traditionally, great reliance has been put upon the proven, demonstrated performance of stone from a particular geological source or even particular quarries and companies. That is, a given product or supplier has acquired a reputation for quality which is, in effect, a form of quality assurance. This remains a most important aspect of the dimension stone industry.

Quality control, in its simplest form, consists of the periodic or continuous inspection and testing of intermediate and final products to determine whether the product complies with specifications. Non-compliant material is rejected as waste probably resulting in significant financial loss since the faulty product has incurred part or all of the processing costs. This system may or may not instil confidence in the customer who may consequently decide to conduct additional acceptance tests and inspections himself. The system is thus inherently wasteful of materials and effort. It is to be expected that all producers of stone products will exercise some form of quality control such as checking dimensions throughout the processing stages and submitting samples of the final product to the tests stated in the specification.

The ultimate objective of quality assurance, QA, systems, however, is to instil confidence in the customer that the product will be of adequate quality for the intended use and that acceptance testing is unnecessary when the customer purchases from an accredited supplier. This system was introduced with the argument that it should confer competitive advantages upon accredited suppliers and economic gains through less wastage of non-compliant materials. It is described in the British Standard BS 5750 which is identical to the European Standard EN 29000 (British Standards Institution, 1987) and to ISO Standards 9000-9004.

This quality standard allows a company to select one of three parts under which it will be assessed. Usually part 2 (ISO 9002) is the most appropriate for a quarry since it deals with manufacturing processes without the design element nor subsequent servicing. Accreditation can also be at three levels; first, second and third party. Self accreditation or first party is unlikey to instil much confidence in customers but second party accreditation, where the customer inspects the quality system of the supplier, is not uncommon where long established commercial relationships exist. Third party accreditation is by an independent organisation such as the British Standards Institution itself.

The introduction of a quality system comprises several stages starting with a declaration of the quality policy by the board of directors of a company and culminating with the production of a quality manual containing details of procedures that must be followed during the manufacturing process to ensure quality. One of the most important aspects of QA systems is the preparation of this manual and methods of maintaining records that the procedures were followed. The system must be subjected to periodic review to seek improvements and to an annual audit by representatives of the accrediting organisation to ensure that the system is indeed being completely and correctly implemented. A quality system has much greater scope than quality control which may form a part of it. Procedures must be written and implemented, for example, to ensure that operators are adequately trained, that machines are correctly set-up, adjusted and maintained and that measuring instruments are regularly inspected or calibrated. The system extends to procedures for the receipt and processing of orders, packaging and labelling and investigation of faults and complaints. It is usually necessary to appoint explicitly a Quality Manager and define management responsibilities with respect to quality. Therefore, it can be seen that the introduction of QA systems represents a large investment of time and effort by a company.

Whereas the concept of QA in a manufacturing process may be relatively easy to understand, the stone industry is beset with one major problem in that the feed material is a natural rock subject to variation in properties. It cannot be as readily specified as, say, the steel rod entering a machine shop or cement supplied to a concrete batching plant. The planning of a dimension stone quarry is a skill learned through experience and the selection of blocks for processing is a subjective judgement also largely based upon training and experience. The quarry operator will need to emphasise this factor and demonstrate a good knowledge of the geology of the deposit to obtain accreditation. At the present time, the quality of a block cannot be assessed by non-destructive test methods, although certain traditional tests do exist. One of these, ringing, consists of striking the raised block and listening for a ringing sound like a bell which denotes that the block contains no fissures. This test is useful for blocks of soft limestones, but strong, hard rocks such as granites and compact limestones may ring despite the inclusion of fractures.

Ultrasonic tests have been tried to identify fractures but not adopted. The testing and inspection of blocks of slate by splitting upon the cleavage and pillaring planes has been described, see §6.4.13.

Dye penetration tests to detect cracks have proved useful for testing slabs before they are finally fixed into place to form cladding. At this stage in the construction process it may be necessary to cut or drill holes in the slab to accommodate fixings or to remedy errors in the previous preparation of the slab to receive fixings. Therefore, there is an opportunity, especially with thin cladding sawn from granite, for cracks and flaws to be introduced. In addition, the slabs may have been damaged during transport and handling. The slab is cleaned by washing with water after which a colourless solution of a fluorescent dye is painted onto the surface. It is then examined under ultra-violet light which will identify the trace of cracks that have imbibed dye.

Porous stones cannot be tested in this manner but wetting by water will often identify cracks which assume a persistent darker colouration as the surface dries. Obviously, no non-destructive test gives information upon colour or textural changes within the block. Therefore, if blocks from a new source, having no established reputation, are offered there is no reliable, independent method of testing the quality of this source except processing itself. One solution to this problem is to trade the stone in slab form rather than block so that it is much less likely that faults remain concealed in the rock. Indeed, the sawing of just one face on a block may reveal major faults as illustrated in Fig. 6.34. However, there are obvious disadvantages to this practice. First, except for strong hard rocks such as granite, which is commonly traded as slab, the slab will require more expensive packaging and protection during transport than blocks. Second, the receiving masonry works will almost certainly contain primary saws capable of slabbing blocks and the operator will be reluctant to pay the supplier to carry out the slabbing work. In the UK, quality systems appear to have been introduced only by a few large companies producing slate, sandstones and Portland stone.

6.6. Examples of British stone quarries and mines

The following descriptions of selected quarries and mines were compiled from information collected during visits augmented by information contained in literature references. They are intended to illustrate the previous text and should not be used for sourcing or specifying stone. For this purpose the reader is referred to well known catalogues e.g. *The Natural Stone Directory*, and to the quarry operators themselves.

In particular, the information given upon output or capacity is indicative only and should be carefully interpreted. Tonnages may be variously quoted as total amount of rock moved, volume of block extracted or tonnage/area of finished, sawn and polished stone. Clearly, these figures are not directly comparable, neither are they absolutely fixed.

In general the output of a dimension stone quarry in the UK is very small compared to that of a typical aggregate quarry which produces at least 100 000 tonnes per annum and maybe as much as 5 million tonnes per annum. Annual outputs of finished stone products i.e. blocks, slabs and slates, from stone quarries and mines range from 1000 tonnes for a small mine to about 20 000 tonnes for a large quarry.

6.6.1. Coombefield limestone quarry, Portland, Dorset

Introduction

The 'Isle of Portland' is, in fact, a peninsula defining the western extent of Weymouth Bay on the south coast of England because the mass of the island is connected to the mainland by a causeway of shingle. Portland Stone has become famous throughout the world largely owing to the extensive use of this stone for buildings in London. This fashion was initiated in 1619 by Inigo Jones who selected the stone for the Banqueting Hall in Whitehall and, of course, established by Wren who used Portland Stone in many churches including St. Paul's Cathedral.

Fig. 6.34. Sawn blocks showing flaws identified by wetting (a) and inspection (b) & (c) (Courtesy of Natural Stone Products Ltd).

Fig. 6.34. *(continued).*

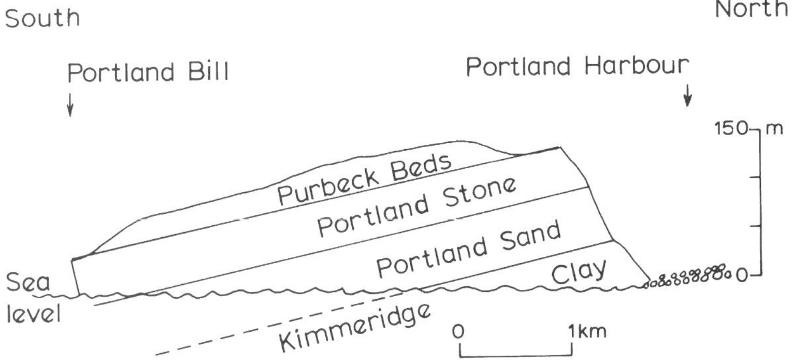

Fig. 6.35. Simplified section of the Isle of Portland.

General geology
Geologically the peninsula comprises the southern limb of an anticline having an east-west axis. The beds of Jurassic limestone dip gently at 2° to 3° from the northern heights, which rise to about 160 m above sea level, towards the southern-most point of the island, Portland Bill, see Fig. 6.35.

The geological sequence is illustrated diagrammatically in Figs 6.35 and 6.36. The useful stone beds are overlain by thin soils and 9 to 14 metres of Purbeck Beds which are known locally as 'Rubble'. They comprise clays and thinnly bedded limestones. The lowest 3 metres of the Purbeck Beds comprise a hard, brittle limestone which is difficult to cut. Beneath this 'Capstone' is the first bed of Portland masonry stone having a thickness of between 3 and 4 metres which is called the 'Roach'. In descending order there then follow two further beds of freestone; the first of thickness between 2 and 3 metres, the 'Whitbed', and the second of thickness between 1 and 2 metres, the 'Basebed'.

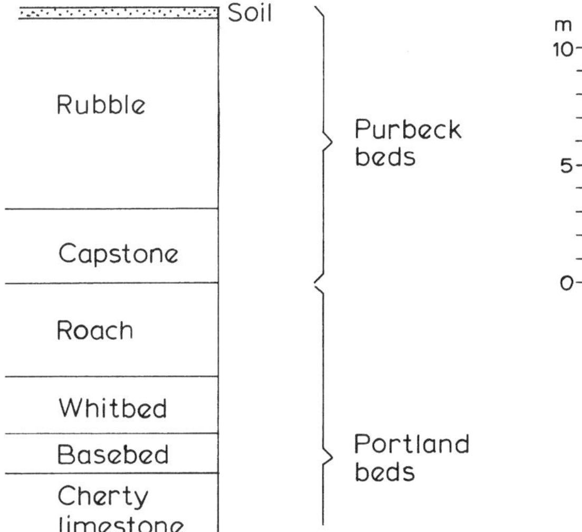

Fig. 6.36. Diagram of the geological sequence in Coombefield quarry.

Underlying the Portland Stone there are approximately 25 metres of an unworkable cherty limestone then the Portland Sand (sandstone), and then the Kimmeridge Clay (Anon 1962).

Utilization of strata

The 'Rubble' has little value and most is tipped to waste usefully backfilling the voids created by other exhausted quarries on the island. Some walling stone and crazy paving can be recovered from these thinnly bedded limestones.

The 'Capstone' is extracted to produce armourstone and the remainder is crushed, together with waste from the masonry stone extraction, to produce dry (uncoated) roadstone. The sale of aggregates contributes significantly to the viability of the stone quarries in addition to disposing of a material that would otherwise be waste.

The 'Roach' is a white, strong, hard and durable limestone that has been used in harbour walls. The most notable features, however, are the cavities and shell casts which impart a characteristic and attractive appearance which is exploited for both internal and external

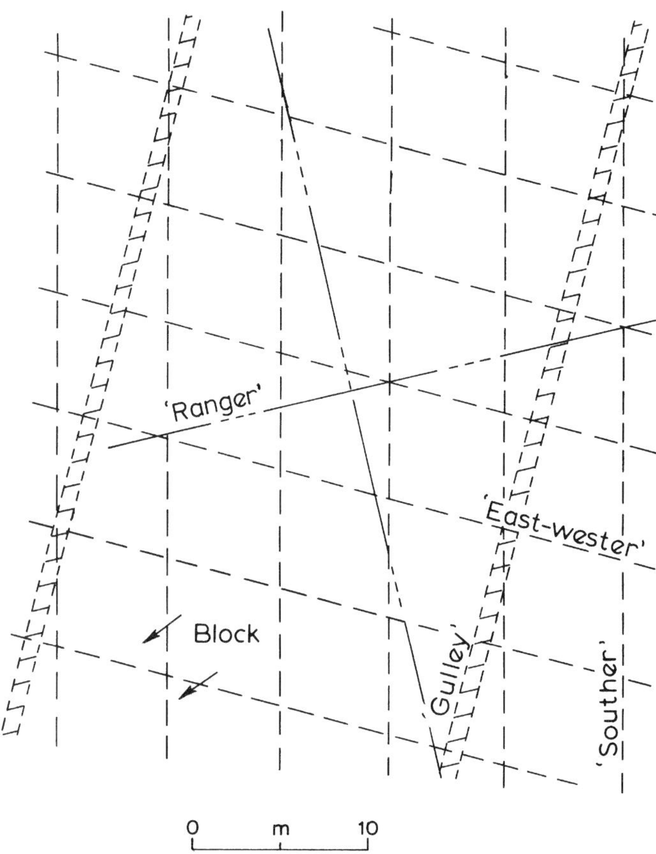

Fig. 6.37. Diagram of the joint systems on the Isle of Portland.

cladding. Owing to its texture, it cannot be sculpted or worked other than by sawing and polishing unless filled with mortar.

The 'Whitbed' and 'Basebed' are both white oolitic limestones that may be sculpted; that is they are 'freestones'. The demarcation between the two is not always definite so the bed thicknesses vary. The 'Roach', 'Whitbed' and 'Basebed' comprise the Portland Stone.

Geological structure
The principal structural feature is a series of parallel, expanded joints called 'gullies' which trend NNE–SSW at intervals of between 20 and 30 metres. A second set of closed joints, which are orientated north–south, are called 'southers' and the third well developed joint set, the 'east-westers', cross these obliquely. The 'east–westers' are, in fact, almost normal to the gullies. The latter two joint sets conveniently divide the beds into blocks having the shape of a parallelogram, see Fig. 6.37. Unfortunately, in some areas, two further, less well defined joint sets occur known as 'northeasters', which describes their orientation, and 'rangers' which are normal to these. Where these joints are developed the blocks are spoilt for dimension stone production.

Extraction
The space between two parallel gullies was traditionally referred to as a 'quarry' and was worked by a team of men using a single crane to lift blocks. Today, the extraction of blocks still exploits the 'southers' and the 'east–westers' to define the blocks in plan. The bedding planes are exploited wherever possible to produce individual blocks having the full bed depth. The back of the block is defined by an 'east–wester' such that the face is orientated approximately east–west also. The two lateral surfaces are created using the principle of plugs and feathers although the hammer-driven plugs and separate feathers have now been replaced by an integrated system incorporating hydraulic cylinders manufactured by Darda, see Fig. 5.37. The parallel, 38 mm diameter holes, spaced at approximately 150 mm, are drilled to a depth of about 2 metres by Tamrock, top-hammer or drifter drills mounted on a quarry bar and operated remotely, see Fig. 5.67.

The block is lifted from the bed using small charges of blackpowder which usefully moves the block forward by about 50 mm. The charges, weighing approximately 500 g, are loaded into plastic tubes which are inserted into the blast holes drilled on the bedding plane at spacings of about 1.5 metres. The blast ratio is about 5 tonnes of stone per kilogram of blackpowder and clay is used as stemming. Once the block has been freed it can be manoeuvred and removed from the face by the wheeled loader (FEL) fitted with a single tine or fork attachment, see Fig. 5.48. This machine is capable of lifting blocks weighing up to 35 tonnes and transporting them within the quarry or loading them onto trucks.

At other quarries on the island the blocks are lifted and transported by crawler cranes which replaced the derrick cranes and were introduced to increase productivity.

The block is then further sub-divided on the quarry floor into blocks of 10 tonnes or less using mobile drifter drills, see Fig. 5.27, and the hydraulic splitters. Blocks are marked with a code number and volume and then stored within the quarry before sale to masonry works. Details of the stored blocks are held upon a computerised data base. There is no processing at the quarry of ARC Ltd. but the parent company (Hanson PLC) presently owns the nearby works of Bath and Portland Stone Ltd. at Easton.

An important aspect of a quarry operation on this scale is the liaison between the marketing and the production of the various products, including aggregates, and the three types of dimension stone. The planning and development of faces must ensure that all materials are available without the creation of an excessive inventory of stockpiled materials. Potential output of block is 20 000 m^3 per annum but is currently less than 10 000 m^3 (Anon 1990; Anon 1993).

6.6.2. Monk's Park Mine, Bathstone mine, Wiltshire

Introduction
Monk's Park mine, near Corsham, Wiltshire, produces blocks of a creamy white limestone. Locally, the same bed of stone has also been worked at Doulting (used in construction of Wells Cathedral and Glastonbury Abbey) and at Box (used in such buildings as Longleat House and Lacock Abbey and extensively in the buildings of Bath).

In fact, these limestones have been worked by man for nearly 2000 years including by the Romans. Outcrops in the valley of the Avon were extensively exploited by quarrying to produce stone for the buildings cited above and for less famous public buildings and private houses of Bath and its environs. The opening of the Kennet and Avon canal in 1810 offered cheap transport into the valley of the Thames and to the markets of Oxford and London. Then, around the year 1840, the beds of stone were exposed by the engineer I. K. Brunel when driving the railway tunnel for the Great Western Railway through Box Hill. This led to greatly increased mining activity when the quantity and quality of the stone were seen together with the advantage of immediate access to rail transport via a spur line entering the mine workings immediately adjacent to the tunnel portal. Stone was also despatched from Corsham railway station, which was connected to other mine workings by mineral railways all over the country. There is no processing at Monk's Park mine and blocks are supplied directly to masonry works including the Bath & Portland Stone company also owned by Hanson plc.

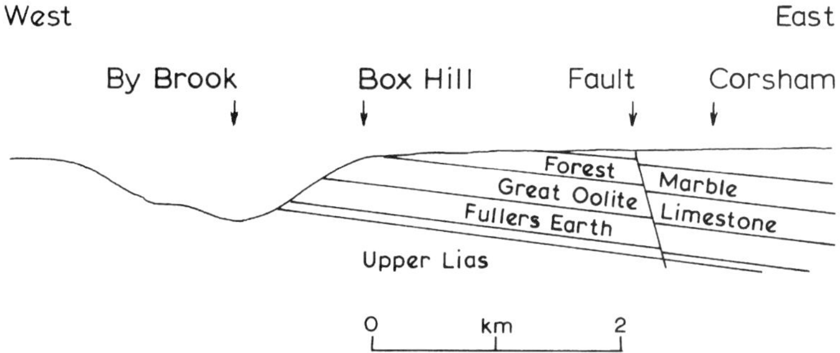

Fig. 6.38. Geological section in the vicinity of Monk's Park mine.

Geology

The oolitic limestone is of Jurassic age and comprises the bed known as the Great Oolite Limestone which is worked over a large area of the UK. Indeed, the Jurassic limestones are the principal source of building stone in the UK. The local names given to particular limestones are contentious but the name 'Bathstone' is claimed by producers within a radius of 12 miles around the city of Bath itself. The same limestone is given other names such as 'Cotswold Stone' in the area of the Cotswold Hills where it is extracted at Temple Guiting, Westwood (Bradford-upon-Avon) and Combe Down, amongst other sites. Near Bath the sedimentary beds dip gently to the southeast from their outcrops in the valley of the river Avon and its tributaries as shown in Fig. 6.38.

The local geological sequence is:

- Great Oolite
  - Cornbrash, a hard limestone exposed at surface under a covering of soils (absent at some other locations owing to erosion).
  - Forest Marble, thin beds of clays (including Bradford clay) and limestones.
  - Great Oolite Limestone, approximately 8 metres of free-stone.
  - Fuller's Earth Series, chalky limestones and clays.
- Inferior Oolite
  - Rubbly oolitic limestone but found elsewhere as a free-stone.
- Upper Lias
  - Silts and clays.

The Cornbrash is too hard to cut for dimension stone. The beds in the Forest Marble are generally too thin but the lowest bed of coral limestone, the Ragstone, has been quarried for walling stone. At Monk's Park it forms a strong roof to the mine. The Great Oolite Limestone at Monk's Park is creamy white and is valued for the mellow, honey colour that it assumes on weathering. The thickness of beds of the oolite varies from 150 to 700 mm but the minimum useful bed thickness is 300 mm. The 'main' joints are vertical and orientated north–south. These are crossed by the 'sleeker' joints which are also vertical but orientated east–west. There are occassional small faults.

Extraction

The general arrangement of the mine is as shown in Fig. 4.15. The landowners located the stone beds by sinking shafts which are now usefully employed for ventilation and as an emergency exit only. The stone is removed via the incline which has a gradient of 1 in 2. The same incline also affords access for men to the beds of stone approximately 30 metres below the surface.

Ventilation was naturally induced but is now assisted by fans suspended in the driveways to prevent any accumulation of radon gas. There is no hazard from dust since the oolite contains less than 1% silica but a mobile dust collector is employed. Ingress of water is not a serious problem because the limestone floor of the mine is pervious and the overlying Bradford Clay produces a seal above the workings. The water table is about 10 metres below the mine workings and, like most mines and quarries in the area, the workings of Monk's Park mine are contained in a hillside above the river valley to avoid water problems.

Blocks are extracted exactly as described in §5.3.10.5 and shown in Figs 5.50 and 5.51. The face between the pillars is known as the 'breach' and the slot cut above the top lift to permit the upper blocks to be raised is known as the 'jad'. In the past, heavy saws called 'frog bobs' were used to cut the stone except for the rear face where long, thin saws called 'razzers' were used. The mechanical saws, introduced around 1950, are Samson arc shearers more commonly found in coal mines and are capable of cutting to a depth of between 2.5 and 3 metres. Most blocks are lifted by cranes onto bogies which are then hauled to the bottom of the incline by locomotives. However, within old stopes used for storage, the blocks may be manouevred by cranes.

At this mine the recovery of stone by the room-and-pillar mining method is about two-thirds when allowance is made for pillars. Of course, there is further loss during extraction, which may amount to between 30 and 50%. Potential output from a single stope or heading employing 4 men is about 20 m^3 of block per day. There is no viable market for the waste which is packed into old stopes underground. The blocks are moist when freed and are said to contain 'quarry sap'. When first raised to the surface they must be protected from frost until the moisture or 'sap' has evaporated after which they will suffer no damage from frost action. Those produced during the winter are either stored underground in old stopes (rooms) or in sheds constructed for that purpose on surface or taken directly to the masonry works. During spring and summer it takes about four weeks for a block to dry in the open stockyard. Some blocks contain 'blue hearts' which eventually oxidize to the normal colour of Bathstone upon exposure and weathering in the open. No problems caused by marcasite nodules in the oolite are encountered at this mine.

As with all oolitic limestones from the area around Bath, precautions must be taken when using the stone in exposed parts of a building, for example, end copings, cornices and canopies. These should be shielded by lead sheeting or other means. Then, provided that correct bed orientations are used, no damage from weathering alone should be evident for many years. Most damage occuring to limestone buildings is, in fact, found to be caused by acidic pollutants produced by the combustion of fuels containing sulphur and de-icing salt applied to roads and pavements.

6.6.3. De Lank granite quarry, Cornwall, UK

Introduction

The De Lank quarry is located near St. Breward, Cornwall on the western flank of the granite intrusion forming Bodmin Moor. It takes its name from the De Lank river that flows west towards the River Camel through the quarry and which supplies water to the processing works. The quarry is closely associated with the nearby Hantergantick quarry which also extracts a silver-grey granite using very similar methods. The centralized works also process stones from other quarries in the UK, including at the present time the famous Shap granite, imported granites and sandstones.

Geology

The geology of the granite is relatively simple and does not pose problems of stability or variable quality through mineralisation or alteration. The rock is massive with widely spaced joints (see Fig. 5.23c) but it exhibits 'rift' or 'grain' with preferential cleavage in three 'ways', see Fig. 5.19. An elvan dyke, which ran approximately west to east near the quarry, has been quarried for roadstone and the narrow pass created now provides the access to the De Lank quarry.

Extraction

The quarry has been stripped of the shallow overburden over the complete extraction area. Further expansion of the quarry is presently constrained by the ownership boundaries, the position of the processing plant and the course of the river. With respect to visual intrusion, noise and dust, the quarry is very well screened by the preservation of a rim of rock around the entire area of the excavation, process plant and waste tips and the narrowness of the access road mentioned above. To permit maximum recovery of the granite a derrick crane is used to raise blocks from the quarry faces and also to move materials and equipment within the quarry and to remove waste. The men obtain access to the working benches by ladders. At present, the flame jet is employed as the most effective method of cutting the granite where no convenient joints can be exploited. Consideration is often given to 'stitch drilling' and the use of 'diamond wire saws' in terms of potential for reducing costs and increasing cutting rates. In the near future it may be that no quarry in the UK will be using the flame jet.

A block is defined by the free-way, which is in the plane of the horizontal base, and two lateral surfaces which are the toughway. The rear face or 'back' is the secondway. If no joint exists to create the lateral and rear surfaces these are cut using the flame jet, see Fig. 5.46. Paraffin is burnt in oxygen to create temperatures of around 5000°C. The cutting rate is low at 0.5 m^2/hour and the noise levels for the operators would be high at between 110 and 120 dBA. Therefore, they wear ear defenders. At Hantergantick diesel fuel is burnt in compressed air but noise levels are even greater. The block is then freed on the free-way by a small charge (2–3 kg) of black powder inserted into a 75 mm hole drilled on the free-way and stemmed with a mixture of soil and drill cuttings. The block may be further reduced in size within the quarry by use of relatively short plugs and feathers which are inserted into shallow, closely spaced holes drilled by a pneumatic hand drill.

Processing

The blocks are trimmed and cut into slab by the two primary circular saws each of 3 m diameter, one at each quarry. These saws are automated so that they can be programmed to cut several blocks consecutively and continuously without supervision and outside the working hours of the quarry. They are fitted with 'silenced' blades. There are also two slightly smaller saws of diameter 2.7 m and 2.5 m respectively. In addition, consideration is being given to the purchase of a fixed diamond wire saw for cutting blocks.

Secondary circular diamond saws cut the slabs into smaller sizes and produce tiles. No frame saws are used.

The secondary circular saws at Hantergantick are also used to create a rough profile in large work pieces as described in §6.4.6. before masons break out the webs and finish the piece with pneumatic tools. Several cubicles connected to dust extractors have been constructed at both works in which masons dress individual stones whilst wearing combined visors and helmets which incorporate an air filtration system, see Fig. 5.6. 'Dolly pointing' or 'bush hammering' are popular finishes for granite at the present time.

Both works contain modern, automated polishing machines and a milling machine is located at De Lank to produce curved pieces and profiles on the edges of slabs. The automated flame texturing machine is often employed to finish the granite and paving sawn from imported stone.

Disposal of waste is a problem and in the past it has been allowed to partially obstruct and obscure the river. Today, the waste is tipped carefully in the valley above the river and thought is being given to the removal of this material to permit salmon to ascend the river once again. Unfortunately, there is no viable additional market for crushed rock aggregates in the area and, in an attempt to reduce the quantity of waste generated, a guillotine has been installed to produce setts and bricks from process waste pieces.

6.6.4. Kirkby slate quarry, Cumbria, UK

Introduction

The Kirkby quarry of Burlington Slate Ltd. is located near Kirkby-in-Furness just outside the southern border of the Lake District National Park. The same company operates seven other slate quarries in the area some producing the well-known Cumberland or Lakeland green slate which is used for cladding and architectural

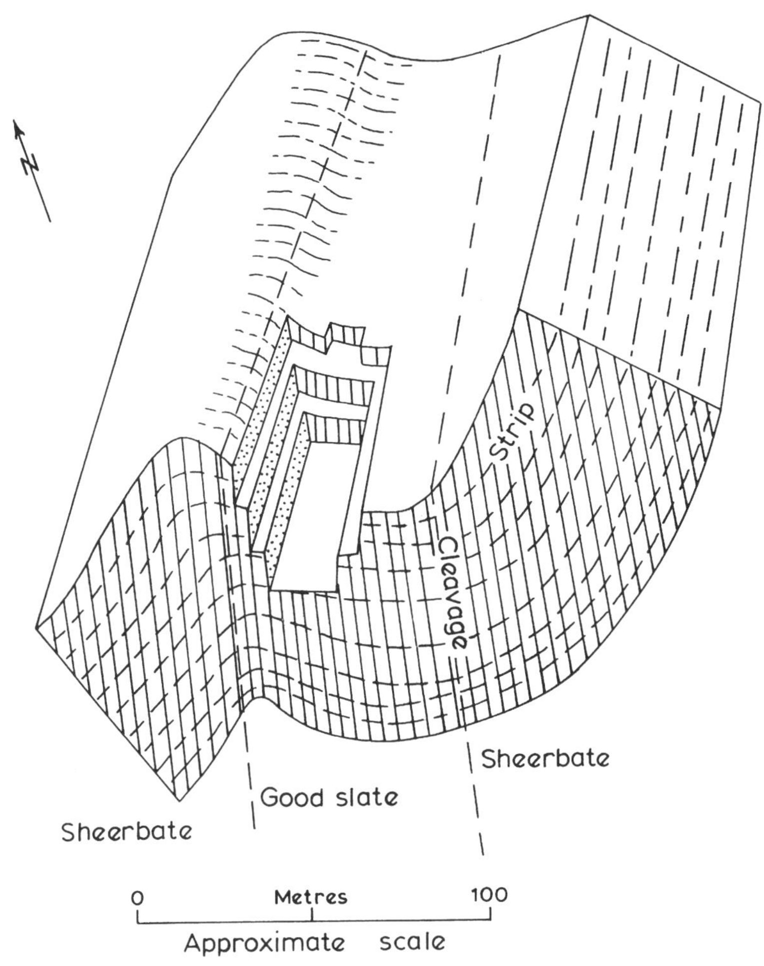

Fig. 6.39. Diagram of the geology and slate quarry at Kirkby.

purposes as well as roofing. However, the blue-grey slate at Kirkby, the largest of the quarries, is split or riven primarily into roofing slates which have an excellent reputation for durability and quality. The centralized processing plant or masonry works is also located at Kirkby.

Geology
The slates, which extend across the southern Lake District, were created by compression of Silurian silty mudstones during the Acadian orogeny of the Devonian period. The cleavage created by this compression generally lies in a plane parallel to the axis of folding and is inclined at angles of greater than 75° to the horizontal.

Laminations or bedding caused by variations in the sedimentary environment are still visible in the slate and are called 'strip'. However, it is the structural geology which determines the quality of the slate and the feasibility of the extraction of blocks. The best quality of slate is found where the original bedding planes are nearly horizontal and, thereby, normal to the approximately vertical cleavage such as in the cores of folds, especially anticlines. Where the cleavage is not at right-angles to the bedding the slate is referred to as 'sheerbate' and is waste. Vertical joints normal to the cleavage are also exploited in the extraction of blocks. Kirkby quarry lies within the northern limb of a large anticline which has an axis trending NE–SW and which plunges at 20° towards the north east. Minor folding on this limb has produced a narrow belt of slate having approximately horizontal bedding, see Fig. 6.39. Therefore, the quarry is a linear excavation lying parallel to the axis of the anticline and which increases in depth to the north until limited by the thickness of overburden. Exploration is difficult since core drilling is unlikely to identify the small-scale folding and structural features. It may be necessary to drive exploration edits.

Extraction
Overburden is removed by hydraulic excavator which loads both rigid and articulated dump trucks. The stripping ratio is high with total waste generation, including processing waste, amounting to about 90%. Thus, disposal of waste and the creation of tips present a significant operating problem in a scenic and recreational area. Some waste may be sold as general construction fill or even as sub-base for large road construction projects but local prices are low and opportunities are rare. Therefore, the company is now expending much effort upon the revegetation of tips and is investigating all means to reduce waste during extraction and processing.

Over the years the management of the quarry has investigated or considered several alternative methods of extraction to increase productivity and output. The use of explosives alone was too wasteful and line-drilling or stitch drilling was both too slow and too wasteful. A mechanical chain saw might be used in the softer Welsh slates but was not applicable at Kirkby.

Until 1985 the quarrymen used helical wire saws with sand as an abrasive to make horizontal cuts but they

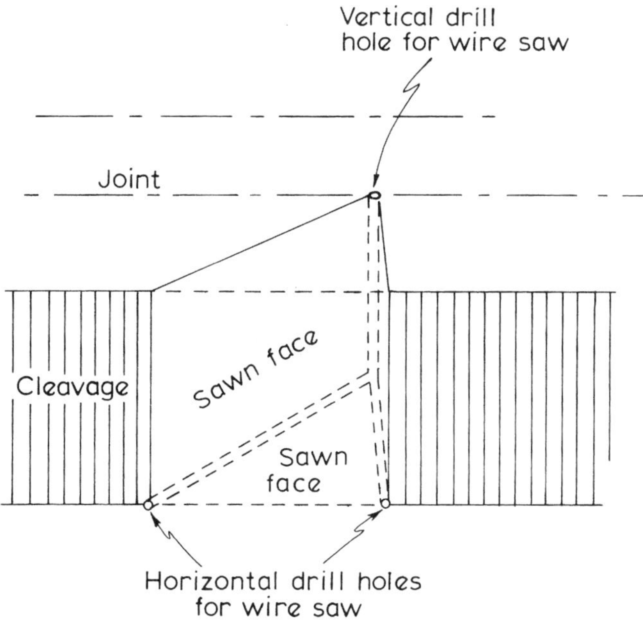

Fig. 6.40. Diagram of the removal of the first block of slate from a new face at Kirkby quarry.

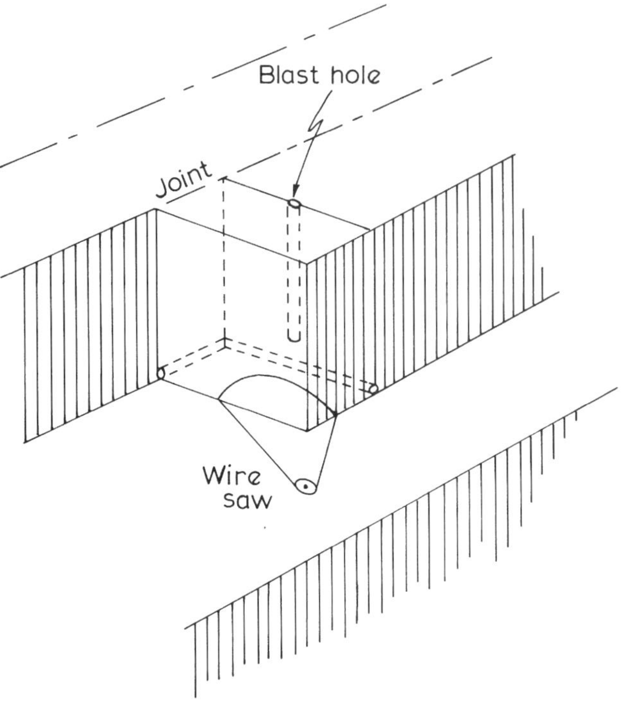

Fig. 6.41. Method of block production at Kirkby quarry.

were amongst the first to investigate diamond wire saws after their development in Carrara. It was found that the diamond wire cuts at about ten times the rate of the helical wire. Rates of 6 to 7 m^2/hour are achieved in the blue-grey slate and 13 to 14 m^2/hour in the green slate. The cut face is also smoother resulting in less wastage during processing. Continuing research and development by manufacturers of diamond wires is steadily increasing the service life and improving the economics.

Extraction of blocks on each bench, which are about 10 metres high, commences with the face of the block perpendicular to the plane of a vertical joint surface and parallel to the cleavage. In order to create the first of these faces on a new bench a triangular wedge of slate is removed from a point somewhere near the middle of the bench. A vertical cut is made with the wire saw at an angle across the cleavage for which purpose it is necessary to drill three intersecting holes, one vertical and two horizontal, as shown in Fig. 6.40. The wedge is then undercut with the wire saw and broken out along the cleavage plane. This procedure has proved less wasteful and damaging than the previous practice of 'heaving out' a first rectangular block with explosives. The rectangular block could not be undercut although both sides were sawn. Subsequently blocks can be removed from the bench in both directions towards the walls of the quarry. A block is removed by exploiting the joint surface and undercutting the block with the wire saw now that access is available for equipment to drill a horizontal hole along the lower edge of the rear face, see Fig. 6.41. The block is finally freed on the cleavage plane by employing a small charge, less than 1 kg, of black powder loaded into one or more blastholes drilled behind the block. The block topples forward onto a pile of quarry waste deliberately placed there to prevent damage to or breakage of the block. The block may be further sub-divided on the quarry floor. Blocks are lifted by wheeled loaders fitted with forks and transported by flat-bed trucks to the works (Anon 1990). Output is about 65 tonnes per day of block.

Processing

The blocks of blue-grey slate are sawn into slabs of standard sizes for roofing tiles using circular diamond saws. These slabs are then split by hand-chisel into slabs having a thickness equivalent to four tiles. Using a broad chisel the slab is then split by the skilled 'river' into tiles. The traditional ragged chamfered edge is then created using a rotary shear. The yield of slates is about one third of the original block. The blocks of green slate are trimmed by the large diameter primary circular saw and then sawn into slabs by a diamond frame saw. Slabs are then further reduced in size by circular diamond saws before polishing on belt-polishers to produce tiles and cladding (Anon 1990).

6.6.5. Penrhyn quarry, Bethesda, Gwynedd, north Wales

Introduction

Welsh slate has been exploited on a huge scale although many of the workings are underground and not immediately visible. In fact, there are several areas of slate working created by the outcrops of slate of different ages in the river valleys that disect the mountainous terrain.

The general trend of the outcrops is southwest to northeast and three of the most productive areas are:

(i) the zone containing Nantlle, Dinorwig and Penrhyn
(ii) Blaenau Ffestiniog and surrounding areas
(iii) the zone extending from Corris to Aberllefeni

The slates of the first named zone are Cambrian whilst the latter two are of Ordovician age. In all cases the beds of slate are now steeply inclined so that they are known locally as 'veins'. The cleavage is also steeply inclined, often sub-vertical, reflecting the compressive forces that were exerted from the southeast. Therefore, the pillaring plane tends to cut across the vein and the joint plane can be nearly horizontal, see §5.3.2.8 (Williams 1991; DoE 1995; Lewis 1976; Lindsay 1974). Penrhyn quarry is located near Bethesda, Gwynedd, in north Wales and is named after the lord of the estate of Penrhyn near Bangor. To be more exact, the quarrymen built the town of Bethesda as a place to live! A railway was constructed over a distance of about 6 miles to the shores of the Menai Straits where a harbour was constructed for the distribution of the famous 'Cambrian purple' slate all over the world. The huge excavation of the north pit commenced in 1785 and was worked by galleries in a similar manner to that described below but without the motorized machines. Extensive use was made of aerial ropeways, inclines and water balances to raise slate and waste. The workings were, and still are, drained by a tunnel driven so that it empties into the Afon (river) Ogwen.

The geology and present method of working by the Nantlle Slate Company of the steeply dipping beds of the same slate at Nantlle are very similar to those described below although the scale of the operation is much smaller. At Dinorwig, situated between the two, the same slate again outcrops and was worked by creating galleries in the form of terraces on the mountain side. However, these are now abandoned.

Geology

The general dip of the 'vein' is 45° to the southeast and the cleavage is near vertical at 80° to the horizontal dipping in the same direction The best purple and blue states are bounded by faults parallel to the cleavage to create a 'vein' of width about 100 metres, see Fig. 6.42. The 'hard' grey slate to the east is not suitable for roofing slate and the demand for the red and green slates that occur to the west is low. Weathering has extended to a depth of up to 50 metres as shown by the presence of clay and iron staining of the cleavage surface. The slate is

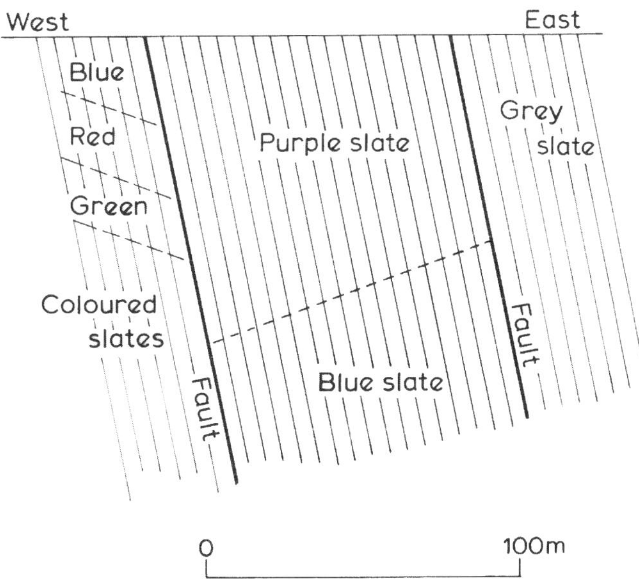

Fig. 6.42. General geology of Penrhyn quarry.

highly fractured by the natural faults, joints and dykes which has important implications upon extraction.

Of paramount importance is the cleavage of the slate which is variable. Best slate cleaves to thicknesses of 4 mm or less and these are often described as 'soft' in that they exhibit some flexibility. These include the Cambrian purples and blues and the blue-grey slates of Ffestiniog. Other slates are unsuitable for roofing and are sawn into memorials, plaques, architectural items, paving, tiles and walling stone. These are described as 'hard' and appear brittle. In between are slates that can only be split to produce thick roofing slates termed 'strong' or 'heavy' grades.

Igneous dykes often cut across the 'veins' and the cleavage and reduce the yield of suitable blocks. There also appears to be an association between dykes and parallel joints, locally called 'knives', which further reduce the yield of blocks. Joints or 'heads' are often spar filled and can be useful, if conveniently spaced, to define two of the surfaces of a block, the 'head joint' and the 'foot joint'. Otherwise, frequent joints reduce block size and yield.

The original bedding plane usually cuts obliquely across the cleavage and, in most cases, is of no concern. Occasionally, however, 'crych du', which may be remnant bedding or slate derived from more coarsely sized sediments, causes a perturbation or inflection of the cleavage plane which must be removed from the block by sawing.

Slates comprise essentially micas (predominantly sericite with some muscovite and illite), quartz and chlorite with minor feldspar, hematite and carbonaceous material such as graphite. The different colours have been attributed to the varying proportions of these minor mineral constituents. In the purple Cambrian slate, in particular, light green spots and stripes can occur. These have no effect upon the splitting or the durability of the slate but may create an undesirable appearance in roofing. Of course, such slate is also generally unsuitable for engraving. These 'reduction' spots and stripes have been attributed to different chemical microenvironments, probably having reducing conditions, within the original mudstone. Alternatively they may be caused by the locally low concentrations of hematite or graphite/carbon in the mineral assemblage.

Palffia are small circular, planar features of diameter between 2 and 50 centimetres. Their cause is unknown. Typically they cut obliquely across the cleavage and produce small iregularities and depressions upon the surface of riven slate. In the worst case, the slate may actually be holed. It has proved very difficult to predict or identify the occurrences of palffia and spots by exploration drilling.

Surprisingly, although much has been written of the history of communities based upon slate production and for that matter, stone in general, there is no recent authoritive text upon the petrology of slate which cites explanations of the many flaws and imperfections. An

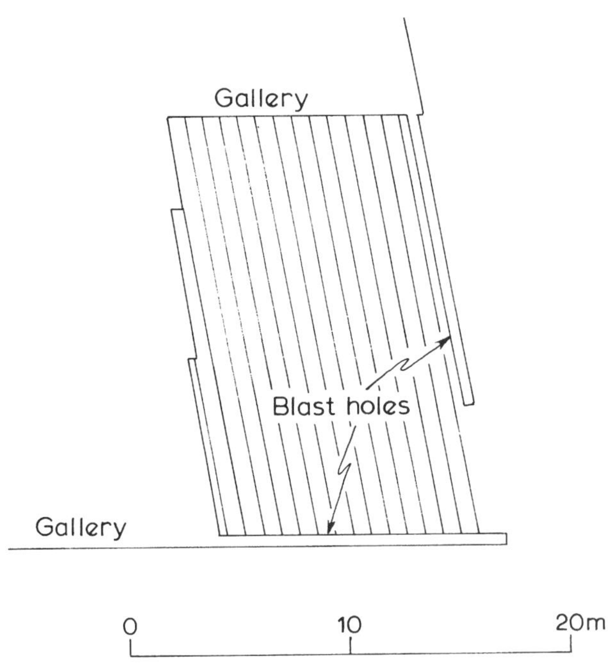

Fig. 6.43. Section of bench at Penrhyn quarry showing blastholes and cleavage.

Fig. 6.44. Hydraulic pick splitting blocks of slate (Courtesy of Alfred McAlpine Slate Products Ltd).

example of an interseting historical text is Behre (1933). This seems to reflect a lack of quantitative research in this subject.

Extraction

As can be appreciated from Fig. 6.42, when the slate is extracted the hanging (east) wall literally overhangs the excavation unless substantial volumes of overburden are removed. A collapse of this wall, probably induced by the weight of tips placed above the quarry, has closed the original north pit, since the description was published in 'Quarry Management' (Anon 1984, 1997). Extraction now takes place from the south pit and the northern excavation is being filled by waste tipping.

Overburden is removed by conventional drill and blast operations using slurry or emulsion explosives because blast holes are typically wet! The quarry has been developed upon benches, locally called 'galleries', of height of 20 metres. Blocks are removed from the eastern faces only so that the quarry expands in an easterly direction and gradually progresses south. Several horizontal blast holes are drilled at the level of the gallery to undercut the block and one or two are drilled on the plane of cleavage. Black powder is the explosive used to shake-up or disaggregate the naturally defined blocks although some breakage will occur at the base of the block unless a 'foot joint' exists. One concealed face of the block, normal to the quarry face, breaks along the pillaring plane, see Fig. 6.43. Potential blocks of slate are then selected by the operator of the hydraulic excavator who loads blasted material onto rigid body dump trucks for delivery either to the inspection area or the tipping point. At the inspection area, close to the waste tipping point, the blocks are examined and split on the cleavage plane by an hydraulic hammer fitted to the chassis of a crawler excavator, see Fig. 6.44. A wheeled loader fitted with forks handles the blocks and loads the good slabs onto the demountable flat-bed body of an articulated dump truck for transport to the processing plant, see Fig. 6.45. Output of slates is about 20 000 tonnes per annum for which it is necessary to move 4 million tonnes of rock per year.

As described above, the entire operation is mechanized and directed towards maintaining this high level of output so that the large market share of roofing slates won by the present operator can be supplied without interruption. A more selective method of extraction exploiting 'foot joints' might produce a greater yield of blocks but this would be at the expense of output. Extraction would be slower and the haul roads on the galleries would be difficult to maintain in a suitable condition for dump trucks.

Fig. 6.45. Articulated truck fitted with flat-bed to carry slate blocks (Courtesy of Alfred McAlpine Slate Products Ltd).

Processing
The principal product of the quarry is roofing slate, the production of which is described in §6.4.13. Waste slate finds some uses as crushed rock aggregate, granules and filler powder.

6.6.6. Aberllefenni mine, Powys, Wales

Introduction
Aberllefenni slate mine is situated in the valley of the river Dulas near Corris, itself a small town surrounded by abandoned slate mines. It is operated by a company which specialises in the production of memorials and architectural items, for example, cladding, cills, lintels and copings.

Geology
The 'vein' of slate is nearly vertical at an inclination of 85° and narrow; only 21 metres. The cleavage is also vertical and parallel to the walls of the vein which is bounded on one side by granite and by inferior slate on the other. The slate is blue-grey in colour, almost black when wet, but does not cleave readily into roofing slate. It is massive in form exhibiting very few joints, palffia, spots or other flaws. Therefore, it can be sawn into large slabs and beams. When polished the slate is almost featureless in appearance and ideally suited for engraving.

Extraction
The vertical inclination and narrowness of the vein mean that it would be uneconomic and impractical to extract the slate by quarrying. Therefore, the slate is mined.

The mine is entered through a horizontal adit in the side of the mountain and all extraction takes place below this level. Above the adit the slate has been extracted by previous mining.

Ventilation is naturally induced, air entering through the adit and leaving through the upper levels which connect to the surface at higher elevations. All equipment is pneumatically or electrically powered so that there are no engine exhaust fumes to remove.

The method of winning slabs of slate is shown in Fig. 5.54. The adit, which contains the rail haulage system, is driven in the footwall along-side the vein. The vein is divided along its length into rooms or chambers for extraction and pillars to be left to prevent collapse of the walls. To create a chamber a tunnel is driven across the vein from the adit or level to the hanging wall. This is then developed laterally to prepare the vaulted roof of the eventual chamber. A cable crane is then rigged across this chamber for the purpose of raising slate blocks up to the haulage level.

At this point it is worth noting that suspended walkways are required by the Mines Inspectorate to enable the roof and cable suspension points to be inspected. Extraction of slate then proceeds in a downward direction. The first stage is the excavation of a 'box cut' by drilling and blasting to create the initial face of height about 2 metres. Thence forward, blocks are sawn on the pillaring plane and undercut using either a wire saw or a chain saw capable of cutting to a depth of 2.1 metres. The teeth of the saw are tungsten carbide but PCD, polycrystalline diamond, is being considered. Finally, the block or slab is split from the face on the cleavage plane using plug and feathers. Thus, maximum size of slab is $2 \times 1 \times 0.3$ metres which weighs about 2.5 tonnes. The slabs are then raised and loaded onto bogies by the cable crane. An electric locomotive hauls the blocks along the adit to the road. No waste is taken out of the mine and output is about 100 tonnes per month of finished slate.

Processing

Processing comprises sawing and polishing using the Jenny Lind. When requested, slab will be riven on one face but otherwise all faces are sawn. For structural members, such as lintels, and fire surrounds it is important that the piece is sawn so that the length contains the cleavage and pillaring planes. The processing of the slate creates very little waste.

6.6.7. Slate mines and quarries of Blaenau Ffestiniog, Gwynedd, Wales

Introduction

By road or railway, Blaenau Ffestiniog is about 12 miles inland from the sea near Portmadog, north Wales. Once again it was the slate mines of the area which caused 'Madock's port' to be developed and also the construction of the railway which is now a well known tourist attraction. Historically, this area has been of great importance and all slate was extracted by mining. The complex of workings known as Oakeley quarry was once the largest slate mine in the world. All of these mines are now inactive but several are open as tourist attractions (1995) including Gloddfa Canol and Llechwedd. However, extraction of slate continues in quarries operated by several companies.

Geology

There are several, essentially parallel, 'veins' in the district separated by beds of chert, greywacke, inferior slate and igneous intrusions. The most important are named the Old Vein, the New Vein and the North Vein

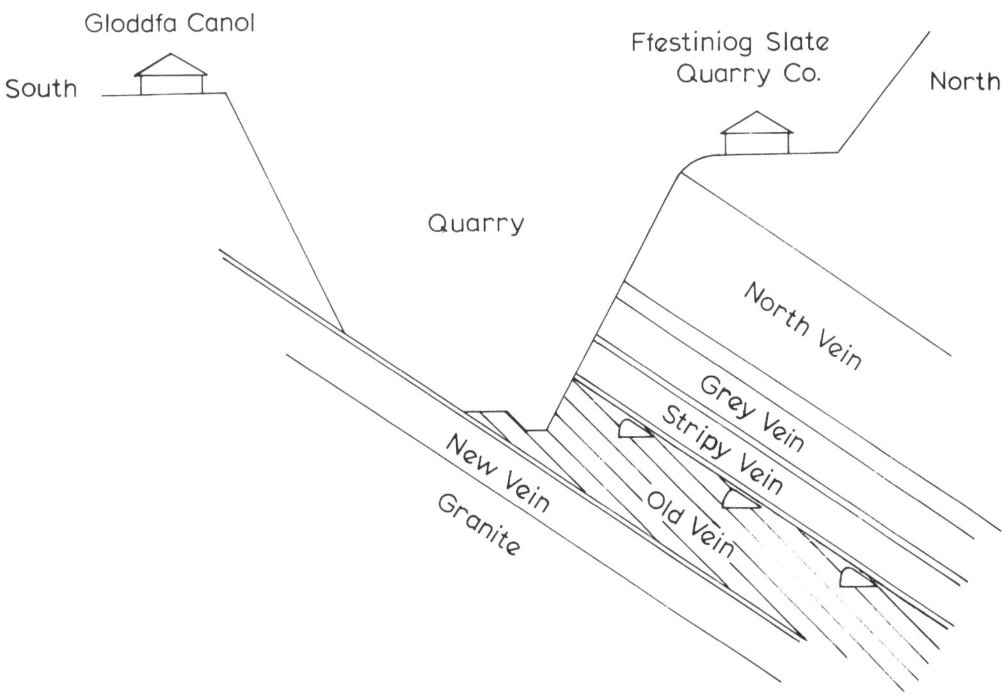

Fig. 6.46. Diagram of the Ffestiniog quarry workings for the recovery of pillars of slate from abandoned mines.

Fig. 6.47. Quarry showing the pillars of the Oakeley mine (Courtesy of Ffestiniog Slate Quarry Co. Ltd).

of which the two former veins have been extensively worked. Several dykes cut across these veins. Typically the veins dip to the north at an angle of 30 to 40° and disappear into the mountain sides under rapidly thickening overburden. The cleavage is at a slightly greater angle than the dip. For example, in the Oakeley mine the dip of the vein is about 35° and that of the cleavage about 45°. The slate is blue-grey and of varying quality with respect to cleavage. The slate from the Old Vein, in particular, is considered to be amongst the best in the world for roofing.

Extraction

The present quarry operations are uncovering the pillars left by the earlier mining operations described in §5.3.10.6 and illustrated in Fig. 5.53 (Isherwood 1980, 1988). This is a major task only made possible by modern earth moving equipment and is shown digrammaticaly in Fig. 6.46. It is hindered by the facts that the area is undermined, that the land surface is steep, that tips of waste overly much of the ground and that buildings have sterilised some slate. A view off the quarry workings showing several pillars and the processing plants is given in Fig. 6.47. In addition, the deep mine workings have flooded to the level of the drains that discharge into local rivers and the water must be pumped to expose the pillars.

Theoretically, the pillars should contain 50% of the original slate but it is apparent that pillars were robbed by the departing rockmen. This gives some problems of instability of faces and fractures in slate caused by collapse of pillars.

Wherever possible foot joints, head joints, pillaring and cleavage are used to define blocks and additional breakage is minimized. Blast holes for black powder are drilled on the cleavage or pillaring planes as necessary, see Fig. 5.47. The blocks are removed by an hydraulic excavator and then examined on the quarry floor. Plug and feathers are employed to split the block into slabs suitable for the saws, see Fig. 5.26, before they are loaded onto a flat bed truck.

Processing

The principal product is roofing slate, the production of which is described in §6.4.13. Slate which will not split for roofing is sawn into tiles, memorials, paving and walling stone. Slab is also engraved although some slate contains crystals of pyrite which precludes its use for this purpose. Disposal of waste is a problem in an area which already contains so many tips. Some waste slate, especially the green slate, is crushed into granules to coat roofing felt and slate powder is also produced for the manufacture of synthetic slates.

6.6.8. Birchover gritstone quarry, Derbyshire

Introduction

The quarry is located at an elevation of over 300 metres within a plateau above the village of Birchover, near Matlock. The high ground known as Stanton Moor has been created by erosion of the surrounding area by the River Derwent flowing through Darley Dale to the north and east and the Rivers Lathkill and Bradford flowing to the west. Birchover quarry is now owned and operated by Natural Stone Products Ltd but was previously known as Ann Twyford's quarry and has an historic reputation for grindstones and millstones. In addition to its use as building stone in houses and churches it was also used extensively in bridges, dams, aqueducts and reservoirs. Today the building stone is used in the local area and in cities and towns where sandstone is a traditional material of construction such as Manchester, Sheffield, Harrogate and Wakefield. In 1997, the quarry fulfilled a large contract to supply stone blocks which were assembled into columns for the New Parliamentary Building in Westminster. The contract was unusual in that the columns were load-bearing and the specifications extremely demanding.

Geology

The quarry exploits the Namurian sandstone commonly called the Millstone Grit Series which overlies the Carboniferous limestone. The Millstone Grit is generally considered to have been formed by consolidation of sediments deposited in a shallow sea as a delta produced by rapid erosion of high ground to the south. In the local area of Birchover the stratigraphic sequence comprises Monsoldale limestones overlain by the Longstone mudstones and then the Namurian sandstones, siltstones and mudstones with the highest stratum being the Ashover Grit which is exploited by the quarry. In many places the softer sediments beneath the more resistant gritstone have been eroded so that isolated remnants of the gritstone remain as outliers on the top of hills and forming spectacular escarpments, ridges and standing stones. Birchover quarry is situated in such an outlier almost entirely surrounded by limestones. The gritstone is buff to pink in colour and is a fine to medium textured sandstone.

Although some evidence of current bedding is evident in the quarry faces, bedding planes are completely absent except for one or two shale bands in the upper levels. The present operator believes that the deposit may have been formed by the rapid filling with sandy and gritty sediments of a depression in the sea-bed created by faulting. An approximately east–west fault with downthrow to the north has been identified just south of the quarry. Consolidation of the sediments has created a deep pocket of massive gritstone beneath the bedded sequence of later gritstones, see Fig. 6.48. The principal structural feature is the presence of a set of persistent, approximately vertical joints which cut across the quarry in a roughly east–west direction. These joints give the appearance of having been formed by slumping of the

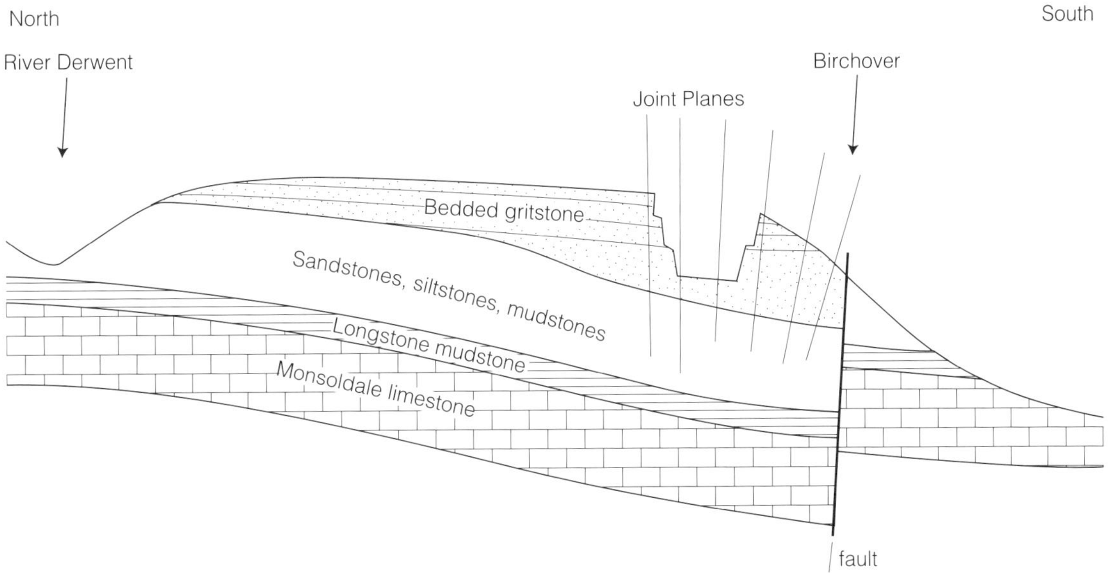

Fig. 6.48. Geological section of Birchover quarry.

Fig. 6.49. Hydraulic claw removing a sandstone block from Birchover quarry (Courtesy of Natural Stone Products Ltd).

deposit towards the escarpment to the south. They rotate from the vertical in the direction of the escarpment and display evidence of widening of the aperture towards the surface. Occasional pockets of consolidated silty, clayey sand are encountered in the quarry which must be rejected together with shale bands by selective extraction.

Extraction

Historically the overlying bedded gritstones were cut into building stones, millstones and grindstones. Today the beds are extracted for restoration work and walling stone. The lower massive gritstone is extracted for building stone owing to the large blocks that may be removed from the faces. Blocks are produced by disaggregation of the rock mass using a back-hoe excavator fitted with a small toothed bucket or a claw, see Fig. 6.49. Wherever possible the vertical joints are exploited to create one face of the block, the 'back'. Where convenient horizontal or vertical joints do not exist blasting with black powder and safety fuse is employed to break the rock. Owing to the large size of the natural blocks it is likely that further sub-division of the block on the quarry floor will be necessary before pieces can be transported to the processing plant by wheeled loader. Blasting is employed at present although expanding powders and Cardox have been tested. For the purpose of the present contract to supply columns the blocks are transported to a storage area where they are inspected, numbered and sampled. A range of tests for strength and durability is applied before the satisfactory blocks pass on to processing.

Processing

The processing plant has two, diamond, mono-blade frame saws which are used for trimming the blocks and two circular diamond saws of 1.6 and 3.0 metres diameter. The frame saws are favoured because they are capable of accepting larger blocks than the circular saws which are used to cut trimmed blocks into slab and walling stone. A milling machine is used to machine the sawn blocks to exact dimensions as, for example, required by the Parliamentary Building Project. A diamond core drill has also been installed for this contract to drill holes in blocks to accept the steel tension bolts that run through each column. Chamfers are cut on the edges of blocks using powered hand tools and the blocks are finished by rubbing using powered Carborundum discs. A guillotine has been installed to manufacture walling stone from waste and the thinnly bedded strata.

Process water is recirculated through concrete lagoons to remove suspended solids. Output is about 50 cubic metres per week.

References

ANON 1962. The quarrying of Portland limestone. *The Quarry Manager's Journal*, June, 1–8.

——1984. A slate operation diversifies. *Quarry Management*, March, 131–136.

——1990. Burlington slate into the nineties. *Mine & Quarry*, December, 8–10.

——1990. Mechanisation at Portland boosts block output. *Stone Industries*, October, 27–29.

——1993. ARC put the record straight on Portland. *Stone Industries*, October, 36–37.

——1994. Slate without waste. *Quarry Management*, May, 33–34.

——1997. A superquarry in the making. *Mine and Quarry*, March, 24–27.

ASHURST, J. & DIMES, F. G. 1984. *Stone in Building*. Stone Federation, London.

BEHRE, C. H. 1933. Slate in Pennsylvannia, State of Pennsylvannia Geological Survey.

BRITISH STANDARDS INSTITUTION 1987. BS 5750 *Quality systems*, Milton Keynes.

BRUCE, A. 1989. Natural stone production in Aberdeen, *Quarry Management*, February, 13–15.

CIRIA/CUR. 1991. *Manual on the use of Rock in Coastal and Shoreline Engineering*. Special Publication 83, London.

CLIFTON-TAYLOR, A. & IRESON, A. S. 1983. *English Stone Building*. Gollancz, London.

DEPARTMENT OF THE ENVIRONMENT 1995. *Slate Waste Tips and Workings in Britain*. HMSO, London.

HARTLEY, R. & BJERKAN, M. 1994. Rock flow systems in coastal and shoreline engineering. *Quarry Management*, 19–24.

ISHERWOOD, J. 1980. *Candles to Caplamps*. Gloddfa Canol Slate Mine.

——1988. *Slate from Blaenau Ffestiniog*. AB Publishing, Leicester.

LEWIS, M. J. T. 1976. *Llechi slate*. Gwynedd Archives Service, Beaumaris.

LINDSAY, J. 1974. *A History of the North Wales Slate Industry*. David & Charles, Newton Abbot.

O'NEILL, H. 1961. The working of the Aberdeen granites. *Quarry Manager's Journal*, Dec., 479–490.

SCHAFFER, R. J. 1972. *The Weathering of Natural Building Stones*, BRE Report 18, Building Research Establishment, London, 17–19.

WARLAND, E. G. 1953. *Modern Practical Masonry*, second edition. Pitman, London.

WILLIAMS, M. 1991. *The Slate Industry*. Shire Publications, Princes Risborough.

7. Rock fill

7.1. Introduction

Where natural ground is excavated and used as bulk fill in civil engineering works, it is categorized as either earth fill or rock fill. The distinction is important from two points of view:

- from a technical standpoint the difference in performance of the two types of fill is significant, rock fill generally exhibiting superior engineering properties to earth fill
- from a contractual standpoint the difference in the effort required to excavate the materials is significant, rock being more difficult to excavate and generally requiring blasting or ripping

The concept of rock fill construction has undergone some radical changes over the years. Before heavy compaction machinery was available, loose dumped rock fill was used to build dam and railway embankments. The 22 m high South Fork dam built in 1852 in Pennsylvania had a downstream shoulder of rock fill; its failure due to overtopping in 1889 ruined a large part of the city of Johnstown and 2209 people died (Jansen 1980). In the middle of the 19th century dams were built by gold miners in California entirely of dumped rock fill. Subsequently, in the first half of the 20th century, dams 100 m high were built in California using dumped rock fill. Large settlements of the rock fill frequently occurred during construction and reservoir filling. Techniques adopted to reduce settlement involved the use of sound rock with a minimum of fines and sluicing with large volumes of water.

With the advent of modern compaction plant it became feasible to place rock fill in layers of a thickness which could be adequately compacted. Using this approach a well graded rock fill with some fines was found to give superior performance. Since large highway embankments are a relatively recent development, nearly all highway rock fills have been constructed in this way as have most modern rock fill dams and railway embankments.

High-quality rock fill is usually quarried at depth and there may be considerable quantities of overlying weathered overburden. There are obvious economic and environmental advantages if such weathered material can be used in the fill operation. Low grade rock fill, or soft rock fill as it is sometimes called, can be considered a transition between earth fill and rock fill and has found increasing use. In a soft rock fill the fines fill the voids between the coarser particles and a maximum density is obtained after compaction.

The use of rock fill in civil engineering structures is a major subject which can only be briefly summarized in this chapter. In June 1990 a NATO Advanced Study Institute was held at LNEC Lisbon on rock fill structures. The proceedings of this two week meeting (Maranha das Neves 1991) provide a useful account of many aspects of the subject.

7.2. Functions and required properties

7.2.1. Applications

The properties required of rock fill are directly related to its function in a particular application. Rock fill may be used in a variety of engineering structures including the following:

- highway embankments
- embankment dams
- foundations for buildings
- gabions

The most common use of rock fill is probably in highway embankments. These are often of modest height but may be of considerable length. The use of rock in highway embankments tends to be governed by locally available material.

Rock fill has also been used extensively in the construction of embankment dams and some of the highest dams in the world are built of rock fill. Nurek dam in Tajikistan is 300 m high with an embankment volume of $58 \times 10^6\,m^3$. As rock fill has a relatively high permeability it is usually necessary to provide a watertight element such as a clay core within the embankment (see Fig. 7.9), or a concrete or asphalt membrane on the upstream slope, see Fig. 7.11.

Shortage of good building land increasingly leads to construction on filled ground and it is not uncommon to place engineered fill to an appropriate specification to form the foundation for buildings. Large volumes of opencast mining backfills, some of them rock fills, have been placed and compacted to engineering specifications so that buildings and roads can be built over them when the opencast operation has been completed.

Gabions are steel wire or plastic mesh baskets filled with rock and they are usually used in situations where land is at a premium or soil protection is required. They have many applications in civil engineering, particularly on highways where soil retention is necessary.

The different applications of rock fill have significance for the degree of selection and control which it is either necessary or practical to exercise during fill placement. In most applications it will be important that the parent rock material is strong, durable and chemically inert.

7.2.2. Slope stability

Where rock fill is used to form an embankment above ground level, it is important to ensure that the rock fill has sufficient strength for the slope to remain stable. Slope failure involves shearing of the rock fill in which rock fragments must move over or between each other. This motion is opposed by friction and obstruction, giving rise to 'shear strength'. The shear strength will be influenced by the size, shape, gradation and strength of the rock fragments that make up the fill. These factors can be conveniently expressed in terms of the internal angle of friction or shearing resistance, ϕ. The shear strength of a particular rock fill is also a function of both the packed density of the fill and the stress level. In simple terms the shear strength (τ) of the material is related to the normal effective stress (σ') and the angle of shearing resistance (ϕ') by the expression:

$$\tau = \sigma' \tan \phi'.$$

A full explanation of shear strength and its use in slope stability is given by Bromhead (1986) and Hoek & Bray (1981).

Rock fills are generally characterized by high shear strength, particularly when they have been heavily compacted and, therefore, they have the ability to be constructed at steep slopes. For a heavily compacted rock fill the angle of shearing resistance, ϕ', will be particularly large at low confining stresses where the maximum, or peak, strength is associated with strongly dilatant behaviour. After the peak strength has been reached, further displacent reduces the strength to the constant volume, or critical state, angle of shearing resistance, ϕ'_{cv}. This is illustrated in Fig. 7.1. For a loose rock fill the maximum shear strength will be close to the constant volume angle of shearing resistance. The angle of repose of the loose rock fill, which is the slope angle that loosely tipped rock fill naturally adopts, is also similar to the constant volume angle of shearing resistance and is typically 35° to 40°.

The dams built of dumped rock fill in California in the second half of the nineteenth century were up to 30 m in height and had slopes as steep as 1 vertical in 0.5 horizontal (63°) (Galloway 1939). The construction of slopes steeper than the angle of repose of the loose rock fill, was achieved by hand placement of stone to form a rubble retaining wall. In recent years different construction techniques have been adopted for the construction of rock fill embankments. The use of modern heavy earth-moving machinery has led to rock fill being placed in layers typically 0.5 m to 1.5 m deep and compacted with heavy vibrating rollers. This method results in very dense well graded rock fills with strength and deformation properties greatly superior to those of the uncompacted, uniform sized rock fills previously used. Yet, as de Mello (1977) pointed out, slopes have tended to become flatter.

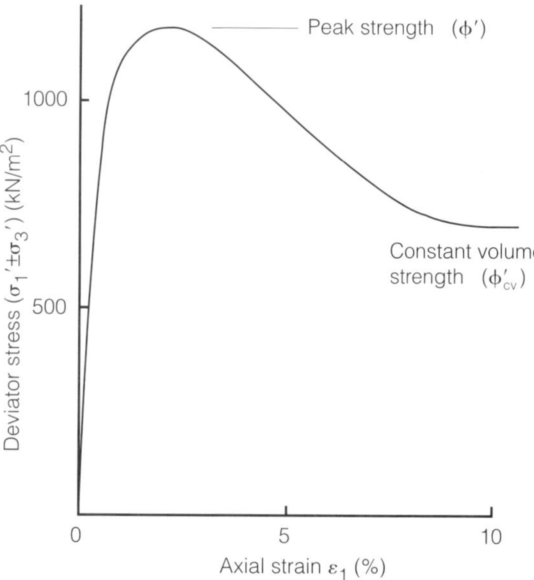

Fig. 7.1. Drained triaxial compression test on heavily compacted basalt rock fill with confining pressure of 100 kPa (after Charles & Watts 1980).

The ability of a slope to remain stable is assessed by the ratio of the restoring force to the disturbing force which is known as the factor of safety (F). It would seem that some modern rock fill structures may have slopes with high factors of safety that do not fully utilize the shear strength properties of the fill. An acceptable value for the factor of safety obtained in a stability analysis, say, $F = 1.5$, may have been based on conservative assumptions about the shear strength of the compacted rock fill, say, $\phi' = 40°$.

The pronounced curvature, particularly at low stresses, exhibited by Mohr failure envelopes for compacted rock fills, which is shown in Fig. 7.2, has formed an obstacle to the use of realistic shear strength parameters in stability calculations as analyses have usually been based on linear failure envelopes. It is now feasible both to measure the shear strength parameters of a compacted rock fill (Charles & Watts 1980; Perry 1994) and to use these realistic parameters in slope stability analyses (Charles & Soares 1984; Perry 1994).

7.2.3. Deformation

Some of the most complex deformation situations involving rock fill occur with embankment dams where there are several different types of fill materials in various zones within the embankment. However, the most difficult situations occur in those applications where even small movements may cause problems such as the following:

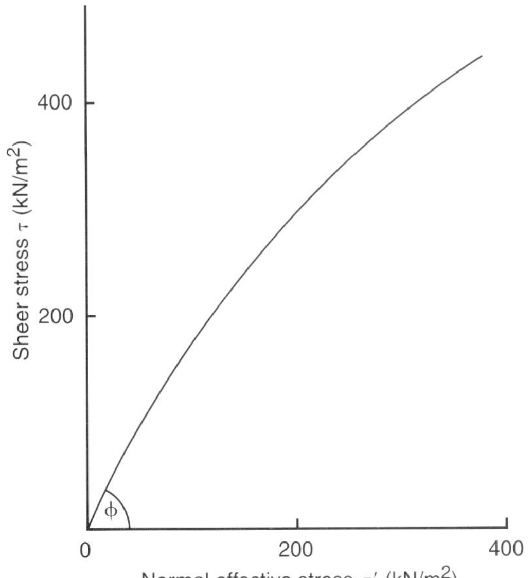

Fig. 7.2. Curved Mohr failure envelope for heavily compacted slate rock fill (after Charles & Watts 1980).

- where settlement sensitive structures are built on the rock fill
- where a road passes from a rock fill embankment onto a rigid structure such as a bridge

In these cases it is imperative to reduce post placement fill settlement.

Applied stresses within the rock fill will increase during fill placement due to the weight of overlying layers of rock fill, but the compression of the rock fill that occurs at this stage will normally be of little practical consequence. It is the movements that occur subsequent to fill placement which are normally of most significance. Compression of rock fill is associated with crushing of points of contact and rearrangement of rock fragments and particles which may be caused by a change in effective stress or changes in moisture content. Changes in effective stress can be caused by, for example:

- the rise and fall of the groundwater level within the rock fill
- the weight of buildings constructed on the rock fill

Poorly compacted, unsaturated rock fill is likely to be susceptible to collapse compression when first inundated as an increase in moisture content may weaken the parent rock material and lead to further crushing at points of contact. An increase in moisture content could occur in the following situations:

- submergence of rock fill by a rising groundwater level
- downward percolation of surface water through the rock fill
- downward percolation of water escaping from drains in the crest of an embankment

The effect of inundation on an unsaturated rock fill can be examined in an oedometer test carried out on a sample of the rock fill compacted to the field density at the field moisture content.

The compressibility of rock fill can be measured in large oedometer tests and Fig. 7.3 shows the compression of some heavily compacted rock fills measured in a one metre diameter oedometer (Charles 1991; Charles & Penman 1988). Large oedometer tests have led to the following conclusions about the compressibility of rock fills (Kjaernsli & Sande 1963; Sowers *et al.* 1965):

- compressibility decreases with increasing strength of the rock particles
- compressibility decreases with increasing density of the fill
- compressibility is smaller for smooth surfaced materials
- compressibility is smaller for a broad grading
- the major mechanism is the crushing of highly stressed points of contact between particles which in turn results in some reorientation of particles

Oedometer tests and field monitoring have also shown that the rate of continuing settlement of rock fill under constant applied stress is similar to the secondary compression behaviour of clays. This conclusion is important as, in many situations the long term compression of the rock fill will be more important than the immediate compression that occurs during rock fill construction.

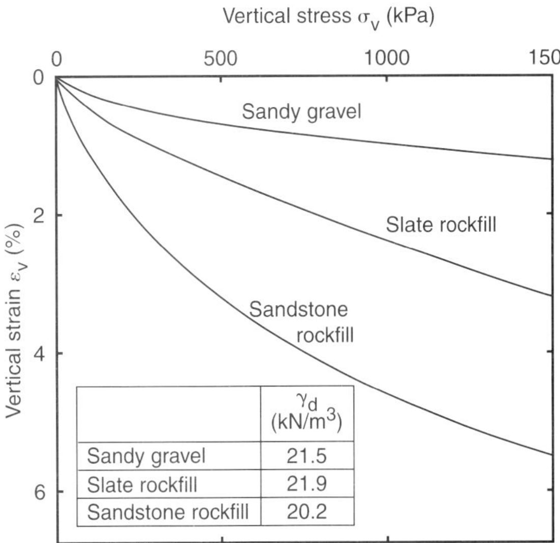

	γ_d (kN/m³)
Sandy gravel	21.5
Slate rockfill	21.9
Sandstone rockfill	20.2

Fig. 7.3. Compressibility of heavily compacted rockfills measured in one metre diameter oedometer (after Charles & Penman 1988).

Heavy compaction of the rock fill during placement can greatly reduce the creep rate of the rock fill at low stresses.

7.2.4. Dynamic behaviour

Vibration can cause compression of a rock fill by the rock particles being rotated and rearranged into a denser packing. Therefore, compaction of rock fill during placement can be achieved by the use of a vibrating roller. Such compaction is beneficial and the more effective the compaction, the less vulnerable the rock fill will be to volume reduction when subjected to any subsequent dynamic loading which could be associated with, for example, a seismic event.

7.2.5. Permeability

There is usually a general requirement that permeability should be sufficiently large to allow water to drain away and prevent the creation of excessive water pressures (pore pressure) during construction by the saturation of voids associated with the finer material in the fill. If water cannot escape the pore pressure reduces the

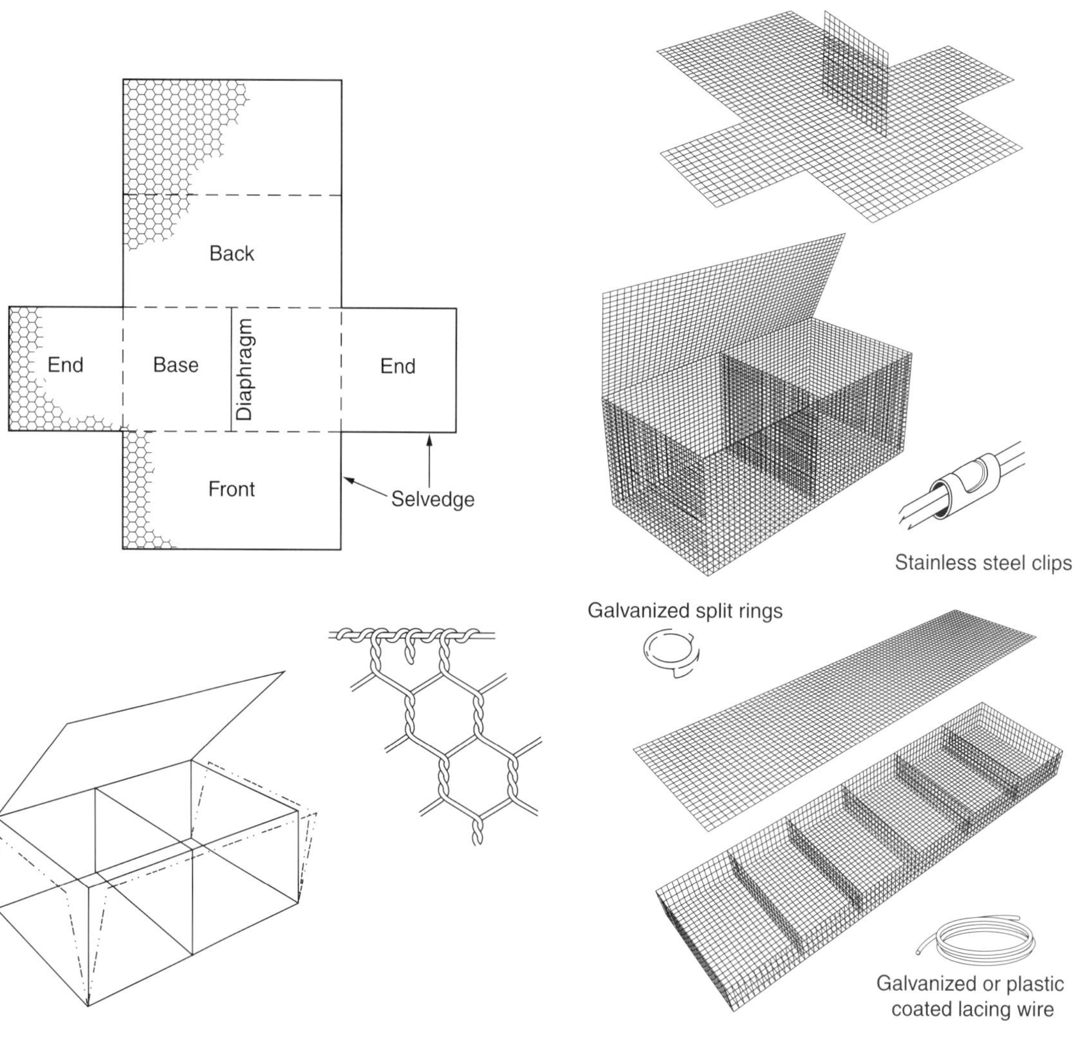

Fig. 7.4. Types of gabion cage (after BS 8002; BSI 1994).

effective stress level (σ') thereby reducing the shear strength (τ). In some applications, such as embankment dams, there may be more specific permeability requirements. While heavy compaction should produce a fill of relatively low compressibility it also creates more fines and it is important that the percentage of fines is not so large that the permeability (hydraulic conductivity) of the fill is reduced below, say, 10^{-5} m/s. The permeability of a rock fill can reduce very rapidly as the percentage of fines increases and it is usual to specify an upper limit of the order of 10% for the percentage of particles finer than 0.06 mm.

7.2.6. Gabions

Gabions are large cuboid shaped baskets or mattresses which are made of steel wire, square welded rod or plastic mesh as illustrated in Figs 7.4 and 7.5, and filled with rock. The size of gabions vary but they are commonly 2 m to 6 m long, 1 m to 2 m wide and in depths of 0.3 m, 0.5 m and 1 m.

Gabions are permeable and flexible. These two qualities make them ideally suited for retaining materials and for construction on soft ground. They can be used for the following purposes:

- to build retaining walls
- to stabilize or repair earthwork or natural slopes
- to construct revetments
- to provide protection against erosion protection for watercourses and to provide protection against erosion by the sea or rainfall

Where gabions are used to construct retaining walls, for example to retain soil for a widened highway or to provide extra ground for a development, the gabions take the form of baskets and are placed one on top of the other. Some designs require the gabions to be tied together while others rely on the friction between the gabions to prevent movement. The walls should be constructed to a batter to enhance their appearance and to resist overturning. Gabions can be used to strengthen, stabilize, repair and reinstate existing slopes as well as being used as a method of new construction.

For revetments, the lining of rivers and canals, or coastal protection, gabions in mattress form are used. These gabions have a large areal extent compared to their height and have a low cellular structure. Their permeability allows water behind the structure to drain away when water levels fall. In some cases a filter material may be used between the soil and gabion to prevent wash-out of the soil behind the gabions.

The rock pieces used in the gabion have to be of a grading which prevents them passing through the mesh. The size of the mesh opening is, therefore, taken as the minimum size of rock fill. The maximum size of fill is usually two thirds the minimum dimension of the gabion or 200 mm whichever is the smaller. This requirement is

Fig. 7.5. Gabions in use for road construction (Courtesy P. G. Fookes).

to allow the rock in the gabion to be placed to fill the gabion well. As gabions should be filled by hand to prevent damage to the gabion mesh, handling of the material is also a consideration. In environmentally sensitive areas, the rock fill in the outer zone of the gabion can be placed in patterns or placed to give the semblance of a dry stone wall. To allow for settlement of the gabions, especially in a wall, the gabions should be slightly overfilled.

For the long-term stability of an individual gabion, the rock fill should meet an appropriate strength requirement. This is specified in terms of the ten-per-cent fines test. The minimum value required in the UK for highway construction is 50 kN. This ensures that the rock fill will not fail due to point contact of the rock pieces as the weight of gabion, and gabions above, is increased. Durability requirements are assessed using a crystallization test (Ross & Butlin 1989).

It is important that consideration is given to the corrosion resistance of the gabion. For temporary works the wire used to form the gabion cage may be uncoated. However, for permanent structures the wire is usually either galvanized or polyvinyl chloride (pvc) coated. Galvanized wire gabion cages are subject to corrosion attack if aggressive soils are in contact with the cage. Tests should, therefore, be undertaken to determine the aggressivity of the soils in terms of chloride ion content, sulphate content, pH, redox potential, soil resistivity and soil moisture content. If the soil is going to cause corrosion of the gabion cage then pvc coated wire should be considered and the pvc coating should be at least 0.25 mm thick and bonded to galvanized wire. The bonding should be sufficient to prevent capillary water entering between the coating and the wire. Both pvc and galvanized wire can be damaged by abrasion and their use should be avoided where granular materials may fall or wash against them.

7.3. Laboratory testing

7.3.1. General

The large size of rock fragments used in typical rock fills causes particular difficulties in determining the engineering properties of rock fill. Rock fragments with a dimension as large as 1m or more have sometimes been used in rock fills. It is clearly impractical to design equipment that could test such material. The largest triaxial testing equipment in the world can only accommodate samples of up to about 1 m in diameter and is thus only suitable for testing rock fill with a maximum particle size of 150–200 mm. Even this size of equipment is not widely available and a single test at this scale is extremely expensive.

The unavailability of large-scale testing equipment means that possible approaches to scaling down the field particle size distribution for laboratory tests need to be examined. These matters are not easy to resolve as particle fracturing can influence the behaviour of rock fill and the particle size distribution may change significantly during the course of a test. The simplest approach is to remove all the oversize material and test what is left although this procedure assumes that the finer fraction is representative of the whole. It has been suggested that it is preferable to test a material with a grading parallel to that of the field grading. However, this latter approach requires far more work in sample preparation and has the disadvantage that the tested sample may have an excessive quantity of fines.

7.3.2. Index and classification tests

With the difficulty and expense of carrying out strength and compressibility tests, there is much interest in correlating index and classification test results with engineering behaviour.

Particle strength, hardness and durability

The properties of the individual fragments of rock will have a significant influence on the behaviour of the rock fill. Particle strength and hardness will control the amount of particle breakdown and crushing of points of contact which occur during compaction and subsequent loading.

Long-term performance of the fill will be affected by the durability of the rock. Rocks are affected by wetting and drying; the strength of saturated rock fragments may be much less than the strength of the fragments when dry. Weak rocks such as shales will swell or disintegrate when exposed to atmospheric wetting and drying and are thus permanently weakened.

Properties of strength and durability can be measured in several ways:

- the uniaxial compressive strength (q_u) of cylindrical specimens of rock can be measured but considerable time and effort is required to prepare the cylindrical sample of rock for this standard test
- in the point load strength test (Broch & Franklin 1972) cylindrical specimens or irregular lumps of rock are loaded to failure between the conical platens of a portable tester
- in the slake durability test (Franklin & Chandra 1972) the resistance of a rock to wetting and drying cycles is assessed by immersing samples in water and noting the rate of disintegration; this test is useful for relatively weak rocks which are sensitive to the test
- the aggregate crushing test has been used to assess the suitability of a material to form a rock fill (Perry & Parsons 1986)
- the saturation moisture content or water absorption can give an indication of the weathering potential

Particle size distribution
The behaviour of rock fills will be influenced by their particle size distribution (PSD). They can be described as well graded where there is a wide range of particle sizes or uniformly graded where all the particles are within a narrow range. The determination of the particle size distribution of a representative sample by sieving will be a major task where the fill contains large rock fragments.

The percentage of silt and clay size particles (i.e. finer than 0.06 mm) is important as, when this percentage is high, the rock fill will cease to perform as a granular soil. The critical magnitude of the fines content is likely to be in the range of 10% to 25% by weight with regard to shear strength and 10% to 15% with regard to permeability.

Moisture content
Water is invariably present in fill materials; the amount of water, expressed as percentage by mass of the dry solid particles, is termed the moisture content (w). BS 1377: 1990 Part 2 describes the definitive method of moisture content determination by oven drying at 105°C to 110°C. As rock fills usually have a very wide range of particle sizes, the moisture may be very non-uniformly distributed throughout the fill.

Compactness
The compactness of a fill is a function of method of placement and the subsequent stress history. The following parameters are related to the compactness of the fill:

- voids ratio (e)
- porosity (n)
- dry density (ρ_d)
- dry unit weight (γ_d)
- air voids (V_a)
- density index (I_D)

These parameters are closely related as the following relationships demonstrate:

- $n = \{e/(1+e)\}\,100\,(\%)$
- $\rho_d = \{\rho_s(100-n)\}/100$
- $\gamma_d = \rho_d g$
- $V_a = \{1 - (\rho_d/\rho_w)[(\rho_w/\rho_s) + (w/100)]\}\,100\,(\%)$

where ρ_w is the density of water (1.0 Mg/m^3), w is the moisture content (%), ρ_s is the particle density (for many rocks 2.6 to 2.7 Mg/m^3), g is the acceleration due to gravity (9.81 m/s^2).

The density index (I_D), which is sometimes termed relative density, is a useful way of relating the *in situ* dry density of a granular fill (ρ_d) to the limiting conditions of maximum dry density (ρ_{dmax}) and minimum dry density (ρ_{dmin}).

$$I_D = \left(\frac{(\rho_d - \rho_{dmin})\rho_{dmax}}{(\rho_{dmax} - \rho_{dmin})\rho_d}\right) \times 100\,(\%)$$

For a rock fill containing large rock fragments, there will be great difficulties in measuring the three dry densities needed to compute I_D.

7.3.3. Shear strength tests

Triaxial testing equipment is commonly used to measure shear strength. Drained compression tests are often the simplest tests to perform and most closely resemble field conditions, but in some situations undrained testing may be required. Strain rate should not greatly affect the measured strength. Figure 7.1 shows the deviator stress plotted against axial strain for a drained triaxial compression test on a heavily compacted rock fill at low confining pressure.

The direct shear test is appropriate for testing free draining granular soils. However, the failure plane is very closely defined in the test and an unrepresentatively high value of shear strength may be measured for a rock fill due to the failure plane being constrained to pass through an artificially large number of rock particles.

Most field conditions will approximate to plane strain rather than the axisymmetric stress conditions in the triaxial test. Plane strain testing equipment also has been used to measure drained shear strength parameters of rock fills but the equipment is not widely available.

As the shear strength of rock fill is a function of both density and stress level, it is essential that test samples are compacted to an appropriate density and sheared under an appropriate confining pressure if strength parameters measured in the laboratory are to be applicable to the field situation. When triaxial tests are carried out to derive shear strength parameters for a limit equilibrium slope stability analysis, values of cell pressure should be used such that the stresses in the triaxial test correspond to the range of stress which will be encountered on potential critical failure surfaces in the embankment slopes. Figure 7.2 shows a curved failure envelope typical of a heavily compacted rock fill.

7.3.4. Compressibility tests

Rock fill compressibility is most commonly measured under conditions of one dimensional compression in a large oedometer as the test has a number of advantages:

- the deformation of a rock fill structure due to a change in stress or moisture content can often be related to the behaviour of the rock fill measured in the test
- the test is relatively simple to perform even at a large scale
- it is easy to carry out creep tests at constant applied load

A considerable number of large oedometers tests has been carried out on rock fill materials (Kjaernsli & Sande 1963; Sowers *et al.* 1965; Fumagalli 1969; Marsal 1973;

Penman & Charles 1976). The rock fill is compacted in layers with an electric vibrating hammer to the field density. The one dimensional compression behaviour of most rock fills on first loading is non-linear and so it is important to determine the compressibility over a range of stress that is applicable to the field situation. Figure 7.3 shows the compressibility of a number of heavily compacted rock fills as measured in a one metre diameter oedometer.

In some cases the unloading and reloading stress strain relationships can be of interest. This will be the case for deformations in the upstream rock fill of a central core dam due to reservoir drawdown and refilling. The stiffness is much greater than on first loading.

Poorly compacted unsaturated rock fill is likely to be susceptible to collapse compression when first inundated. The effect of inundation on an unsaturated rock fill can also be examined in an oedometer test by flooding the sample at an appropriate stress level.

7.4. Excavation

7.4.1. General

At present excavation of strong rock is accomplished economically by blasting and weak rock is excavated by machine. Modern explosives used in rock excavation by blasting almost entirely fall into the high explosive category and can be divided into gelatins, emulsions, slurries and ANFOs (Ammonium Nitrate/Fuel Oil mixtures) in approximately decreasing velocity of detonation. Black powder is the only surviving example of a low explosive which deflagrates rather than detonates and, although used extensively for rock before the early 20th century, finds no application in modern highway rock excavation, see §5.3.3.2.

Ripping is used on weaker materials which can be broken up using steel tynes or rippers mounted on a crawler tractor. The material is then scraped or dug ready for loading and transportation to the fill site.

As well as the need for an excavation to produce rock of a grading suitable for use as a fill material, there will also be a requirement in an engineering application such as a highway cutting that the excavation itself remains stable for a long period of time. The following sections on excavation by blasting are based on Matheson (1995).

7.4.2. Instability induced by excavation using explosives

Considerable damage can be caused to a rock slope by the uncontrolled use of high explosives. In civil engineering applications the major effect of blasting is one of increasing disturbance of pre-existing natural discontinuities. Presplit faces show little change from those of natural exposures unlike bulk blasted faces which tend to show a dramatic increase in discontinuity dilation which can be the principal cause of the resulting instability.

Standard seismic refraction techniques (Matheson 1985) have been used successfully to determine the extent of the blast disturbance. This application depends on a low velocity layer being formed in the disturbed rock with its dilated discontinuities in contrast to the relatively high velocity layer in the natural, undisturbed rock mass with tight discontinuities and acoustically coupled rock blocks. The width of the zone of disturbance can vary from two to four metres with smooth and trim blasting, and from six to eight metres with bulk blasting. Increasing instability in the final face is associated with increasing widths of disturbance. There is no disturbance in most natural slopes and those formed by presplit blasting.

Closed circuit television (CCTV) techniques have been used to measure directly the nature and extent of the disturbance and to verify the findings of the seismic refraction profiling (Gunning 1992). A skid mounted camera is inserted into holes drilled into the rock face and the depth of insertion is measured using a tape attached to the camera head. Observation and video recording are performed simultaneously through either a forward or a side viewing head. The discontinuity positions and dilations can be determined from a detailed scan of the borehole wall. Results verify that dilation of discontinuities is the main feature of the zone of disturbance measured by seismic refraction techniques.

The choice of excavation method involves predicting the damage that may be induced, then minimizing the damage to the final face whilst ensuring that the rock is fragmented sufficiently to allow mucking out. The two methods commonly used are presplit blasting and fragmentation blasting, but only presplit blasting appears to eliminate damage entirely.

7.4.3. Presplit blasting

This form of controlled blasting is designed to minimize damage in the final face (Matheson 1983, 1986). Closely spaced holes drilled along the proposed design slope are relatively lightly charged. The presplit charges are detonated simultaneously forming discontinuities along the design slope. Bulk blasting techniques are then used to fragment and loosen the rock in the excavation area. The presplit discontinuities limit disturbance arising from the bulk blasting and leave the rock forming the design slope in as near as possible its natural condition, thus minimizing induced instability in the final face, see §5.3.2.7. A presplit face is shown in Fig. 7.6.

The type, charging and detonation of the explosives used in presplitting require careful control. Hole diameter, hole spacing and explosive charging have proved to be fundamental, dependent variables which should not be varied unnecessarily. The explosive charges must be of sufficient strength to ensure that presplit fractures

Fig. 7.6. Presplit face.

are formed between boreholes and these fractures must be in existence before the disturbance caused by the bulk blasting reaches the proposed design slope. There must, therefore, be a delay between the detonation of the presplit and the bulk charges and a lower limit of 50 milliseconds has proved satisfactory. There is no upper limit and time intervals of days and weeks are commonly used.

Accurate drilling is vital and the setting up and close monitoring of the initial stages of drilling have been found to be extremely important. The orientation of drill rods and drill holes can be defined in terms of a dip (the angle from the horizontal) and an azimuth (direction of dip). Deviation of drill holes with depth can prove to be a problem, even when the initial alignment has been accurately set. Deviations tend to relate to the type of drill and the drilling technique, rather than the rock conditions. However there is a tendency for drills to deviate towards the normal of any hard and soft layering that exists in the host rock. A simple drill orientation device has been developed to help accurate alignment of drill rigs and measurements of drill hole orientation (Matheson 1984). The design of the device makes it largely independent of rig type and drill rod diameters and the accuracy is adequate for most surface excavations where precision drilling is required. Its use has considerably increased the accuracy of drilling presplit holes and it is usually specified on trunk road projects.

Successful presplit faces have been formed in a wide variety of sedimentary, metamorphic and igneous rock types, ranging from intensely fractured phyllitic schists to block fractured granitic intrusions. Individual presplit lifts of up to 27 m and presplit faces up to 62 m high are being used with great success. Nevertheless, caution is necessary in the use of presplit blasting as the technique alone is not the answer to all slope stability problems.

7.4.4. Fragmentation blasting

Fragmentation blasting is employed to break up the blocks naturally present within a rock mass to a size consistent with the intended use. In highway cutting excavations, after blasting the blocks must have a size distribution that is able to be easily loaded and transported by mechanical plant out of the excavation area and, if required as fill, must be within the specified grading. The degree to which fragmentation occurs when bulk blasting depends on the range of block sizes originally present in the rock mass, the natural block size distribution (NBSD) and the blasting technique. This bulk use of explosives is in complete contrast to presplit blasting which employs carefully controlled blasting to form the design slope, see §5.3.3.5.

7.4.5. Ripping

Ripping is an inexpensive method of providing rock fill where the *in situ* material is discontinuous or relatively soft. A crawler tractor is fitted with one or more steel tines or rippers which breaks up the rock as the tractor moves forward. The output of the ripper will depend not only on the material it is working but also on the power of the machine and the number and dimensions of the tines, see §5.3.2.9. The fragmented material is removed by a bulldozer and loaded by a backactor onto a dump truck for transport to the fill area. The output of a ripper is, therefore, also influenced by the capacity of the bulldozer. Inadequate capacity for the backactor and dump trucks can be overcome by stockpiling material. However, it is good practice in this type of construction to match the different types of plant for excavation, haulage, placement and compaction to ensure maximum efficiency.

7.4.6. Assessment of excavatability by blasting or ripping

If a rock mass could be excavated without introducing new discontinuities then the distribution of sizes characteristic of the volume of the excavated rock would identical with the Natural Block Size Distribution (NBSD) within the rock mass. The NBSD is analogous to the Particle Size Distribution (PSD) of a soil. The actual Block Size Distribution (BSD) in the excavated material depends on both the original NBSD and also the method of excavation, see §5.3.2.3. In strong rock having a coarse NBSD explosives are required to reduce blocks sizes to a level at which they can be handled by mechanized plant and, if required, used as rock fill. If this is not accomplished then secondary breakage of the larger rock block will be required which is time consuming and expensive.

Techniques of estimating both the NBSD and the BSD have been developed (Wang *et al.* 1992) which rely on the use of field data on the spacing and orientation of discontinuities within the area to be excavated. The data can be obtained by extrapolation from outcrop mapping, from scanlines on surface exposures, or from CCTV scanning of holes drilled into the rock mass. BSD can be estimated using either the Bond-Ram model (Bond 1959; Cunningham 1982) or the Kuz-Ram model (Kuznetsov 1973). Both models have been incorporated into computer programs that allow the effects of varying the blast pattern and explosive charging to be estimated.

In theory the highway engineer is able to calculate the NBSD of a rock mass and choose a technique of blasting which will fragment the rock mass to a BSD consistent with efficient loading and transportation, and a size range suitable for use as rock fill if required. However, these methods of prediction need to be fully tested in the field.

The techniques of minimising natural and induced instability on a rock face have been incorporated into the Optimum Design Technique for Rock Slopes (Matheson 1992). This dual approach is essential as instability is cumulative and one method cannot compensate for deficiencies in the other. For example, presplit blasting cannot compensate for a rock slope design orientation out of harmony with the host geotechnical conditions. The objective is to improve whole life costs by increasing stability and reducing costly remedial work and maintenance.

Whether to rip or blast will depend on the intact rock strength, the spacing of fractures and the abrasiveness of the rock. These different parameters have led to classifications based on seismic velocity (Caterpillar Tractor Company 1982) or point load strength and fracture spacing (Pettifer & Fookes 1994), see also §5.3.2.9.

Seismic velocity is the velocity at which a ground-borne vibration, usually the longitudinal or compression wave component, travels through a rock mass. The velocity is dependent on the stiffness of the rock and in particular the number, spacing and width of discontinuities. The higher the number of discontinuities the slower the wave will travel. The measurement of seismic

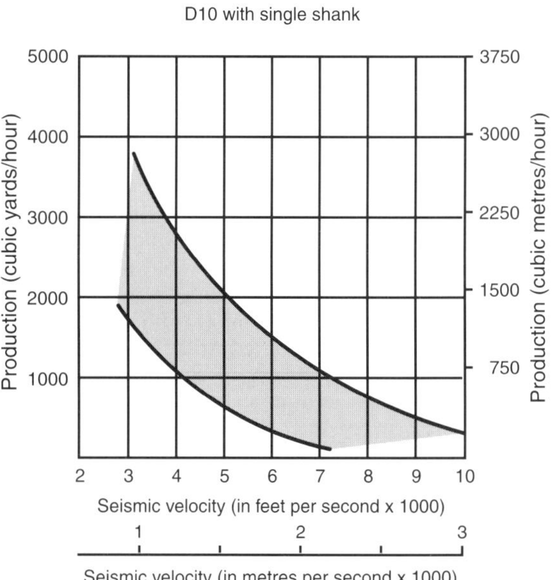

Fig. 7.7. Estimated ripper production (after Caterpillar Tractor Company 1982).

velocity is non-destructive, fast and relatively straightforward. Consequently its use in excavation has been promulgated by excavation equipment manufacturers, notably the Caterpillar Tractor Company, as a means of quickly assessing the rocks mass characteristics and hence the best use of their plant. Figure 7.7 is an example for one particular type of ripping plant, a Caterpillar D10 crawler tractor, and shows how the assessment of the productivity of ripping is made. Figure 7.8 illustrates another method by which seismic velocity and/or rock type can be used to assess productivity for the same machine.

Graphical methods are particularly useful for rapid assessment of excavatability during initial site surveys or where test data are not available. The graphical method of Pettifer & Fookes (1994) as shown in Fig. 5.21 is particularly suited for assessing whether blasting, ripping or hard digging is required. In particular it gives guidance on the type of excavation plant that is needed for ripping. The assessment is based on the point load index and the discontinuity spacing index, which are the two geotechnical properties which most effect excavatability. The point load test is explained in Appendix B. The discontinuity spacing index is the mean number of fractures per metre of a line, known as a scan line, across the site. A three-dimensional discontinuity spacing index, calculated on a unit volume basis or from actual spacings, should be used wherever possible since this gives a realistic impression of average block size. Figure 5.21 does not consider other factors such as plant selection and cost and is purely based on geotechnical property considerations. Also it is stressed that predictions made using the graph need to be compared with the performance actually achieved and revisions will be required as more powerful excavation equipment become available.

A statistical approach based on productivity has been used in Australia (MacGregor *et al.* 1994). A large database of information on geological, ripping and laboratory data has been interrogated and regression lines plotted through the data. Correlations have been calculated which allow a prediction to be made of the likely productivity of ripping plant. The calculated productivity is used for assessing the output of the site and determining whether or not ripping is economically feasible.

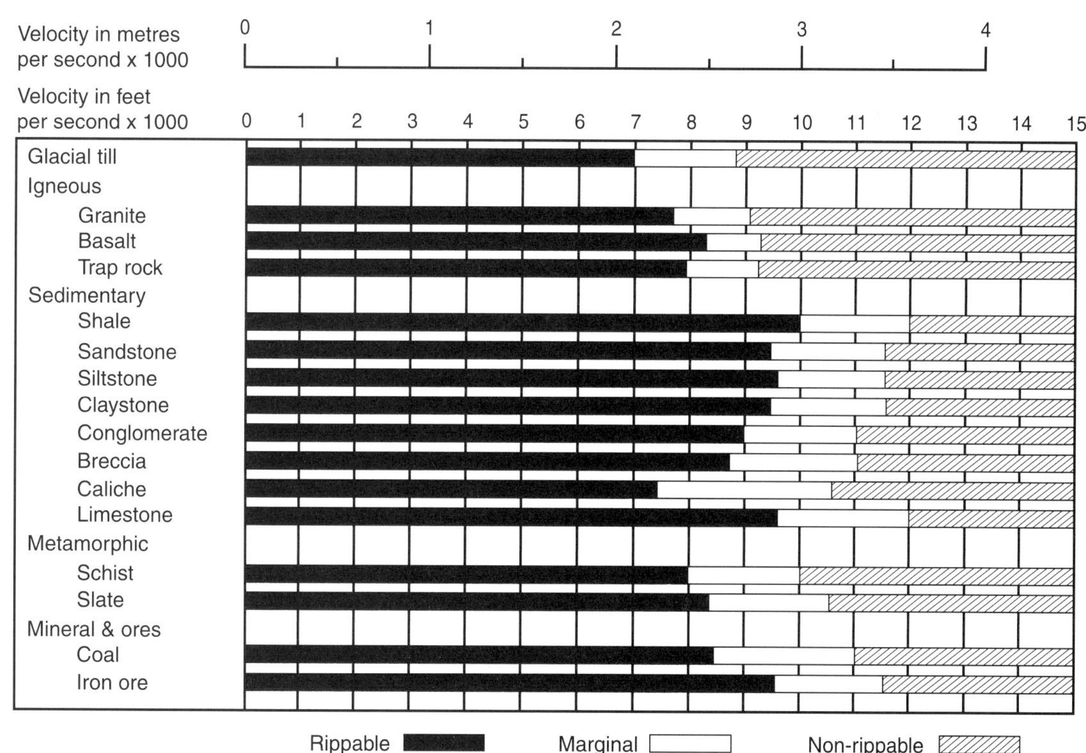

Fig. 7.8. Multi or single shank D10 ripper performance (after Caterpillar Tractor Company 1982).

7.4.7. Treatment of instability of cutting slopes

Treatment of instability should only be required where it has not been possible to ensure stability by design, or where there have been deficiencies in the design process, or poor construction practice. General guidance has been given by Fookes (1976). In highway rock engineering four basic techniques are available; removal of unstable rock, strengthening of the rock forming the face, support of the rock face, and containment of falling rock. In extreme cases reprofiling of the slope may be necessary. The use of any particular treatment technique depends mainly on the nature and scale of the instability, the geotechnical conditions present, the geometry of the slope area, and the risk to road users. Techniques of hazard and risk assessment for slopes have been described by McMillan & Matheson (1997, 1998).

7.4.7.1. Removal of unstable rock
Where practical, the first approach to instability in a rock slope is to consider removal of the unstable rock using either hand scaling, mechanical plant, or the local use of small explosive charges. Removal is low in cost, usually fast to perform, and can be totally effective in the short term. However, problems can arise if block sizes or volumes are large, access difficult, or the risk particularly high. All techniques require careful consideration of slope stability, geotechnical conditions and an evaluation of the implications in the long term.

7.4.7.2. Strengthening of rock face
In general strengthening techniques are expensive and, in some situations, of questionable cost-effectiveness. Their use tends to be confined to circumstances where other methods cannot be employed and where block sizes are relatively large. Where unstable rock blocks cannot be removed without adversely affecting the stability of the rock slope, techniques of strengthening the face can be employed. All situations require a careful analysis of the geotechnical conditions, the possible failure mode, the most appropriate technique of strengthening, and the most effective method of installation.

In highway projects, the common strengthening techniques are rock bolts, anchors and dowels. With rock bolts, holes are drilled by hand or machine, bolts inserted, an anchorage established, the bolts stressed to their working load, and the holes back grouted to prevent corrosion. Depending on the situation, bolts can be from 3 m to 10 m in length, and be either anchored at a particular point or continuously bonded. Anchors are similar to rock bolts but generally longer, composed of multiple steel strands, and are invariably anchored at a particular point only. Dowels are generally short, and are continuously bonded to the host rock, see §5.3.2.6.

A long design life is required for highways, up to 120 years, and so double corrosion protection is specified. Increasing use is being made of stainless steels for similar reasons. Although extended claims regarding stress retention and corrosion protection are made, there is considerable doubt over the ability of some systems to sustain high levels of stress over their design life and to provide the expected degree of corrosion protection. Often strengthening techniques appear to be used for peace of mind rather than as primary aids to stability.

7.4.7.3. Support of rock face
If key areas of instability are given support early enough then face stability can be maintained, and upward progressive failure of a rock face is halted, see §5.3.2.5. The type and extent of the treatment depends on whether material is being lost through weathering of the minerals in the rock or through block fall, or both. Weathering can be arrested by placing a protective layer of sprayed concrete, mass concrete or masonry on the face; the rock is then protected from weathering and the face supported against further failure. The extent of such treatment can vary according to the geotechnical circumstances from small local areas of 'dentition' to that of the entire face.

Progressive deterioration through block fall can sometimes be prevented by providing judicious support before the volume involved in the failure becomes too large. The loss of key areas on a face can be compensated for by installing support buttresses, walls, or beams. These generally are of concrete with a local masonry finish and are usually keyed in or pinned to the rock mass using dowels or bolts. The technique is particularly effective at treating small areas of failure, where further loss of material would increase the risk of larger failure occurring. Where the techniques do not involve bolting they tend to be inexpensive and effective, and can easily be made to blend into the rock face. A comprehensive description of available rock support systems is given by Hoek & Brown (1988).

7.4.7.4. Containment of falling rock
The principle of containment involves allowing a certain level of rock fall to occur but preventing such falls from being a danger to road users while in the highway cutting. The extent of rock removal, strengthening, or support required for full stability is thus often considerably reduced, and costs are minimized. Techniques vary according to the block sizes involved, the profile of the rock face, and the geometry of the side slope. They include netting of the face to contain falls of small sized material near the face, rock traps, fences, barriers, and earth or rock bunds to prevent larger blocks or volumes of rock reaching the carriageway. In using such techniques maintenance is not entirely avoided and regular checks on the integrity of netting and fences, and periodic cleaning of debris filling in the area between the face and containment barrier, are still required. The lower cost of such containment measures compared to

that which would be required for removal, strengthening and support in a full treatment of face instability, make them increasingly attractive. Although rigorous engineering techniques are available to design containment structures, considerable subjective judgement is needed to estimate both the size and timescale of the failures. An evaluation by a qualified and experienced engineering geologist is an essential requirement.

7.4.8. Environmental impact

Increasing emphasis is being paid to the environmental impact of highway construction. Attention is being focused on rock engineering works to reduce environmental impact and make them aesthetically acceptable. Pressure is also being exerted to design and to construct remedial work such that it blends into the local countryside. Unsightly concrete support walls, conspicuous bolts, or obvious netting in full view to road users are becoming unacceptable where alternative options exist. Road alignments, side slope profiles, the appearance of rock faces, and the conspicuousness of remedial treatments can all be engineered with existing techniques. Cosmetic issues can be considered at both the design and the construction stages, but are likely to add considerably to the costs of highway construction. A similar situation arises in the case of blast vibration which, although seldom producing measurable damage, is often intrusive to those living nearby, see §5.2.3.4.

7.5. Placement and compaction

7.5.1. General

Rock fill is a very coarse material containing particles with maximum dimensions typically of about 500 mm and, where a fill has both these large particle sizes and in addition fine material to fill the interstices between the coarser particles, only certain types of compaction plant will be effective in attaining the highest possible density in the layer. The thickness of the layer placed will be dictated by the maximum particle size; normally it is considered that the thickness should be such that the maximum particle size is no more than two thirds of that thickness (Forssblad 1981). For the interstices to be filled by migration of the fines downwards through the layer, a number of conditions need to be fulfilled:

(a) The rock fill should be spread so that the coarser material does not accumulate on the surface of the layer. Experience has shown that this is best achieved by dumping the rock fill on top of and behind the edge of the advancing fill surface and using a heavy bulldozer to push the material beyond the edge. This causes the larger particles to roll to the bottom of the layer and fines to fill the voids between them, thus creating a dense layer, the surface of which consists mainly of the finer material (Williams & Stothard 1967). The spreading of a separate layer of fine material on the surface of the rock fill should be avoided as it could substantially reduce the effective depth of compaction by vibrating rollers (Forssblad 1981).

(b) The fines mixed with the coarser material must be non-cohesive so as to be capable of being vibrated or washed through the layer. The presence of cohesive fines makes the achievement of a satisfactory state of compaction extremely difficult.

(c) A heavy vibrating roller with a large amplitude of vibration is required to ensure that vibrational stresses extend to the bottom of the thick layer. Towed vibrating rollers or self-propelled single roll vibrating rollers are generally most appropriate for this purpose. Forssblad (1981) recommended amplitudes of 1.5 to 2 mm and frequencies of 25 to 30 Hz for rock fill compaction. The shell of the vibrating roll must be of high grade steel to accommodate the large stresses that arise during the vibratory compaction of rock fill.

Prior to the development of the heavy vibrating roller, it was common practice to sluice the fill with an excess of water from high pressure hoses so that the water passing downwards through the layer conveys fines until the voids were filled. This process could cause damage to the surrounds, however, and could be detrimental to the long term performance of the rock fill embankment if the foundation soil was cohesive and so weakened by the increase in moisture content.

When rock fill is relatively uniformly graded and completely devoid of fines, it can be assumed to be already in a well compacted condition as placed, in that inter-granular contact will prevent any further rearrangement of the particles. Material with these properties is often used for drainage layers which are placed at the bottom of fills, particularly where large horizontal flows of water are expected, e.g. on flood plains.

Although engineered rock fills are normally selected, placed and compacted to minimize settlement and ensure adequate bearing capacity, there are certain situations where this may not be feasible and occasionally there may be applications where it is not necessary. For example, end dumping has to be used to fill below water level. The rock used in this situation should have the following characteristics:

- it should be durable, especially resistant to degradation by wetting and drying cycles (protection against wave action is provided by armourstone)
- it should have a coarse grading with very little fine material which would tend to be removed by the water

In some cases it may be necessary to densify the end dumped rock fill by some deep compaction technique such as dynamic compaction. This can be carried out as soon as a platform of rock fill has been established above water level. Above this level the rock fill can be placed and compacted in layers as an engineered rock fill. In remote areas of the world where a less demanding standard of performance can be accepted, there may be circumstances in which it is considered that end dumping will provide a technically adequate solution.

7.5.2. Low grade rock fill

Embankments are often constructed of materials which are intermediate in character between rock fill and earth fill and which are variously described as low grade rock fills or soft rock fills. Quarries may yield large quantities of such materials before sound, strong rock fill is reached and there are clear economic advantages if such materials can be used.

Shale

Clay shale has characteristics between those of a clay soil and intact rock. Although initially intact and often difficult to excavate and handle, the dominant clay mineral makes shale sensitive to the effects of water and initially rock-like material can degrade on exposure to wet weather to a very weak plastic clay. The extent to which clay shales weather varies considerably, however, and the variations in their properties cause problems in selecting compaction specifications which ensure that adequate densities are attained. The two principal tests used in the United States for durability classification of shales, listed by Strom (1980), are the jar slake test (based on observed behaviour of shale when soaked in water) and the slake durability test (measuring the degradation when the shale is placed in a wire-screen drum rotated under water). The latter test is specified as ASTM Test D 4644, American Society of Testing and Materials (Annual publication) and described by Brown (1981).

The classification tests can be used to divide the shales into three main categories, (Strom 1980):

- Soft non-durable shales are excavated and treated as cohesive soil. Sufficient breakdown of the aggregations usually occurs during the normal earthmoving operations so that the material is compacted in thin layers to typical requirements for soil compaction.
- Hard, non-durable shales need to be compacted to the requirements for soil but, to carry out the compaction processes effectively, additional operations are needed involving the breakdown, removal or separate excavation of the coarser, hard particles that would be incompatible with spreading in thin layers. Materials in this category also include weak, non-durable shale interbedded with rock layers such as limestone. Thus, hard but nondurable shale has to be intensely degraded during excavation, placement and compaction and finally densified to a specification appropriate to the soil type to which it would eventually deteriorate. A compaction–degradation test (Hale *et al.* 1981) is used to indicate the degree of difficulty with which this would be accomplished. When the shale strongly resists efforts to break it down, special wetting and heavy rolling procedures may be required.
- Hard, durable shales can be treated as rock and compacted accordingly.

In a review of laboratory test methods aimed at classifying shales according to their potential breakdown during and subsequent to embankment construction, Bailey (1976) discussed problems of site control. It was recommended that shales that are resistant to mechanical breakdown but are prone to weathering, leading to collapse problems when contained within an embankment, should be degraded before reaching the fill area and undergoing compaction. Thus, a more satisfactory state of compaction can be achieved than would be the case with larger aggregations of clay particles. On occasions water has been added to the shale to aid breakdown and improve compaction.

Bailey (1976) summarized experiences in the United States with construction trials involving shale. Such trials have served primarily as compaction equipment trials and often have provided a measure of the variability in the behaviour of the shale. It was recommended that only one factor should be varied at one time, and sufficient test samples taken to allow for the variability of the material and the imprecise control of the compaction energy. No conclusion was possible regarding the relative merits of method or end product compaction specifications for shales, or what the end product should be except in very general terms. Experience with compaction trials on shales in Indiana has indicated that the following factors should be considered:

- shale type and initial condition
- moisture content and its variability
- type and size of compactor
- number of passes
- layer thickness and the total number of layers
- foundation material type and stiffness
- weather conditions

Currently, in the United Kingdom, the use in highway construction of shales and other argillaceous rocks as rock fill for starter layers is prohibited (MCHW 1 1994). A starter layer forms the base of an embankment where construction is over soft ground and creates a stable platform on which to construct and support overlying weaker embankment layers. Coarse granular material for use as general bulk earthworks rock fill in the UK is required to have a 10% fines value in excess of 50 kN and this value is likely to preclude the use of most, but not all, shales.

Rock fill with cohesive fines

If significant quantities of cohesive fine material are associated with large rock particles it is impossible to achieve a migration of the fines downwards through the layer by the use of vibration. The alternative of sluicing with water would not be successful because of the cohesive nature of the material. Thus it can be expected that the cohesive element of the fill can only be compacted in relatively thin layers as per normal compaction practice. As the presence of the large particles precludes the use of such thin layers, a satisfactory compaction could not normally be carried out. The only solution is to remove the coarse particles such that thin layer compaction can be achieved. The type of compaction plant in use will determine the thickness of layer that can be compacted, and the maximum particle size remaining in the fill should not exceed two-thirds of the layer thickness. The maximum thickness of stony cohesive material that may be compacted by a vibrating roller is 275 mm, provided that the vibrating roller has a mass per unit width of vibrating roll exceeding 5000 kg/m. With such a combination of machine and layer thickness the maximum particle size allowable in the fill material would be $(\frac{2}{3}) \times 275 = 183$ mm.

Forssblad (1981) took a different view, however, in discussing the compaction of morainic soils based on experience in Sweden. These materials often contain stones with a very large particle size and include a significant clay fraction; Forssblad contends that compaction in thick layers is much more economical than compaction in thinner layers involving the removal of the large stones. Morainic soils have been compacted successfully in Sweden in layer thicknesses of 0.7 to 1.0 m using heavy vibrating rollers with a mass on the vibrating roll of 10 to 15 t. Such large vibrating rollers are uncommon in the United Kingdom but where the scale of the work is sufficiently large and the fill materials are similar in nature to morainic soils their use could well be justified.

In France, compaction of large rock particles with cohesive fines is included in the specifications for earthworks construction, Ministere de l'Equipement *et al.* (1992). The material is considered unsuitable for use as fill if the fines are excessively wet (strength too low) or excessively dry (compaction too difficult). At intermediate moisture conditions compaction is considered viable using either vibrating rollers, pneumatic-tyred rollers or tamping rollers. Specified layer thicknesses vary from 200 mm to 650 mm depending upon the material class and the type of compactor; however, the maximum particle size is restricted to two-thirds of the layer thickness and this will obviously often dictate the use of a thicker layer with a commensurate increase in the size of compactor.

7.5.3. Trial fill placement

Where large quantities of rock fill are to be placed, it will usually be advisable to carry out excavation and placement trials prior to commencement of the main earthworks. As an example, rock excavation and compaction trials were carried out as part of the preliminary investigations into building the Pennine section of the M62 motorway which included the 73 m high Scammonden dam (Williams & Stothard 1967). As a result of the trials which took place in 1964, a specification was written which included detailed grading limits for the rock fill, see §7.6.1.

A trial to determine the procedures for the construction and control of compaction of rock fill for embankments on the Rabat to Casablanca motorway is described by Jakani (1987). Rock blasting trials were included to establish a drill-hole pattern that yielded an appropriate grading with minimal amounts of excessively large particles. The material was spread in layers 800 mm thick by a heavy bulldozer which was also used to tow the heavy vibrating roller for compaction. Various methods of compaction control were tried:

- plate bearing tests with a 600 mm diameter plate were used but the results were too scattered for a reliable interpretation to be made
- *in situ* density measurements were also made but the tests were time consuming and, because of the large particle sizes, it was impossible to establish a laboratory maximum dry density
- levels were taken of the surface layer to deduce whether or not there was any significant settlement but none was registered

It was concluded that careful planning of the rock blasting would be required to ensure the most effective grading of the fill material and that a heavy vibrating roller with a roll loading of more than 3500 kg per metre width should be used. The compaction should be to the method specification developed in France for soils (Ministere de l'Equipement *et al.* 1992).

7.5.4. British practice for specification and control

Because of the large particle sizes involved and the thicknesses of layer that these sizes necessitate, the compaction of rock fill is normally to the requirements of a method specification, that is, the type of compaction plant, the maximum thickness of layer and the minimum number of passes are laid down. Where the *in situ* state of compaction has to be determined by achieving a specific end product requirement, large scale replacement tests may be performed. These involve the excavation of large holes with depths equal to the thickness of the compacted layer and of sufficient volume to ensure that representative samples of the fill material are obtained. All material removed from each excavation has to be weighed and its moisture content determined. The volume of the excavation is determined either by lining the hole with a plastics-sheet and determining the

Table 7.1. *Compaction of rock fill for highway works in the United Kingdom using single roll vibrating roller*

Mass per metre width of vibrating roll (kg)	*Maximum final thickness of compacted layer (mm)*	*Minimum number of passes*
up to 2300	unsuitable	–
over 2300 up to 2900	400	5
over 2900 up to 3600	500	5
over 3600 up to 4300	600	5
over 4300 up to 5000	700	5
over 5000	800	5

volume of water required to fill the cavity to surface level, the water-replacement method (British Standards Institution 1990), or by determining the weight of a fairly single-sized granular material, pea gravel for example, required to fill the cavity and converting the weight to a volume from a separate calibration of the material in a container of known volume (Williams & Stothard 1967). The mass of material involved can amount to several tonnes for the normal type of rock fill and the laborious nature of the operation discourages its application other than in trials or research situations.

The more usual way of controlling the compaction of rock fill is by a method specification. The current specification for highway works in the United Kingdom (MCHW 1 1994), requires the use of single-roll vibrating rollers for compaction of rock fill to ensure that a high amplitude of vibration is achieved. Only the heavier machines available for civil engineering works are approved for such work. Table 7.1 gives the thicknesses of layer and numbers of passes for the limited number of categories of vibrating roller specified in the United Kingdom for highway works.

Information about rock fills used in some UK embankment dams is presented in Tables 7.2 and 7.3. Table 7.2 illustrates embankment dam practice in rock-fill placement in terms of layer thickness, the weight of the vibrating roller (VR) and the number of passes. Table 7.3 gives an indication of average porosity (n) and air voids (V_a). It was not possible to include all the relevant details in these two tables. The layer thickness and method of compaction may have been changed during construction of the embankment, some water may have been added to the rock fill and there may have been more than one type of rock fill used in the embankment. Furthermore, some of the quoted density results may be less reliable than others, being based on far fewer test data or incomplete information.

In addition to information on achieved densities in heavily compacted rock fills in embankment dams, some information has been provided in Table 7.3 for two rock fills used as opencast mining backfills. At Horsley the backfill consisted mainly of mudstone and sandstone; at Tranent of mudstone, siltstone and sandstone. Neither fill was systematically compacted. The densities were determined from small samples and can only be a crude guide to the condition of these two very variable fills.

The five dams had porosities in the range 15% to 27% and this could be regarded as typical for modern well graded heavily compacted rock fills. In contrast the two opencast backfills had much higher porosities, 33% and 37% respectively.

Table 7.2. *Field placement of rock fill (Charles 1991)*

Dam	*Date*	*Rock fill*	*Layer (m)*	*Pass no.*	*VR Wt tonne*
Balderhead	1965	shale	0.8	2	8.5
Scammondon	1969	sandstone/mudstone	0.9	5	11.5
Llyn Brianne	1971	mudstone	0.9	4	13.5
Winscar	1974	sandstone	1.7	4	13.5
Marchlyn	1979	slate	1.0	4	13.5

Table 7.3. *Field density of rock fill (Charles 1991)*

Location	*Structure*	ρ_d *(Mg/m³)*	w *(%)*	ρ_s *(Mg/m³)*	n *(%)*	V_a *(%)*
Balderhead	embankment dam	1.94	9	2.66	27	10
Scammonden	embankment dam	2.02	7	2.69	25	11
Llyn Brianne	embankment dam	2.35	3	2.75	15	7
Winscar	embankment dam	2.03	6	2.60	22	10
Marchlyn	embankment dam	2.25	4	2.81	20	11
Horsley	opencast backfill	1.70	7	2.54	33	21
Tranent	opencast backfill	1.54	9	2.45	37	23

[ρ_d = dry density of fill, ρ_s = particle density, w = moisture content].

7.5.5. Other national practice for specification and control

The previous sub-section has dealt with UK practice and the situation in some other countries is now briefly reviewed.

Germany

A useful description of the requirements for rock fill is given by Rosenheinrich (1978). Rock fill has to be placed evenly over the whole area to be filled and only well graded material should be placed in the upper 1 m of the fill. The largest particle size used should not exceed two-thirds of the allowable layer thickness. Minimum requirements for compaction of rock fill is in the form of an end-result specification and is expressed in terms of relative compaction with the normal Proctor test (2.5 kg rammer method) as the laboratory standard. Minimum relative compaction values vary from 100 to 103% for material placed within 0.5 m of the formation level, and 95 to 97% for material placed below that level. The actual values within these ranges depend on the classification of the rock fill.

The difficulties of *in situ* measurements of density and laboratory compaction tests with coarse granular material has led to an additional specification in terms of the results of platebearing tests. The determination is made of E_2, the modulus of deformation on the second loading cycle of the plate. Escario *et al.* (1980) give the equation for the determination of the modulus of deformation as follows:

$$E_2 = 0.75d(\Delta\sigma/\Delta s)$$

where d is the plate diameter, normally 300 or 600 mm, $\Delta\sigma$ is $0.7\sigma_{max} - 0.3\sigma_{max}$, σ_{max} is the maximum load applied and Δs is the increment of deformation between $0.3\sigma_{max}$ and $0.7\sigma_{max}$. The specified maximum thickness of layer depends on the type of material to be compacted and on the required level of compaction. Dynamic types of compaction are regarded as the most effective, particularly vibrating rollers and vibrating-plate compactors, with dynamic forces sufficiently large to transfer the smaller particles such that they fill up the interstices between the larger particles. It is also considered most effective to compact fills from the outside towards the middle, with the compactor moving at a steady, uniform speed, avoiding excessive speeds of travel which may result in inadequate densities in the layer. Overlapping of the adjacent tracks traversed by the compactor should be maintained at about 100 to 200mm

USA

In the construction of rock fill, it is recommended (Transportation Research Board 1990), that the correct sequence of operations is to dump the rock on to the layer under construction. The material is then pushed by a bulldozer over the leading edge of the layer, is thoroughly wetted, and then compacted with heavy equipment. Finer material must be applied to the top of the layer being compacted to fill any voids.

South Africa

Specific mention of rock fill procedures is made in National Institute for Transport and Road Research (1982) where it is recommended that the rock is spread by bulldozing to its correct position to avoid arching within the dumped material. Rock should not exceed a maximum dimension of two-thirds of the layer thickness. Materials which fracture easily or weather readily should be grid-rolled in order to break them down to satisfactory dimensions for the layer, since this may otherwise result in loose zones within the layer.

Belgium and France

The compaction of embankments in rock fill poses particular problems, according to Centre de Recherches Routieres (1978), because of the difficulties of determining whether the required density has been achieved. The design engineer in Belgium is advised to specify the thickness of layer to be placed, the type of compactor and the number of passes. This form of specification is similar to that used in France (Ministere de l'Equipement *et al.* 1992).

7.6. Case studies

Six case histories are presented to illustrate the performance of rock fill.

7.6.1. Scammonden dam

Construction of the 73 m high rock fill embankment commenced in 1967 and was completed in 1969. The embankment, which is located some 10 km west of Huddersfield, is a dual purpose structure, forming both a motorway embankment and an embankment dam. A cross section of the embankment is shown in Fig. 7.9. The wide crest carries the M62 Pennine motorway and an upstream sloping soft clay core forms the watertight element of the dam. Reservoir impounding commenced in 1969 and the reservoir was full in 1972.

In 1964, prior to embankment construction, extensive trials were carried out to study methods of quarrying, placement and compaction (Williams and Stothard 1967). It was found that multi-row blasting produced a well graded fill that could be placed and compacted to a high density. Ripping and single row blasting were unsatisfactory.

As a result of the trials a specification was written for the rock fill and grading limits were specified for construction. No single piece of rock was to have a

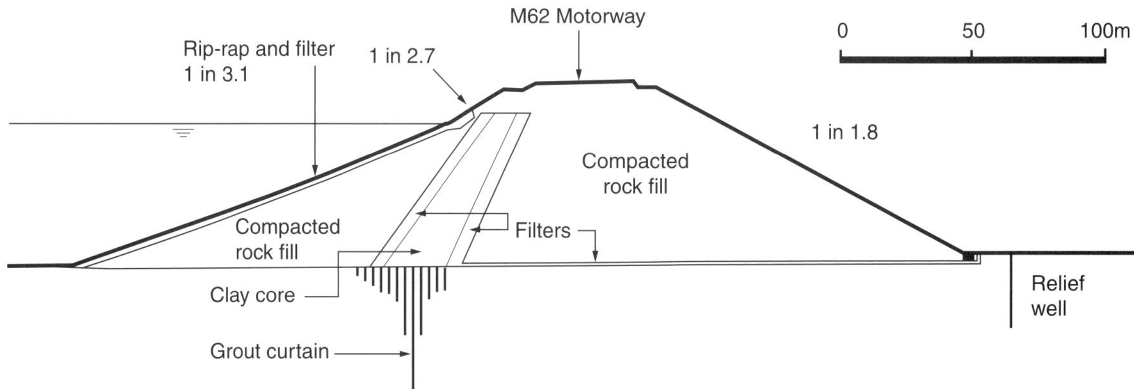

Fig. 7.9. Cross section of Scammonden dam (after BNCOLD 1983).

volume greater than 0.4 m^3 or a dimension greater than 0.9 m. The percentage passing the 76 μm sieve was specified as 0–5%. Rock fill was to be placed by tipping on the surface of the layer at least 4 m back from the advancing face and then pushed forward over the face. No rock fill was to be placed when the moisture content of the material finer than 19 mm exceeded 12%. Compaction of each layer was specified as either 8 passes of an 8 tonne vibrating roller or 12 passes of a 5 tonne vibrating roller.

The 3×10^6 m^3 of rock fill for the dam were excavated from the adjacent motorway cuttings. The valley is in the Millstone Grit series of the Carboniferous system and the strata consist of alternating horizontal layers of sandstone, mudstone and shale. The embankment was principally constructed of sandstone, but there are three mudstone zones in the middle of the embankment. Grading tests were regularly carried out on 25 tonne samples from the blast face. The rock fill was placed on the embankment in 0.9 m thick layers and compacted with 5 passes of an 11.5 tonne vibrating roller. Oversize pieces were fragmented by a drop ball on the embankment. Density tests were carried out using the pea gravel replacement method in an excavated hole having a volume of approximately 1 cubic metre.

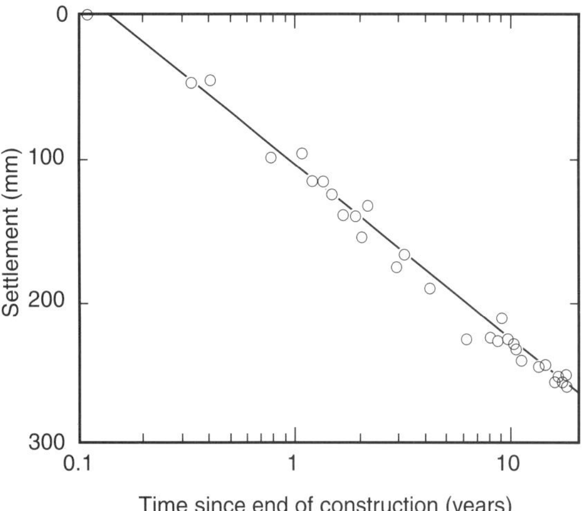

Fig. 7.10. Settlement of crest of Scammonden dam (after Charles 1991).

At times of heavy rain the dump truck tyres churned up the fines to form a slurry and it was feared that this might lead to weaker layers in the fill. However when trial pits were taken down through two layers of fill, no evidence of these relatively smooth surfaces was found. There was an absence of voids with densely packed fines between the larger rock fragments.

BRE measurements of the deformations of the embankment during construction have been described by Penman *et al.* (1971). Monitoring of the movements has continued over the last 20 years and the settlement of the crest of the high embankment is shown in Fig. 7.10 plotted against logarithm of time (Charles 1991).

7.6.2. Roadford dam

Roadford dam forms a 37×10^6 m^3 reservoir which supplies southwest and north Devon (Wilson & Evans 1990). The embankment was built in 1988 and reservoir impounding commenced in October 1989. The reservoir was full early in 1991.

The 41 m high dam is constructed of low grade rock fill. An asphaltic concrete membrane on the upstream face of the embankment forms the watertight element. A cross section of the embankment is shown in Fig. 7.11. The Upper Carboniferous strata at the dam site and quarry consist of rapidly alternating mudstones, siltstones and sandstones. Near the surface the weathering

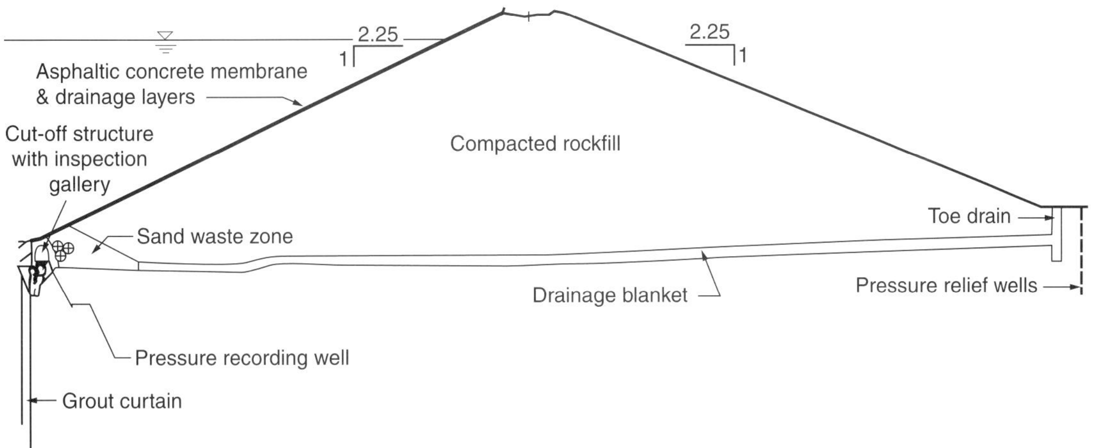

Fig. 7.11. Cross section of Roadford dam (after Evans & Wilson 1992).

of the mudstones is extensive. When an exploratory quarry was opened the material was classified into three types related to the depth below ground level and weathering characteristics. It was considered that an embankment could be constructed of the less weathered materials obtained from depths greater than 4 m.

Samples of the rock showed that there was an average of one per cent by weight of iron pyrites (Millmore & Bell 1994). The mineral was considered to be potentially degradable and leaching tests were carried out to simulate the effects of weathering. Both laboratory tests and trial embankments confirmed that the chemical constituents of the formation could lead to the oxidation of iron pyrites to produce dissolved metals and acidic drainage water. Measures were taken to minimize the oxidation process and mitigate polluting discharges.

The dam construction contract was let early in 1987 and further compaction trials were undertaken which showed that the addition of water caused the compacted surface to become slurried. Embankment construction commenced in June 1988 and the $1 \times 10^6\,m^3$ embankment was completed by October. The embankment was formed of equal quantities of sandstone and mudstone quarried on site (Evans & Wilson 1992) and the specification required that the embankment fill should be built of rock defined in Table 10 of BS 5930: 1981 as fresh, slightly weathered or moderately weathered. Excavation was initially carried out by face shovel loaders assisted by a ripper but to maintain output more powerful rippers were introduced and the material was pushed towards the loaders. This method of working produced a well blended and consistent material (Wilson & Evans 1990).

Samples from the quarry were tested for particle density (specific gravity), moisture content and grading. The fill was generally drier than expected with a mean moisture content of only 4.4%. After ripping and loading the maximum rock size was usually not greater than 0.5 m. From the gradings of material below 106 mm it was concluded that the fill had a slight excess of fines. It was expected that the material would be weather susceptible but there were only a few occasions when it was necessary to stop fill placing after heavy rain. Compaction was to a method specification which required a 450 mm finished layer thickness. Some 149 density cubic test holes with a dimension of 800 mm were excavated during embankment construction and the gravel replacement method was used to measure the volume. On completion of the density measurement, the test hole was filled with water and a falling head permeability test was carried out. The average permeability (hydraulic conductivity) was 1.5×10^{-4} m/s. By July 1989 the dam was ready for impounding and the reservoir was full early in 1991.

Embankment deformations have been monitored during construction, reservoir filling and subsequently. Since reservoir impounding, settlements have continued at a reasonably constant rate apparently unrelated to water load. There has not been the steady reduction in settlement rate observed, for example, at Scammonden. This has been attributed to additional settlement in the embankment associated with an increase in moisture content (Evans & Wilson 1992).

7.6.3. Queen's Valley dam

The Queen's Valley dam was planned to form a $1.2 \times 10^6\,m^3$ reservoir on the island of Jersey (Bridle 1988). The embankment was completed in September 1991. Impounding commenced in December 1991 and the reservoir was full by June 1992. The 34 m high dam was built from ignimbrite rock fill with a watertight element provided by a 600 mm wide central dense bituminous concrete core. Figure 7.12 shows a cross section of the embankment.

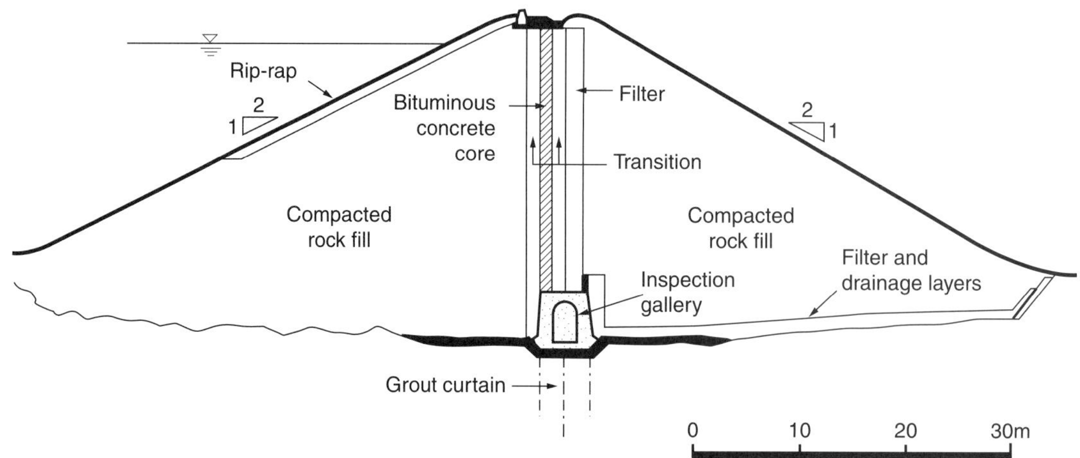

Fig. 7.12. Cross section of Queen's Valley dam (after Bridle 1988).

For economic reasons it was essential to use all the suitable material that was found in the quarry and the general excavation as fill in the embankment. The design of the dam was based on two categories of rock fill, with the lower quality rock fill containing more fines being used downstream of the core. In the downstream rock fill the material finer than 0.063 mm was restricted to a maximum of 12%.

Fig. 7.13. Rock fill placement at Queen's Valley dam; dumping and watering the fill.

Trials were carried out on both categories of rock fill to establish satisfactory methods of placing and compacting the fill and to measure mechanical properties. Density, moisture content, grading, permeability and shear wave velocity were measured in field trials and the results were used to design appropriate laboratory tests to assess the strength and deformation properties of the fill. A 2.1 m wide towed vibrating roller with a static weight of 11.7 tonnes was used in the trials. In general the trials indicated very satisfactory results in terms of the densities and gradings which were achieved. Figure 7.13 shows the rock fill being dumped several metres behind the edge of the advancing fill surface during dam construction. The fill is being pushed forward by a bulldozer in Fig. 7.14. The compacted surface of the rock fill is shown in Fig. 7.15. Densities of both categories of fill in the dam embankment were about 2.1 Mg/m^3.

Deformations during construction are largely a function of the compressibility of the rock fill and the height of the embankment. The low compressibility of the compacted rock fill ensured that there were no large movements during construction or reservoir filling; observations indicated a maximum movement during construction of only a few centimetres.

7.6.4. Loch Lomondside A82 highway

The Camus nan Clais to Hollybank section of the A82 highway runs along the western shore of Loch Lomond in Scotland. The improvement of this section of the A82 has been completed and the road was opened in 1987. At two locations there was not sufficient shore between the steep hillsides and the loch itself to construct the highway along a new alignment. To cut into the hillside at these two locations was not possible due to the presence of a landslip at one site and the need for an excessively high cutting at the other. It was, therefore, decided to construct the new road along the shoreline in the Loch and on rock fill. Howison & MacDonald (1988) describe the design and construction of this scheme.

At the South Camus Bank location, see Fig. 7.16, the slope of the loch consisted of organic silt and peats overlying sands and gravels at a depth of about 4 m. In order to displace the mantle of soft material below the water level, rock fill was placed by bottom opening dump barges in 8 m wide bands working from the shore to the embankment toe (Stage 1). Each band was completed before the next was placed. In Stage 2 rock fill was placed in 1 m layers at the toe of the embankment to

Fig. 7.14. Rock fill placement at Queen's Valley dam; pushing fill over advancing face.

Fig. 7.15. Rock fill placement at Queen's Valley dam; compacted surface of fill.

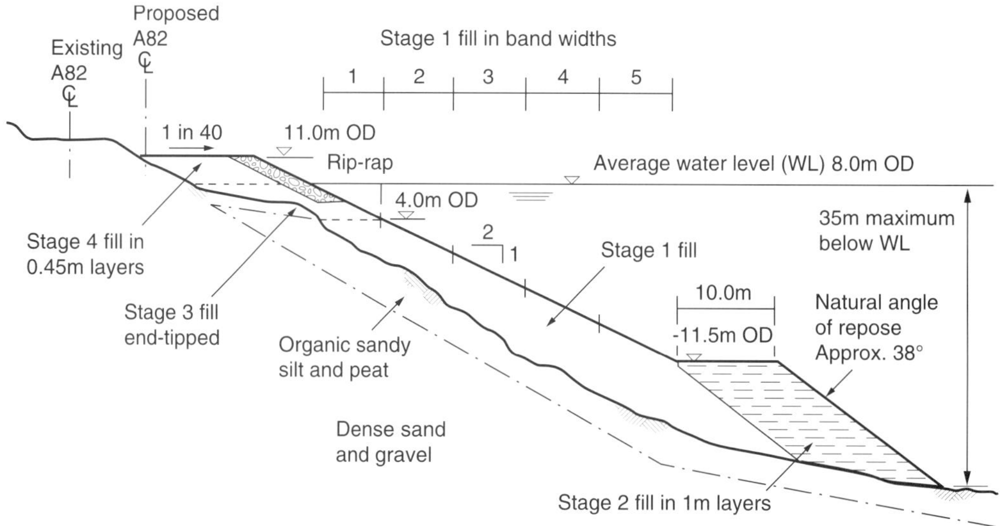

Fig. 7.16. Sequence of fill placement at A82 South Camus Bank (after Howison & Macdonald 1988).

improve the stability. Stage 3 required the end tipping of the fill at around the average water level for the loch and finally Stage 4 was fill placed in 450 mm layers above the water level. Rip-rap was placed at the mean water level to protect the embankment slope.

At the location at Wades Bridge Bank the geology of the site was slightly different in that the organic silts and peat were sandwiched between two granular layers. Therefore, rather than displace the soft material the design philosophy was based on containment and improvement of shear strength with time. The rock fill embankment profile was similar to that at the South Camus Bank location but the rock fill was placed in layers, each 1 m thick from the base of the embankment to the top. The toe bund (Stage 2 of the South Camus Bank) was constructed first. Fill was placed slowly to allow an improvement in the shear strength of the soft material to be achieved.

At a third location, Caravan Site Bank, rock fill was used to infill a small bay between two headlands. The ground conditions were good, consisting of loose sands and silts overlying dense granular material. Conventional rock fill embankment construction was undertaken in 1 m thick layers.

The construction below water level of the $189 \times 10^3\,m^3$ of fill was undertaken with two barges of 120 tonne and 80 tonne capacity. The maximum rock size permitted on the barges was 450 mm and the rock was placed at locations established using a grid of surface marker buoys. Monitoring of the loch bed and embankment slope was carried out using a narrow beam echo sounder with confirmation of these surveys by divers.

At South Camus Bank the displacement technique worked well with monitoring showing that 4 m of soft material was moved down slope and the final fill quantity was less than that assessed at the tender stage. At Caravan Site Bank more settlement occurred than was expected and the quantity of fill was increased accordingly. However, at Wades Bridge Bank problems occurred both in the northern and southern sections. In the northern section penetration of the loch slope and base was more than expected as the toe bund was placed. Once stability of the toe bund had been achieved subsequent placement of the embankment went much as expected. In the southern section the toe bund was placed with little difficulty. However, as the rock fill behind the bund was placed a major displacement occurred and about 15 000 cubic metres of material moved down and beyond the embankment toe. Filling resumed at the toe and proceeded steadily to the surface, the displacement having removed much of the underlying soft material. Settlement pins and inclinometers have been installed in the embankments and are showing movement similar to that that predicted in the design.

7.6.5. Llanddulas to Glan Conwy section of the A55 highway

The A55 highway runs along the north coast of Wales providing an important strategic link in the area. This section runs between cliffs of boulder clay and the sea. Sea defences were incorporated within the highway earthworks and both the sea defences and highway earthworks contained a high proportion of rock fill. The design of the rock fill structures is described by Springett & Stevenson (1984) and the construction by Rowland *et al.* (1988).

Figure 7.17 shows a typical cross section through the highway works. The whole embankment structure is formed on a 600 mm bedding layer of crushed rock (100 mm to 150 mm size) placed on a plastic filter membrane whose purpose is to prevent finer material contaminating the rock fill and weakening the foundation, and to provide a stable working platform. The sea defences consist of a rock fill core of 250 mm to 500 mm size material. The primary armour on the slope of the embankment is formed by two layers of 5 tonne Dolos units laid to a density of 45 per 100 square metres. Just over half were placed in the base layer and the remainder in the top layer. The 22 000 Dolos units were cast on site in the open to allow easier access. Production was not delayed by one day due to bad weather during the whole of the 15 months casting period and frost was not a problem. When the gantry crane for lifting the units was thought to be vulnerable to high winds a crawler mounted crane from the adjacent storage area was used.

Primary armour at the embankment toe consisted of 3 tonne rock boulders. Secondary armour consists of 1 tonne or 2 tonne rock boulders. The rock armour is keyed into the beach at the outer face of the defences to a depth of about 2.5 m. Landward of the sea defences, the road embankment was constructed of earth fill overlying a base rock fill layer of 100 mm to 550 mm size material. Wave screen armour, with a nominal weight of 300 kg, was placed against the road embankment. Carboniferous limestone was used throughout for the rock fill and was obtained from local quarries. Pulverized fuel ash (PFA) was used as a lightweight fill on the embankment, and road pavement foundation and layers constructed on the PFA. The road was opened ahead of time in two stages in 1984 and 1985.

7.6.6. New Hong Kong airport

7.6.6.1. Introduction

The construction of the 1248 ha platform for Hong Kong's new airport at Chek Lap Kok was one of the largest civil engineering projects ever undertaken in South East Asia, see Fig. 7.18.

The work consisted of dredging approximately 67 million m^3 of soft marine clay, excavating and placing 118 million m^3 of soil and rock won from Chek Lap

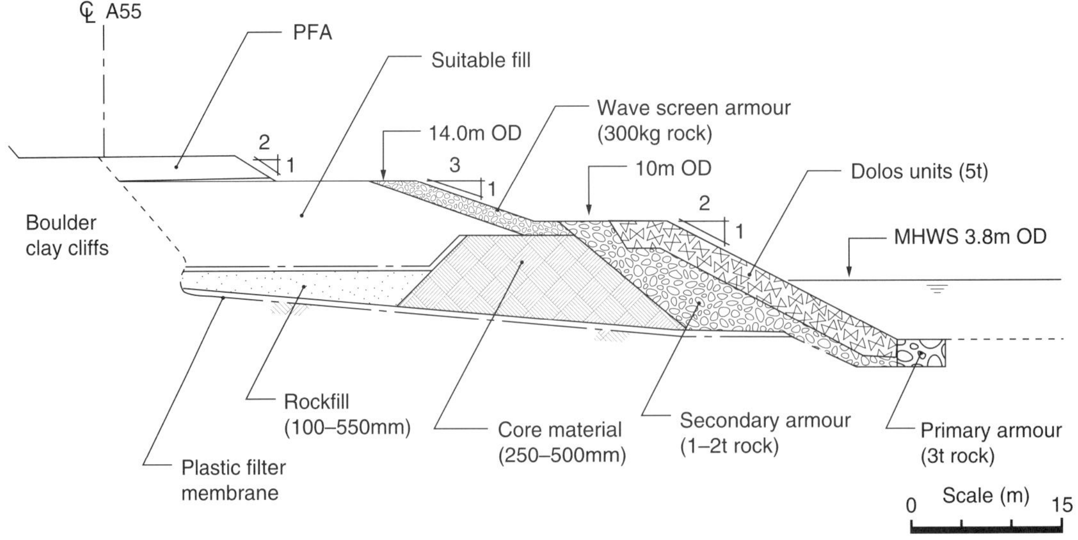

Fig. 7.17. Typical cross section through A55 road embankment and sea defence works (after Springett & Stevenson 1988).

Fig. 7.18. Chek Lap Kok, August 1996, showing completed platform.

Kok, Lam Chau, West and East Brothers Islands and the dredging and placement of 76 million m^3 of landfill from marine borrow areas. Surrounding the platform is 13.2 km of sea wall, both sloping (formed using rock fill) and vertical (formed using concrete blocks). The levelled islands of Chek Lap Kok and Lam Chau form approximately one quarter of the airport platform; the remainder is reclamation formed from various fill materials.

On 30 November 1992 the Airport Platform Contractors Joint Venture (APCJV) were awarded the contract on a fixed lump sum basis of approximately HK$ 9 billion.

7.6.6.2. Geology

Hard Rock. Chek Lap Kok and the neighbouring small island of Lam Chau are formed predominantly of Mesozoic fine to medium grained granite with associated rhyolite, intruded by Tertiary basalt and lamprophyre dykes. The granite is generally closely to moderately jointed (typical of Hong Kong), while the rhyolites tend to be very closely to closely jointed. A major north–south striking fault formed a prominent valley that bisected the former island; minor local faults, shear zones and veining were common. A variable thickness of completely decomposed rock formed a veneer over much of the island, generally 0.5 to 3 m thick but

Table 7.4. *Fill types used at Chek Lap Kok (ref. to Fig. 7.19)*

Fill type	*Description*	*Source*	*Use*	*Areas*
A	Hard and durable rock, formed from bulk blasting. The allowable grading ranged from 2 m boulders to silt. In practice the as-excavated material was generally a well graded rock fill ranging from 600 mm boulders to a medium gravel.	Slightly to moderately weathered rock, generally grade II or III. Obtained from bulk blasting of the former islands of Chek Lap Kok and Lam Chau.	In areas requiring the characteristics of durable rock fill i.e. low sensitivity to earthquake induced settlement and liquefaction, low creep and free draining. Seawalls and Southern Runway.	Southern runway and taxiway.
B	The allowable grading ranged from 300 mm boulders to clay with up to 50% fines. In practice the as-excavated material was generally a silty clayey, gravely sand with boulders and cobbles (20 to 100 mm). Occasionally large boulders were present.	Highly to completely decomposed rock and residual soils. The metasedimentary material obtained from the Brothers Islands was not considered hard and durable and was therefore classified as Type B. Generally machine excavated.	In areas of piling, tunnelling and deep excavations with associated dewatering. Capping layer for utilities and pavements.	East and west vehicle tunnels and APM tunnel extension. General capping layer.
C	Marine sand, with a small gravel content. The mineralogy is predominantly quartzitic, but includes some calcareous content.	Marine borrow areas within Hong Kong Territorial waters.	In areas of general fill, piling, tunnelling and deep excavations with associated dewatering. Capping layer for utilities and pavements.	General areas. Midfield.
A/B	Mixture of Type A and B.	Completely to moderately decomposed rock. Both blasted and machine excavated.	General fill areas. Stabilizing blanket of material bottom dumped on the dredged surface prior to endtipping.	General areas. Northern runway landside.
Sorted processed rock	Large hard durable boulder for armour rock or durable graded rock fill for filter layers and underlayers.	Slightly to moderately weathered rock, generally grade II or III. Obtained from bulk blasting. Small proportion imported.	Sloping seawalls.	Sloping seawalls.

becoming over 20 m deep in the vicinity of the major fault (Langford 1994).

The former Brothers Islands, a sedimentary inlier,- were composed of metasediments, generally metasandstone and graphitic siltstone. High grade graphite was mined from West Brother island until the late 1960s for use in nuclear power stations.

Superficial Deposits. The offshore Quaternary geology comprises a complex sequence of interbedded clays and sands of an alluvial/marine origin, overlain by Holocene marine clays (James *et al.* 1994). The onshore superficials, usually found either at the base of valleys or in small bays, generally comprised either typical flood plain sediments, sands and clays, or beach sands and gravels.

7.6.6.3. Fill types

The reclamation was formed from three basic fill types, designated as Types A, B and C, the description and use of which are listed in Table 7.4. A number of other fill types were also produced for specific uses, such as in the construction of the seawalls that surround the reclamation.

7.6.6.4. Fill allocation plan

A simplified fill allocation plan is shown in Fig. 7.19. The rationale behind the fill allocation plan was influenced primarily by the requirements of a fast track project together with relating fill types to specific future construction and fill performance requirements. This careful planning significantly reduced the time consuming and costly requirement of extensive sorting and processing of the blasted rock, the exception being for armour rock and underlayers for construction of the sloping seawalls.

7.6.6.5. Blasting, excavation and placement of fill

The bulk blasting and excavation to formation level of Chek Lap Kok and Lam Chau, and the placement of 118 million m^3 of rock fill, had more in common with a quarrying or mining operation than normal earthworks. At peak production, the works were reputedly the worlds fourth largest operational open cast mine, see Fig. 7.20.

Bulk blasting techniques were used to fragment the rock to an extent that would both allow excavation and produce an as-blasted fill of the required grading. To cater for the large quantities of explosives required

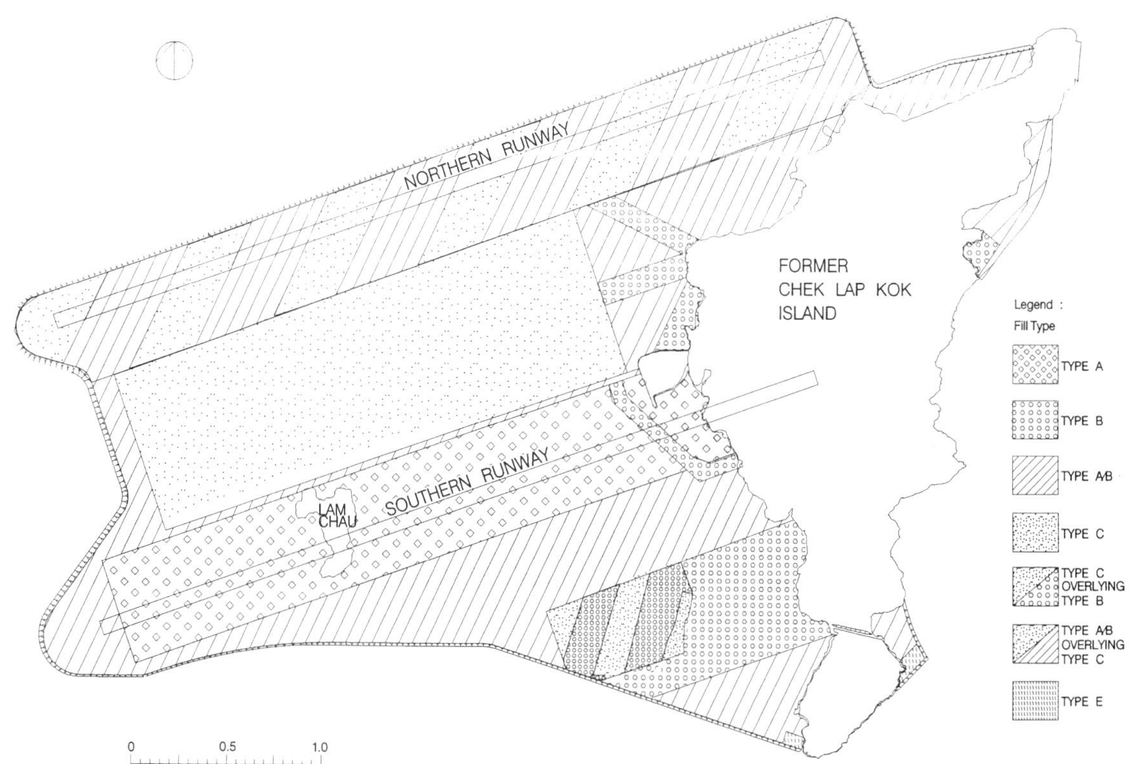

Fig. 7.19. Fill allocation plan.

Fig. 7.20. Excavation of rock fill from blasted benches, December 1994.

for blasting, a bulk ANFO, a mixture of fuel oil and ammonium nitrate, and slurry manufacturing plant was established on site. The explosive mix used comprised 30% ANFO and 70% emulsion for wet holes and 100% ANFO for dry holes. Typical blasting parameters are set out in Table 7.5

Blasting was generally carried out twice a day, using between 40 and 50 tonnes of explosives for each blast and producing about 80 000 m^3 of fragmented rock.

Table 7.5. *Typical blasting parameters*

Blast hole diameter (mm)	165 to 216
Burden (m)	5.0 to 6.5
Spacing (m)	6.0 to 7.5
Sub-drill depth (m)	1.5 to 2.0
Total depth (m)	13.5 to 15
Weight explosive per hole (kg)	150 to 240
Bench height (m)	12 to 13

In all about 40 000 tonnes of explosives were used. Twelve percussive drilling rigs drilled over 2700 km of blast hole, producing about 85 million m^3 of fragmented rock. Sixteen excavators, with a bucket capacity of up to 22 m^3 were used to load a fleet of 67 dump trucks, (Caterpillar 785s and 777s), with a capacities of up to 136 tonnes.

The majority of the fill obtained from Chek Lap Kok was directly end tipped. In areas where there was concern over tip face stability, either a stabilizing blanket of rock fill or sandfill was first barge-dumped on the dredge surface, or a policy of tipping short of the tip face and using bulldozers to push the fill over the tip face was adopted. Adherence to this policy meant that only a small number of minor failures occurred at the tip face.

7.6.6.6. Seawalls

The construction of the seawalls (Neville-Jones & Leutchford 1994) required the production and selection of 450 kg to 5 tonnes armour rock, various underlayer grades and seawall core material. The seawall core rock was selected at the blast face and consequently did not require additional processing. The finer underlayer materials were produced by crusher and mechanical screening process. The remainder of the rock was processed using backhoes for armour rock smaller than 900 mm, scalping buckets for those of intermediate size and individual selection for 3 to 5 tonne armour rocks. The scalping bucket consisted of a bucket frame with spaced bars set to the required rock size.

In the early stages of the project, no particular effort was made to produce rock of the sizes required for use as armour rock. It later became obvious that a short-fall was likely and the day-to-day blasting operation was modified to maximize armour rock production.

7.6.6.7. Quality Control of rock fill

The primary quality control of the rock fill was carried out by a visual assessment of the weathering state, durability and grading of the rock. This was carried out principally at the blast face, and dictated the final destination of the fill. In addition, samples of the material were reviewed at the tip face prior to end tipping.

Bulk grading tests of the fill were carried out at a frequency of 1 test for every 10 000 m^3 of fill. The grading tests were done using a 'bunk bed' of grading screens with apertures of 900, 300 and 75 mm. Additional testing was also carried out where the fill was required for use as an aggregate.

7.6.6.8. Properties of the rock fill

In general, no ground treatment was undertaken at Chek Lap Kok during the placement stages and consequently the end tipped or bottom dumped rock fill is in a relatively loose state. Limited areas of the site were surcharged, primarily to reduce settlement in the underlying alluvium. However, surcharging also proved effective in reducing creep within the fill. One area of the site was subjected to dynamic compaction (DC) in order to improve the settlement characteristics. The DC was carried out on an area of rock fill directly adjacent to a vibrocompacted sand fill in order to reduce the differential settlement between these fill types.

The saturated density of the Type A and A/B below the water table has been estimated to be approximately 22 kN/m^3 which equates to a bulking factor of 1.35. Although no ground treatment of the upper layer of fill (above the water table) has been carried out, the tracking action of the considerable number and size of plant required to construct the platform has resulted in this zone being, in general, in a dense state. The equivalent load per tyre contact area for the haul trucks greatly exceeds conventional heavy compaction plant. Large-scale water replacement tests have been performed in Type A/B fill with results typically in the range of 23 to 24 kN/m^3.

The permeability of the Type A and A/B fills below the water table is extremely high. In general it was not possible to measure the actual permeability using pumping tests, due to the inability to create a significant drawdown. The assumed value is thought to be in the range of 10^{-3} to 1 m/s. The permeability of the Type B (CDG) was typically in the range of 10^{-7} to 10^{-5} m/s.

It was neither necessary nor feasible to carry out strength tests on either the Type A or A/B fills. However based on the side slope angle of fill stockpiles around the site an internal angle of friction of 45° would be applicable in the loose state, and considerably greater strength could be mobilized when compacted or partially saturated.

For design of reclamations, the creep and stiffness characteristics are extremely important. The instrumentation for the airport platform has been described by others (Newman *et al.* 1995; Ayson & Lang 1996). Approximately 40 extensometers have been installed through the fill and underlying alluvium and anchored into the underlying bedrock in order to monitor subsurface settlement of the platform. A number of these were extended up through the surcharge fills constructed at various locations on the platform. These have allowed complete time settlement curves to be determined. A typical result for compression of the fill due to surcharging is shown in Fig. 7.21. It can be seen that settlement is a time dependent process. It is of note that the initial compression of the fill is not immediate but takes place over 2 to 3 weeks. Based on the known high permeability of the fill the settlement is not considered to be a consolidation process but more related to creep.

Creep is usually assumed to commence 0.1 years after completion of filling. This period is generally used as a mathematical convenience. However, it is useful to define the settlement which occurs in the first 0.1 years as being the constrained modulus and settlement thereafter

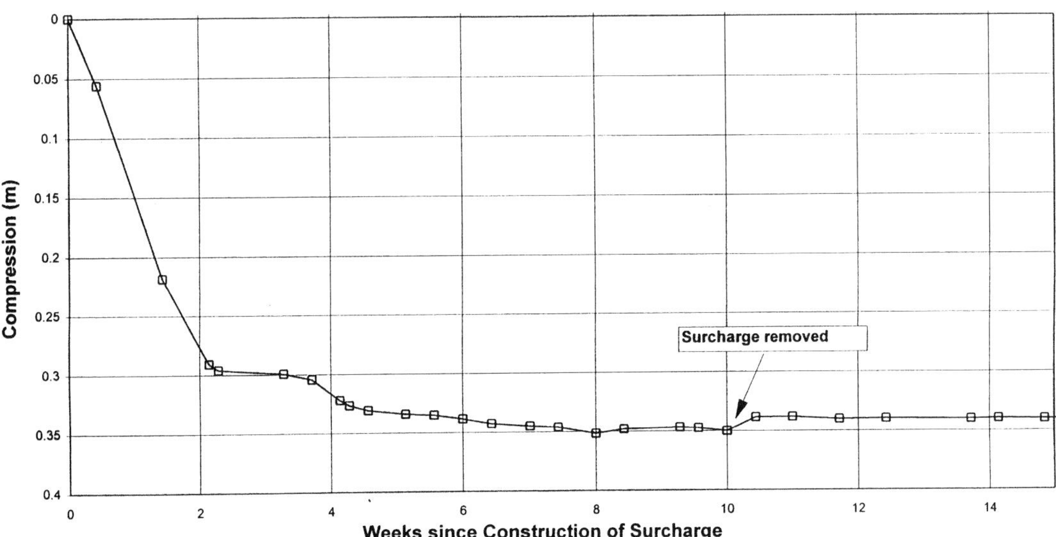

Fig. 7.21. Compression of fill due to surcharge.

as creep settlement. It should be noted that neither of these values are elastic parameters, as there is little to no recovery on unloading. Compression parameters derived in this way show that both Type A and A/B fill have similar characteristics. The compression of the 20 m thickness of rock fill below the water table was typically in the range 200 to 500 mm for a surcharge load in the range 100 to 160 kN/m^2.

The Type A fill below the water table has a constrained modulus in the range 20 to 50 MN/m^2 and

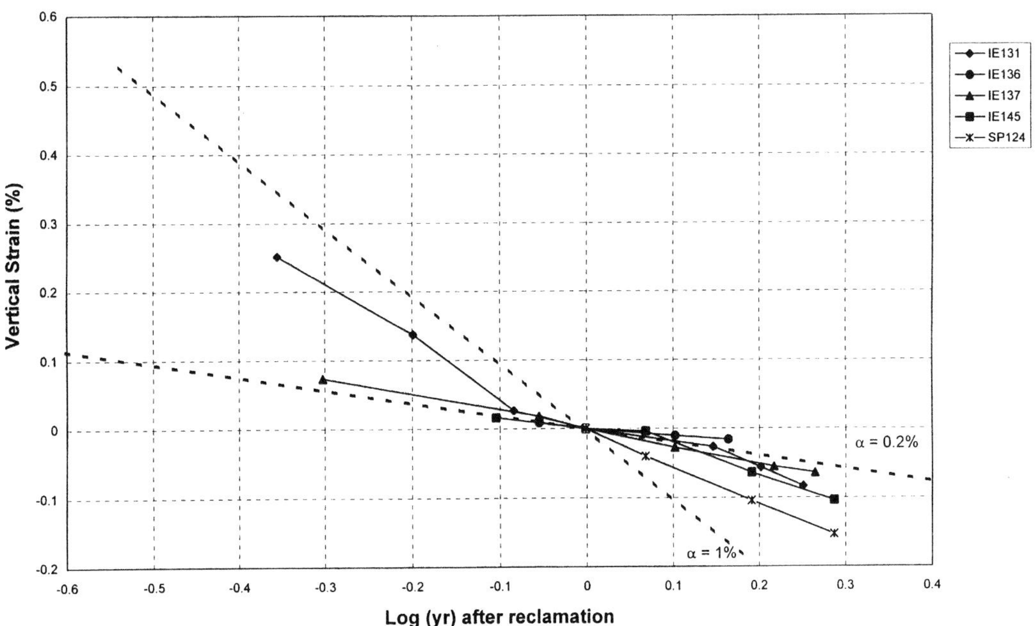

Fig. 7.22. Log time–strain plot of fill type A.

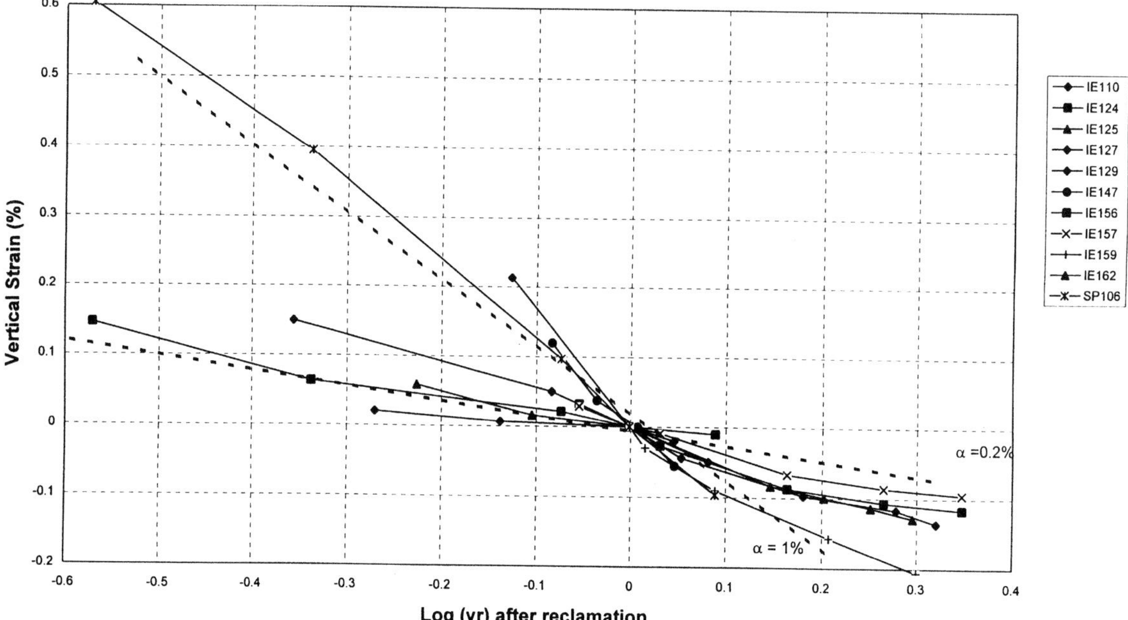

Fig. 7.23. Log time–strain plot of fill.

the Type A/B fill in the range 10 to 40 MN/m^2. Care must be taken when considering these values, as fills had been in place for variable periods prior to surcharge loading, and were subject to different surcharge heights.

From the extensometers installed in the reclamation, up to three years of monitoring data have been collated, and are available to enable creep parameters to be determined. The logarithmic creep parameter (α) for Type A has been determined to be in the range 0.2 to 0.5% per log cycle of time and Type A/B in the range 0.3 to 1.0% of log cycle of time. Typical results derived from extensometers in the fill are shown in Figs 7.22 and 7.23. For comparison purposes the creep measured in each extensometer was determined on a common base of one year after completion of the reclamation at the location of the extensometer. Total creep was calculated from 0.1 years after reclamation.

In addition to the above stiffness values, plate load tests have been carried out on the compacted Type A/B fill above the water table. Subgrade reaction in the range 100 to 300 kPa/mm has been determined for 300 mm diameter plates.

7.6.6.9. Conclusion

From start to the substantial completion of the reclamation took approximately 31 months and involved the movement of about 350 million m^3 of material, equivalent to two tonnes per second over the 31 months. At the peak of the works, 2 hectares of reclaimed land were being formed each day.

The rapid pace of construction was at least in part achieved by the use of a carefully programmed fill allocation plan taking best advantage of the various fill types available. This minimized the requirements for fill processing and ensured that the fill placed in a particular area met the specific engineering requirements of the future planned construction.

This approach also minimized the requirement for ground improvement of the reclamation fill thereby reducing both cost and time. To date the performance of the reclamation has met with the design requirements for the follow-on facilities and is expected to do so throughout the operational life of the airport.

Acknowledgements. Section 7.6.3 on Queen's Valley dam is included by kind permission of The Jersey New Waterworks Company Limited.

References

AMERICAN SOCIETY OF TESTING AND MATERIALS. *Annual Book of ASTM Standards*. ASTM, Philadelphia.

ANON 1990. Tropical residual soils: working party report. *Quarterly Journal of Engineering Geology*, **23**, 1–101.

——1994. *Manual of Contract Documents for Highway Works*. Volume 1: Specification for highway works (MCHW 1). Her Majesty's Stationery Office, London.

AYSON, I. J. & LANG, C. 1996. Survey Monitoring and Instrumentation Techniques Adopted During the Construction of Hong Kong's New Airport at Chek Lap Kok. *Proceedings of the 8th FIG International Symposium on Deformation Measurements, 25–28 June 1996, Hong Kong.* Dept. Land Surveying and Geo-Informatics, Hong Kong Polytechnic University.

BAILEY, M. J. 1976. Degradation and other parameters related to the use of shale in compacted embankments. *Joint Highway Research Project-76-23*, Purdue University, Indiana.

BNCOLD 1983. *Dams in the UK 1963–1983*. British National Committee on Large Dams, London.

BOND, F. C. 1959. Confirmation of the third theory. *American Institute of Mining & Metallurgical Engineers, Annual Meeting in San Francisco.*

BRIDLE, R. C. 1988. Selection and design of the waterproofing element for Queen's Valley dam, Jersey, Channel Islands. *Transactions of 16th International Congress on Large Dams*, Vienna, **2**, 643–653.

BRITISH STANDARDS INSTITUTION 1981. *Code of Practice for Site Investigations.* BS 5930: 1981. BSI, London.

——1990. BS 1377: 1990. *Methods of Test for Soils for Civil Engineering Purposes* (in 9 parts). BSI, London.

——1994. BS 8002: 1994. *Code of Practice for Earth Retaining Structures.* BSI, London.

BROCH, E. & FRANKLIN, J. A. 1972. The point-load strength test. *International Journal of Rock Mechanics and Mining Science*, **9**(6), 669.

BROMHEAD, E. N. 1986. *The Stability of Slopes.* Surrey University Press.

BROWN, E. T. 1981. *Rock Characterization Testing and Monitoring. ISRM Suggested Methods.* Pergamon, Oxford.

CATERPILLAR TRACTOR COMPANY 1982. *Caterpillar Performance Handbook.* Caterpillar Tractor Company, Preoria, Illinois.

CENTRE DE RECHERCHES ROUTIERERS 1978. *Code of Practice for the Geotechnical Investigations of Road Alignments.* Volume 2 Survey of problems (in French). Recommandations CRR-R42/78, C. R. R Brussels.

CHAIGNE, P., LEFLAIVE, E. & SCHAEFFNER, M. 1980. A new concept for compaction specifications for road embankments (in French). *International Conference on Compaction.* Editions Anciens ENPC, Paris, Vol II, 493–9.

CHARLES, J. A. 1991. Laboratory compression tests and the deformation of rock fill structures. Chapter 5 of *Advances in Rock fill Structures* (ed. Maranha das Neves E), pp. 73–95.

—— & WATTS, K. S. 1980. The influence of confining pressure on the shear strength of compacted rock fill. *Géotechnique*, **30(4)**, 353–367.

—— & SOARES, M. 1984. Stability of compacted rock fill slopes. *Géotechnique*, **34(1)**, 61–70.

—— & PENMAN, A. D. M. 1988. The behaviour of embankment dams with bituminous watertight elements. *Transactions of 16th International Congress on Large Dams*, San Francisco, **2**, 693–705.

CUNNINGHAM, C. V. B. 1982. Rock fragmentation related to blast design. *Quarry Management and Products*, December, 820–824.

DE MELLO, V. F. B. 1977. Reflections on design decisions of practical significance to embankment dams. *Géotechnique*, **27**, 281–354.

ESCARIO, V., LOPEZ-CORRAL, A. & SERRANO, A. 1980. Correlation between plate bearing tests and deformations originated by a 10 t axle load for compaction control of earthworks. *International Conference on Compaction.* Editions Anciens ENPC, Paris, Vol II.

EVANS, J. D. & WILSON, A. C. 1992. The instrumentation, monitoring and performance of Roadford dam during construction and first filling. *Water Resources and Reservoir Engineering. Proceedings of 7th Conference of British Dam Society*, Stirling. Thomas Telford, London, 157–165.

FOOKES, P. G. 1976. Stabilization and control of local rock falls and degrading rock slopes. *Quarterly Journal of Engineering Geology*, **9**, 37–55.

FORSSBLAD, L. 1981. *Vibratory Soil and Rock Fill Compaction.* Dynapac Maskin AB, Solna, Sweden.

FRANKLIN, J. A. & CHANDRA, R. 1972. The slake-durability test. *International Journal of Rock Mechanics and Mining Science*, **9**, 325.

FUMAGALLI, E. 1969. Tests on cohesionless materials for rock fill dams. *Journal of Soil Mechanics and Foundations Division.* American Society of Civil Engineers, **95**, January, SM1, 313–330.

GALLOWAY, J. D. 1939. The design of rock fill dams. *Transactions of American Society of Civil Engineers*, **104**, 1–24.

GUNNING, A. 1992. CCTV borehole surveying and its application to rock engineering. International Society of Rock Mechanics: *Eurock '92*, Chester. British Geotechnical Society, Telford, London, 174–178.

HALE, B. C., LOVELL, C. W. & WOOD, L. E. 1981. Development of a laboratory compaction degradation test for shales. *Transportation Research Record 790*, Transportation Research Board, Washington DC, 45–52.

HOEK, E. & BRAY, J. W. 1981. *Rock Slope Engineering.* Institute of Mining & Metallurgy, London.

—— & BROWN, D. F. 1988. Rock support. *Mining Magazine.* October 1988.

HOWISON, J. A. & MACDONALD, A. 1988. Trunk Road A82: the Loch Lomondside road: conception to implementation. *Proceedings of the Institution of Civil Engineers*, **84(1)**, 497–517.

JAKANI, A. 1987. Earthworks – drainage – subgrade. Report from Morocco. *PIARC XVIII World Roads Congress*, Permanent International Association of Road Congresses, Paris, 61–75.

JAMES, J. W. C., EVANS, C. D. R., CROSBY, A. & HUMPHREYS, B. 1994. An interpretation of the marine geology for the replacement airport at Chek Lap Kok, Hong Kong. *British Geological Survey Technical Report WB/93/34R.*

JANSEN, R . B. 1980. *Dams and Public Safety.* US Department of the Interior, Denver.

KJAERNSLI, B. & SANDE, A. 1963. Compressibility of some coarse grained materials. *Proceedings of European Conference on Soil Mechanics and Foundation Engineering*, Wiesbaden, **1**, Deutsche Gesellshaft fur Erd und Grundbau, 245–251.

KUZNETSOV, V. M. 1973. The mean diameter of the fragments formed by blasting rock. *Soviet Mining Science*, **9**, 144–148.

LANGFORD, R. L. 1994. HKGS, *Geology of Chek Lap Kok*, Sheet Report No. 2 Geotechnical Engineering Office, Hong Kong.

MACGREGOR, F., FELL, R., MOSTYN, G. R., HOCKING, G. & MCNALLY, G. 1994. The estimation of rock rippability. *Quarterly Journal of Engineering Geology*, **27**, 123–144.

MARANHA DAS NEVES, E. (ed.) 1991. *Advances in Rock fill Structures*. Kluwer, Dordrecht.

MARSAL, R. J. 1973. Mechanical properties of rock fill. *In*: HIRSCHFELD, R. C. & POULOS, S. J. (eds) *Embankment Dam Engineering* – Casagrande Volume. Wiley, New York, 109–200.

MATHESON, G. D. 1983. *Presplit Blasting in Highway Rock Excavation*. Departments of Environment and Transport, TRL Report LR 1094. Transport Research Laboratory, Crowthorne.

——1984. *A Device for Measuring Drill Rod and Drill Hole Orientations*. Departments of Environment and Transport, TRL Report SR 817. Transport Research Laboratory, Crowthorne.

——1985. The stability of slopes exposing rock. *Proceedings of the International Symposium on Failures in Earthworks*. Institution of Civil Engineers, London, 295–304.

——1986. The design and excavation of stable slopes in hard rock, with particular reference to presplit blasting. *International Symposium on Rock Engineering and Excavation in an Urban Environment*. Institution of Mining and Metallurgy, Hong Kong, 271–283.

——1992. Highway rock excavation. *Explosives '92*, Leeds. Institute of Explosives Engineers, London, 139–154.

——1995. Aspects of highway rock engineering in the UK. *In*: EDDLESTON, M., WALTHALL, S., CRIPPS, J. C. & CULSHAW, M. G. (eds) *Engineering Geology of Construction*. Geological Society, London, Engineering Geology Special Publications, **10**, 169–187.

MCMILLAN, P. & MATHESON, G. D. 1998. Rock slope hazard assessment: a new approach. *In*: MAUND, J. G. & EDDLESTON, M. (eds) *Geohazards in Engineering Geology*. Geological Society, London, Engineering Geology Special Publications, **15**, 177–184.

——1997. A two-stage system for highway rock slope risk assessment, *International Journal of Rock Mechanics and Mining Sciences*, **34**, 3–4.

MILLMORE, J. P. & BELL, J. E. 1994. Roadford reservoir – environmental experiences. *Transactions of 18th International Congress on Large Dams*, Durban, **2**, 659–672.

MINISTERE DE L'EQUIPEMENT DU LOGEMENT ET DES TRANSPORTS 1992. *Construction of embankments and formation layers* (in French). Service d'Etudes Techniques des Routes et Autoroutes, Laboratoire Central des Ponts et Chaussees, Paris.

NATIONAL INSTITUTE FOR TRANSPORT AND ROAD RESEARCH 1982. *Construction of Road Embankments*. Technical Recommendations for Highways TRH 9 NITRR, Pretoria.

NEWMAN, R. L., PINCHES, G. M., LANG, C. & PEART, M. 1995. Preliminary Aspects of the Instrumentation of the Reclamation for the New Hong Kong Airport at Chek Lap Kok, *HKIE Annual Geotechnical Seminar 'Instrumentation'*.

NEVILLE-JONES, P. & LEUTCHFORD, D. 1994. The construction of 13 km of seawall for Hong Kong's new airport at Chek Lap Kok. *Proceedings of Conference on Advances in Coastal Structures and Breakwaters*. Institution of Civil Engineers, Thomas Telford, London.

PENMAN, A. D. M. & CHARLES, J. A. 1976. The quality and suitability of rock fill used in dam construction. *Transactions of 12th International Congress on Large Dams*, Mexico, **1**, 533–556.

——, BURLAND, J. B. & CHARLES, J. A. 1971. Observed and predicted deformations in a large embankment dam during construction. *Proceedings of Institution of Civil Engineers*, **49**, May, 1–21.

PERRY, J. 1994. A technique for defining non-linear shear strength envelopes, and their incorporation in a slope stability method of analysis. *Quarterly Journal of Engineering Geology*, **27**, 231–242.

—— & PARSONS, A. W. 1986. *Assessing the Quality of Rock Fill: a Review of Current Practice for Highways*. Department of Transport, TRL Report RR60. Transport Research Laboratory, Crowthorne.

PETTIFER, G. S. & FOOKES, P. G. 1994. A revision of the graphical method for assessing the excavatability of rock. *Quarterly Journal of Engineering Geology*, **27**, 145–164.

ROSENHEINRICH, G. 1978. The placing and compaction of rock fill (in German). *St u Tiefbau*, **32**, 4, 10–16.

ROSS, K. D. & BUTLIN, R. N. 1989. *Durability Test for Building Stone*. BRE BR141. Building Research Establishment, Watford.

ROWLAND, S. B., JOHNSON, K. A . L. & WENDES, J. 1988. A55 Llanddulas to Glan Conwy – construction. *Proceedings of the Institution of Civil Engineers*, **84**(1), 965–988.

SOWERS, G. F., WILLIAMS, R. C. & WALLACE, T. S. 1965. Compressibility of broken rock and the settlement of rock fills. *Proceedings of 6th International Conference on Soil Mechanics and Foundation Engineering*, Montreal, **2**, 561–565.

SPRINGETT, M. & STEVENSON, T. D 1988. A55 Llanddulas to Glan Conwy – design. *Proceedings of the Institution of Civil Engineers*, **84**(1), 939–964.

STROM, W. E. JR. 1980. *Design and construction of shale embankments*: Summary. Report FHWA/TS-80/219. Army Engineer Waterways Experiment Station, Vicksburg, Mississippi.

TRANSPORTATION RESEARCH BOARD 1990. *Guide to Earthwork Construction*. State of the Art Report 8 TRB, Washington.

WANG, H., LATHAM, J.-P. & MATHESON, G. D. 1992. The design of fragmentation blasting in surface rock excavation. International Society of Rock Mechanics: *Eurock '92. Rock Characterization*, Chester. British Geotechnical Society, Thomas Telford, London, 233–238.

WILLIAMS, H. & STOTHARD, J. N. 1967. Rock excavation and specification trials for the Lancashire-Yorkshire Motorway, Yorkshire (West Riding) Section. Paper No 6972, *Proceedings of Institution of Civil Engineers*, **36**, 607–631.

WILSON, A . C. & EVANS, J. D. 1990. The use of low grade rock fill at Roadford dam. The embankment dam. *Proceedings of 6th Conference of the British Dam Society, Nottingham*. Thomas Telford, London, 21–27.

8. Armourstone

8.1. Introduction

Man has been involved in the construction of harbours and the protection of vulnerable sections of the coastline since antiquity. The use of large blocks of rock to armour such structures also has a long history, but it is only within the last century that the design of structures using natural rock materials has been treated scientifically.

This chapter is primarily concerned with the use of undressed stone, of various types, in marine structures. The complexity of the design of such structures and the factors affecting them are addressed elsewhere, for example by the Construction Industry Research and Information Service (CIRIA) and the Centre for Civil Engineering Research and Codes (CUR) (Netherlands) in their joint 'Manual on the use of rock in coastal and shoreline engineering' (CIRIA/CUR 1991), by the Institution of Civil Engineers (ICE) in 'Design Of Breakwaters' (ICE 1988) and by the US Army Corps of Engineers in the 'Shore Protection Manual' (US Army Corps 1989).

8.1.1. Objectives

As a consequence of the number and variety of types of structure and of their locations worldwide, it is most appropriate to consider the rock used in a general way dealing with block size, grading, rock density and durability, as well as with extraction, processing, transport and placing. Therefore, a general review is given covering the design requirements of the materials specified for most marine structures which use natural rock in their construction and also similar structures such as river bank, river scour and dam face protection.

The special nature of the marine environment imposes severe constraints both on the design and the construction of coastal defence structures and this in turn imposes limitations on the geometric, physical and mechanical properties of the rock used. Later sections of this chapter will review the specifications and tests appropriate for these materials in relation to their in-service performance.

8.1.2. Marine structures

Marine structures may be grouped into the following six broad categories:

1. Rubble mound breakwaters and reefs
2. Shoreline protection and sea walls
3. Groynes
4. Artificial beaches (and beach nourishment)
5. Floating breakwaters
6. Piers and quays

Although there are many examples of artificial materials such as concrete and asphalt forming all or part of these structures, natural rock is commonly the major component used in the construction of structures in the first four groups listed above. Rock facings and armouring are being used increasingly at the present time as a consequence of economic, practical and environmental considerations in the design.

Rubble mound structures are widely used as breakwaters for harbour and coastal protection, and in modified form for coastal defence structures. Their designs make use of a variety of rock gradings and require careful specification of block shape, and of physical and mechanical properties. A typical cross section of such a structure is illustrated in Fig. 8.1.

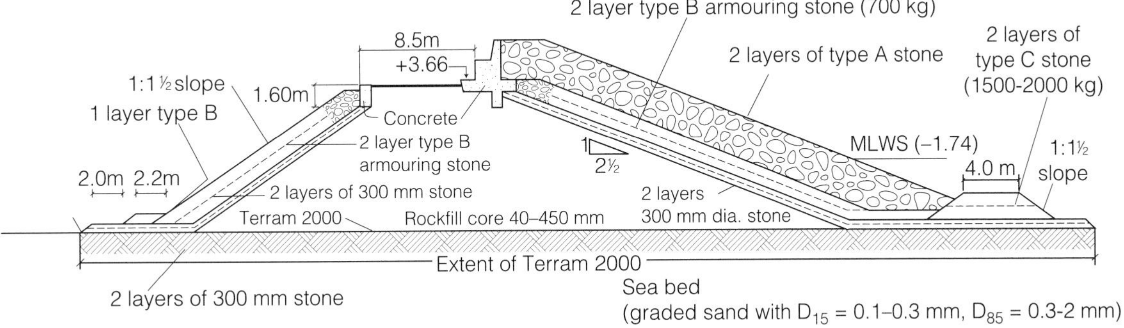

Fig. 8.1. A typical cross section of a rubble mound breakwater, seaward face to the right. The original North Breakwater, Bangor, Northern Ireland (after Bell 1984).

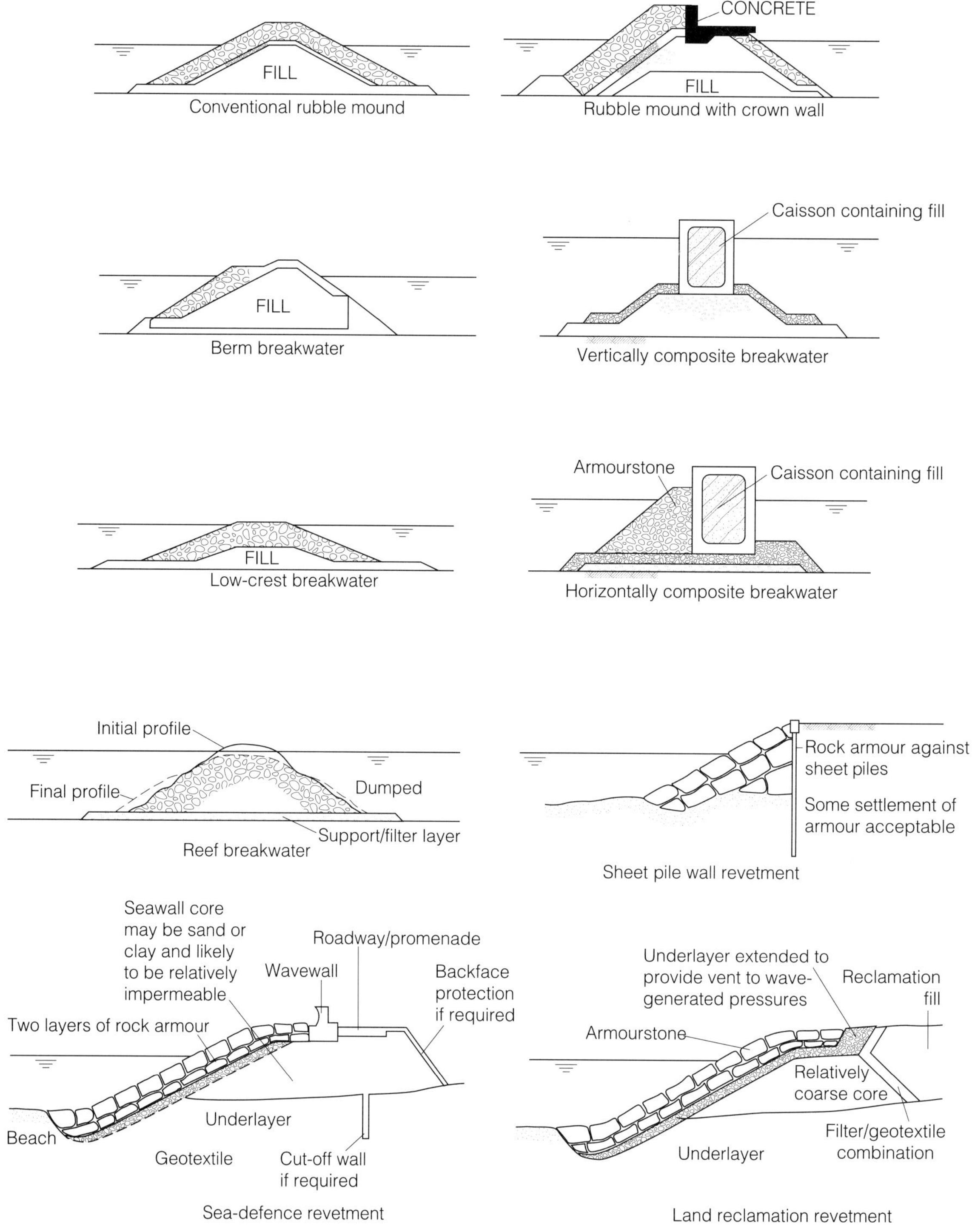

Fig. 8.2. Some examples of cross sections of rock armoured marine structures.

The principal advantage of an open textured rubble mound structure is that the wave energies are dissipated to a considerable extent by turbulence generated within the voids between adjacent blocks. Thus, wave energies are largely dissipated as turbulence and heat rather than reflected back, as would be the case with a vertical sea wall. The effect is to reduce wave run-up and overtopping of the structure. Consequently, size, shape, packing of blocks on the face of the structure, and slope angle of the face are all key factors which control the effectiveness of energy dissipation.

As the forces acting on breakwater structures have become better understood, it has been recognised that wave attack on the exposed face of a rubble breakwater will tend to move material of the outer layers of the structure so as to develop an 'S'-shaped profile. Thus, two types of structure can be designed. The first where the structure and armouring is massive enough to withstand storm damage up to a defined limit and remain static and the second where either an 'S' shaped profile is built into the original design of the breakwater by incorporating a toe berm, a gently sloping section near mean water level or, alternatively, initial storm wave action is allowed to move material on the structure so that it develops a flatter more stable profile within the tidal range. This last type of re-profiling design is referred to as a dynamically stable structure and can use smaller sized stone blocks than equivalent static designs.

Variations of the rubble breakwater designs are also employed in coastal and sea wall protection. Some typical examples are illustrated in cross section in Fig. 8.2. An energy spending beach is the best form of coastal protection and where a beach fronts a sea wall or natural shoreline special protection may not be required. However, undercutting of sea walls, particularly during storm conditions, is common often as a result of a general lowering of beach levels which may occur when beach materials are removed by longshore transport and not replenished. As a consequence, some form of toe protection, usually as large blocks or rip-rap is either incorporated into the original design or forms part of remedial measures undertaken at a later date.

Groynes are a common feature on many beaches and act to stabilize the beach by trapping sediment and reducing the longshore drift of beach materials. Traditionally, these structures were constructed of hardwoods and formed vertical fence-like barriers extending perpendicular to the coastline. In the last three decades the

Fig. 8.3. A general view of Malaga beach regeneration scheme showing rock groynes and offshore rubble mound breakwaters (courtesy Director General Ports and Coasts, Spain).

use of rubble rock groynes in place of the traditional types has become increasingly common, partly because of their better energy dissipating characteristics and partly because they are considered more environmentally sympathetic, though usually the cost differential between hardwood and rock groynes is small. However, such structures and coastal revetments can be ideally suited to construction from imported marine transported rock and have now become more viable with the development of coastal quarries in Scandinavia, Spain, France, Ireland and elsewhere, and with the introduction of large rock carrying barges. The increasing sophistication of groyne field design for the stabilization of amenity beaches (see Fig. 8.3), and modern environmental considerations have also contributed to the increasing use of rock groynes round the world.

The importance of beaches both for coastal protection and as a leisure amenity has led to extensive beach nourishment schemes and the construction of artificial beaches. The bulk of materials used for beach construction and nourishment are sea dredged. However, some beach nourishment schemes involve the use of cobble, and larger size materials, which are sometimes used to stabilize beaches in energetic marine environments (CIRIA 1996).

8.1.3. Non-marine structures

Large natural rock blocks, either as single sized, or more usually as widely graded material (rip-rap), are commonly used in the construction of river training schemes, bank and river bed protection and stabilization. Such materials are also used in the prevention of scour around bridge piers, where river flows have been constricted, in closure works and for the protection of dam faces from wind generated wave action.

Important to the design of such schemes are the full ranges of velocities of current flows and their directions, including the possible extremes of turbulent flows during flood conditions. Also the shape, slope and nature of the pre-existing bed or bank, its bearing capacity and other geotechnical parameters are important for the development of an appropriate design in a particular instance.

The size and grading of the rock material to be used, the permeability and thickness of the layer and the necessity for a granular filter or geotextile beneath the protective 'armour' layer will depend on the particular design application and the hydraulic and geotechnical conditions prevailing. Such design considerations are covered in publications by PIANC (1987, 1989); by the US Army Corps of Engineers (1989) and Thorne *et al.* (1995).

Although many different types of natural and artificial materials are used in river training and similar stabilization schemes, rock in the form of rip-rap or in gabions, see §7.2.1, is very commonly used. Rip-rap is usually preferred to single sized material as it exhibits a better resistance to scour for a given median block size in the grading (D_{50}), see §8.3.1 (Simons 1995).

As with marine structures, stone used in these applications must be durable and the density, block shape and angularity will all be important factors to be considered during the design stages of a project.

8.1.4. Materials requirements

Large volumes of rock are used in the construction of marine and coastal defence structures. As an example, the construction of the new Hong Kong Airport and related developments were estimated as requiring 9.3 million tonnes of rock per year for coastal protection and related marine structures over the period 1990–1995 (Fowler & Earle 1990), see §7.6.6. A single large breakwater constructed in Iceland required 1 847 000 tonnes of rock, of which 80% was core and 20% armourstone.

Figures for the annual consumption of armourstone in the UK and the rest of Europe are difficult to estimate, partly because of the commercial sensitivity of the information and partly due to the wide fluctuations in demand depending on the number and sizes of marine construction projects in progress at any particular time. Thomas (1996) suggests that an estimate for the annual demand for rock armour in the UK runs at 1.2 million tonnes. However, this estimate excludes works associated with harbours and coastal defences which are funded by private bodies. Thus it is reasonable to suggest that in the UK the consumption of armourstone larger than 0.5 tonne (based on a five-year average) is of the order of 1 to 1.5 million tonnes per annum but this figure might be doubled in any one year depending on the construction of a major marine project in that year as demonstrated by Rees-Jones & Storhaug (1998).

Although primary armourstone blocks up to 20 tonnes have been produced and used, the geological constraints of discontinuity spacing in rock masses limit the maximum size of blocks that can be obtained from a given source. Typically the maximum size of primary armourstone blocks commonly available is 10 tonnes and smaller. As a consequence of this limitation, designers favour concrete armour units as primary armour where conditions require the use of very large units; alternatively they design structures to take account of the likely dimensions of the available rock materials.

Typically conventional designs require the primary armourstone, the secondary armourstone and the underlayers to be single size, or within narrow size gradings. Both the constraints on block size and their geometric shape are carefully specified at the design stage. Most commonly, equant (cubic, prismatic or pyramidal) blocks are required.

Generally, primary armourstone will be specified by its weight (W) or mass (M), where $W = Mg$ (g is the acceleration due to gravity), and, depending on the design requirement, a median weight between 1 and 10 tonnes is commonly required although much larger blocks may be required for exposed breakwater sites or in deep water. Similarly secondary armour and underlayer material is typically specified by weight or mass with the median value ranging upward from about 0.1 tonne, depending on the particular design requirement.

In addition to the requirement for particular rock sizes specified within a narrow grading, some marine structure designs, particularly those for coastal protection revetment schemes and for river bank protection, require the use of rip-rap, usually with a top size that is less than one tonne and with a wide grading downwards to perhaps 0.2, 0.1 or 0.05 tonne, see §8.1.3.

8.1.5. Material quality evaluation

Rock selected for use in a marine structure such as a breakwater may be subject to severe conditions, particularly during storms. The rock must be able to withstand rapidly fluctuating and severe hydraulic pressure changes, impact due to movement, abrasion and attrition, wetting and drying, thermal cycling, and possibly freeze/thaw, salt and solution damage. Thus, rock selected for use on marine structures, particularly that chosen for primary armour on the inter-tidal zone where conditions are most severe, will require physical and mechanical properties able to withstand the storm conditions specified in the design of the structure and the extremes of local environmental conditions.

The testing and evaluation of these properties is as important as the control of shape, size and grading in meeting the design specification of a given structure. Many of the tests to evaluate armourstone quality have been modified from appropriate National Standard tests that were originally designed for aggregates, while others have been specifically designed to determine armourstone quality. The objective of all these test procedures is to ensure that a rock selected for a marine structure will be strong enough to withstand breakage, both during handling from quarry to structure and during its service life on the structure and will also be sufficiently durable to avoid significant wear or degradation in-service so that the original design criteria are not compromised. Typical specification requirements in the selection of rock are discussed in §8.6 and the test procedures relevant to these specifications in §8.5.

8.2. Definitions

8.2.1. Introducing armourstone terminology

Rock is used in coastal structures in a wide variety of ways. Monolithic masonry wall structures are rarely constructed today because of the high costs involved in comparison with the use of other materials such as concrete but rock is increasingly used for random rubble armour where the dissipation of wave energy is important. Armourstone, according to the definition in the draft European CEN Standard (March 1996), consists of stones of different sizes and irregular shape which are used in hydraulic protection and regulation structures. They are typically large equant blocks of rock usually considered to have masses greater then 0.25 tonnes. The armour layers used on hydraulic structures are composed of these blocks which are normally laid so as to maximize both interlock between blocks and the void volumes between them.

Armouring in the context of coastal engineering implies permanent protection to a structure in water. Such armour may consist of blocks of rock or concrete units of the appropriate size if rock is not available. Depending on the design criteria limitations the rock armour has to be massive enough either to remain static under storm conditions or to assume an eventual stable configuration after an initial period of movement and sorting (i.e. re-profiling) by wave action during the first few periods of major storm activity.

In the majority of rubble mound breakwater and rock armoured sea defence structures a range of rock gradings are required in the design. The larger sized blocks such as those required for primary armour are usually specified in terms of physical, mechanical and durability characteristics and by shape and mass. Smaller sized materials such as filter and core material must meet appropriate physical, mechanical and durability criteria and are specified on particle shape and screen sizes as for aggregates (Smith & Collis 1993). The change in specifications from one based on size to one based on mass arises from the practical difficulties of screening blocks of large size. The typical transition from size to mass specification occurs when the required material exceeds 250 mm (CIRIA/CUR 1991), but this depends in part on the processing equipment available.

The relationship between volume and mass (M) depends on the rock density (ρ) but with irregular shaped large blocks size is most conventionally defined as the side length of the equivalent volume cube (D_n) sometimes called the nominal diameter where:

$$D_n = (M/\rho)^{1/3}.$$

Another possible size definition uses the equivalent volume sphere (diameter D_s).

The grading of rock is also important in specification since natural quarry blocks will range in mass. The conventional means of presentation is the cumulative grading curve which is based on the percentage of blocks lighter by weight than a particular block weight. Thus, W_{50} expresses the median block weight with 50% by weight heavier and 50% lighter than this value. Similarly W_{85} and W_{15} express the values where 85% and 15% by weight respectively of blocks or particles are lighter than these values. The ratio W_{85}/W_{15} is commonly used to give an indication of the width or steepness of a grading curve, and the following descriptions are normally applied (CIRIA/CUR 1991).

	W_{85}/W_{15}
Narrow or 'single sized' grading	1.7–2.7
Wide grading	2.7–16.0
Very wide or 'quarry run' grading	1.6–125+

It has been recognized in Europe that there are many advantages to the producer, designer and user in introducing a standard series of grading classes. The draft CEN Standard (1996) designates armourstone gradings in terms of lower and upper nominal class limits and also accepts that undersized and oversized armourstone blocks may be present in a given grading specification. The draft standard defines three groups of gradings as follows:

Coarse gradings:	the nominal upper limit is defined by a square aperture sieve size between and including 125 and 250 mm.
Light gradings:	the nominal upper limit is defined by a mass between and including 25 and 300 kg.
Heavy gradings:	the nominal upper limit is defined by a mass of more than 300 kg.

The standard recommends further subdivision into five gradings for each of these groups and provides test procedures for their determination. The details of these gradings are given in Tables 8.1, 8.2 and 8.3, which are

Table 8.1. *Requirements for the particle size distribution of coarse gradings*

Grading	*45/125 mm*	*63/180 mm*	*90/250 mm*	*45/180 mm*	*90/180 mm*
Passing sieve (mm)	*Cumulative fraction (% by mass)*				
360	–	–	98–100	–	–
250	–	98–100	90–100	98–100	98–100
180	98–100	90–100	–	90–100	80–100
125	90–100	–	0–50	–	–
90	–	0–50	0–15	–	0–20
63	0–50	0–15	–	0–50	–
45	0–15	–	0–5*	0–15	0–5*
31, 5	–	0–5*	–	–	–
22, 4	0–5*	–	–	0–5*	–

* Fragments.

Table 8.2. *Requirements for the mass distribution of light gradings*

Grading	*5–40 kg*	*10–60 kg*	*40–200 kg*	*60–300 kg*	*15–300 kg*
Less than mass in kg	*Cumulative fraction (% by mass)*				
450	–	–	–	97–100	97–100
300	–	–	97–100	70–100	70–100
200	–	–	70–100	–	–
120	–	97–100	–	–	–
80	97–100	–	–	–	–
60	–	70–100	–	0–10	–
40	70–100	–	0–10	–	–
30	–	–	–	0–2*	–
15	–	–	0–2*	–	0–10
10	–	0–10	–	–	–
5	0–10	–	–	–	–
3	–	–	–	–	0–2*
2	–	0–2*	–	–	–
1, 5	0–2*	–	–	–	–

* Fragments.

Table 8.3. *Requirements for the mass distribution of heavy gradings*

Grading	*300–1000 kg*	*1000–3000 kg*	*3000–6000 kg*	*6000–10 000 kg*	*10 000–15 000 kg*
Less than mass in kg			*Cumulative fraction (% by mass)*		
22 500	–	–	–	–	97–100
15 000	–	–	–	97–100	70–100
10 000	–	–	–	70–100	0–10
9 000	–	–	97–100	–	–
6 500	–	–	–	–	0–5*
6 000	–	–	70–100	0–10	–
4 500	–	97–100	–	–	–
4 000	–	–	–	0–5*	
3 000	–	70–100	0–10	–	–
2 000	–	–	0–5*	–	–
1 500	97–100	–	–	–	–
1 000	70–100	0–10	–	–	–
650	–	0–5*	–	–	–
300	0–10	–	–	–	–
200	0–10	–	–	–	–
200	0–5*	–	–	–	–

* Fragments.

taken from Tables 3, 4 and 5 of the draft standard and the test procedures are summarized in §8.6 and Appendix B. It should be noted that the coarse grading 90/180 mm is a narrow grading designated for special applications like gabions.

There is a general design preference for angular equant shaped blocks for the construction of armour layers. Translation of this preference into specifications of acceptance/rejection criteria can lead to difficulties unless the geometric shape of blocks can be adequately quantified. With natural irregularly shaped blocks shape specifications using axial ratio measurements is one possibility, but they must be clearly defined and be amenable to objective measurement. The maximum (X) intermediate (Y) and minimum (Z) dimensions of an enclosing cuboid can be used since their ratios will distinguish cubic, tabular and elongate shapes (Thompson & Shuttler 1975). A more practical scheme, which is objective and is readily measurable, has been proposed in the CIRIA/CUR manual as follows:

- z: Sieve size (i.e. the smallest square hole that a block in optimum orientation will pass through)
- l: Maximum axial length (the distance between the two most distant points on the block)
- d: Thickness or minimal axial breadth (the minimum distance between two parallel straight lines between which a block could just pass)

The draft CEN standard uses the same definitions for l and d but relabels them L and E respectively. The L/E aspect ratio may be considered a satisfactory means of defining gross shape for specification purposes. However, using these definitions it must be remembered that an $L:E$ ratio for a cube is 1.74:1 and only a sphere will have a ratio of 1:1. Thus specifications requiring a length to breadth ratio of say 2:1 or 3:1 must also clearly define the system of measurement used, i.e. whether an enclosing cuboid system or L/E system as defined in the CEN standard is in use.

The preference for angular shaped blocks rather than rounded ones has led to shape specifications that include less quantifiable and more descriptive shape classifications that are based on silhouette diagrams or photographs of various shape classes. BS 812 (1975) illustrates six shape classes: rounded, irregular, angular, flaky, elongate and flaky elongate which were intended to be applicable to aggregate particles while the CIRIA/CUR Manual (1991) illustrates five shape classes on photographs of blocks used in wave flume experiments. They are elongate, tabular, irregular, equant, semiround and very round. There appears to be no clear consensus view of shape classes and no clear distinction between basic particle shape and the degree of rounding.

Attempts to quantify degree of rounding have been based on silhouettes of particles such as the mathematically based systems comparing sphericity and roundness, (Krumbein & Sloss 1963) or quantifying shape using Fourier analysis to give numeric shape descriptors (Latham & Poole 1987). Indeed success in correlating Fourier shape descriptors to hydraulic performance has been useful in the refinement of rock armour stability formulae in taking account of shape effects (Bradbury *et al.* 1990). However, these are essentially laboratory methods and difficult to apply to large armour blocks on site. Consequently, more subjective visual methods are usually employed.

Photographic areas of block shapes

In agreeing compliance with specification for 3 tonne limestone and gabbroic armour blocks for shore protection works associated with the construction of a power station in the Middle East, difficulties were experienced in applying acceptance/rejection criteria to individual armourstone blocks in terms of geometric shape and particularly with respect to their degree of rounding.

Sources of rock of appropriate quality for armourstone were limited in the region. A satisfactory practical, if subjective, method of assessment was devised based on the comparison of blocks with an 'atlas' of photographs of acceptable/unacceptable block shapes, some of which are illustrated in Fig. 8.4.

A more basic approach to classifying natural rock blocks in terms of their shape is to take account of the number, orientations and spacings of natural discontinuity planes within a rock mass since these discontinuities will be a primary control on the block shapes obtained by quarrying, provided the discontinuities are well developed.

In rock masses where three sets of discontinuities are present and are essentially perpendicular to each other, block shapes will naturally tend to be cubic, tabular or elongate depending on the spacings between discontinuities in each set. In situations where one or more sets of discontinuities are inclined at an angle to the others, pyramidal and wedge shaped blocks would be produced, the precise shapes depending on the spacings between adjacent discontinuity planes in each set. Where more than three principal sets of discontinuities are present more complex block shapes are possible but it may be possible to describe them either as a combination of the shapes noted above, or in terms of the simpler shape to which they most closely approximate. An illustration of the variety of shapes commonly formed is given in Figs 8.5 & 8.6. Rounded blocks are developed as a result of weathering processes, for example corestones as illustrated in Fig. 8.4D, or as a consequence of geological transport or as a result of abrasion and damage during production and handling. Depending on the original block shape, the rounding will tend towards the discoidal, ellipsoidal or spherical.

8.2.2. Terminology used for rock in marine structures

Primary rock armour forms the outer protective layer on the structure and is usually placed in random arrangement in one or two layers. Interlock is maximized by careful placing of the individual blocks during construction since this is important for the potential stability of the layers, see Fig. 8.7. The mass of individual armour blocks is a most important factor in all design equations relating to rock armoured structures. Thus, the design specification will include a block mass, weight or size requirement. The grading of armour blocks will also be specified and has been typically of a 'single size' or narrow grading with limits set for acceptance of oversize and undersize blocks. The size of primary armour blocks required will depend upon the conditions under which they are to be used and on the design of the structure. Although designs involving primary rock armour blocks up to 25 tonnes have been constructed, more typically specifications require blocks of 10 tonnes and smaller as primary armour.

Equant block shapes are preferred and most designers avoid tabular blocks for primary armour although they have been used successfully in some structures at Holyhead, Anglesey, and there is some limited experimental evidence to suggest that they can be used to form a stable primary armour layer (Bradbury *et al.* 1990). Acceptable ratios of length (l) to thickness (d) of 3 : 1 or 2 : 1 have been specified.

Specifications for primary armourstone will also require the blocks to be adequately strong and durable since they will be subjected to very aggressive conditions particularly in the intertidal and splash zones were wave attack and wetting and drying conditions are most extreme. It is usual for designers to specify a series of tests to cover the physical, mechanical and durability aspects of the material and these will be covered in §§8.3 and 8.5. A particular requirement for armour blocks is that they should not break into two or more pieces either during transportation, handling and placement, or during their service life on the structure. Two distinct breakage modes are recognized, Type 1 where the block breaks into two or more major pieces along flaws and Type 2 is where breakage occurs along new fractures usually resulting in edges or corners being knocked or sheared off, see Fig. 8.8. Incipient flaws or planes of weakness are often difficult to detect in large blocks and special 'drop tests' have had to be developed for specification purposes, see Fig. 8.22.

Secondary rock armour (and sometimes **tertiary armour**) may be used in rubble mound breakwater structures as a support layer for the primary armour, see Fig. 8.9. As with the primary armour, turbulence within voids between blocks in the secondary armour layer helps to dissipate and absorb the incident wave energies rather than reflecting the waves back. Thus the requirements for mechanical strength, durability and shape will be similar to those required for the primary armour.

Fig. 8.4. A selection of typical armourstone block shapes subjectively defining angular (A), sub-angular (B), sub-rounded (C) and well rounded (D).

Fig. 8.4. (*continued*).

Fig. 8.4. *(continued)*.

C

C

D

D

Fig. 8.4. (*continued*).

Fig. 8.5. A selection of armourstone block shapes resulting from simple patterns of three intersecting joint planes present in the original rock mass.

Interlock between adjacent blocks and with the primary armour layer is very important for the stability of the whole structure. However, since these layers are partly protected by the primary armour the size of the secondary armour blocks can be smaller and is typically about one tenth that of the primary blocks. This size differential is considered to provide the optimum shear keying between the primary and secondary layers. The principal constraints on the designer will be to insure that the secondary armour blocks have adequate interlock and that their size and strength will be sufficient to support the primary armour and will not allow individual blocks to become dislodged and removed through gaps in the primary layer during storm conditions.

Tertiary armour is specified in some designs and acts as a support layer for the secondary armour. The blocks will be smaller in size than those in the secondary layer and like filter layers must not allow smaller sized

Fig. 8.5. (*continued*).

material to be 'piped' through the layer by the forces of hydraulic suction generated by the wash of waves against the structure. In its turn the blocks in the tertiary layer must not be dislodged and removed through gaps in the outer layers.

Rip-rap (sometimes referred to as 'pell-mell') rock materials may be used as supporting layers for the primary armour and also as the outer armour layer in river bank protection and coastal defence schemes or in dynamically stable breakwater and coastal defence structures, see Fig. 8.10. They are very widely graded materials which are usually placed in bulk (i.e. tipped rather than placed block by block). Specifications are often restricted to indicating a maximum and minimum grading limit, but an even distribution of block sizes between these limits is desirable and elongate prismatic or tabular shapes should be avoided. Since rip-rap material is subject to movement and wear during handling and placing, as well as in service, adequate strength and durability characteristics are essential and are usually specified in terms of appropriate laboratory test criteria, see §8.5.

The **underlayers** and **filter layers** which lie between the armour layers and the core materials of the breakwater or sea defence structure are composed of relatively small rock particles and perhaps are better described as rock

Fig. 8.6. A selection of more complex block shapes resulting from complex sets of joint planes present in the original rock mass.

Fig. 8.6. (*continued*).

Fig. 8.7. Example of primary armour on a rubble mound coastal defence system.

aggregate materials. The rock used must be sufficiently strong and durable for its purpose with low water absorption characteristics. Particle shape must be equant and specifications usually set low limits on the proportions of flaky and elongate particles that are acceptable particularly for filter media.

One of the major problems concerning rubble mound breakwaters and related structures is the tendency for fine material present in the core of the structure to be sucked (piped) through the outer layers of the structure by the hydraulic action of the waves. This can lead to subsidence and in extreme cases to de-stabilization of the outer layers and collapse of the structure. Thus the design of the filter layers to prevent piping is critical to the stability of the structure. In recent times geotextiles have been used in some designs as a replacement for the conventional filter layers but they are easily ruptured, less porous than rock filter underlayers and less absorptive which can be detrimental to the stability of the outer armour layers.

The **core** of rubble mound structures is by far the largest volume of material in most designs. A typical design of breakwater structure may require 80% by volume of core material with only a 20% requirement for armour and other materials. In the majority of structures core material is 'quarry run' material, that is material produced by the quarry with a minimum of processing.

The provision for the long term maintenance of such structures is an important aspect which will be incorporated into a good design. This leads the designer to carefully consider the future availability of repair materials, storage areas adjacent to the structure and access for plant to the site and onto the structure itself, perhaps by the provision of a permanent roadway along the crest.

In a general context modern practice is moving towards structural designs which maximise the use of the total quarry output, thus minimising material produced at the quarry which has to be discarded or used for other purposes, see §8.3.2. This practice, coupled with the increasing use of dynamically stable designs using rip-rap, is leading towards a more economic use of natural materials and to the creation of 'softer', more environmentally satisfactory marine structures.

8.3. Functions and required properties

8.3.1. The coastal defence and breakwater environment

By their nature coastal defences and breakwaters are either shoreline or nearshore structures. In a world survey (Stickland 1984) 75% of breakwaters were found to be constructed in depths of water which are less than 15 m. Thus the nearshore bathymetry and geomorphology together with the prevailing wave directions and wave climate are important considerations in coastal and shoreline engineering design. Other factors of importance will include the bearing capacity and ground conditions of the submarine site, the fetch fronting the structure, tidal and other current flow directions and strengths, and general climatic parameters such as prevailing wind direction and strengths and the magnitude and frequency of storm conditions. Factors relating to the environmental impact of the structure must also be considered for a proposed development. An environmental assessment or environmental impact assessment is often required by the authorities in whose jurisdiction the project falls. The objectives of such an assessment are to ensure that the proposed development is environmentally sensitive, and to minimize environmental damage. It must also provide sufficient information for the regulating authorities to make environmentally informed decisions.

The EC directive 85/337 (1985) required environmental assessment to be a mandatory part of the planning

(a)

(b)

Fig. 8.8. Incipient fracturing of armour blocks: (**a**) Type-1 fracture; (**b**) Type-2 fracture.

process for major projects and indicates four subject areas that should be addressed. This assessment will cover both the construction and the completed stages of the work. The four areas are:

1. Human beings, fauna and flora.
2. Soil, water, air, climate and the landscape.
3. The interactions between the factors listed in 1 and 2.
4. Existing material assets and the cultural heritage.

Both the physical and environmental factors will vary greatly from location to location and from structure to structure. The physical factors typically are such that they may well show significant variation even for

Fig. 8.9. Example of primary armouring showing the underlying secondary armour layer on a coastal defence structure.

different parts of a single structure. Thus the evaluation of all the physical and environmental factors required during project planning and design have two primary objectives:

Fig. 8.10. Example of rip-rap used in the Tees Barrage (courtesy of Bardon (England) Ltd).

1. The development of an appropriate design which is fit for its intended purpose.
2. To assess the effect the project will have on the environment.

Consequently a well designed coastal structure will, in addition to being fit for the purpose and durable over the period of its design life, also have a minimal or acceptable and predictable impact on the local and wider environment.

Rock is very commonly used as the major, and in some cases the only, construction material for such structures. The extraction, handling and placing of rock together with its quality will have implications which relate to both the objectives given above.

8.3.2. Required rock properties for coastal engineering

Although there are numerous types and designs of coastal defence structures in current use the rock materials from which they are constructed may be categorized into primary armour and underlayers, rip-rap, filter materials and core or fill as described in §8.2.2.

The cores of the great majority of rubble mound breakwaters and similar coastal defence systems are composed of rock fill or quarry run material because of their relative cheapness although it should be noted that the core may represent as much as 50% of the cost of the structure. Usually specifications require the grading of the fill to be controlled with limits on the maximum block size and, owing to the possibility of piping, a limit or exclusion of fine materials below a specified minimum particle size. Removal of fines is usually accomplished at the quarry by screening or using loaders fitted with buckets having grid bases. Other criteria typically specified are bulk density and compliance with appropriate durability and strength tests.

Granular filter layer materials are placed to prevent erosion, scour or migration of fine materials from the core. The design is usually based on the geometric considerations of the packing of particles of specified size such that finer particles beneath cannot migrate through the pore spaces in the overlying filter layer irrespective of the hydraulic loading conditions. The classic rules for filter layers were validated by Terzaghi (1922) and a full treatment of filter media design, requirements and properties is given by Terzaghi & Peck (1964). However, the studies of Terzaghi & Peck relate only to unidirectional flow not the oscillating flow encountered in marine structures. Application of filter rules to real materials under the hydraulic loading conditions prevelent in breakwaters requires various corrections to be taken into account. Extensive testing has been carried out by Pilarczyk (1984) and the practical application of filter design for coastal engineering is discussed in the Manual on the use of rock in coastal and shoreline engineering (CIRIA/CUR 1991). Filter media must also be durable and strong with good load spreading characteristics. Filter media including filters for marine works are reviewed in '*Aggregates*' (Smith & Collis 1993)

The primary armour layers and underlayers are normally closely specified according to the particular design requirements of the structure. However, if very narrow grading limits are specified for the armour layers the majority of the quarry output may then be unsuitable for the project. On the other hand, good practice will ensure that the size distributions and volumes of the materials available for construction are taken into account at the initial design stage.

Extraction of blocks at the quarry inevitably leads to a range of block masses and so the material produced will be graded to a greater or lesser extent. The trend towards the development of standard gradings has already been discussed in §8.2.1. The distribution of block sizes is most easily visualised from the steepness of the cumulative grading curve; the steeper the slope the narrower the size distribution.

Conventionally the overall steepness of the curve is often defined by the W_{85}/W_{15} ratio. Sometimes the cube roots of this value is used to provide an indication of the steepness, which is taken as approximately equivalent to the D_{85}/D_{15} ratio determined from the cumulative curve of the sieve diameters of the sample. New specifications should normally refer to the appropriate standard gradings given in Tables 8.1, 8.2 or 8.3. However, some specifications only indicate the median block mass required for the design. In such cases it is essential that the tolerances of over and undersized blocks allowable in the design are also specified.

Rip-rap is usually applied to material which has a wide grading and usually a relatively low median weight (for example, $W_{50} = 0.3$ tonne). The required properties of such materials are similar to those of armourstone in that the individual blocks should be hard, durable and free from flaws but, because they are likely to be moved about due to wave action, they should also be resistant

Table 8.4. *Typical current requirements and specifications for breakwater and coastal defence structures*

Geometric characteristics	*Range in use*	*Typical specifications*
Primary armour		
Block weight	1–15 tonne	Depends on design
Block shape (L/E)	1.5:1–5:1	3.:1
Grading $(M_{85}/M_{15})^{1/3}$ or (D_{85}/D_{15})*	1.7–2.7	2.5
Incipient flaws (drop test†)	0–5%	5% maximum
Underlayers		
Block weight	3–0.5 tonne	Depends on design
Block shape (L/E)	2:1–4:1	3:1
Grading (D_{85}/D_{15})	1.7–2.7	2.5
Filter layers		
Block size (sieve size D_{50})	300–1 mm	Depends on design
Block shape (B.S. flakiness index)	10–30	30 maximum
Grading (sieve sizes)	Wide, depends on design	10% maximum undersize fines
Core/Fill		
Maximum block size	200–1000 mm	Depends on design
Grading (D_{85}/D_{15})	1.8–2.5	15% fines maximum

* Definition CIRIA/CUR (1991) Notation.
† Drop Test: CIRIA/CUR (1991), Section A2.11, pp. 529.

Table 8.5. *Typical requirements and specifications for breakwater and coastal defence structures, physical, mechanical and durability test characteristics for moderate to severe sea conditions*

Property	*Armour layers*			
	Static	*Dynamic*	*Filters*	*Core*
Relative density	2.5 min	2.5 min	2.5 min	2.5 min
Water absorption (%)	3.0 max	3.0 max	3.0 max	10.0 max
Uniaxial compressive strength (MN/m^2)	100 min	100 min	120 min	100 min
Aggregate crushing value (ACV)	35 max	25 max	30 max	35 max
Aggregate impact value (AIV)	20 max	25 max	30 max	35 max
Aggregate abrasion value (AAV)	20 max	15 max	20 max	35 max
$MgSO_4$ Soundness (%)	15 max	12 max	12 max	30 max
MAV*	0.004 max	0.0013 max	–	–
Micro Deval Test†	20 max	10 max	–	–

* Mill abrasion value, giving the fractional weight loss per 1000 mill revolutions CIRIA/CUR, Section A2.9, pp. 524, (1991).
† AFNOR (1987), LCPC (1989).

to impact damage and abrasive wear. Taking account of the practical difficulties associated with production in the quarry, the US Corps of Engineers (1983) usually specify a grading envelope for rip-rap. They further recommend that the lower limit of the median block size (D_{50}) should be required to withstand the expected shear forces exerted by the currents and that the upper limit of particle size should not exceed five times the lower limit for a given D_{50}. The lower limit of the largest blocks (D_{100}) should not be less than twice the lower limit of the D_{50} stone. They also recommend that the bulk volume of blocks lighter than D_{15} should not exceed the volume of voids present in the layer without this lighter stone.

An indication of some of the more typical values for block masses and sizes commonly used in the construction of rubble mound structures with slope angles in the range 1:2 to 1:3 is given in Table 8.4. Generally slope angles of revetment structures tend to be steeper than those of breakwaters. However, the mass of primary armourstone blocks and consequently of underlayers and other parts of the structure are critically dependent on the local wave climate and the slope angle of the structure so there are many exceptions to the typical values given in Table 8.4.

8.3.3. Design requirements, rock weight and grading

The requirement for rock used in marine structures and particularly as armouring to be both strong and durable is quite clear. However, estimation of the weight of armour blocks can be made from rock density and volume and is critical to the particular design in that the block mass selected for primary armour will control many other aspects of the design. A number of equations have been proposed for estimating armour weight in a given situation.

In concept these equations relate damage levels to significant wave height, wave period, storm duration and the relative density and weight of the armourstone for a particular structure.

As has already been noted, armourstone block sizes are controlled by the natural frequency and spacing of discontinuities (joints and bedding) in the quarry, see §§4.2.3 and 5.3.2.2. The equations clearly indicate the importance of relative density and the block size or weight of the armourstones in resisting damage under wave attack. The interrelation between block size, relative density and mass makes it possible to devise nomograms such as that illustrated in Fig. 8.11 taken from Fookes & Poole (1981) provided the block shape is essentially regular.

Poor quality control over the grading of armourstone is one of the most frequent causes of construction difficulties and contractual disagreements. Even experienced quarry operators may produce stone with an uneven block mass distribution which may fall outside the specified range. Consequently careful quality control procedures should be in place at the quarry. Ideally quality control measures should be in operation:

- at the quarry during production
- during loading/unloading of transport
- before and during placing, see Fig. 8.12.

As already noted, armourstone gradings are normally specified by weight, so nomograms of the type illustrated can form a useful field guide and be satisfactory if the blocks produced have good prismatic shapes (e.g. some well bedded sedimentary rocks). However, quarry operators normally use one or more of the following quality control methods in order to meet specification:

1. Weighed blocks representing upper and lower mass limits, marked with their mass are used as a visual check on production material by the quarry workers.

Design equations

One of the best known of these is the Hudson formula (1958)

$$W = \frac{H^3 w_r}{Kd(Sr-1)^3 \cot\theta}$$

where W is the weight of the armour unit, H is the wave height, w_r is the unit mass of stone, Sr is the specific gravity of armour unit, θ is the armour slope angle and Kd is the stability coefficient (Kd is taken as 3.5 for breaking waves, and 4.0 for non-breaking waves for angular stones in two layers; for a no damage condition).

The most recent edition of the shore protection manual recommends that H is taken as the average of the highest 10% of all waves and that the value of Kd for breaking waves should be revised downward from 3.5 to 2. Some of the other equations are reviewed in a report of the Permanent International Association of Navigational Congresses (1976). However, more recently research taking account of random wave attack has led to Van der Meer (1987) proposing equations for plunging and surging waves which have gained rapid acceptance, though they are more difficult to use because a sensitivity analysis should be performed for all the parameters in the equation to achieve the best design

Plunging waves: $$H_s/\Delta D_{n50} = 6.2P^{0.18}(S/\sqrt{N})^{0.2}\xi_m^{-0.5}$$

Surging waves: $$H_s/\Delta D_{n50} = 1.0P^{-0.13}(S/\sqrt{N})^{0.2}\sqrt{(\cot\alpha)}\xi_m^p.$$

These apply to waves in deep water conditions. Similar equations with different numerical constants (6.2 to 7.7 and 1.0 to 1.4) are appropriate for shallow water conditions. Here H_s is significant wave height at toe of structure (average of the highest $\frac{1}{3}$ of waves), $\xi_m(-)$ is a surf similarity parameter (describes the form of the wave breaking on the structure), α(degrees) is the breakwater slope angle, $\Delta(-)$ is the correction to the armourstone density in sea water, $\Delta = \rho_a/\rho - 1$, $\rho_a(\mathrm{kg/m})^3$ is the mass density of stone or unit, $\rho(\mathrm{kg/m})^3$ is the mass density of water, D_{n50}(m) is the nominal diameter of stone, $D_{n50} = (M_{50}/\rho_a)^{1/3}$, $P(-)$ is the notional permeability coefficient of the structure (normal range is from 0.1 to 0.6, minimum to maximum), $S(-)$ is the damage level (depends upon breakwater slope angle and ranges from 2; no damage, to 17; failure) and $N(-)$ is the number of waves (up to a maximum of 7500 when the structure has reached equilibrium).

2. Blocks are weighed directly with a load cell attached to the handling equipment.
3. Blocks are weighed indirectly on the truck using a weighbridge.
4. Bulk weighing of blocks and calculation of individual mean block weight, see Fig. 8.13.

Estimation of block weight from the volume of the enclosing cuboid and relative density can be corrected by direct weighing and a correction factor calculated. With blocky equant shapes this correction factor often works out in a range around 0.55 (see Gauss & Latham 1995).

Light gradings in the region of 10 to 300 kg are most readily determined indirectly from the bulk weight using a weighbridge and calculating the mean block weight by carefully counting the blocks in the bucket of the loader. Combining this method with a visual assessment of the class limit (CL) ranges of the blocks ELCL (Extreme Lower), LCL (Lower), UCL (Upper) and EUCL (Extreme Upper), see Fig. 8.14, and then weighing of individual stones as a check on the visual assessments will usually provide data sufficient for specification requirements.

Blocks below about 200 mm maximum dimension may be graded by conventional screening methods. The 200 mm limiting size is set by the limitations of the mechanical strength of the grid bars on a typical grizzly.

The relative bulk density of rock is important particularly with respect to the armour layers of a marine structure. In broad terms relative density of rock will range from 3.3 tonnes/m^3 for some ultrabasic dense dark coloured igneous rocks rich in iron to about 2.0 tonnes/m^3 for some porous chalks. Although there are many exceptions bulk densities can be related to rock type as illustrated by Table 8.6.

8.3.4. Durability

Durability is one of the most important characteristics to be considered when selecting rock for use in a

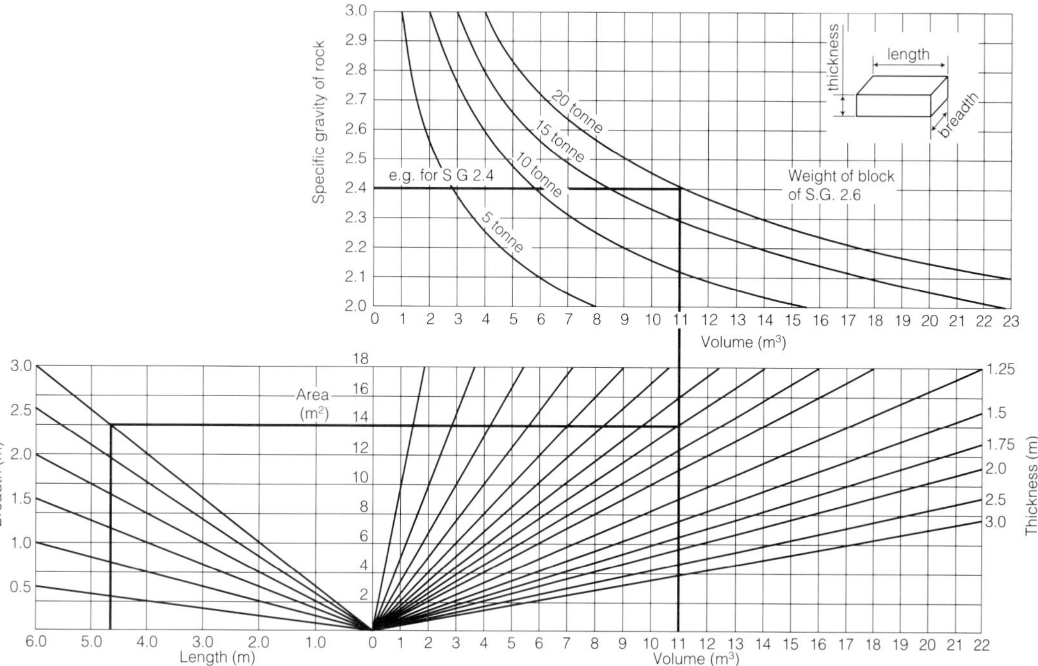

Fig. 8.11. Nomograms for field use, relating relative density, block shape and rock volume to rock mass for prismatic block shapes. The dashed line gives an example of a 20 tonne block (Fookes & Poole 1981).

marine environment. In this context, durability may be defined as the ability of a rock to retain its physical and mechanical properties while resisting degradation in engineering service.

The marine environment is exceptional in that wave action, particularly during storm conditions can exert very large transient mechanical and hydraulic forces on engineering structures and will also subject the materials within the tidal and supratidal zones to cycles of wetting and drying with salt crystallization and redissolution.

Thus, for rock armoured structures the individual blocks may be subjected to movement leading to fracture, abrasion from blocks moving against each other, attrition from wave born shingle or sand and spalling of surface layers due to wetting/drying or salt crystallisation/solution cycles. These aggressive agencies are most severe along the intertidal zone of the structure and are most effective at degrading the rock if it has suffered geological weathering, see §2.4, hydrothermal alteration or is cut by incipient fracture planes, see §2.3.

Both geological weathering and hydrothermal alteration of existing rock can result in alteration to some or all of the minerals it contains and may also cause incipient fractures to develop. Many reviews and discussions of the effects of weathering on the engineering properties of rocks have been published, for example Dearman (1974), Ollier (1975), Fookes & Poole (1981), Fookes (1991) and Price (1995). A brief review of weathering is also given in §2.4 of this book.

Durability or resistance to wear or deterioration is also of importance for rock aggregates. In §7.5.4 of the working party report, '*Aggregates*' (Smith & Collis 1993) methods of testing rock aggregates are reviewed and separated into tests for mechanical deterioration or wear and physico-chemically activated deterioration.

Rock used in armouring a marine structure requires testing to demonstrate its fitness for purpose and consequently a number of the standard test procedures for aggregates have also been applied to rock for marine use. The most commonly used of these aggregate tests which relate to durability include the determination of water absorption, sulphate soundness, freeze–thaw and crushing strength tests. A brief discussion of the applicability and interpretation of these and other tests are given in §8.5. As the use of rock and particularly armourstone for coastal structures has increased considerably in recent years, special tests for armourstone have been proposed and are now sometimes required by the specification. These special tests are also briefly reviewed in §8.5 but the practical details of the methods are given more fully in the text and in Appendix 2 of the

Fig. 8.12. Individually weighed 0.3 tonne granite armourstone blocks, rejected by quality control inspector because of poor shape or incipient flaws.

Manual on the use of rock in coastal and shoreline engineering (CIRIA/CUR 1991).

8.4 Extraction, processing and placing

8.4.1. Introduction

It has already been noted in §§5 and 6 that the extraction of large blocks for dimension stone and armour is significantly different from the quarrying methods used for the production of fragmented rock for aggregates.

As already indicated in §§4.2.3.2 and 8.1.4 the fundamental limitation on maximum block size depends on the discontinuity spacings in the rock mass being quarried. In practice, quarried stone blocks rarely exceed 10 tonnes and the proportion of large blocks in 'as blasted' material is often quite low, typically of the order of 5% or less of the output although this figure can sometimes be improved by careful blast design.

8.4.2. Quarry production

There are very few quarries which are dedicated to the production of armourstone blocks only. The two principal sources of armourstones are aggregate quarries which set aside and stockpile large size blocks during the course of extraction and production, and dimension-stone quarries which may also stockpile armourstone

Fig. 8.13. Loading of armourstone blocks into a truck for bulk weighing.

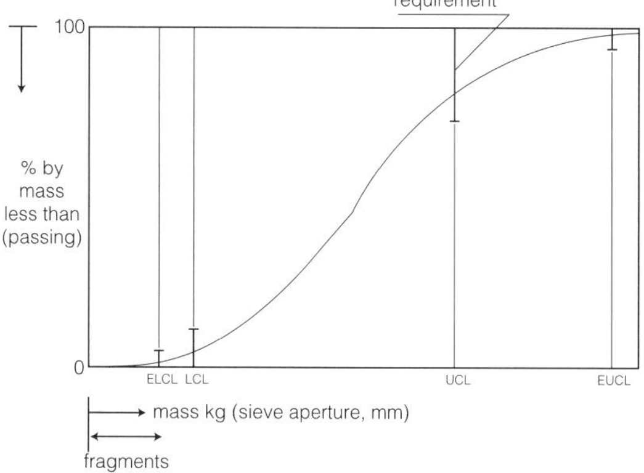

Fig. 8.14. Class limits of coarse, light and heavy gradings (CEN Draft Standard 1996).

blocks which are blocks found to be unsuitable for cutting. In some cases temporary dedicated quarries are opened local to the construction site to supply the materials for a particular project though the maximum block sizes obtainable will be dependent on the geological characteristics of the source. Where large blocks are scattered over a land surface, for example in glaciated regions, these are sometimes gathered up and used as armouring. However, in many such cases it is difficult to obtain a sufficient quantity of large blocks and often the individual stones are rounded and difficult to 'lock into' the armour layer.

Blast design in aggregate producing quarries maximizes fragmentation of the quarry rock into usable sizes for crushing and screening with oversize and undersize material minimised. With careful evaluation of discontinuity spacing and adaptation of the blast design (CIRIA/CUR 1991), the yield of top size material may be increased by two or three fold. The three factors affecting the size and proportion of armourstone obtainable from a given quarry are:

1. The geological characteristics of the rock.
2. The properties of the explosives and the detonation methods used.
3. The blast design.

The geological characteristics and block size have already been discussed in relation to discontinuity spacing, see §8.2 and 2.3, and degree of weathering, see §2.4, but strength, elasticity, density, porosity and permeability are all characteristics of the rock which will modify its behaviour during blasting.

There are many studies of blasting and rock fragmentation, such as those of Bergman *et al.* (1974, 1983). Armourstone production is discussed by Wang *et al.* (1991) and is also addressed in §§5.3.3 and 5.3.8.

In general terms blast design for high armourstone yields contrasts with high fragmentation blasting as follows:

1. Low specific charge and explosives should have low shock energy and higher gas energy.
2. Large burden and small hole spacing, spacing to burden ratio 1 or less.
3. Bench height 2 to 3 times burden.

Table 8.6. *Typical dry bulk densities for some common rocks used in marine structures*

Rock type	*Mean value* (t/m^3)	*Typical range* (t/m^3)	*Notes*
Igneous rocks			
Granites	2.66	2.6–2.8	
Syenites	2.70	2.6–2.9	
Gabbros	2.95	2.8–3.4	
Eclogite	3.38	3.3–3.6	
Dolerites	2.89	2.6–3.2	
Basalts	2.74	2.7–3.0	vesicular varieties have lower values
Andesites	2.65	2.5–2.9	
Sedimentary rocks			
Quartzites	2.64	2.6–2.7	
Sandstones	2.40	2.0–2.8	excluding porous soft sandstones
Greywackes	2.68	2.6–2.7	
Limestones	2.40	2.2–2.6	excluding porous chalks
Metamorphic rocks			
Granite gneisses	2.65	2.5–2.8	
Schists	2.80	2.6–3.2	
Slates	2.78	2.7–2.8	

Figures from Carmichael (1982) and other sources.

4. Stemming length large usually larger than the burden.
5. Small blast hole diameter typically 50 or 75 mm.
6. Single row blast hole design.
7. Holes should be fired instantaneously rather than with delays.
8. High concentration bottom charge, low concentration column charge.
9. A small primer located centrally.

8.4.3. Handling and transportation

Oversize stone blocks may be reduced by splitting using methods similar to those described in §5.3.9. The selection of blocks of appropriate size is generally done by eye in the first instance by the machine operator who may use a variety of simple rules of thumb to judge the size.

A variety of handling equipment exists for selecting, moving and transporting the stone. These are discussed briefly in §5.3.9 of this book and more fully in Section 3.4.2 of the CIRIA/CUR Manual (1991). With the development of super quarries in Scandinavia, increasing use is made of barge transportation by sea. Barges with capacities up to 3000 tonnes or drive on drive off pontoons with capacities of up to 20 000 tonnes are used, see Figs 8.15 and 8.16. Methods for the safe loading and unloading of these vessels range from crane mounted grabs to on-board machines capable of moving the blocks across the decks.

Although road transport has the advantage of flexibility, see Fig. 8.17, it is typically much more costly than sea transport. Road transport of materials during construction can be very intensive and environmentally disruptive causing excessive noise, possible damage to property and risk to other road users. This has led to prohibition of road transport of rock in a number of districts in the UK. However, the large quantities of material carried by barges can increase unloading and handling costs on-site and bad weather can cause unexpected delays in delivery and unloading, Fig. 8.18.

8.4.4. Placing

Static rubble mound armoured structures need to be constructed so that individual blocks in the armour layers interlock to produce a stable structure able to resist movement by wave attack. However, it is also necessary to retain a high macro-permeability in the armour layer as the turbulence created in the voids between armourstone blocks is the principal dissipating mechanism for the wave energies.

The detailed method of placement of armour layers and the general construction of breakwaters and similar structures are determined by the particular structural design, its precise function and the local marine conditions. However, the methods used can be divided into land-based and water-borne operations each with its own advantages and disadvantages.

Fig. 8.15. Example of a side loading armourstone carrier.

Fig. 8.16. Loading of an armourstone carrying barge, Scandinavia (photography courtesy of J.-P. Latham).

Fig. 8.17. Loading 0.75 to 3 tonne armour blocks for transportation overland.

With land-based operations, the crest width, elevation, the angle of slopes and width of berms and aprons are constrained by the dimensions of the trucks and cranes and the reach of the cranes, see Fig. 8.19. The work front is usually small and centred around the position of the crane(s) so the various construction phases follow rapidly on each other. By contrast waterborne operation require a minimum depth of about 3 m below

Fig. 8.18. Barge unloading armourstone for the construction of off-shore breakwaters (photograph courtesy of R. Trayner, Arun District Council).

low water. The crest elevation and size of the structure is determined by the hydraulic constraints on the design. The work front is usually large to allow space for barges and shipping to manoeuvre and anchor. A loading terminal for barges is required before construction can start but the work front is not constrained and work can be initiated and proceed at several locations. With land-based operations, an existing road system can be used for transport from quarry to the site but supplies of materials must be transported over the breakwater to the construction front. Typically the placing of individual armourstones to interlock satisfactorily into the armour layer is more accurately carried out using a land based crane or hydraulic grab, see Figs 8.20 and 8.21. Accurate positioning of block below water introduces additional problems, involving special positioning systems and monitoring with divers or underwater camera systems.

Although static primary and secondary armour layers are normally placed as individual blocks with care being

Fig. 8.19. Crestline roadway allowing access for transport and equipment.

Fig. 8.20. Claw grab crane placing armourstone, Dibba Harbour.

taken to achieve a minimum of three point stable support and to ensure that specified surface profiles and slope angles are obtained, core material, rip rap and materials for dynamically stable structures are normally dumped in bulk. Care is taken to minimize disturbance to material already placed and to minimize segregation of grading. Consideration must also be given to the risk of damage during the construction either by the construction equipment or from storms occurring before the structure is fully armoured.

8.5. Testing and evaluation

The reasons for testing rock materials for use in marine structures may be itemised as follows:

Fig. 8.21. Hydraulic claw grab placing armourstone on the Dawlish Warren coastal defence.

1. To assess the quality (fitness for purpose) of the rock.
2. To assess variability from a given source.
3. To compare the quality of material from two or more sources.
4. To assess the variability of material supplied.
5. To predict in-service performance and durability.
6. To check compliance with specification.

As has already been noted in §8.3.4 a number of the tests applied to armour and other rock materials to be used in a marine environment were designed for use in assessing rock aggregates. Some of these tests are equally applicable to rock for marine structures while others require careful interpretation. The special aspects and requirements of marine environments, especially in the case of armour rock has led to the development of special tests for rock materials to be used in marine application. A brief summary of appropriate test methods is given below. A more comprehensive and detailed account appears in Section 3.3 of the CIRIA/CUR Manual (1991) and in CEN drafts for comment, CEN (1996). Precise information concerning particular test methods are given in the appropriate national standards or original references.

8.5.1. Petrography

Methods of petrographic examination are described in various national standards such as ASTM C295 (1985) which are applicable to aggregate materials. Rock armour and similar materials require a petrographic examination which is broad in scope which will recognize and quantify the variability of the material, identify flaws and potential planes of weakness and the degree of weathering as well as identifying the rock type. The Methylene Blue staining test (Stewart & McCullogh 1985), (Hills & Pettifer 1985) and (ASTM C837, 1988) is carried out on 10 to 14 mm crushed rock and provides information concerning clay mineral contents. Alternatively, examination of petrographic thin sections and the use of x-ray powder diffraction techniques can provide more detailed information relating to the degree of weathering of particular rock samples. The CIRIA/CUR Manual recommends the methylene blue test as suggested by the International Society for Rock Mechanics (ISRM) (Brown 1981) and also the index ratio of sound to unsound constituents (Irfan & Dearman 1978).

An excellent detailed methodology for selecting sample materials to be used for armourstone is given in the CEN Draft Standard (1996) which covers selection and sample reduction methods both at the production and delivery points and also provides a series of clear definitions. An up to date summary of test methods applicable to armourstone is also given by Latham (1996).

8.5.2. Size, shape and grading

Grading of small sizes is normally carried out by sieving after washing. The methods described in BS 812 are appropriate for particles of 75 mm downwards allowing a cumulative grading distribution curve of percentage by mass passing the sieve sizes to be calculated. Larger sizes can damage the test sieves but sizes between 31.5 and 200 mm nominal diameter may also be graded by using specially designed sieves. A satisfactory method is based on the Dutch draft standard NEN 5181 (1988). Details of the method and the calculation of the cumulative size distribution curve is described in the CIRIA/CUR Manual, Appendix 2.1.

In the determination of gradings for quarried stone blocks with mass greater than 25 kg, the blocks are either weighed individually, or individual masses are calculated by indirect methods such as bulk weighting, see §8.3.3. The CEN draft standard recommends that test samples should comprise of a minimum number of individual stones as indicated in Table 8.7, which outlines two alternative methods for determining the cumulative grading curve in terms of weight.

Particle shape of fine gradings below 200 mm may be determined by standard methods appropriate to aggregates. A good equidimensional approximately cubical shape is preferred for filter and core materials and may form part of the specification. BS 812 provides two standard methods which give indices which measure departure from equidimensional shapes. The first of these is the Flakiness Index, BS 812 (1989) which gives the weight percentage of particles whose minimum dimension is less than 0.6 times its mean dimension. The mean dimension is the arithmetic mean of the side dimension of the limiting square hole sieve sizes. Thus the mean dimension would be 12 mm for a 10–14 mm aggregate. The minimum sample size is 200 particles and the method is only applicable to gradings over 6.3 mm.

Table 8.7. *Number of stones in test portions*

Standard grading	*Minimum number of stones heavier than fragments*
10 000–15 000 kg	25
6 000–10 000 kg	30
3 000– 6 000 kg	60
1 000– 3 000 kg	90
300– 1 000 kg	140
Light grading	200

The second is the Elongation Index. This is the weight percentage of particles whose long dimension is greater than 1.8 times the mean dimension. A good review of shape classification is given in §7.5.1 of '*Aggregates*' (Smith & Collis 1993).

Tests that are available for characterizing the shape of larger particles in the 'light' and 'heavy gradings' that are used for rip-rap and primary and secondary armouring include the method described in Annex E of the CEN Draft Standard (1996) were L and E are measured on the number of blocks as indicated in Table 8.7. This method is based on an earlier Dutch test method (NEN 5182) described in CIRIA/CUR (1991) which requires measurement of a minimum of 50 blocks. In both cases the number of stones with L : E or l : d ratios greater than 3 are reported.

8.5.3. Density and water absorption

The relative density of rock used in marine structures is a most important parameter and is an essential test for all gradings. Water absorption is normally determined at the same time as relative density and is important because of its relationship with the durability characteristics of the rock.

Numerous national standard test methods are available, for example BS 812 and ASTM C127-84. These test procedures use distilled water and small corrections are required when considering relative density with respect to sea water (density 1030 kg/m^3). Variation between the various test methods is often negligible for similar sized test pieces, so that any appropriate method may be used for design purposes. However, for durability evaluation, differences in method may be significant and the definition of density must be established. Latham (1996) suggests that measurements should be made on at least ten representative cores or lumps for each homogenous rock source.

8.5.4. Strength related tests

Rock used in marine structures and particularly rock armour blocks must resist breakage and fracture while being handled and while in service. Some rock types, particularly if they are weathered, are profoundly weakened on immersion in sea water so that testing of breakage should be carried out on saturated samples to simulate inservice conditions.

A variety of *in situ* and laboratory tests are available and range from direct determination of uniaxial compressive strength to indirect methods such as sonic velocity measurements. The tests in common use and referred to in specifications are summarised below. If a more detailed account is required reference should be made to the CIRIA/CUR Manual, Latham (1996) and to the appropriate national standards.

8.5.4.1. Block Integrity Drop Test
This test checks an individual block or a stockpile of armour blocks for the possibility of hidden flaws or planes of weakness in order to predict breakage during handling and while in service.

The test is based on dropping 50 blocks through a distance of 3 m onto a platform built of blocks of similar grading and of the same rock type, see Fig. 8.22. A breakage index is calculated from the median sample weight before the test (Wi) minus the median weight after test (Wf) divided by the original median weight i.e.

$$\text{Breakage Index} = \frac{Wi - Wf}{Wi} \times 100$$

8.5.4.2. Fracture toughness (K_{Ic})
Uniaxial compressive strength of intact rock can be determined on cut cylindrical rock specimens and gives a value for the crushing strength but is rarely required as other tests which more closely simulate the marine working conditions are considered to be more appropriate. As tensile fracture is one of the principal forms of damage associated with armourstone the determination of fracture toughness (K_{Ic}) (the ease with which a crack will propagate through the mineral fabric starting from an existing flaw in the rock) provides a useful indication of a rock's potential for fracturing.

A satisfactory test procedure is described by ISRM (1988) which uses a cylindrical cut specimen of rock which has a chevron shaped slot cut across the diameter at one end. The fracture toughness is calculated from the force exerted perpendicular to the cylinder to split the specimen into two halves at the slot.

8.5.4.3. Point load strength
In many respects the point load strength index is an excellent method of assessing mineral fabric strength. The method uses a hand operated hydraulic jack mounted in a rigid frame to split rock samples between a pair of conical plattens. The details of method are described by ISRM (1985) but more recent work (Latham 1996) suggests that for evaluation of armourstone at least 12 samples from at least ten randomly selected armourstone blocks should be used and that the highest and lowest results from the set should be excluded when calculating the average strength. With anisotropic rock the strength parallel to the plane of weakness is the value to be reported.

The apparatus is portable and specimen testing is rapid so it is a simple and convenient tool for field use for the rapid assessment of a potential quarry source of armourstone and for quality control. However, although it may be used on irregular rock samples the results obtained should not be considered as precise as those obtained from a series of uniformly cut blocks or cylindrical samples.

8.5.4.4. Aggregate impact strength tests
Impact resistance is an important consideration for large rock blocks during handling and placement, and also

Fig. 8.22. Example of a drop test in an Omani quarry.

if they are subject to movement while in service. Standard aggregate tests are commonly used to assess this characteristic. The aggregate impact value, BS 812 and variants of it are the most commonly specified tests. The AIV is determined by dropping a 14 kg weight through 381 mm onto an aggregate sample contained in a steel cup. The amount of crushed material passing a 2.36 mm sieve after 15 blows is determined. This provides an indication of the sample aggregate's resistance to impact damage. A wet dynamic crushing test method based upon a Dutch standard is described in Appendix A2.5 of the CIRIA/CUR Manual (1991). It is similar to but improves on the relevance of the BS method to armourstone by controlling the shape of the test aggregate, removing flaky particles and testing the aggregate in a saturated condition.

However, coarse grained rocks can give high test results which do not necessarily imply that the rock will be unsatisfactory in service. Thus, crushing tests should be interpreted with care with attention being given to the grain/crystal size and to the standardisation of the aggregate test samples.

8.5.4.5 Resistance to abrasion

Abrasion resistance values can be interpreted to give an indication of how quickly a rock will wear and become rounded through abrasion from water-borne sand and shingle or through movement on a dynamically stable structure. A number of tests are specified several of which were designed for testing the abrasion characteristics of road stones such as the aggregate abrasion test or the Los Angeles test. These tests are not ideal as simulations of the abrasive wear experienced by rock in marine structures and in recent studies new tests have been designed and are gaining acceptance. These tests include the French wet micro Deval test, LCPC (1989) which simulates rock to rock surface grinding, but has been criticised on the grounds of poor reproducibility and discrimination between samples. The QMW mill abrasion test, CIRIA/CUR, Appendix 2 (1991) which rolls specimen blocks against each other in a water flow which constantly removes fine material, gives good discrimination between samples. Finally, in the Sandblast test (Verhoef 1987) the sample is abraded in an air blast containing quartz sand particles. This gives good discrimination between relatively weak rocks but is not so satisfactory for very hard, strong rocks.

8.5.4.6. Sonic velocity

There is considerable interest in using sonic and ultrasonic sound wave propagation through large rock samples to evaluate the intact strength of the rock and detect incipient flaws. Sonic methods have been the subject of much research, e.g. Dearman *et al.* (1987). The methods are very sensitive to degree of saturation and test specimens require careful preparation. Although research continues, it is potentially a valuable technique for assessing microfractures and is already used by the Laboratoire Central des Ponts et Chaussees (LCPC) in France to give an 'Index of Continuity' for microfractured rock.

8.5.5. Durability tests

The requirement for rock which will be durable in a marine environment has been discussed in §8.3.4. The most commonly used tests are either the ASTM C88, BS 812, part 121 (1989) sulphate soundness tests or variations on them. These methods involve test samples of aggregate being subjected to cycles of immersion in a magnesium or sodium sulphate solution followed by oven drying. Repeated crystallization of a range of salt hydrates and their dissolution set up bursting pressures in pores and microcracks within the rock leading to its disaggregation. The degradation weight loss measured after five cycles of soaking and drying gives the soundness value for the rock. This test causes a more severe degradation than similar tests carried out using a sodium chloride solution. This is because sodium chloride does not form hydrates on crystallization as does sodium and magnesium sulphate.

In temperate and cold climatic conditions resistance to freezing and thawing cycles may require evaluation. The method suggested in the CIRIA/CUR Manual is developed from German and Dutch standards and subjects at least 20 blocks with a minimum mass of 10 kg to 25 freeze–thaw cycles. A 0.5% weight loss in more than one piece or the development of open cracks is taken as failure to resist freeze–thaw.

A particular problem encountered in Holland with imported alkaline basalt is a deterioration referred to as 'Sonnenbrand' (sunburn) which is usually attributed to the transformation of nepheline and possibly albite into analcite during the solidification of the rock. These changes lead to internal stresses which with alternating heating and cooling cause the rock to degrade. The recommended test involves boiling cut slices of the basalt for 36 hours in distilled water which are then allowed to dry. On remoistening the cut surfaces with a damp cloth, star shaped spots with radiating hair cracks are indicative of basalts likely to be subject to this type of degradation.

8.5.6. Field tests

A number of the test methods outlined above make use of equipment which is sufficiently portable to be used in the field or on-site. Dealing with the determination of grading by weighing large blocks in the heavy and light grading categories requires heavy equipment normally only available at the quarry or construction site. The drop test is also only appropriate for quarry or site use.

Other tests, which may be undertaken either in the laboratory or in the field, include the density and water absorption determinations, the point load strength index test, the AIV test and parts of the petrographic investigation. In particular the petrographic variation between armour blocks or across the face of a quarry can only be assessed onsite, though the petrographer may need to select samples for more detailed laboratory study.

Hardness of rocks may also be measured directly in the field using the Schmidt impact hammer test which is used to determine the Schmidt Rebound Hardness value. This hand held device measures the rebound of a spring loaded hammer after striking the rock surface. The result is influenced by the surface preparation of the rock and by cracks or cavities close to the site where the hammer strikes the surface. Usually the mean reading of a number of replicate readings is taken. Several versions of the test device are available with hammers covering a range of energy release values. Type 'L' is appropriate for most fresh igneous rocks.

8.6. Specifications

Many aspects of specification for quarried rock for use in marine structures will be site and design specific. The economic consideration of developing a particular design to incorporate as much of the source quarry output as possible with minimum wastage is becoming increasingly important for modern projects. Some guidance relating to specification is given in the revision of draft of BS 6349 (British Standards, 1997) but the more general aspects of specification and typical values or ranges of values for tests are summarised below and in Table 8.5.

8.6.1. Gradings

The requirements for particular gradings will depend upon the design requirement and availability, but all heavy and light gradings are classified by weight with appropriate class limits set as indicated in §8.3. Coarse gradings are usually defined in terms of minimum and maximum acceptable proportions of the total weight which will pass through standard sieve sizes.

8.6.2. Shape

The heavy and light gradings will be specified in terms of the L/E ratio with a specific limitation (usually $\leq 5\%$) on the percentage of blocks with a L/E value greater than 3.

8.6.3. Density and water absorption

A minimum rock density is usually specified with limits of acceptance for example, an average density of 2600 kg/m^3 with 90% of blocks with densities greater

Failure of breakwater, St Paul's Island, Alaska

A case history of a breakwater design, failure and modification has been presented by Weckmann & Watts (1988) and relates to a shore connected harbour breakwater at St Pauls Island, Alaska. The original design of this 610 m long rubble mound breakwater followed a conventional three layer system consisting of a graded quarry rock core with two layers of 8–17 tonne armourstone on the seaward side at a slope of 1 on 2.5. The head section had a slope of 1 on 3 and was to be 17–24 tonne stone. The authors showed a typical cross section, see Fig. 8.23. Difficulties in obtaining armour blocks of these sizes necessitated a modification of the design to a berm breakwater concept which in theory was to maximize the use of all stone sizes produced at the quarry. This design used 0.75–8 tonne stone for the outer layer with a median size of 1.5 tonnes, for most of the 18 m wide berm on the seaward side. A core section was also designed into the berm, see Fig. 8.23. A length of 265 m with a maximum crest height of 8.5 m above MLLW was constructed and completed in October 1984.

Substantial damage resulted from two winter storms of 1984 which generated waves up to 9 m high with a period of 16 seconds. Approximately 150 m of crest and 100 m at the water line of the armour layers were lost as a consequence of these storms and material from the head section was transported into the harbour area during these storms producing reef-like mounds. Breaching of the breakwater trunk was also observed during the first and most severe December storm.

Following the damage of 1984 the breakwater was redesigned to include a 60 m concrete dock. The new design was selected for 7.6 m breaking waves and this required armourstone of 14 tonnes on the trunk and 18 tonnes on the head section of the breakwater with slopes of 1 on 2.5 and 1 on 3 respectively. The crest was also raised to 11.3 m above MLLW. This new breakwater was completed by January 1986. Although subjected to several periods of severe storm between 1986 and 88 no significant displacement of armourstone has been observed and hydraulic model tests have indicated that the slope could in fact be steepened to 1 on 2 along the seaward face provided 18 tonne armourstone was used.

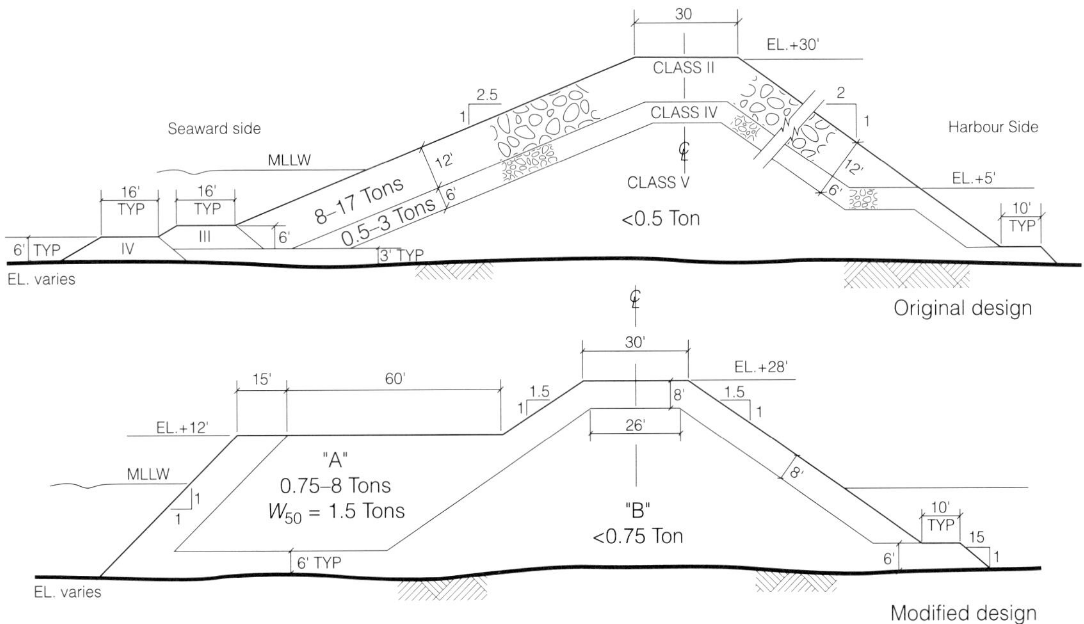

Fig. 8.23. Cross section of the St Pauls Island harbour breakwater.

than 2500 kg/m^3 is typical. Water absorption is an indicator of rock durability. The limit for water absorption is usually 3% or less though this value may have to be relaxed in exceptional circumstances where only marginal quality rock is available.

8.6.4. Durability

In addition to water absorption values specifications aimed at ensuring good durability characteristics may include a statement that deleterious secondary minerals shall not be present and that a magnesium sulphate soundness or similar test must not exceed a certain maximum value (the CIRIA/CUR Manual suggests magnesium sulphate soundness values of less than 2% for rock of excellent quality, less than 12% for good quality and less than 30% for rocks of marginal quality). With the CIRIA/CUR freeze/thaw test, weight loss must be less than 0.5% for good quality and less than 2% for marginal quality material. There may be additional requirements relating to absence of visible cracks in the specimens after testing.

8.6.5. Block integrity

Armour blocks should be free of visible cracks, planes of weakness, voids or other flaws which could lead to breakage during handling. A low drop test breakage index may also be specified, for example less than 2 or 5%, though there is little practical experience to support these values at the present time. Latham (1996) suggests that specifications which include a drop test should ideally be coupled with appropriate sonic velocity surveys before and after the blocks are dropped.

8.6.6. Impact resistance

Specifications may include limiting values for the aggregate impact test or similar dynamic crushing test such as described in Section A2.5 of the CIRIA/CUR Manual. In this test the aggregate samples are water saturated and it is recommended that materials exhibiting values of less than 30% are marginal and those giving less than 20% are good quality rock. However, these figures are currently the subject of debate because coarse grained igneous rocks of excellent quality sometimes give high results.

An average point load index carried out in accordance with the ISRM (1986) method provides an alternative method of assessment. It is suggested that rocks of marginal quality will have a value of at least 4.0 MPa while good quality material should exceed 40 MPa.

Fracture toughness testing is not widely used because of its expense and the specialist nature of sample preparation and test apparatus. However, it is an excellent test, with good repeatability for assessing performance with respect to corner breakage and loss of angularity. The CIRIA/CUR, Appendix A1 (1991) suggest values of 0.8 MPa m$^{1/2}$ and 1.4 MPa m$^{1/2}$ as minimum values for marginal and good quality armourstones respectively.

Example of a coastal defence specification

An outline of the specification for Phases 2 and 2a of the Morecambe Bay Coastal defence works given to quarry contractors has been published by Clark (1992).

Total materials requirement:

Core fill	5400 tonnes
Bed stone	24 400 tonnes
Armourstone	71 000 tonnes
Total	100 800 tonnes

Armourstone gradings:

% Mass	Mass (tonnes)	Diameter (metres)
85	3.5	1.09(D_{85})
50	2.0	0.90(D_{50})
15	0.7	0.64(D_{15})

(The maximum and minimum masses of any individual block shall be 0.5 t and 5.0 t respectively).

The stone used (limestone) should be of suitable angular shape, dimension and mass, hard and durable, sound and free from laminations, weak cleavage planes and undesirable weathering; and should be of such a character that it will not disintegrate or erode from the action of air, water, salts, wetting and drying, freezing and thawing or impact due to wave action. It shall also be capable of being handled and placed without undue fracture or damage.

Representative samples of at least 100 tonnes shall conform with the above specification to within ±10%.

The contractor shall ensure that the stone brought to site complies with the above grading to within 10% by adopting the following procedures.

(a) The weight of the individual rocks with the exception of Category D (0.7 tonnes) shall be measured at the source by a suitable loading machine fitted with an approved weight measuring device which shall be calibrated every 5000 tonnes loaded or monthly whichever is the sooner. The Contractor shall supply the Engineer with copies of all the calibration certificates pertaining.

(b) Every load of stone delivered to site shall consist of stones of weight that fall into one of the categories shown below with the ratio of loads and nominal number of mean weight blocks per load as shown in the following table. Representative samples of at least 100 tonnes shall conform with the above specification to within ±10%.

Category	Mass	% By weight	Load ratio	Nominal no. of mean weight blocks per load*
A	$>M_{85}$	15	1	4
B	M_{50}–M_{85}	35	2	7
C	M_{15}–M_{50}	35	2	13
D	$<M_{15}$	15	1	30

* This figure is based on load weight of approximately 18 tonnes.

The bedstone shall satisfy the following gradings:

% Passing by weight	Equivalent sieve size (metres)
85(D_{85})	0.35
50(D_{50})	0.25
15(D_{15})	0.15

The maximum and minimum equivalent sieve size of bedstone shall be 0.40 and 0.10 metres respectively. The core stone shall be natural stone with nominal sizes ranging from 1 mm to 150 mm with no stones retained on a 200 mm sieve.

8.6.7. Abrasion Resistance

Resistance to abrasion may be specified by limiting values obtained from a variety of test methods. The aggregate abrasion value (BS 812) will give values better than 5 for good quality igneous rock but may range up to 10 for good quality Carboniferous limestone. Modern specifications favour abrasion mill values using the micro Deval test or the QMW Mill Abrasion test. Recommendations from this last test suggest that the abrasion index should be less than 0.002 for rock of excellent quality; less than 0.004 for good quality and less than 0.015 for marginal materials.

8.7. Case histories of coastal protection projects

8.7.1. St Paul's Island, Alaska (see text box on p. 323)

8.7.2. Morecambe Bay, England (see text box on p. 324)

References

AFNOR 1978. L'association Francaise de normalisation (AFNOR pp. 18572), *Essai d'usure micro-Deval.*

American Society for Testing and Materials 1963. Standard C88, *Soundness of aggregates by use of sodium sulphate or magnesium sulphate.*

——1984. Standard C127-84, *Specific Gravity and Absorption of Fine Aggregate.*

——1985. Standard C295-85, *Standard Practice for Petrographic Examination of Aggregates for Concrete*, Philadelphia, USA.

——1988. Standard C837, *Methylene Blue Index for Clay Test.*

Bell, A. K. 1984. Figure 11, 85 Discussion contribution. *Breakwaters Design and Construction.* Thomas Telford, London.

Bergman, F. C. 1983. Effects of explosives properties, rock type and delays on fragmentation in large model blasts. *In*: Holmberg, R. & Rustan, A. (eds) *1st International Symposium on Rock Fragmentation in Blasting.* National Swedish Board for Technical Development, 71–74.

——, Wu, R. C. & Edi, U. W. 1974. Model rock blasting measures effects of delays and hole patterns on rock fragmentation. *Engineering Mining Journal*, Mining Guidebook Systems for Emerging Technology June 1974, McGraw-Hill, New York, 124–127.

Bradbury, A. P., Latham, J.-P. & Allsop, N. W. H. 1990. Rock armour stability formulae – influence of stone shape and layer thickness. *Proc. 22nd Int. Coastal Engng Conference.* American Society of Civil Engineers.

Brown, E. T. 1981. *Rock Characterisation Testing and Monitoring ISRM Suggested Methods*, Pergamon, Oxford.

British Standards Institution 1975. BS 812, PART 1: *Methods for Sampling and Testing of Mineral Aggregates, Sands and Fillers.* BSI, London.

——1989. BS 812, SECTION 105.1: *Flakiness Index.* BSI, London.

——1984. BS 1200: *Specification for Building Sands from Natural Sources – Sands for Mortars for Bricklaying*, BSI, London.

British Standards Institution 1989. BS 812 Part 121. *Method for Determination of Soundness.* BSI, London.

——1997. BS 6349: Draft revision of BS 6349: part 1, *Maritime Structures, Part 1 Code of Practice for General Criteria*, BSI, London.

Carmichael, R. R. (ed.) 1982. *Handbook of Physical Properties of Rocks*, Vol II. CRC Press, Florida USA, pp. 1–345.

CEN European Standard E383 1996. *Draft European Standard E383* as submitted to CEN members March 1996.

CIRIA/CUR 1991. *Manual on the Use of Rock in Coastal and Shoreline Engineering*, CIRIA Special Publication 83, CUR Report 154, London.

CIRIA 1996. *Beach Recharge Materials – Demand and Resources.* CIRIA Report R154.

Clark, G. 1992. Material production from aggregate quarries for Phase 2 and phase 2a of the Morecambe Bay coastal defence works *In*: Latham, J.-P. (ed.) *Report on the Proceedings of the Seminar on Armourstone.* Queen Mary and Westfield College, London University, 135–144.

Dearman, W. R. 1974. Weathering classification in the characterisation of rocks for engineering purposes in British practice. *Bull. Int. Assoc. of Eng. Geol.*, **9**, 33–42.

——, Turk, N., Irfan, Y. & Rowshanei, H. 1987. Detection of rock material variation by sonic velocity zoning. *Bull. Int. Assoc. of Eng. Geol.*, **35**, 1–8.

EC Directive 85/337 1985. *On the assessment of certain public and private projects on the environment.*

Fookes, P. G. 1991. Geomaterials. *Quarterly Journal of Engineering Geology*, **24**, 3–15.

Fookes, P. G. & Poole, A. B. 1981. Some preliminary considerations on the selection and durability of rock and concrete materials for breakwaters and coastal protection works. *Quarterly Journal of Engineering Geology*, **14**, 97–128.

Fowler, P. & Earle, Q. 1990. The Hong Kong quarrying industry 1992–2000, A decade of change. *Proceedings of a seminar, Hong Kong Branch Institute of Quarrying.*

Franklin, J. A., Broch, E. & Walton, G. 1971. Logging the mechanical character of rock. *Trans. Inst. Min. Metall.* (Section A: Minerals Industry), **80A**, 1–9.

Gauss, G. A. & Latham, J.-P. 1995. The drop test for armourstone integrity. *In*: Thorne, C. R. *et al.* (eds) *River, Coastal and Shoreline Protection.* Wiley, Chichester, 481–499.

Hills, J. F. & Pettifer, G. S. 1985. The clay mineral content of various rock types compared with the methylene blue value. *J. Chem. Tech. and Biotech.*, **35A**, 4, 168–180.

Hudson, R. N. 1958. *Design of Quarry-stone cover layers for rubble mound breakwaters*, US Corps of Engineers, W.E.S. Research Report 2-2.

Institution of Civil Engineers (ICE) 1988. *Design of Breakwaters, Proceedings of the Eastbourne Conference 1988.* Thomas Telford, London.

International Society of Rock Mechanics (ISRM) 1985. Commission on testing methods, suggested method for determining point load strength (revised version). *Int. Jnl of Rock Mechanics, Mining Science and Geomechanics Abstracts*, **22**, 51–60.

——1988. Commission on testing methods, suggested method for determining the fracture toughness of rock. *Int. Jnl. Rock. Mech. Min. Sci. and Geomech. Abstr.*, **15**, No. 2, 71–96.

IRFAN, T. Y. & DEARMAN, W. R. 1978. The engineering petrography of a weathered granite in Cornwall, England. *Quarterly Journal of Engineering Geology*, **11**, 233–244.

KRUMBEIN, W. C. & SLOSS, L. L. 1963. *Stratigraphy and Sedimentation*, 2nd Edition. Freeman, San Francisco.

L.C.P.C. 1989. *(Laboratoire Central des Ponts et Chaussees) Les Enrochments*, Rapport de la Ministère de L'Equipment du Logement des Transports et de la Mer.

LATHAM, J.-P. 1996. *Assessment and specification of armourstone quality from CIRIA/CUR (1991) to CEN (2000?)*, *Quarterly Journal of Engineering Geology*.

—— & POOLE, A. B. 1987. The application of shape descriptor analysis to the study of aggregate wear. *Quarterly Journal of Engineering Geology*. **20**, 297–310.

LCPC 1989. *"Les Enrockments" Ministère de l'équipment du logement, des transports et de la mer*, Laboratoire Central des Ponts et Chaussées.

OLLIER, C. D. 1975. *Weathering*, Longman, Edinburgh.

NEN 5181 1988. *Determination of particle size distribution*, Draft of standard of the Netherlands, March.

PERMANENT INTERNATIONAL ASSOCIATION OF NAVIGATIONAL CONGRESSES (PIANC) 1976. *Final report of the International Commission for the Study of Waves*, Bulletin No. 25, Vol. III.

——1987. *Risk consideration when determining bank protection requirements*, Bulletin No. 58.

——1989. *Economic methods of channel maintenance*, Bulletin No. 67.

PIANC 1987. Risk consideration when determining bank protection requirements. Bulletin No. 58.

——1989. Economic methods of channel maintenance. Bulletin No. 67.

PILATCZY, K. K. W. 1984. Filters. *In*: HUISIN'T VELD (ed.) *The Closure of Tidal Basins*, Delft University Press.

PRICE, D. G. 1995. Weathering and weathering processes. *Quarterly Journal of Engineering Geology*, **28**, 243–252.

REES-JONES, R. G. & STORHAUG, E. 1998. Meeting the demand for rock armour and its grading specification. *In*: LATHAM, J.-P. (ed.) *Advances in Aggregates and Armourstone Evaluation*. Geological Society, London, Engineering Geology Special Publications, **13**, 87–90.

SIMONS, D. B. 1995. Fundamental concepts of rip-rap use for channel stabilization, *In*: THORNE, C. R. *et al.* (eds) *River, Coastal and Shoreline Protection*, Wiley, Chichester, 1–15.

SMITH, M. R. & COLLIS, L. 1993. *Aggregates: Sand, Gravel and Crushed Rock Aggregates for Construction Purposes*, 2nd Edn, Geological Society, London, Special Publications, **9**.

STEWART, E. T. & MCCULLOUGH, L. M. 1985. The use of the methylene blue test to indicate the soundness of road aggregates. *J. Chem. Tech. and Biotech.*, **35A**, 4, 161–167.

STICKLAND, I. W. 1984. Theme paper, State of the Art. *Breakwaters Design and Construction*, Thomas Telford, London, 1–8.

TERZAGHI, K. 1922. Der grandbuch an stauwerken and seine verhütung. *Die Wasserkraft*, **17**, 445–449, Reprinted in *From Theory to Practice in Soil Mechanics*. Wiley, New York, 114–118.

—— & PECK, R. B. 1964. *Soil Mechanics in Engineering Practice*. Wiley, New York.

THOMAS, R. S. 1998. The outlook for rock armour and beach recharge. *In*: LATHAM, J.-P. (ed.) *Advances in Aggregates and Armourstone Evaluation*. Geological Society, London, Engineering Geology Special Publications, **13**, 59–63.

THOMPSON, D. M. & SHUTTLER, R. M. 1975. *Rip-rap Design for Windwave Attack – a Laboratory Study in Random Waves*, Report Ex. 707, Hydraulics Research, Wallingford.

THORNE, C. R., ABT, S. R., BARENDS, F. B. J., MAYNORD, S. T. & PILARCZYK 1995. *River, Coastal and Shoreline Protection*. Wiley, Chichester.

US ARMY CORPS OF ENGINEERS 1983. *Engineers technical letter*, 1982 Hydraulic Design Conference, 1110–12, 284.

——1989. *Shore protection manual*, 4th Edition, Coastal Engineering Research Centre, US Govt. Printing Office, Washington DC.

VAN DER MEER, J. W. 1987. Stability of breakwater armour layers – design formulae, *Coastal Engineering*, **11**, 219–239.

VERHOEF, P. N. W. 1987. Sandblast testing of rock. *Int. Jnl. Rock Mech. Min. Sci. & Geomech. Abstr.*, **24**(3), 185–192.

WANG, H., LATHAM, J.-P. & POOLE, A. B. 1991. *Blast design for armour stone production, parts 1 and 2*. Quarry Management, July–August 1991.

WECKMANN, J. & WATTS, G. M. 1988. *Berm breakwater failure at St Paul Harbour, Alaska*. 21st International Conference on Coastal Engineering, Malaga, Abstracts Book, Paper 180, pp. 353–354.

9. Stone for buildings and civil engineering

9.1. Introduction

This chapter deals with uses of shaped natural stone in buildings, in their immediate surroundings and in civil engineering works. Stone in this type of use is normally termed dimension stone. The chapter deals mainly with initial construction uses of natural stone; the repair of stonework in existing buildings is covered in Chapter 10.

The initial part of the chapter defines building or dimension stone and discusses the development from stone originally being a locally available utility material to today's uses of stone from all over the world for mainly decorative purposes. This is followed by descriptions of the use of natural stone in the construction of various elements of buildings and its use in nearby areas, for example as paving or street furniture. Section 9.4 describes a design methodology for the selection of stone for different uses. Sections 9.5 and 9.6 cover the functional requirements and the tests that can be used to determine them.

This chapter is intended to provide some basic guidance on the choice and use of stone appropriate to different cases.

Dimension stone is defined by Ashurst & Dimes (1977) and Shadmon (1996) as any rock that is cut and worked to a specific size or shape for use in building and that the stone should be free from fractures, tough and devoid of minerals that can break down chemically or by weathering. The surfaces of the finished blocks may be dressed by one or more mechanical treatments, for example honing, or flame texturing.

9.2. Forms of construction and uses of stone in buildings

Stone masonry, if not the first building material to be used by mankind because that distinction probably belongs to timber, is certainly the most durable: Parts of Egyptian temples, more than 2500 years old are still standing as is the dry-jointed Lion Gate of Mykenai, and even when ancient monuments have fallen into ruins, their stones have survived and often been re-used in later, usually lesser, buildings.

Traditionally, building stone was extracted and used within the immediate local region – which resulted in the evolution of building design to take into account the materials available and their qualities. The exceptions were major buildings where stone was imported for architectural or aesthetic reasons or because of the absence of suitable local materials. Developments in transport methods now allow materials not only to be moved across the UK but also to be imported from almost any country in the world – leading to their use in regions or countries which are very different from their traditional areas as seen in Fig. 9.1 which is a view of the Cabot Square within the recent development of Canary Wharf, London Docklands. In some cases the initial driving force for the use of a particular stone is the cost or colour – and only then are its qualities questioned. Some balance is needed so that the design takes account of the stone's properties or, if the design is fixed, only stones of suitable quality are used. This raises the question of how quality can be assessed and which qualities are important for a particular stone or design.

The durability and weathering resistance of stone masonry means that it can be exposed on external elevations of buildings, without requiring any surface coating, such as rendering. It is also highly versatile, in terms of structural forms, having been used through the ages for walls, pillars, arches, vaults and domes.

Fig. 9.1. Cabot Square, Canary Wharf showing a range of imported stone cladding and paving.

Where cheaper alternatives, such as brick, were available the cost of extracting and working dimension stone has led to its use being restricted to more monumental buildings since the late middle ages. In arid mountainous regions it is, however, still used extensively for vernacular buildings, i.e. buildings local to the area made from local materials. Eighteenth and nineteenth century civil engineering relied heavily on natural stone masonry, particularly where its strength, impermeability and abrasion resistance gave it a clear advantage over the alternatives: brickwork and the concrete then available. After the post-war fashion for exposed concrete, natural stone is now being specified for an ever increasing number of uses in buildings and their surrounding areas. It is also still used in civil engineering structures, but on a much reduced scale.

Current uses of dimension stone in buildings can be described under the following headings:

- Load-bearing and self-supporting masonry
- Masonry facades to framed buildings
- Cladding and linings
- Roofing
- Flooring
- Miscellaneous elements

Civil engineering uses can similarly be sub-divided into:

- Structural uses
- Facing and cladding
- Hard landscaping

9.2.1. Load-bearing and self-supporting masonry

The term load-bearing masonry is, in the building industry, usually understood to mean masonry that supports loads and/or resists forces additional to those due to its own weight. Self-supporting masonry is similarly understood to support only its own weight, although it often has to resist wind loads, e.g. as free-standing garden walls. A good introduction to the use of both load-bearing masonry and masonry facades to framed buildings can be found in the 'classic' work by Warland (1929) and the more recent book by Hill & David (1995). A recent, rare example in the UK is the Hindu temple, or Mandir, in Neasden, London, see Fig. 9.2. The temple was constructed from Bulgarian limestone blocks supported on a plinth of Sardinian granite and the interior is lined with intricately carved marble from India and Italy.

Fig. 9.2. Hindu temple or Mandir, Neasden, London.

9.2.1.1. Through-thickness walls, piers and arches

In this form of construction the whole thickness of the masonry is made up of stones laid with fairly thin mortar joints. Alternatively, as in some ancient Mykaenean, Inca and Indian masonry, the stones were cut so accurately that they were laid with dry joints that were so tight that one cannot today force a feeler gauge in. The horizontal joints between layers, or courses, of stones of the same height, are known in the trade as bed joints; the vertical joints between stones are known as butt joints, but sometimes, mainly in brickwork, they are called perp-ends. The stones are laid in bond so that a stone in one course overlaps the butt-joint in the course below; in this way, the wall is not divided into narrow stacks of stones, separated by continuous vertical butt-joints. Usually the stones are also bonded through the thickness of walls where the wall is of greater thickness than a single stone. A stone in the course above will overlap a butt joint, which is parallel to the face of the wall, in the course below. This is important for the integrity and strength of the wall, as otherwise there can be a tendency for it to split down the middle of its thickness into two thinner part-walls, or leaves.

The stones may be dressed, i.e. cut or sawn to have plane, fairly smooth, surfaces on five faces (wall face, bed-joint faces above and below and two butt joints) with square corners, whilst the joint face towards the interior of the wall is usually left square, but rough. Walls, or leaves of walls, built with such stones, are known as ashlar. An example of a traditional ashlar building is shown in Fig. 9.3. Alternatively, stones are cut to size and roughly squared with hammer and chisel, but the faces are left rough. Walls, or leaves, built with this kind of stones, are known as coursed squared rubble, see Fig. 9.4.

Fig. 9.3. Traditional building constructed with ashlar walls.

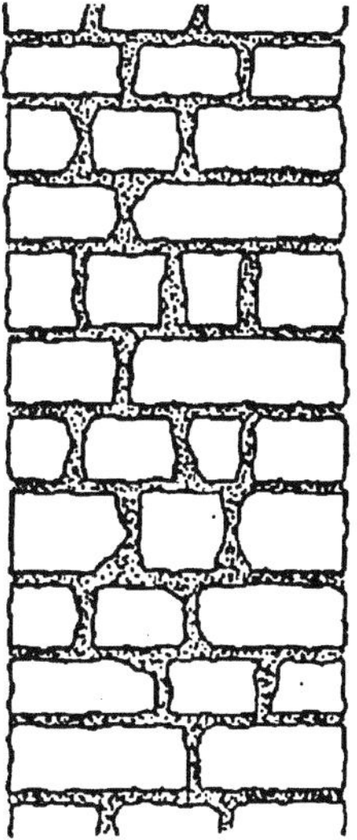

Fig. 9.4. Section and elevation of a coursed squared rubble wall.

For both ashlar and coursed squared rubble, the height of stones in one course is constant, but the height of different courses may be different, so as to allow the best possible utilisation of the available stone blocks and to enable features such as window sills to be placed at predetermined heights. The maximum height of the courses is dictated by the largest size of stone that can be consistently extracted, worked and transported. In traditional buildings this varied considerably: in a 19th century housing estate in Bradford, the facing work and stones were cut to brick size, whilst at York Minster the 15th century masonry has courses up to 400 mm thick. What is described above, is referred to as coursed masonry walls, as opposed to the cruder random rubble masonry walls, in which the stones are only roughly trimmed, see Fig. 9.5, to fit the 'valleys' and 'ridges' of the layer of stones below.

Columns in Egyptian temples were often single shafts of granite; columns in Greek temples were usually constructed of complete 'drums' of stone. However, from the middle ages onwards, the more common practice in Europe has been to build piers as if they were just walls with similar plan dimensions in both directions. A notable exception is the use of shafts of polishable limestone, e.g. 'Purbeck Marble' in many English cathedrals. Bonding is even more important for piers, in view of the higher load per unit of horizontal area that they have to carry.

In arches, the stones usually have to be wedge-shaped, to allow uniform thickness of the mortar joints; such stones are known as voussoirs. Voussoirs may be of uniform height, resulting in the upper surface to the arch, to which the wall supported by the arch must fit, being curved. The wall stones must be cut accordingly. Alternatively, to enable voussoirs to be integrated into the coursing of the ashlar of a wall, they may be cut with horizontal and vertical upper faces and will thus have five sides perpendicular to the face of the wall, see Fig. 9.6.

Fig. 9.5. Elevation of a random rubble wall.

So far the emphasis has been on load bearing masonry as found in early churches and monumental buildings. Where larger scale brick manufacture was introduced, it became uneconomic to use stone for the whole thickness of walls and its use was restricted to the visible face(s) or even just to the ornamental parts of walls, see §§9.2.1.4 and 9.2.2. Today in temperate, and sub-arctic climates, an additional factor mitigating against through-thickness use of stone for external walling is its relatively poor thermal insulation properties.

There has recently been some interest shown by post-modernist architects in using natural stone in, more or less, the traditional way for monumental buildings. There have also been some recent designs, in which fairly slender stone piers are used at ground level to support the facades and floors of multi-storey buildings, see Fig. C7 in Appendix C. Such piers sometimes have to be pre-stressed, in order to give them the necessary resistance against horizontal forces.

However, the widest use of stone in through-thickness masonry today is likely to be in the form of coursed rubble or random rubble in vernacular buildings in areas where timber is scarce and where at the same time bricks and/or concrete blocks would have to be imported at high cost. For such buildings, the stone will usually be won locally and dressed, if at all, on site.

Many of these areas are subject to frequent earthquakes and in some places the vernacular building practice incorporates horizontal timbers in the walls to improve the resistance to seismic movements. Where this is not the case, it is fairly easy to provide some tensile resistance in new walls and sometimes it can be 'retrofitted'. Equally important for earthquake resistance is prevention of distortion of the original, usually rectangular, plan shape of the walls; this can sometimes be simply provided by pairs of crossing diagonal ties. Anti-seismic codes of practice, such as Eurocode 8 (EC8), usually aim at total protection against the largest predictable earthquakes and their requirements are often impractical in these remote areas with poor populations.

9.2.1.2. Dressed stone leaves with rubble-and-mortar core
Two skins, or leaves, of stone, dressed to form the two faces of the wall, were interspersed by a core made up of stone rubble and mortar. Similarly large piers had an outer skin of dressed stone with a rubble-and-mortar core, see Fig. 9.7. This is the construction found in the majority of English mediaeval churches and castles and its use continued right up to the late 19th century; the piers of Winchester Cathedral and some of the piers of St Paul's Cathedral had rubble cores. In both cases, the weakness of these piers contributed to the problems that

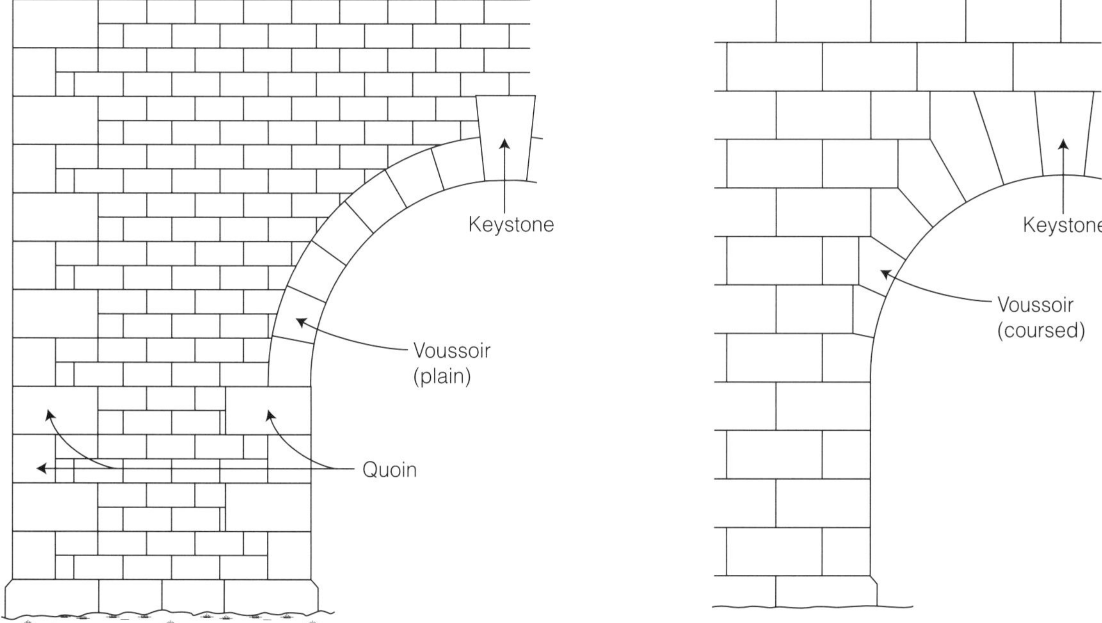

Fig. 9.6. Elevation of voussoirs and bonding to courses.

had to be dealt with in the first half of this century. In a 19th century housing estate in Bradford this form of construction was used for the external walls, and these were suffering from bulging, due to freezing of water, that had entered the core from overflowing gutters.

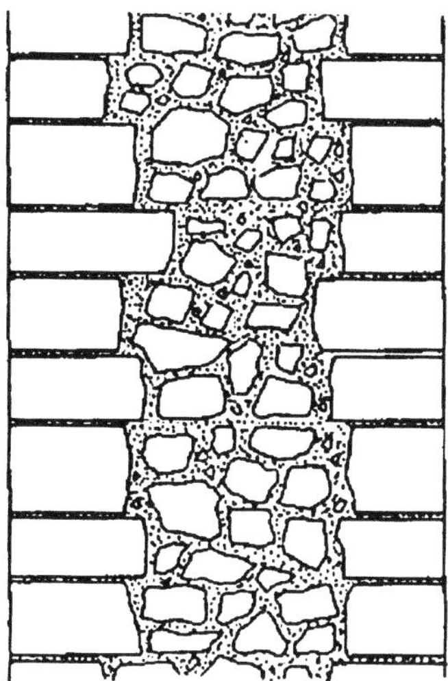

Fig. 9.7. Section through an ashlar and rubble-core wall.

The construction of such walls and piers proceeded as follows: the skins or leaves were built up a few courses and the rubble and mortar mix was then tamped into the core space, using the skins as 'permanent formwork'. The rubble would have consisted largely of the waste from the working of the face stones in the mason's yard close to the building. It seems unlikely that the primitive means of transport then available would have been used to freight waste from quarry to building site. Some of the face stones would protrude further into the core than the majority, providing some bonding of the face leaves to the core and thus, indirectly, to each other. In thinner walls, bonding stones may have extended all the way from the front face to the back face. The 'raison d'être' of this form of construction was obviously economics; mortar and rubble waste being cheaper than dressed stone.

The rubble-and-mortar filling of the core was, in effect, a primitive concrete. There is, in principle, no reason why this construction technique should not be employed today, using a core filling of concrete. What militates against such a revival is primarily the limited resistance of the face leaves against being overturned by the pressure of the wet concrete. This limits the height of wall that can be built 'in one go' and thus leads to slow construction. There may also be some anxiety about chemical reaction between some of the constituents of modern Portland cement and certain kinds of stone e.g. limestones.

9.2.1.3. Outer leaf of external walls

Where stone of good weathering quality and acceptable appearance is available at reasonable cost, its use for the outer leaf of external walls, in combination with an inner leaf of blockwork with the necessary insulation properties, and usually with a cavity, becomes attractive, particularly for dwelling houses of one or two storeys. Such use will often be encouraged, or even required, by the local planning authority in order to preserve the character of the neighbourhood. In such construction, the loading from the floors and roof will usually be carried by the inner blockwork leaf, but the outer stone leaf will have to contribute to the stability of the wall as a whole and also to resist its share of lateral (wind) loads.

Granites in some locations may give off small amounts of radon, a radioactive gas and special measures to prevent a build-up of radon in the inhabited rooms from the underlying rock may be necessary (BRE 1992; BRE 1993). However, where such granites are used as the outer leaves of external walls to houses or as internal flooring or lining these precautions are not necessary.

9.2.1.4. Facing, bonded and/or cramped to backing masonry or in situ *concrete*

Where bricks became freely available, and where there was no requirement for an interior stone finish, it was no longer economical to construct internal walls, nor the whole thickness of external walls of stone. In fact, where good facing bricks were available, stone was often relegated to quoins (see Fig. 9.6) window surrounds and corniches on external walls. Where, however, a facade in the Classical style was desired, stone was used as a facing to a backing masonry of brick. This style and form of construction became very fashionable in the first three quarters of the 19th century. The requirements of the building regulations, in force until the passing of the 'new' London Building Act 1909, led to very thick walls on multi-storey buildings, but this gave scope for deep articulation of architectural features on the facades. The outside face would be smooth ashlar, shaped in places to create pilasters and/or half-columns, pediments, cornices and whatever else was thought by the architect as enhancing the owner's prestige. The style was sometimes referred to as 'Banker's Roman'. The stone masonry was built up 'in step' with the brickwork and bonded into it by some of the stones being deeper than the rest. The minimum depth of the facing stones would be equal to the width of a brick: 100 mm (~4 inches), whilst the 'bonding stones' would usually be about 210 mm deep in a 330 mm thick wall and 320 mm in a 440 mm, or thicker, wall leaving a uniform internal brick face to receive plaster since exposing isolated stones on the inside face could cause plaster problems, see Fig. 9.8. The bond with the brickwork required that the courses of the stonework had to be multiples of the brick courses, i.e. for 'standard' brickwork with four courses to the foot: 152 mm (~6 inches), 228 mm (~9 inches), 305 mm (~12 inches), etc.

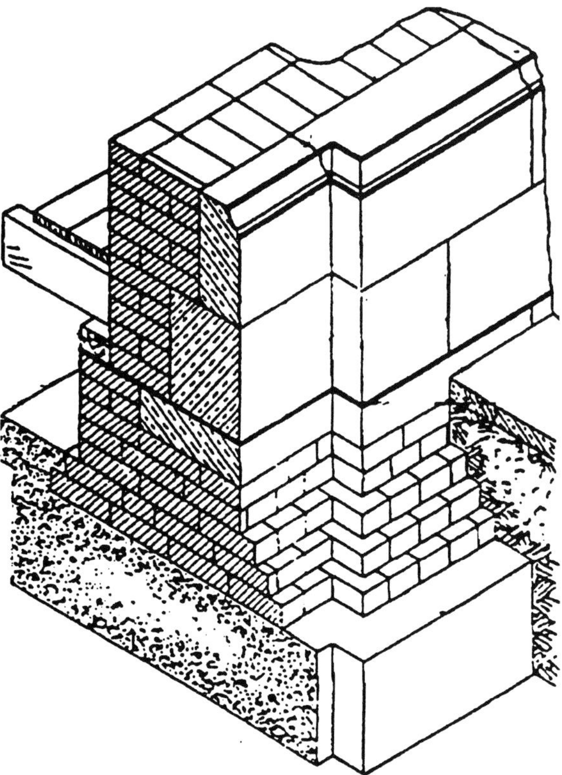

Fig. 9.8. Isometric section/elevation of a stone-faced brick wall.

In some instances, decorative features were cantilevered too far to be secured by bonding alone. They were then restrained by metal cramps, usually in the shape of an inverted square-cornered U with the crossbar embedded in a groove and the vertical legs in holes in the top of the stones. Cramps of bronze were sometimes used in very important buildings, but wrought iron was the usual material. Early practice was to envelop and embed the iron in lead, in order to protect it from rusting, but towards the end of the 19th century, embedment in Portland cement mortar became the norm. The lead would sometimes split, or be corroded by the lime mortar, and the cement mortar was often porous; the consequent lack of effective rust protection is to-day causing problems in some buildings.

A last magnificent, if somewhat idiosyncratic, example of the stone-faced self-supporting wall is Lutyens' Britannic House on Finsbury Circus in London, see Fig. 9.9. In this building, however, the floors are supported on a steel frame, whilst the heavily sculpted and decorated facade walls envelop the steel stanchions,

Fig. 9.9. Britannic House, Finsbury Circus, London.

which do not carry the weight of the wall. As this is a seven-storey building, the 'regulation thickness' at ground floor level is about one metre. The cost and time involved in the construction of such thick walls led to the abandonment of load bearing walls in multi-storey buildings, and their replacement by infill walls to steel frames. There is, in principle, no reason why the backing could not be blockwork or *in situ* concrete. Blocks were however not available in the heyday of this form of construction, and concrete would have to be cast in shallow pours, a few courses deep at a time. There are therefore few, if any, examples of these alternative backings to stone faced walls.

9.2.1.5. Mortar, its function and influence on masonry properties

Whilst this book is primarily about the use of stone, the mortar affects so many aspects of the performance of masonry, that some discussion here is appropriate. In the dry-jointed masonry, mentioned in §9.2.1.1, each block of stone was cut and dressed to very precise dimensions and then laid directly on the blocks below and against the adjacent block without any intervening layer of mortar. This was a very laborious process, but necessary to ensure stable bedding of the stones, in the absence of mortar.

The technique has another drawback. However meticulous the dressing of the stone, it is often impossible to insert a thin knife blade anywhere in the joints, the stones only bear on each other over a small proportion of the bed joint surface so that the bearing stresses at the contact points are very high indeed. This does not create any problems away from the edges; the lateral components of the stresses, as they spread out from the contact points, cancel out each other; there are no stresses to cause load splitting. If, however, a 'hard' point occurs at the edge of the bedding surface, i.e. at the face of the wall, then the inclination of the stresses, as they converge towards the contact point, produces a horizontal force, which is only resisted by the tensile strength of the stone. If that is overcome, a thin sliver of stone is split off: the face of the stone spalls, see Fig. 9.10.

The introduction of mortar joints overcomes these problems. It eliminates the need to produce very smooth and plane bedding surfaces on the stones and the hardened mortar provides contact, and hence load transfer, over the entire area of the bed joints, with elimination of the high stresses at the contact points. This highlights one of the prime purposes of mortar: to keep the stones apart; **Not**, as is sometimes assumed by engineers, to glue them together. Another purpose of mortar is to seal the joints to keep the weather out of the building. All these benefits are, however, not achieved without some disadvantages. The mortar joints limit the strength of the masonry and ingredients of some mortars may react chemically with the stone.

When a body of any solid material is compressed, it becomes shorter in the direction of the compressing force and slightly wider at right angles to the direction of the force: this is easily demonstrated by squeezing a soft rubber. This deformation is displayed by stones as well as mortar joints but, because most stones are less deformable than the hardened mortars, the joints tend to spread out more than the stones. The tendency of the

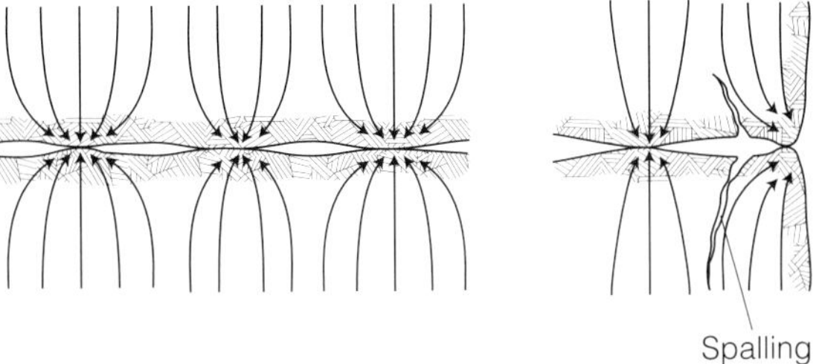

Fig. 9.10. Stress flow in dry-jointed masonry.

Stress, strain and modulus of deformation

The compressive bearing stress on a bed joint is the vertical load on the joint, divided by the area of the joint. This stress is the same for the stone and for the mortar joint.

The compressive strain of a mortar joint is the amount the joint becomes thinner under stress, divided by the original thickness. The compressive strain of a stone is the amount its height reduces under stress, divided by its original (unloaded) height. For the same stress, the compressive strain of the mortar joint is usually greater than that of the stone.

The modulus of deformation is the stress divided by the strain. This is usually higher for stone than for mortar.

The lateral strain of any material is the amount it expands at right angles to the direction of the primary stress. This is proportional to, but smaller than, the compressive strain. The lateral strain of the mortar in a joint is usually larger than that of the stone.

These definitions do not apply to all materials under all stress conditions; they are, however, adequate for the purpose of this chapter.

mortar to spread out more than the stone, coupled with the fact that the relatively rough surfaces of the stones prevent the mortar sliding between the stones, leads to the mortar exerting a horizontal outward drag on the stones. When this drag overcomes the tensile strength of the stones, which is always much less than the compressive strength, the stones crack, the wall or pier splits into slender skins or shafts which then buckle, see Fig. 9.11. It is this mechanism, which is more pronounced for weak mortars than for strong ones, that causes failure of masonry, not crushing of the stones. The net result of the above is that the compressive strength of masonry, depending on the mortar, may be no more than 20 to 40% of the compressive strength of the stone.

As the strength reduction is less severe for strong mortars, there may be a temptation to use strong mortars, based on Portland cement. This temptation must, however, be resisted for two reasons:

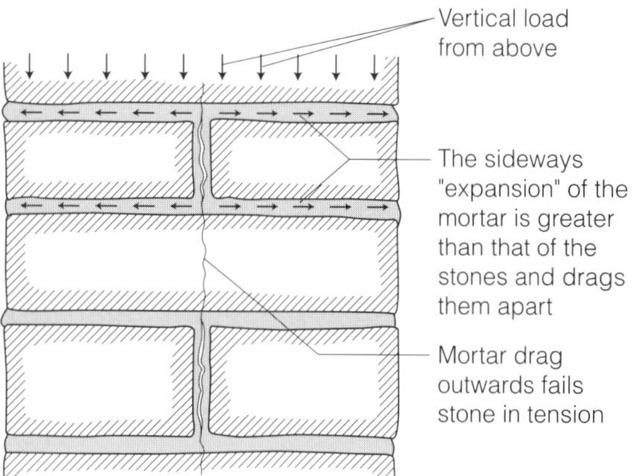

Fig. 9.11. Strains in mortar jointed masonry.

Firstly, if subsequent to construction, foundation movement should take place, any cracks would follow the joints, usually in a diagonal zigzag pattern, provided that the mortar was not too strong. With too strong a mortar, however, the cracks will go through the stones and be far more difficult to make good in a visually acceptable way.

Secondly, some of the constituents of Portland cement may react deleteriously with certain stones, accelerating decay. Furthermore, being very impermeable, cement mortars may interfere with the natural draining down of absorbed rainwater and thus accelerate damage, due to frost and salt crystallisation.

Pure lime mortar is, however, not without problems of its own: The lime is made by first heating limestone so as to convert the calcium carbonate (calcite) to calcium oxide, so-called 'quicklime'. This is then slaked with water to produce calcium hydroxide 'slaked lime', which is subsequently mixed with sand to produce the mortar. The slaked lime takes up carbon dioxide from the atmosphere and reverts to calcium carbonate. This is what causes the mortar to harden, but it is a very slow process. It is in fact so slow that in new construction, the use of pure lime mortar dictates the height of wall that can be raised in a week. It also means that the mortar joints are vulnerable to weather erosion for quite a long time after completion. The Roman builders overcame this drawback by substituting crushed fired clay brick for some of the sand; this acted as a pozzolan and enabled the mortar to begin to harden in the absence of air. Many naturally occurring limes contain impurities which have the same effect on the lime. Because they enable the lime to harden under water, they are called hydraulic limes.

Many of the limes, used from mediaeval times up to the 19th century, would have contained such impurities to a greater or lesser degree. This could explain why lime mortars were used successfully in old construction, whilst repairs made with modern 'pure' lime, mixed with washed silica sand, free from clay, have been known to be short-lived. Another factor could be that the compaction, given to mortar when re-filling eroded joints (re-pointing), has not been as thorough as during construction, when the stone is bedded into the mortar.

There is also a general consensus that lime slaked the old-fashioned way by being thrown into a pit, or deep vessel, filled with water, and left to settle for some weeks, is superior to 'hydrated lime', produced by blowing steam through the powdered quicklime. The explanation for this is that the 'quenching' in water of the quicklime produces a different crystalline structure and grain size of the slaked lime from that of the steam-hydrated. It could also be that the steam treatment exposes the freshly hydrated lime to atmospheric carbon dioxide whilst it is hot and hence more reactive; this would mean that the lime in the mortar, subsequently made, is already partly carbonated and therefore has lost some of its cementing action. In contrast, the traditionally slaked lime, being saturated with water, is only exposed to the air after being mixed into mortar, laid and dried out.

9.2.2. Masonry facades to framed buildings

As mentioned in §9.2.1.4, the thickness, required by the building regulations for load bearing walls, made this form of construction too slow and expensive for buildings more than two or three storeys high. With the introduction of steel and reinforced concrete frames, the problem was overcome by supporting not only the floors, but also

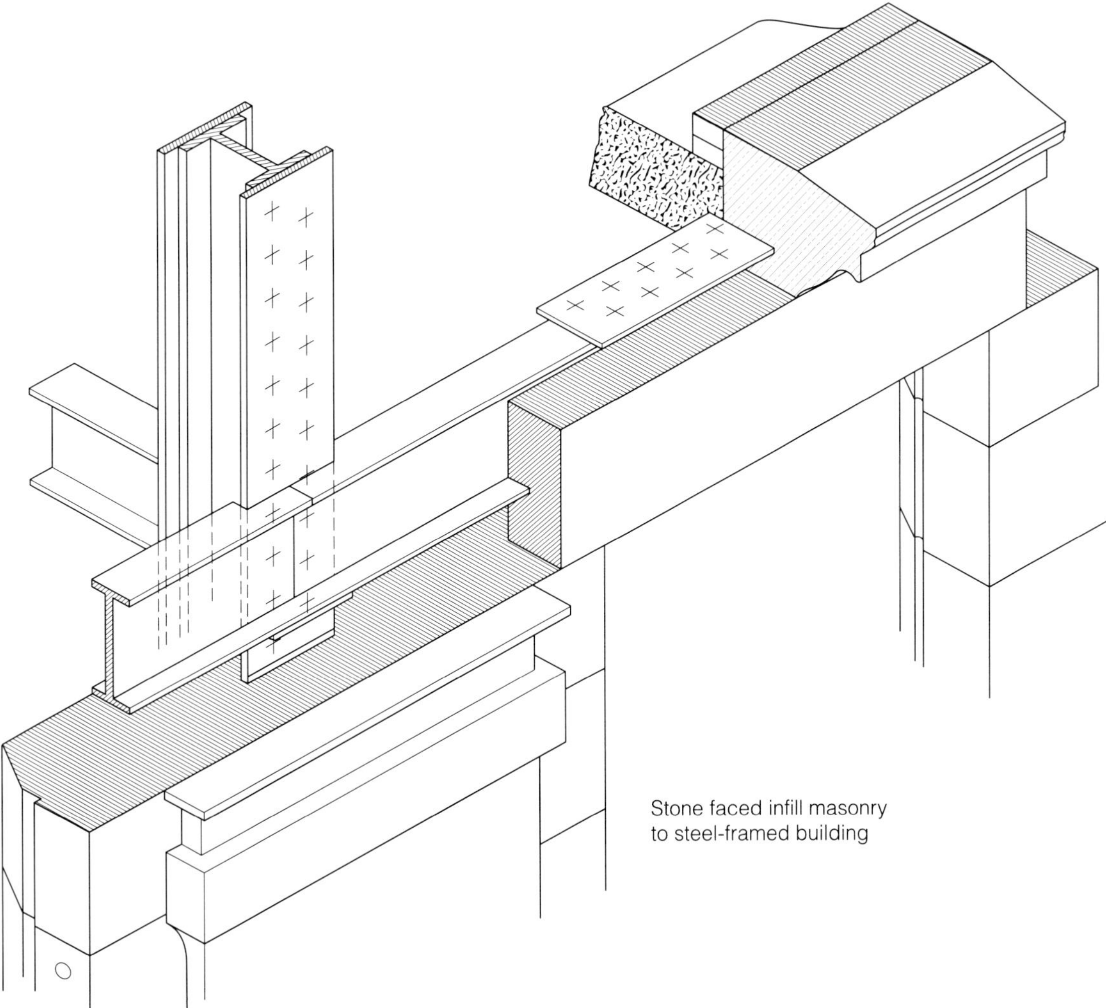

Fig. 9.12. Isometric section/elevation of a masonry wall supported by a steel frame.

the walls, on the beams of the frame, one storey at a time. This meant that the external walls only had to resist wind forces, in addition to carrying their own weight of one storey height. For buildings of, say, more than five storeys, this enabled a drastic reduction of the overall thickness of the external walls. While the influence of the mortar on the strength of the masonry will not be significant for this type of 'infill' masonry, the requirements for chemical and weathering compatibility of stone and mortar are the same.

9.2.2.1. Facing bonded and/or cramped to backing brick- or blockwork, supported floor-by-floor on steel frame

This is largely the same form of construction as that described in §9.2.1.4 but, because the masonry is supported at every floor, its thickness is only governed by requirements for fire resistance, thermal insulation, wind resistance (over the height of one storey only) and decorative features. The backing masonry is built off the floor structure and the stonework is 'wrapped round' the steel stanchions, see Fig. 9.12. After the 1940s, the steel frame was usually encased in concrete, but earlier practice did not provide this corrosion protection and many buildings of this type suffer from cracking of stonework due to rust expansion of the steel members. With the changing fashion in architecture, and the development of cladding techniques, using relatively thin slabs, this form of construction has, since the mid-1960s, been largely superseded by those described in §9.2.3.

9.2.2.2. Facing bonded and/or cramped to backing brick- or block-work, supported floor-by-floor on reinforced concrete frame

This is almost identical to the use described in §9.2.2.1. The nature of the concrete frame does, however, leave more scope for connecting the masonry to the frame by metal ties, etc., and being generally of later date, although the Royal Liver Building in Liverpool dates from 1910, blockwork may have been used for backing to a greater extent. Like that described in §9.2.2.1, this form of construction has been replaced by claddings, as described in the following section.

9.2.3. Cladding and lining to framed buildings

9.2.3.1. Cladding- and lining-slabs, individually fixed

The use of granites, marbles and other stones in the form of relatively thin slabs has long been a popular method of providing prestige natural stone interiors, and durable external stall risers and plinths as well as complete facades to commercial buildings. In this way the benefits of natural stone, its appearance, durability, and weathering characteristics can be gained without the cost penalty inherent in thick stone facing but the reader should also see §9.5.1.5. What sets these uses apart from all other uses of dimension stone is that individual slabs of stone are held in place with metal fixings without bearing on the course of stone below, see Fig. 9.13. As a consequence entirely different technologies have been developed for fixing, jointing and weatherproofing.

The construction of external claddings and internal linings involves the assembly on site of factory cut and finished stone slabs held in place with metal fixings. The methods of cutting and preparing the stone have changed little, although the developments in the machinery used for cutting and preparation allow the contemporary designer to use a wider range of finishes, profiles and thinner slabs than in the past.

The work carried out on site is usually limited to setting fixings in the structure, offering up the stone panels, and then propping the panels, usually with wedges, while the fixing medium sets. Some cutting of stone and/or fixing slots to accommodate construction inaccuracies is usual, but has been known in some cases to initiate fine cracks in the cladding slabs. The preparation of the stones for the fixings may be carried out

Fig. 9.13. Limestone slab supported by a corbel plate and restrained by a cramp.

Fixing

Developments in fixings technology have been wider ranging than that of the slabs. At the beginning of the twentieth century, fixings were usually manufactured from copper alloys; the designs were simple, consisting of load-bearing corbel plates and restaining wire ties which engaged in slots and holes, prepared in the cladding slabs, and which themselves were bedded in mortar-filled pockets or mortar joints in the backing structure. Today there is a large international fixings industry, marketing a wide variety of fixings. Bronze has largely been replaced by stainless steel for external use. The techniques which have been added to mortar fixing include dovetail and other cast-in slots, expanding bolts and synthetic resin anchors. The designs available today range from the simple corbel plates and ties to complex multi-component brackets with sliding adjustment and complete systems which allow for construction tolerances and relative movements of structure and cladding, see Fig. 9.14.

on site depending on whether the specified fixings allow for tolerance, or whether tolerance is allowed for in the position of the fixing on the slabs. However, it is preferable to carry out this work in the factory.

The design of internal lining and external cladding in the UK is usually governed by British Standard BS 8298: 1994. This is because compliance with the stand-ard is the easiest of satisfying the requirements of the Building Regulations. The designer of a new building or refurbishment which requires Building Regulations consent and which includes natural stone facings has the choice of complying with most of the standard, or embarking on the time consuming and often expensive path of justifying a departure or a different approach to

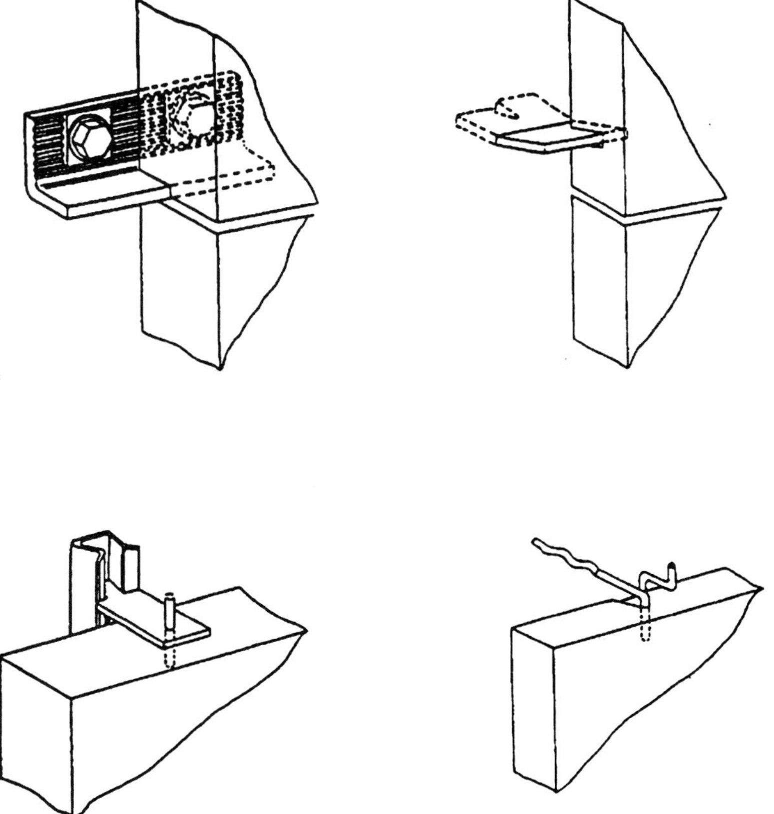

Fig. 9.14. Examples of load-bearing and restraint fixings.

design. The Standard is a code of practice for the design, installation and maintenance of natural stone facings but is currently restricted to slabs attached by support and restraint fixings. It provides general recommendations for many of the aspects of design, and detailed specific prescriptive recommendations for fixing, which take up nearly half of the standard. This includes a table of stone thickness and thickness of stone behind fixings for a number of different types of stone in a range of construction locations. It is recommended that this table is complied with unless the design is supported by structural calculation or performance testing, both of which fall outside the scope of the standard.

The fixing of individual stone slabs direct to the structure of a multi-storey building requires a lengthy period of time in the construction programme for fixing on site, during which scaffolding or other access for the masons and material is required. Cladding systems have been developed since the 1960s which avoid this by using systems which make use of large, storey or two storey panels to which the stone is fixed in the factory. Those based on pre-cast concrete panels are described in §§9.2.3.2 and 9.2.3.3, those based on metal subframes are described in §9.2.3.4.

9.2.3.2. Stone faced pre-cast concrete panels

The conventional technique for fixing stone facings to concrete panels is by the use of a relatively close-spaced stainless steel dowels, so called 'hedgehog fixings', and BS 8298: 1994 requires a minimum of eleven per square metre. These are placed and glued into holes drilled in the back face of the finished stone slabs, which are then laid in the moulds prior to pouring the concrete. Resistance to pullout is achieved by drilling the holes for the dowels at an angle to the perpendicular, with some inclined one way and others in opposition.

The design of these facings in the UK is controlled by BS 8298: 1994 for the same reasons given in §9.2.3.1; compliance enables straightforward Building Regulations approval. The standard has specific requirements for the distribution of dowels, their size, inclination to the back of the stone, penetration into the stone, and embedment into the concrete. It also requires that the slabs are de-bonded from the concrete, and that soft grommets are placed on the dowels at the interface to allow for the relative thermal and structural movement of the concrete and the stone, see Fig. 9.15.

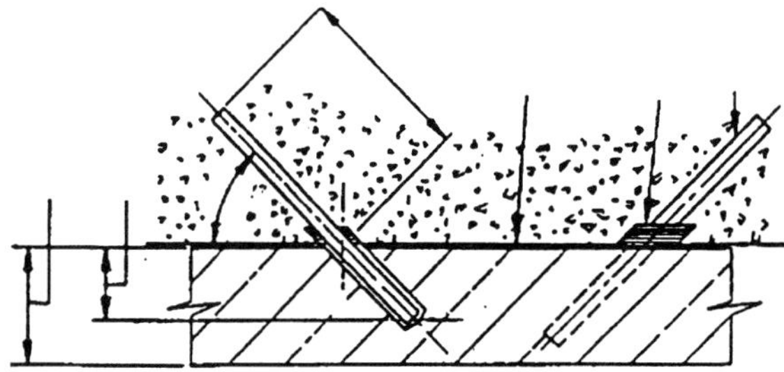

Fig. 9.15. Diagram of dowel fixing of a stone slab to a precast concrete panel.

The advantages of the system are that the stone fixings themselves are simple and cheap, and their installation does not require the skills of a mason. There are of course on top of these costs those of the fixings and installation of the pre-cast concrete panels. There are disadvantages to this technique: including a greater dead weight than many cladding systems, and the difficulty of replacing any stones which are damaged.

9.2.3.3. Sub-frame mounted stone facings

In this method of constructing stone facings, frames are used to support a number of individual stone slabs. The framing is purpose designed and fabricated for each project, often from tubular steel sections with welded joints and hot dip galvanized after fabrication. Frames are typically full storey height and vary in complexity

Stone cladding on precast panels

The consequences for stone cladding design and specification which result from fixing stones on to pre-cast concrete include:

(a) the introduction of movement joints between panels.
(b) the requirement to co-ordinate the stone slabs with the pre-cast concrete design.
(c) the need to provide for the protection, transport and hoisting of large panels and restrictions which arise as a consequence.
(d) the need to devise a replacement technique. If the stones are fixed with a high density of small inclined dowels, replacement is not possible using the original method in the event of damage. The risk of damage leading to the need for replacement occurs during the transport and hoisting of the panels when the stone is vulnerable to breakage. Replacement techniques commonly involve reduced numbers of dowels, angles of dowels to allow the stone to be offered into position and resin fixings for the dowels into the concrete.

from simple designs which support only the stone to complex systems which also support windows in a complete wall structure, see Figs 9.1, 9.16 and 9.17. The individual stone slabs are fixed to the frames in the workshop by intermediate stainless steel or aluminium fixings and the completed fully clad frames are transported to the site for hoisting into position.

It is common in these systems to use continuous extrusions rather than traditional fixings for the stone slabs. One of the reasons for this is that the fixings have to be more robust than for site fixed cladding because of the forces imposed during transport and hoisting There are, however, other systems which employ threaded studs, glued into holes in the back of the stone slabs, to bolt the slabs to a (stainless or galvanized) steel sheet that is welded to the subframe and intended to act as the rain barrier. These techniques were imported into the UK by North American property developers and their architects during the commercial construction boom of the 1980s in response to the pressure for ever faster methods of design and construction to minimize the construction period during which the developer pays loan charges but has no rental income. It is one of the 'fast-track' methods which aim to allow the simultaneous design and construction of the building structure and cladding and minimum assembly time on site. The extra cost of prefabrication can be offset against the concentration of the stone workers' activities in the factory rather than on site, which enables productivity improvements and the opportunity for better supervision and inspection.

Fig. 9.16. Modern building with sub-frame mounted stone cladding behind an older stone masonry tower and building clad with Portland limestone.

Fig. 9.17. Precast concrete sub-frame clad with limestone being lowered into position (Centre West, Hammersmith).

These systems which are sometimes known as 'strongback fixings' are not included in the 1994 edition of BS 8298. The foreword to the standard states that the 'general principles ... of traditional stone cladding apply, with particular attention to the need for articulation and isolation of dissimilar materials'. Any designer contemplating one of these sub-frame systems for a project in the UK should consult the local Building

Stone cladding on sub-frames

The consequences for stone cladding design and specification which result from the introduction of a sub-frame include:

(a) the introduction of movement joints between panels.
(b) the requirement to co-ordinate the stone slabs with the sub frame design.
(c) the introduction of panel fixings with an allowance for building tolerance, which may reduce the tolerances which the stone fixings themselves have to accommodate.
(d) provision for the transport and lifting of large panels and restrictions which arise as a consequence. In particular the benefits of limiting panel weight, and hence stone thickness introduce a new parameter into the equation which balances the size of panels and the cost of fixings.

Control Office at an early stage in the design development to agree what proof of the design will be necessary in order to obtain a Building Regulations approval.

9.2.3.4. Veneer panels

During the 1980s very light weight composite stone faced boards and reinforced stone panels have come to the market, manufactured in Italy and the United States. One manufacturer makes the panels by gluing honeycomb core boards to each side of a slab of stone, typically 20 mm thick with a plastic resin. Following curing of the resin, the stone is cut down the centre to create two panels and the cut surfaces are finished by traditional finishing techniques, see Fig. 9.18. Another supplier uses panels manufactured in Italy which have a glass fibre reinforced polyester sheet backing. The thickness of stone on the face of these panels is typically 7 mm. Another variant also manufactured in Italy consists of slabs of 18mm thick stone into the back face of which a grid of grooves has been cut, and a glass fibre reinforced polyester mesh bonded to it. These composite boards have a natural stone face but are, at the same time, sufficiently light and rigid enough that panels of a size which would have previously required lifting by hoist, can be lifted by two men. This clearly gives a significant advantage in manufacturing and assembly and in the lighter backing structures which are necessary to provide support. The first use of these

Fig. 9.18. Stone veneer panel (part of the stone veneer and layer of glass fibre reinforced resin has been removed to show the aluminium honeycomb) (courtesy of Stone Panels (UK) Ltd).

panels was for interiors and examples include an hotel where the traditional use of stone was ruled out because of load restrictions on the existing structure and subsequently in lifts where the reduction in weight relative to solid stone allowed lower powered lifting machinery and lower running cost.

The honeycomb backed boards have been used externally in curtain walls in the United States and there is a proposal to use the grid reinforced slabs described above for a curtain wall system on a building in the City of Westminster. Either may be installed into framed glazing systems but their use in rainscreen cladding requires special fixing techniques. The honeycomb backed panels are fastened using fixings set into plastic blocks cast into the back after removal of sections of the honeycomb. Fixing is thus entirely dependent on adhesion. The grid reinforced panels may be fixed using special stainless steel fixings developed for ceramic rainscreen tiles which engage in undercut circular holes drilled with a purpose made expanding bit and are thus mechanically fixed.

These materials and the methods of fixing them are still at an innovative stage, their manufacture and use are not covered by any codes published by the BSI and indeed adhesive fixed stone cladding systems are specifically excluded from the terms of reference of BS 8298. The designer wishing to use these products must therefore rely on original research and testing to prove their performance and durability to the satisfaction of himself and the Building Control Official.

9.2.4. Internal flooring and stairs

9.2.4.1. Internal floor paving and stair treads

Internal floor paving is traditionally in the form of slabs or tiles of honed or polished stone laid on a bed of sand or on a mortar screed. The purpose of the screed is to provide a sound base for a finish that is capable of withstanding the applied loads. The majority of traditional floors are laid on bonded screeds without the use of a separating membrane. Recommendations for the design and installation of natural stone floor slabs up to 0.6 m^2 in area are given in BS 5385: Part 5: 1990. However, this code of practice concentrates on the installation of the stone, rather than the selection of the stone. In recent years there has been a trend towards the use of thinner tiles, sometimes as thin as 10mm thick. The thinnest of these are often fixed with adhesives but those between 15 and 25 mm thick can also be laid on traditional sand cement beds. In some cases the slabs are very large and difficulties can be encountered in the handling and laying of these large, thin stones.

Corbella (1990) divides internal flooring into two groups – mass produced and traditional custom made flooring. The mass produced flooring is based around a limited number of unit sizes (for example 300 mm × 300 mm, and 400 mm × 400 mm) with typical thicknesses of 10–20 mm – usually depending on the physical strength of the stone both in production and in use. Recent experience has shown that there are a number of critical factors in the creation of a good stone floor. These include the protection of the floor during the final stages of construction, the use of the correct cleaning and maintenance methods, and the exclusion or removal of moisture from the floor beneath the screed. Failure to meet this last requirement seems to be a major cause of staining of lightly coloured floors, particularly those in white and grey marble.

Thin tiles of natural stone can also be used as cladding on staircases and stair treads. The requirements for this type of use are similar to those for flooring but with an added emphasis on the structural qualities if the stone is to carry any of the load. However, in the majority of cases the load bearing structure is made of reinforced concrete and the stone provides a veneer or cladding.

9.2.4.2. 'Cantilever' stairs and landings

Each tread and landing of these stairs consists of a single piece of stone, built into a wall at one end only. In this way they allow stairways and halls to have an open and spacious appearance. They are therefore mainly found in the grander Georgian and early Victorian Buildings and usually have fairly elaborate wrought-iron balustrades. The structural adequacy of these stairs has always been a challenge to engineers. The bending strength of the individual treads and landings usually appears to be far from enough and the depth of embedment in the wall usually seems grossly inadequate. It is generally accepted that the treads do not act as cantilevers in bending. Each tread receives the reaction from the one above along its upper arris and transmits it plus its own load to the tread below along its soffit groove. As the reactions are offset relative to each other, a moment is created which is transmitted in torsion of the tread to its embedment in the wall. This load transfer is repeated at every tread down to the bottom one which rests on the floor.

At the junction with the landing, a mutual support action can develop from in-plane forces, in the landing and in the stair flight, combining to create a vertical reaction. Quite often, however, junctions are found where this action cannot fully develop, and where considerable bending therefore has to be resisted by the stone landing slab. The load-carrying mechanism of these stairs is thus often very complex and past performance is often the best guide to their structural adequacy, as long as they have not been overloaded, damaged or interfered with during refurbishment work (Beckmann 1994).

9.2.5. Roof cladding

The earliest evidence of the use of stone for roofing in this country is to be found in Roman remains. There is little evidence of use from that time until the fourteen century when it began to be used to provide durable and fire resistant roofing in church and house building. Its use grew to a high point in the nineteenth century following the industrial revolution when slate dominated the roofing industry by virtue of its utility and economy, during the building of the Victorian towns and cities.

The three groups of stones which can be split into relatively thin slabs and have been used extensively in the past for roofing are fissile sandstones and limestones, both of which are sedimentary stones, and metamorphic slates. The geological origin of these three types in described in Chapter 2, their extraction in §5.3.9 and their processing in §6.4.13. There is frequently discussion over the definition of a metamorphic slate but in general it is taken to be a stone which has a fissility independent of the bedding as a result of alteration from its original form by the effects of heat or pressure or both. A number of other stones are described as slates because they split easily and are traditionally used in other countries as roofing materials. However, they are often either mudstones or low grade metamorphic rocks in which the bedding is still present.

The stone roofing industry evolved a rich language over the centuries which varied from place to place and which has largely escaped standardisation. In the following text, the word 'slate', in the singular, refers to metamorphic rock, and 'stone tiles' to the thin slabs of limestone or sandstone used in roofing. The descriptions used by different quarries for various thicknesses of slate also requires explanation. The thinnest slates of 4 or 5 mm can only be riven from the finest slate and are usually described as 'bests'. Thicker slates of up to 8mm are usually known as 'strongs' and 'heavies'. The nomenclature for different slate sizes is discussed in §6.4.13.

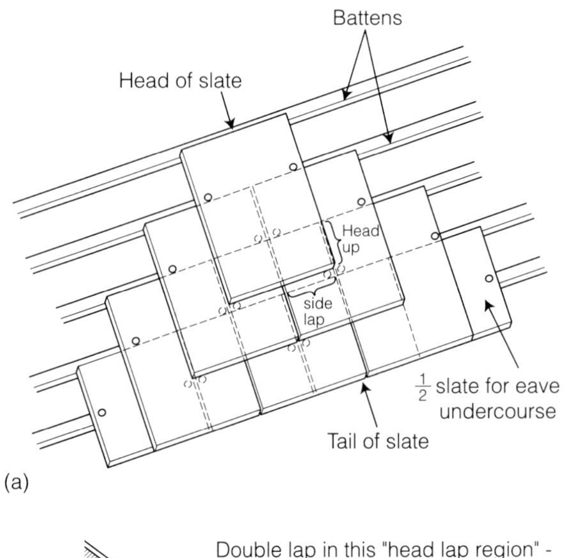

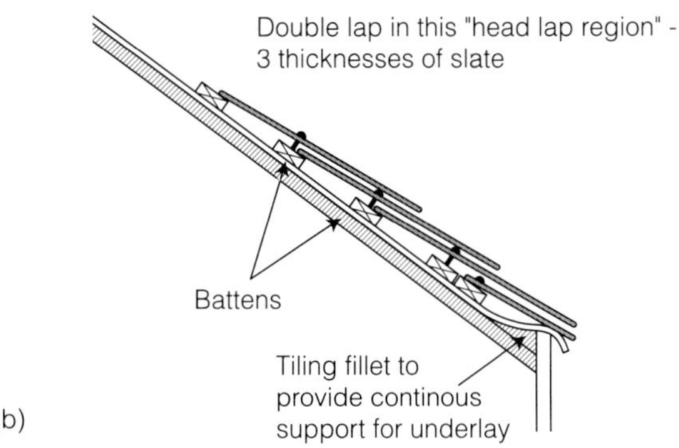

Fig. 9.19. Section through 'Double-lap' slate roofing.

9.2.5.1 Limestone and sandstone roofing tiles

Since the first World War the use of limestone and sandstone for roofing has declined to the point where new stone roofs are very rarely constructed and much of the industry is now concerned with re-roofing work. The future of the craft in the UK is assured on a small scale by Planning Authorities and the listing procedure which require the owners of much of the remaining stone roofed building stock to repair or re-roof using the same material, see Fig. 9.19.

The processes which are carried out to create the individual stone tiles are varied. The traditional method for limestone is to 'frost' the quarried stone slabs by continuous saturation followed by exposure to frost to weaken the laminations and facilitate splitting into individual stone slates with the cleaving hammer.

The methods of constructing new or re-covered limestone and sandstone roofs are much the same today as they were in the nineteenth century. No British Standards cover either the manufacture of limestone or sandstone tiles or their installation, so the contemporary specifier must depend as in the past, on his knowledge and experience and on the same craft technology. This requires study of the locally available stones, a knowledge of the quarries, the stone tiles they produce, this performance in service and the methods of detailing and fixing. A brief description of the principles of stone tiling follow but the detail is beyond the scope of this publication and reference should be made to specialist publications.

Stone tiles vary in size, the largest sandstone slabs may be up to 900 mm or 1200 mm long and may be up to 75 mm thick, limestone up to 900 mm long and between 8 mm and 25 mm thick. The weight of these roofs may be up to 0.16 tonnes per square metre and clearly require a substantial supporting framework, traditionally constructed of oak. The tiles are usually supplied in random sizes, sorted on site and laid in diminishing courses starting with the larger stone slates at the eaves and using progressively smaller tiles up to the ridge. The traditional method of fixing was by oak, or bone pegs driven though holes drilled in top of the tiles and resting on the battens. It is now more usual to use heavy copper or galvanized nails. Each course laps the preceding course by slightly more than half its length to ensure that water passing through the joints between stone tiles falls on to the tile below and is directed back to the outside. Resistance to wind blown rain and snow which may be forced up the underside of the slates is provided by two methods. The first is to provide a lap, which is the distance by which stone tiles lap both the slate above and the next, see Fig. 9.19. The distance required depends on the local conditions and on the pitch of the roof. Stone tile roofs are usually constructed at a pitch of between 50 to 55 degrees and sometimes more. The steeper the pitch, the less the lap required to prevent leakage, but the greater the amount of stone used and weight to be supported. Traditionally the second defence was to seal the joints between stone tiles either by laying on mortar, or by torching. This consists of placing sand/lime/hair in the joints between tiles on the underside of the roof. Now it is usual to fix a layer of waterproof, tear resistant felt below the battens to prevent any leakage through the tiles reaching the interior.

9.2.5.2. Metamorphic slates ('true slates')

Through-out most of the nineteenth and early twentieth century slate dominated the roofing market in the UK for all building types and the roofscapes of our Victorian cities are still composed predominantly of slate, see Fig. 9.21. During the middle and late twentieth century the use of slate declined and domestic quarry output fell from 300 000 tons in 1920 to 50 000 tons in 1985. The reason was the development of alternative products including concrete tiles, synthetic slates and profiled metal for pitched roofs and flat roofing materials with the advantages of low cost and ease and speed of construction. The cost of an installed Welsh slate roof covering is now two or more times the cost of a fibre-reinforced-cement slate roof and three times the cost of a concrete tile roof. Cumbrian and Cornish slate prices are higher still. So whereas natural slate was used universally for industrial, agricultural, commercial, institutional and housing construction last century, its use by the seventies was restricted to the commercial and institutional sectors where it was valued as an attractive, reliable and durable covering, free from the risks associated with the newly developed felt roof coverings.

The introduction of imported slate, mostly from Spain but also from quarries as distant as China and Canada, from the eighties reversed the trend. By competing on cost, undercutting the initial purchase price of Welsh slate by over 50%, imported slate has become competitive with cement fibre reinforced slates (Anon 1996). The commercial success has now given foreign suppliers an

Fig. 9.20. Example of a stone tiled roof.

Fig. 9.21. Example of a building with a traditional metamorphic slate roof.

equal share of the market with domestic slate quarries. The quality of imported slates has not been consistent, and there have been some failures arising from cross graining, mineral inclusions, and weak slate, resulting in the need for replacement after only a few years.

In order that a slate roof is durable and waterproof the designer needs to ensure

(a) that the slate specified is durable
(b) that the slate supplied consistently complies with the standards specified
(c) that the design is competent and takes into account the prevailing weather conditions
(d) that the installation is carried out in accordance with the design and good standards of workmanship and
(e) the suitability of the supporting structure.

There have been several well publicised failures of slate roofs in recent years resulting from failure to satisfy requirements (a), (b) and (d).

9.2.6. Miscellaneous

9.2.6.1. Foundations and plinths
Where stone was the preferred material for walls, it was equally the obvious choice for foundations. On soft ground they would be considerably wider than the wall they were to support and would 'corbel in' at about 45° from the lowest course to the level from which the wall itself would rise. The fact that certain stones could be worked to large slabs, with significant bending strength, led to them being used occasionally to provide spread footings to brick walls, etc. One example of this was found under the brick piers of All Souls' Church, Langham Place, which dates from the early 19th century. The American '*Architect's and Builder's Pocket-book*', by Frank. E. Kidder, from 1905 contains rules for stone foundations. The walls of many modern stone buildings, although often only clad with stone, incorporate a lower course of large facing blocks to emulate the style described above. This course is known as the plinth and is often composed of a very durable stone to resist the more severe conditions of weathering experienced at pavement or ground level. Furthermore, the stone or style of finish to the slabs may be chosen deliberately to contrast with the upper elevation, see Fig. 9.22.

9.2.6.2. Lintels, jambs, sills, padstones, cornices, quoins and ornamental bands
Where openings, wider than the length of the ordinary masonry units, have to be formed in walls, beams of timber or stone are often used to carry the masonry over the opening (the alternative is to form a flattish arch of

Fig. 9.22. Plinth (orbicular granite) contrasting with building facade (limestone).

masonry units, be they brick or stone, over the opening). For external walls, stone lintels have the advantage of being more durable than timber and if the stone can be carved, stone lintels can combine decorative with structural function. Sometimes it may be desired to have complete, projecting stone surrounds to window openings in a stone or brickwork facade. In that case the lintel will bear on stone jambs (the vertical framing members to the window opening) which, unlike the lintel, may be in more than one piece and which in turn straddle the sill, which has to collect the rainwater running down the window and throw it clear of the masonry below. Such stone surrounds are not always as deep as the full thickness of the wall; in that case a timber lintel may carry the inner part of the wall across the opening and the internal vertical reveals may be wood panelled or plastered and the inner sill will be of wood. A stone lintel has to be a single piece, in order to act as a beam, whereas jambs can have bed joints within their height and sills can have butt joints in their length.

Where major floor beams, particularly iron- or steel beams, have to be supported on brick walls, the vertical reaction force from the beam often has to be spread over a greater length of wall than the width of the beam bearing, in order not to cause local crushing of the brickwork. The traditional way of achieving this is to bed a stone block of the required length, usually three or four courses deep, in the brickwork centrally under the beam bearing. The greater compressive strength of the stone enables it to carry the beam without distress and its bending strength allows it to spread the load on the brickwork.

Cornices are horizontal projecting decorative features on walls, most often occurring at eaves level, but also found at certain floor levels on buildings in classical style; they are usually given quite intricate profiles which together with their exposed position require a material that is both relatively easy to shape and very durable. Some limestones when fresh from the quarry are easy to carve, but harden subsequently; these would seem ideal materials for this application. Ornamental bands, mainly on brick buildings, are similar, but do not project like corniches, being mainly flush with the wall face.

It is sometimes desired to provide sharp, well-defined corners on buildings with walls built of rubble, or to visually emphasise the corners of brick buildings. Such corners or quoins are made from stone blocks, square-cut with sharp arisses like ashlar, but generally larger, see Fig. 6.27.

9.2.6.3. Sills and copings

Sills at the base of window openings and copings on the top of vertical walls are often in locations on buildings exposed to wind and rain. As a result they are often constructed from stone that is known to have a good durability or they may be covered, for example with lead sheeting. Both types of unit are very important in the construction of traditional and modern constructions as they are required to protect the core or cavity of the wall from rain penetration. Sills and copings are partly covered by BS 5642 where the standard describes two durability tests for natural slate copings and sills. No tests for any other stone type or any other parameters are recommended in the standard. It is these buildings components, along with string courses, that are usually in the most exposed locations of a building and consequently the most likely to require testing for durability.

9.3. Forms of construction and uses in civil engineering

9.3.1. Structural uses

9.3.1.1. Arch bridges
Stone slabs have been used for short-span bridges since prehistoric times – the 'clapper' bridges on Dartmoor are UK examples – but it was only the invention of the arch that made it possible to span distances that were larger than the individual pieces of stone that could be quarried, worked, transported and handled on site. The Roman engineers built tier upon tier of semi-circular arches of modest spans to carry their aqueducts across deep gorges, whilst the Chinese 700 years earlier had spanned 37 metres with a segmental arch of only seven metres rise. The centreline of a segmental arch is a segment of a circle, rather than a full semi-circle.

The traditional arch bridge in Britain consists essentially of a barrel vault, that is, an arch that is significantly wider than one or two stones, usually segmental and formed of a single 'ring' of stones, see Fig. 9.23. On the edges of the barrel stand spandrel walls that retain a filling of earth or of rubble-and-mortar. This filling forms the base of the road. This form of construction remained in use well into the railway age and the requirements for gentle gradients of the track sometimes led to viaducts with heights that approach those of the Roman structures, but were achieved with tall piers rather than multiple tiers of arches – Blea Moor Viaduct is one example. Single, larger, spans were bridged with elliptical and other arch shapes, see Fig. 9.24.

Scaffolding and centring are necessary for both this form of construction and for concrete arch bridges, but the stone vault and the spandrel walls require large amounts of masons' labour. Stone arches for bridges were therefore superseded by concrete arches in Europe from the early decades of this century. They were, however, extensively used on the Trans-Iranian Railway in the 1930s and would still be economical where good

Fig. 9.23. Single arch bridge, Brig o' Doon, Scotland.

Fig. 9.24. Railway viaduct at Berwick-on-Tweed.

stone and skilled labour are readily available, and if good sand for concrete would have to be transported long distances.

9.3.1.2. Solid bridge piers, abutments and parapets
Segmental and similar 'flattish' arches need abutments to resist their horizontal thrust, and multiple arches, and other multiple bridge spans, need intermediate piers. These are often situated in severe environments, and heavily loaded: abutments by arch thrusts and earth pressures; piers by the weight of the spans and by water currents, or even ice pressure. So where good stone is available, it is the natural material for these structures. Likewise, if the arches and the spandrel walls have been built of stone, it makes sense to use stone for the parapets. Early bridge piers were usually constructed in a similar way to those in the mediaeval churches with a shell of dressed stones and a core of rubble and mortar, but in order to save weight, Telford used cellular construction for the tall piers for his Menai Suspension bridge and for the Pont Cyssyllte aqueduct. A later spectacular use of stone piers for steel bridge superstructure are the approach spans of the Forth rail bridge, built 1882–1889.

9.3.1.3. Through-thickness dams, retaining walls, dock- and quay walls
The spandrel walls, which retain the infill of arch bridges, have been mentioned above. However, anywhere where earth had to be held at a face that was steeper than its angle of natural repose, or where water had to be stored, where environmental actions were usually severe, stone masonry became the natural material for retaining structures. This was particularly so where other materials, such as brick, would have had to be imported from some distance away. As simple dams and retaining walls are gravity structures, the greater density of stone, compared to brick, was an added advantage. For walls to canal locks and for quay walls, the resistance against abrasion and impact from moored boats was also a desirable property, see Fig. 9.25. Whilst the Romans built a number of stone masonry dams to impound the head waters for their aqueducts, the sheer volume of most later dams led to it being superseded by earthfill or rockfill.

9.3.2. Facing and cladding

9.3.2.1. Facings to bridge piers, abutments and parapets
When brickwork became more economical than stone masonry for structural uses, the greater strength of stone would recommend it as a capping, spreading the concentrated loads from the bridge bearings to the masonry of the piers. The greater abrasion resistance of granite and similar stone led to its use as facing to the brickwork where the structure was subjected to abrasion and impact. This would be the case, for example, for the lower part of piers and their cut-waters, see Fig. 9.26, and for tops of quay walls, whilst its superior weathering resistance would point to its use as copings for bridge parapets, cappings to walls, etc.

9.3.2.2. Facings to dams, intake structures and spillways
Whilst earthfill and rockfill generally displaced masonry as the material for the main structure of dam, there were parts of dams and associated structures which required greater resistance to erosion and abrasion. These were, for instance, the upstream faces of dams, exposed to fluctuating water levels in the reservoir, the intake structures to aqueducts and the spillways which had to carry away the excess water of spring floods. For these, stone remained the preferred material until the advent of high-strength concrete.

9.3.2.3. Tunnel linings and portals
Most tunnels have to be lined and, while bricks and concrete are likely to be available and more economical for tunnels through soft ground, there may be

Fig. 9.25. Stone dock walls.

Fig. 9.26. Piers of the new London Bridge clad in Cornish granite.

instances where stone would be used for linings. Even when the main length of the bore would be brick-lined or self-supporting, stone was often, in the heyday of the railways, used to form semi-monumental portals to major tunnels.

9.3.2.4. Facing to precast concrete cladding panels

Just as in building construction, it is nowadays sometimes found economical to use precast concrete panels to protect or decorate civil engineering structures. Planning constraints may at the same time dictate that a stone face is the best, or even the only acceptable, option. This leads to the use of stone as facing to concrete panels. The panels and the stones tend to be larger and heavier than for buildings, but the principle remains the same.

9.3.3. Hard landscaping

9.3.3.1. External paving

Probably the largest consumption of dimension stone for construction purposes on dry land in the past was road paving, whether in the form of large setts or the smaller cubes, favoured for highways and pedestrian areas on the continent. Nowadays, the use of stone for roadways tends to be limited to ornamental driveways on the approach to important buildings. Similarly, whilst stone paving slabs, traditionally referred to as flags, have generally been replaced by pressed concrete, stone in various forms (slabs, setts, etc.) is still used where special effects are desired or where similar material is being replaced or added to. Stone is particularly prominent in pedestrian areas and in conservation areas. Natural stone is suitable for paving, setts and kerbs but consideration must be given to the planned environment of which it is to be a part, and to its durability, detailing and maintenance.

Consideration should also be given to the type of material traditionally used in the location. Pavements and large pedestrian areas in the UK were often paved in slabs of York sandstone or Caithness flags 50 mm to 75 mm thick which are amongst the best stones available for paving. York stone flags have been a familiar part of many city streets since the 18th century having achieved an early popularity as a result of the ease with which consistent slabs could be produced by splitting the stone along its natural bedding planes. Many stones are now produced by sawing from dimension stone blocks but a few are still split on their natural bed to give a riven finish. The key qualities for a good paving slab are strength, high resistance to weathering (particularly salt and ice), abrasion resistance and slip resistance.

Setts used in the UK were traditionally made from Cornish or Scottish granite blocks around 100mm square and 150 mm to 180 mm thick and the worn surfaces of these setts produce the typical 'cobble' streets depicted in Victorian times. In recent times there has been a renewed interest in the use of setts as they can both enhance areas of hard landscaping and give a good, hard wearing surface that has good slip resistance, see §§9.5.2.3 and 9.6.2.6. The renewal in interest has lead to a revival in the production of setts in the UK and also to the use of reclaimed setts. In other countries, setts, often as small as 40 mm cubes, are used to produce patterns in large pedestrian areas, see Fig. 9.27. Many of the patterns are based on curves and fan-shapes with the setts being laid into areas marked out to give the required design.

Fig. 9.27. Hard landscaping using natural stone setts.

9.3.3.2. Kerbs, bollards, etc

In addition to the use of stone for paving and roadways it has also been used for other features in hard landscaped areas for example as kerbs and bollards, see Fig. 9.28. Kerbs were often made of granite with hewn or sawn faces. In many cases they have survived in areas where the original 'matching' setts or paving have long been lost.

9.4. Design methodology

The key to the successful use of stone is identifying and resolving the separate components within the design

Fig. 9.28. Bollard of porphyritic Shap granite, St. Pauls, London.

methodology: the aesthetics of the end appearance, the durability and the future performance.

9.4.1. Strategy

In order to ensure the success of a proposed stone application, it is necessary for the designer to put into practice a design process which ensures that the properties of the material to be chosen match the functional requirements of the application. Published codes of practice provide an adequate framework for the design, selection and construction of many stone applications, but it is important that their scope and limitations are understood. If departures from the code's recommendations or scope are envisaged, then other means of verification of the suitability of design or materials should be obtained. This may require the advice of experts, or special investigations or tests to be commissioned. If an innovative design is proposed then it is particularly important to recognize in what ways that design departs from established practice and to ensure that the design process addresses the areas of innovation.

It is important to recognize that designers can approach the process of selection from either end. This means either that a particular stone is attractive to a designer and an occasion for its use is sought, or conversely, and more objectively, that performance requirements are identified and a selection is then made from the limited palette of stones which comply.

The whole design process can be considered in three parts: briefing, specification and selection, and detailed design. In fact, although these parts are discussed separately below, the design process moves forward as an iterative process with interaction between stages. In a simple example, a stone may be selected initially upon appearance but later rejected for reasons of lack of durability, high cost or low availability.

9.4.1.1. Briefing

The first requirement of good design is a complete understanding of the properties of the materials available, the functions which they are to perform, and the environment in which they will be exposed. The following is a checklist for the parameters to be considered at this stage:

(*a*) *Durability*

Several aspects of durability require consideration. According to BS 7543: Guide to Durability of buildings, building elements, components, products and components, which provides a framework for the whole subject, there are five key points for a stone application.

- The selection of most granites, metamorphic slates, many marbles, and some limestones can ensure a 'long life' of at least 120 years for most of the uses of stone in buildings subject to the correct detail design.
- The same is not true of all the materials used in stone applications. Particular consideration needs to be given to the design of and access to short or medium life components within a stone cladding system, such as sealants, which will require replacement within the lifetime of the building or structure.
- Where stone is subject to physical abrasion such as paving or steps, then consideration is required as to the level of traffic, design life requirement, and resistance to abrasion of the stone proposed
- The life expectancy of stone may be reduced in situations where it may be saturated for prolonged periods, or used in very thin sheets such as roof slates and copings. The use of sandstones and soft limestones in these situations requires special consideration.
- Within the lifetime of the stone it will be subject to weathering to an extent which is determined by the stone type, surface finish, design, environment, exposure and cleaning regime.

The juxtaposition of two different kinds of stone may lead to accelerated decay of one: for example, where areas of magnesian limestone have been replaced with ordinary limestone, the latter is found to deteriorate rapidly where the run-off from the magnesian stone impinges on it. Similarly, where ordinary limestone has been used above sandstone, the sandstone may deteriorate fairly rapidly.

(b) Appearance
The appearance, especially colour, of natural stone is usually one of the principal reasons for its use in buildings. The appearance of finished stone is a function of its composition, formation and the surface finishing, see Fig. 9.29. In order to judge colour, grain, texture pattern, veining, surface finish and variation, samples should be obtained and buildings where the stone has been used should be visited. Viewing should be carried out to investigate the effects of different lighting conditions and wetting on the appearance. For large projects and patterned paving it may be most useful to prepare a visual 'mock-up' before the design is finalized.

If a honed or polished finish is envisaged it should first be checked whether the stone proposed will actually take, and hold a polish in the conditions in which it will be used. For example, marbles loose their polish after two or three years in most climates when used externally, see Fig. 9.30. A lengthy process of sampling may be required to identify the grit size which gives the degree of polish required. The result is also affected by the steps used in grit size before the final polish, the machines used, and the extent of recycling and filtering of water carrying abrasive and stone dust. When the desired finish is achieved on a sample all these variables should be defined and recorded in the specification.

(c) Form
Most of the dimension stone used in the building industry is in the form of slabs for cladding, lining, and paving, or blocks for ashlar which are sawn and machine finished. For more complex shapes and carved features the workability of the stone becomes important and will influence the choice of stone.

(d) Environment
The environment in which stone is exposed influences both the selection of stone type and detailed design. Resistance to frost, water, and pollutants varies between stone types and sources. In order to ensure that an appropriate stone is selected and appropriate detail design is carried out the degree of exposure to the following has to be known:

(i) diurnal temperature variations, during summer and winter
(ii) rainfall, frequency and intensity
(iii) frost/snow: frequency and temperature

Fig. 9.29. Contrasting appearance of the same stone finished by flame texturing (steps) and polished (walls), Cabot Square, Canary Warf.

Fig. 9.30. A large building in UK unusually clad with marble (Vermont), Canary Wharf.

(iv) groundwater: presence and mineral content
(v) wind
(vi) nature and severity of air/waterborne pollution
(vii) aspect: the direction in which the stone faces, see Fig. 9.31.

Records of (i), (ii), (iii) and (v) are usually available; (vi) may require physical and chemical tests.

(*e*) *Cost*
The budget for the construction project is obviously relevant to the selection of the stone. It must be remembered that the total budget must meet both the purchase costs of the stone, including extraction, cutting, finishing and delivery and the installation costs including the costs for fixings.

(*f*) *Availability*
Irrespective of the desirable appearance of a particular stone or its physical properties and durability or its low cost, to be useful in a given project the stone must be available in blocks or slabs of the necessary dimensions and in quantities, especially rate of output, to meet the construction requirements and schedule. It is interesting to note that the Mandir in Neasden used Carrara marble because the marble from Ambaji, India could not be supplied at the required rate. In the past, the first source of processed stone for major projects has been Italy but large suppliers are now established in the USA, Brazil and Australia. Consideration must be given to the output of the quarry, consistency of the rock, limiting block sizes, capacity of processing and shipping or freight schedules if the construction project is not to be delayed. For major projects visits are likely to be made to the processing facilities and the quarry to obtain and confirm this information.

(*g*) *Maintenance*
Thought must be given to the maintenance of the building such as whether natural weathering is acceptable or will periodic cleaning be necessary. Provision must also be made for the replacement of sealants, if used, and damaged stones.

Information on many of these aspects can be obtained from Codes of Practice, industry pamphlets and from samples.

9.4.2. Specification/selection

9.4.2.1. Specification
The specification of stone is carried out in two ways. The first is simply by reference to source, and the second is by performance standard. Specification by source depends on knowledge of the performance of the stone extracted from particular quarries, and from particular beds in each quarry. It remains the method of specification for much of the stone used in the building industry in the UK. Verification of fitness for purpose for stone specified in this way is provided by an empirical process drawn from the successes and failures of the past. Reference should be made to BS 8298 and BRE Digest 420 which give guidance to the use of stone extracted from quarries in the UK and on selection. Some properties of natural building stones from the British Isles are listed in Table C1 in Appendix C.

It should be remembered, when specifying stone, that the nature and origin of a certain stone determines its properties. Two stones that superficially look alike but which have been formed in different ways and or come from different locations, may have significantly different properties. Being a natural product, the properties of a given rock may vary from quarry to quarry and even from one end of the working face to the other within the same quarry. Some knowledge of the geological formations from which a certain stone has to be won and of the mineral make-up of the stone can, therefore, help to avoid specifying it for an unsuitable purpose.

Fig. 9.31. Staining of unknown cause on one facade of a building.

For example: the polishable limestones from Dorset, the so-called 'Purbeck Marbles' only occur in thin beds. This forced the mediaeval cathedral builders to use it as shafts, cut 'on false bed', but their mineral make-up is such as to make them liable to severe weathering, if used externally in exposed positions. This despite the fact that the 'ordinary' limestones from the same area are adequately durable.

There is now a wide range of stone available in western countries which originates from sources all over the world. Some have little or no track record in the UK to provide evidence of fitness for purpose. There is no British Standard for natural stone, and the industry has adopted American ASTM standards for dimension stone in the absence of any other. European standards are in the course of production and are likely to replace ASTM standards in Europe before the end of the century. Separate ASTM standards are published for granites, marbles, limestones, slates, and sandstones, see §9.5. They define limits on the results of standard tests for petrographic composition, density, strength, modulus of rupture, water absorption, and salt crystallisation. Although the specifications provide absolute limits for various properties, these values should not be employed in calculations without reference to the properties of the actual stone to be used. The limits indicate the properties of stones which have performed successfully in the past but it should be understood that this is based empirically on the successes and failures of the stone used in the United States. It should also be noted that they were developed for use in conjunction with American design codes.

It should be borne in mind that the mechanical properties can vary significantly depending upon the direction of stress relative to bedding planes and on the moisture content of the sample.

9.4.2.2. Selection

Two separate selection processes need to be considered. The first is concerned with identifying a type and source of stone for a particular project, and the second concerns the monitoring of quarry output to ensure that only material which conforms to agreed standards is used. The standard ASTM and BS tests referred to above are used in both processes. There is increasing use of petrographic examination by microscope, which is required by the ASTM standards, in order to provide evidence of the structure and indicate likely performance and potential weaknesses of the stone.

Natural stone requires specific and separate consideration from the majority of materials in the construction industry which are man made and capable of manufacture to obtain performance within specified limits which can be checked by simple measurement or tests. Consequently, natural stone requires careful selection combined with quality control to ensure conformance to specified standards. Helpful advice on the selection of stone for cladding has been given by the Centre for Window and Cladding Technology (CWCT 1997).

9.4.2.3. Special considerations for the selection of slate
For roofing slates, the designer may specify slate with a bias toward any combination of appearance, performance or cost. These are related. For instance, the mineralogy of slate determines both colour and performance and so the desire for a green Cumbrian slate is incompatible with maximum durability in areas of high acid pollution because these contain calcite, see Chapter 2. Advice on the properties and performance of domestic slates may be found in the BRE Report 'The building slates of the British Isles'. Advice on slates from other sources must be sought from the quarry or local agent.

All the national standards for roofing slates include requirements for testing and reference should be made to §9.5 for details of these. The UK slate material standard is BS 680 'Roofing slates'. It has requirements for

standard sizes, flatness, and tolerance in thickness of 'graded' slates
integrity by ringing test
weathering

The weathering test is in three parts. These are:

- Measurement of water absorption (which is not to exceed 0.3% after 48 hours immersion). It has been found that many inferior slates have significantly higher absorption than more durable slates and that high absorption can reduce frost resistance.
- Wetting and drying tests to eliminate those slates that delaminate or flake upon repeated wetting and drying. This test can also be used to help identify slates that contain iron pyrites that can cause damage by expansion on weathering. Analysis of the sulphate content can help to identify slates which contain iron pyrites.
- Acid immersion to identify slates with a high calcium carbonate content in the case of slates intended for sites exposed to sulphurous or other acid pollution.

The standard requires that the tests are carried out on samples taken from three slates.

The standard was issued in 1944 (updated in 1971) to enable slates originating from any part of the country to be tested using simple methods and equipment available at the time. The criteria for pass or fail were based on the results of tests on slates of known performance. The standard seems to have been satisfactory for UK slates but the rapid growth in the use of imported slates has lead to a general feeling that extra requirements need to be included. In particular, a test for the strength of the slate and loads it could carry seems to be required. The proposed European Standard should address both this area and those traditionally found in BS 680. However, until that time BS 680 combined with mineral analysis and determination of flexural strength seem to offer a good basis for specification and selection.

9.4.2.4. Quality control
In order to exercise the same control over the quality of stone supplied for a building project the designer of a building project needs to put into place a regime for the sampling, inspection and testing of stone. The use of ASTM and other standards in specifications enable limits to be put on some of the physical and chemical characteristics of stone. They require that colour, texture and variation are controlled by detailed description, by naming, or by comparison with samples approved prior to commencement of supply. During a construction project using stone of variable appearance or texture, for example, the sawing and finishing of slab may be overseen by the customer or a range of acceptable colours and textures defined by specimens selected by the customer.

One form of quality control that is relevant to thin cladding slabs, is the checking for fine cracks that may have resulted from the extraction or working of the slabs

Other standards and tests for slates

In the UK it is still common for the British Standard to be used. However, occasionally other standards are sometimes referred to in the UK. These include the American standard ASTM C 406 and French Norme Francais P32-301. ASTM C 406 includes a requirement to carry out three weathering tests: a water absorption test, a variation on the acid immersion test in which depth of softening is measured in preference to observation of delamination, and a modulus of rupture test. Depending on the results of the absorption and acid immersion tests, the slate may be given any of three classifications which confer life expectancies in the ranges: over 75 years, 40 to 75, and 20 to 40 years depending on geological location and environmental exposure. A constant value of 60 MPa is required for the modulus of rupture test. P32-301 includes tests for frost resistance, pyrite content and calcium carbonate content.

(cutting of fixing slots, dowel holes, etc.) or from rough handling or transport, see also Chapter 5. Such cracks may pre-dispose to detachment of fragments or whole slabs. For polished or honed fine-grained slabs this can be done by wetting the surface and checking whether any dark, and therefore damp, lines remain after the general surface has dried; for coarser-grained stones, such as granites, a fluorescent clear liquid is used and the surface examined under ultra-violet light. As any detached fragment can constitute a danger to life and limb of people walking below such a clad wall, the usual percentage sampling for purposes of quality control is **not** satisfactory in this case; **every** slab should be examined immediately prior to being fixed.

Flame-texturing of the slab surface may induce incipient spalling and/or microcracking, which may lead to reduced durability. Whilst the potentially detached slivers may be less of a hazard in this case, such slabs should be examined for excessive fissuring.

It should be borne in mind that the natural variability of stone, combined with the hazards in extraction, processing and transport may make it necessary to impose quality control on site, immediately prior to the incorporation of the blocks or slabs in the finished works. If such a procedure is intended, it should be described in, and be made part of the contract documents.

9.4.3. Design

The design of a building can be considered from two different points – the visual design and the structural design.

9.4.3.1. General design of facades

The detail design may proceed along various paths. In some instances the architect may limit his input to the main features of the facades and leave the masonry contractor's drawing office to deal with the height of individual course, slab sizes, fixing hardware, etc. In other cases, the architect will, preferably in consultation with a structural engineer and someone knowledgeable from the stone industry, have drawn the detailed layout of the facade, decided on the fixing system, if any, and jointing, leaving the stone contractor to concentrate on schedules of cutting dimensions, fixing slots, etc.

9.4.3.2. Structural design of load-bearing masonry

For load-bearing and self-supporting, as well as for infill, masonry the structural design proceeds in the conventional manner; loads and bending moments, whether from gravity, wind or other sources, are assessed, stresses are calculated and compared with the compressive strength of masonry given in BS 5628, or similar design codes (this will be substantially less than the strength of the stone, due to the effect of the mortar joints, see §9.5.1.1). If these documents do not give reasonable guidance for the stone or the proposed form of construction, tests can be carried out on reduced scale 'wallettes' to ascertain the masonry strength.

9.4.3.3. Structural design of facade cladding

For cladding, basically similar procedures are carried out; the governing 'load parameters' in this case being, bending from wind forces, forces created by restraint from the fixings of movements due to temperature and moisture fluctuations, or movements of the supporting structure relative to the cladding. The obvious most important strength property of the stone is the bending strength but the resistance against pull-out of the fixings that hold the slabs to the backing structure is, if anything, more important unless whole slabs are not to be sucked off the building during high winds and fall to the ground – or onto innocent passers-by on the footway below.

Self weight. Panel dimensions should be established early in the design process because they determine the minimum thickness of stone which can be used and, hence, panel weight. This has a large effect on the choice of support system and on fixing design. Most stone cladding in the UK is designed in accordance with BS 8298 which recommends that stone thickness should be in accordance with Table 4 which relates stone thickness to stone type and location, unless the thickness of stone is proved by calculation. No method of calculation is given.

Lateral loads. In the UK the main lateral forces are due to wind, both pressure and suction. Loads from access equipment and impact load as described in BS 8200 may also have to be considered. Wind loads are stipulated by CP 3: Chapter V or BS 6399, Part 2 1995. In parts of North America, New Zealand and other parts of the world subject to seismic activity, building regulations require calculations to prove the capacity of the support system to withstand inertia forces due to earthquake.

Deflection. Building structures deflect elastically, and plastically as a result of dead and live loads and with respect to large buildings and multi-storey buildings, in particular, the cladding designer needs to allow for these. Cladding system fixings impose point loads on the building structure at the anchor position and, where these are of a high order as can be the case with stone faced pre-cast concrete panels, the horizontal members must be designed to ensure that acceptable levels of deflection are not exceeded.

In many cases the stone cladding is fixed after the heavy elements of construction have been placed and the majority of the elastic deflection has taken place but, where heavy pre-cast concrete panel systems are to be used and the late imposition of a large part of the dead load is inevitable, then it is usual to provide adjustment in the fixings which give a means of compensating for deflection (Tanno 1997)

The cladding systems for large concrete framed buildings also have to accommodate creep and the cladding designer should obtain estimates of the amount of creep which will occur in the structure and allow for these in fixing and joint design.

Shrinkage and creep. Concrete structures are also subject to drying shrinkage and creep. Approximately 65% of the total shrinkage takes place within the first three months. The designer should either allow for the shrinkage and creep and the resulting column shortening in his design, or delay the installation of the cladding until after most of the shrinkage has occurred. It should be remembered that a large proportion of shrinkage will only take place after the building has been closed in and heated.

Thermal and moisture movements. The different rates of thermal expansion of the materials used in stone cladding, and the changes in temperature which occur both as result of diurnal temperature changes, solar heating, and heat exchange through the building fabric result in differential thermal movement for which the design must allow. In extreme conditions a movement of 12 mm can occur in a 30 metre masonry wall. Any attempt to restrain such movement will cause large forces acting on the fixing points in the stone slabs and in the substrate.

Natural stones expand and contract, when saturated and exposed to cyclical freezing and thawing weather conditions. The degree of movement is dependent on the stone type. These movements can cause stress on the support system, structure, and within the stone itself although most cladding designs contain sufficient provision for movement in their jointing systems to allow for this effect. The measures available to the designer to reduce the amount of movement rely on minimising the moisture in the stone. This can be done by sealing joints and by the application of water resisting treatments to the stone. These treatments may however have a limited life and can have undesirable side effects. For example, towards the end of their effective life, they will not exclude all water, but they may still inhibit the drying out of the stone by evaporation and thus aggravate the problem.

Building tolerance. It is usual for cladding designers to specify closer construction tolerances than those usually specified by the engineer for the building frame; and even the latter are sometimes exceeded in practice. Consideration must be given to the likely differences between the designed and the actual clearances between cladding and frame. The cladding designer should then allow for these variations in the fixing design. Shims and slotted holes in the metal components are usually used to provide the adjustment needed.

Cumulative effects. The effects described above can act in concert or in opposition, and calculation of the cumulative effect should be carried out to provide the basis for joint design. A method for determining these effects can be found in Lewis (1995).

9.4.3.4. Design of roof cladding

The functions of a slate roof are to provide a water resistant barrier to rain and snow, and to resist the effects of wind uplift, snow load and self weight. BS 5534 and BS 6399 Parts 2 and 3 provides guidance on all of these subjects. This standard is not referred to in Building Regulations but compliance with it would normally be accepted as evidence of good practice.

The key variables in the design of slate roofs are:

- roof pitch
- slate size
- overlap
- method of fixing

The relationship between roof pitch and overlap described in §9.2.5.1 above also applies to slate roofs. The lower the pitch the greater the overlap required as demonstrated in Tables 4 and 5 of BS 5534.

It is usual practice now to specify a single size of slate within the BS 680 range from 615 mm × 340 mm down to 300 mm × 155 mm. These are faster to lay than random size slates because less sorting is required and this is sufficient to offset the higher prices that are charged relative to random slates. Less wastage results from the production of random slates and this is the reason for the difference in price. Random slates are sometimes specified when the appearance of diminishing courses is required on steeper roof pitches. It is also normal for larger slates to be priced higher than small slates but they are faster to fix because the time taken to fix a 615 mm × 340 mm slate is no more than to fix a 300 mm × 155 mm slate.

It is standard practice to centre nail each slate twice because they are considerably thinner than stone slates. Whereas the self weight of stone is usually sufficient in itself to resist wind uplift when the slates are pegged or nailed at the top only, the thinner slates can lift if fixed this way. If nails were positioned under or close to the joints in the course of slates above, then leakage through the holes would be likely. Nails should, therefore, be positioned close to the edge of the slates, see BS 5534. Nails must be corrosion resistant if they are not to fail before the slate, see BS 5534 for the use of aluminium, copper and silicon bronze nails.

An alternative method of fixing has been proposed in recent years in which stainless steel wire hooks engage in the bottom of each slate and the top of the battens. This offers the advantage that the slates do not have to be drilled hence providing a saving in installation time and costs, and ease of repair. The method is not covered in the British Standard and adequate evidence of performance should be obtained before this method is contemplated.

The cost of a slate roof covering is affected by the slate specified, by the amount and size of slate used and by the cost of fixing. The prices of the cheapest and most expensive natural slates vary by a factor of six or eight. In descending order they are: Cumbrian slate, Welsh slates and imported slates. The design of the roof affects the amount of slate used in two ways. Clearly the steeper the roof pitch for a given plan area, the greater the quantity of slate required. But conversely the shallower the pitch, the greater the head lap required to prevent ingress of wind blown snow or rain and hence the greater the quantity of slate used. A further variable is that larger slates are generally priced higher than small slates. Many slate suppliers will now carry out a price study to determine the most economic configuration of a particular roof.

9.4.3.5. Design of fixings

Methods used to fix stone to buildings in the past are numerous; BS 8298 provides examples of the most commonly used fixing methods. The purpose of this section is to describe the principles to be adopted in fixing design.

Materials. The important properties of the materials used in stone fixings are:

- strength and stiffness
- corrosion resistance
- they should not cause staining or deterioration of the stone.

The materials used most commonly in the UK are various grades of stainless steel and copper and copper based alloys. For recommendations on the use of these alloys including recommended working stresses, reference should be made to BS 8298. The standard does not contain recommendations for the use of any other metals or alloys, but it does note that their use is not precluded if their suitability can be demonstrated. In North America the use of galvanized steel and aluminium alloys for fixings is common. The Masonry Institute of America support the use of hot dip galvanized fixings which are not in direct contact with stone, subject to minimum coating thicknesses, which increase with decreasing fixing thickness. Advice on the life expectancy of galvanized components is available from the Zinc Development Association. (Note: galvanizing does not provide long-lasting protection against corrosion due to sulphurous pollutants and chlorides).

Types of fixing. Fixing types are usually categorized by their function. BS 8298 identifies five types of fixing for stone claddings; some examples of which are shown in Fig. 9.13:

- load bearing fixings
- restraint fixings which provide resistance to wind and other lateral forces
- combined loadbearing and restraint fixings
- face fixings, for situations where hidden fixings are undesirable or impractical
- soffit fixings.

To this list may be added perimeter fixings, such as the continuous extrusions used in the fixing of stone to framed systems.

Fixing design. Fixings may be either purpose designed or selected from manufacturers' standard range of products. The features of fixings which should be considered during the selection or design are:

- strength to resist loads imposed by panel weight, wind, earthquake (where applicable) and other imposed loads
- the ability to accommodate movement which is predicted in the cladding and substructure as result of thermal effects and structural deflection
- the facility for adjustment which may be required to accommodate construction tolerances
- the practicality of installation in a particular system and a particular panel fixing sequence.

BS 8298 contains specific requirements for thickness of stone behind fixings and minimum depth of slots for corbel plates which are related to the type of stone used, location on the building and thickness of stone. There are minimum depths of penetration for dowel fixings etc. and reference should be made to this standard for the selection or design of fixings for UK projects.

If fixings not covered by BS 8298: 1994 are proposed, prototype testing should be carried out. This could include testing of fixings, materials or panels. For example, a test panel held by the appropriate fixings may be placed in a chamber to a form a septum over which a pressure difference is created to determine the resistance against suction created by wind. A useful guide to the type of tests that can be undertaken is given in Lewis (1995).

Fixing anchorages. The method by which fixings are attached to the structure include:

- by mortar fixing of ties into pockets in the structure or joints in masonry backup walls. The acceptable pull out values for these types of fixing is usually achieved by the use of features such as fishtails, perforated plates or wavy tails
- Cast-in slots
- Expanding and resin anchor bolts.

Reference should be made to the manufacturers' recommendations and those of BS 8298. BS 8298 cautions against the use of resin anchors for situations where there is a tensile load because their long term performance has not been proven.

Layout and positions of fixings. The preparation of a layout, indicating types of fixings and locations, forms part of the structural design of the cladding system. This will be determined by the size and weight of the panels, the background structure to which they are fixed, and the load capacity of the individual fixings. There are specific requirements in BS 8298 for the number and location of fixings for individual stone panels and reference should be made to this standard for projects in the UK.

9.4.3.6 Joints

Joints in stone cladding systems are formed at junctions between panels, as movement joints or at the junction with other building elements. Whether or not these joints are filled should be considered at an early stage in the design when it is decided whether the cladding system is to be designed as a sealed system, a rainscreen, or how else it is to function and what level of rain penetration and air movement through the joints is acceptable and, or, desirable. BS 8298 contains recommendations for the provision, detail and construction of joints.

Panel joints. Traditionally panel joints were filled with cement sand or cement/lime sand mortar, but there is an increasing use of elastomeric sealants, particularly for marble and granite claddings. These joints are not intended to accommodate any movement except the thermal and frost expansion and contraction of the panels

Movement joints. Movements joints are used to:

- prevent transfer of vertical loads from one lift of cladding to the next
- prevent transfer of loads from the structure to the cladding
- prevent stresses which would otherwise arise from thermal and other movements listed in §9.4.3.3
- provide a continuous weather seal, whilst allowing movement. The width of these joints depends upon the movement expected, their spacing, and the elasticity of the sealant used.

Junctions with other elements. The movement which panel and movement joints are required to accommodate is usually in one dimension: in the plane of the stone and perpendicular to the joint. Movement in junctions with other building elements may be in two or three dimensions, if there are independent fixing systems, and if the coefficients of thermal expansion or thermal mass of the adjoining elements are different from those of the stone. Careful consideration of the likely movements is required to ensure that the sealant is not overstressed in these joints.

Sealants. Reference should be made to BS 6213 for guidance on the selection and use of sealants. There are two particular aspects of design which warrant discussion here.

- Life expectancy. The probability of the life expectancy of a sealant being lower than that of stone or the whole stone installation was referred to under the heading of durability. Even the manufacturers of sealants do not claim a service life of more than 20 years for the most widely specified sealants: silicones and polysulphides. It is, therefore, probable that they will require replacement several times during the design life of the building. The designer should plan for this and ensure that the joints are reasonably accessible to enable future inspection and replacement.
- Compatibility. There are a number of instances of the use of sealants resulting in the staining of stone, and in some cases expensive remedial works have been carried out to remove staining and re-apply non-staining sealant, see Fig. 9.32 (Anon 1997). New non-staining silicones have been developed in the 1990s specifically for use with marbles and limestones, but nonetheless it is recommended that trials be conducted and previous sealant applications viewed to prove the compatibility of sealant and stone. Other compatibility problems arise from contact between silicone sealants and damp-proof membrane components which contain pitch or bitumen and cause staining of the sealant. Contact should be prevented by specifying products which do not contain bitumen or pitch, a different pitch or bitumen tolerant sealant, or incorporation of a separating layer.

9.4.4. Workmanship

Workmanship is important in all aspects of the construction of buildings. This is particularly so for stonework because its integrity and durability can be affected by defects which are not discernible to the naked eye immediately after completion.

For example, micro- or macrocracking may have been caused by the block, from which the stone is cut, having been extracted by blasting, or extracted by wedging from a face fissured from previous blasting. On a large cladding contract in Australia, where large slabs of Sardinian granite had been specified, almost two thirds of the first shipment were rejected, when dye testing, see §9.4.2.2, revealed serious cracking. It was found that the blocks had been taken from a face from which paving blocks or aggregates had previously been extracted by blasting. The quarry operator was compelled to use another quarry face, some distance away, for subsequent consignments.

Fig. 9.32. Staining of stone by sealant (also showing current bedding of the adjacent sandstone).

Another cause of cracking can be unsuitable techniques for cutting corbel slots and cramp holes. On a large building in London, extensive cracking of the granite cladding slabs was observed. The majority of the cracks followed the lines of the corbel slots on the back of the slabs before continuing in random directions. It was found that many of the corbel slots had been manually enlarged by hammer and chisel to accommodate inaccurate levelling of the corbel plates. Experiments were conducted which showed that cutting corbel slots by water-cooled diamond saw (as had been done at the supplier's workshop) did not cause any cracking, but that enlargement by hand, or by using a non-cooled abrasive disc cutter produced cracking in almost every case.

On the same building, other cracks were found which emanated from hard shims that had been left in instead of being removed prior to the sealing of the movement joint. Some illustrated examples of poor workmanship during construction have been given by provided by Harrison (1997).

Most slate roofing failures investigated in recent years have included elements of poor workmanship. Some of these have been confined to poorly executed details. Others show widespread malpractice including the roof of a large commercial building where the majority of the slates had been punched from the face instead of the back contrary to normal practice and specification. This had resulted in the absence of a countersink, raised nailed heads and the cracking of over 50% of slates on the roof one year after completion. Also the nail holes had been incorrectly positioned too far from the edge of the slates, within the angle of creep, that is the triangular zone under the exposed part of the joint between slates into which rainwater leaks.

To avoid this type of problem, it is necessary to take steps to ensure that adequate standards of workmanship are specified and enforced. The following items should be considered:

Specifications. Relevant parts of BS 8298 'Code of practice for the design and installation of natural stone cladding and lining' may be quoted in their entirety for all normal stone cladding. Guidance on cladding that is outside the scope of BS 8298 can be found in the work of the Centre for Window and Cladding Technology at Bath University. BS 8000 Part 6 'Code of practice for slating and tiling of roofs and claddings' may be quoted in its entirety for slating work.

Skill. It is necessary to ensure that fixers of stone cladding and slates have an adequate level of skill and expertise. This may be approached by specifying that the work is to be carried out only by trained tradesmen, or by taking up references and inspecting work carried out by the proposed subcontractor or by naming subcontractors of known competence.

Inspections. Inspection may be carried out by the Architect and the Clerk of Works, or in the case of engineered cladding, such as for instance 'strong-back cladding', by a specialist Resident Engineer. In some instances, it is apparent that routine inspections by the architect and the Clerk of Works have failed to pick up widespread poor workmanship and breaches of specification. In some instances this may be as the result of inexperience and in others, because many of the defects which can occur are rapidly covered up. Clearly it is important for the architect to establish a planned series of inspections and to ensure that a competent person undertakes inspections. If expertise is not available in the office, then the services of a specialist should be obtained. These services should cover preparation work. An early mock-up or sample, which may be the first section of the cladding or roof to be installed, should be inspected in order to establish a standard before the actual work starts. Then sufficiently regular inspection should be made throughout the installation work to provide assurance that the work is adhering to the established standard.

9.5. Functional requirements of stone for different uses

The properties of a stone depend on the properties of the minerals of which it is composed and on the processes by which the parent rock has been formed up to the time of extraction. In igneous rocks, such as granite, the hard minerals, such as quartz and feldspar, have been 'fused' together during the cooling and solidification of the magma from the molten state. These rocks are, therefore, generally stronger and more abrasion resistant than sedimentary rocks, such as sandstone, in which the quartz grains are only cemented (or 'glued') together by softer minerals such as calcite or iron oxides. Because stones such as granite contain a very high proportion of minerals with similar (high) hardnesses, they tend to 'polish' with wear and become slippery. However, in sandstones the usually softer cementing minerals wear down first, thus reducing their 'grip' on the hard particles which become loose and removed, exposing a fresh rough wearing surface, before they themselves have been worn. A good introduction to the properties of different stone types is given by Winkler (1973, 1994).

For a stone of a given geological classification, the different uses to which it may be put each dictate a different priority to its various properties. If it is to be used as external cladding slabs, weathering resistance and bending strength would be at the top of the list, whereas for internal flooring slabs, wear resistance and slip resistance would take preference. In this section the various properties of stone in general are discussed with reference to the requirements for different uses.

A summary of the functional requirements and properties of dimension stone for different uses is given in Table 9.1.

9.5.1. Structural Properties

9.5.1.1. Compressive strength

As explained in §9.2.1.5, failure of masonry subjected to vertical load rarely takes place by crushing of the stones or the bricks. In dry-bedded masonry, the stones only touch each other at discrete spots on the bed joints and the very high contact forces set up tensile stresses, which lead to spalling at the faces. In mortar-jointed masonry, the mortar extends laterally and 'drags' the units with it; the stones or bricks then split or spall. Walls may then split into two leaves, which then buckle; piers may develop vertical cracks and the separated 'mini-piers' buckle.

All modes of failure of masonry under vertical load are essentially caused by the overcoming of the horizontal *tensile* strength of the bricks or stones, **not** the vertical compressive strength. Current methods of testing the compressive strength of stone (particularly those using cylinder specimens) do, however, produce failures that are largely due to lateral tensile strains, and thus give a reasonable prediction of the behaviour of stone under compressive load.

Design codes of practice, such as BS 5628 lay down permissible loads on masonry in terms of the strength of the units (stone, bricks or blocks), modified by a factor depending on the strength of the mortar (and on the shape of the units, the height-to thickness ratio of the wall or pier, etc.). The Department of Transport in their bridge assessment manual BD 21/93 show a graph, giving the strength of masonry as a function of the stone strength for three different types of masonry. This is much simpler to use than BS 5628, but appears to give somewhat conservative values. In the table below, values of masonry strength, read from the graph BD 21/93 are shown for a range of stone strengths:

Table 9.2 demonstrates that, whilst good stone is likely to be stronger than most concrete, it may still be important to know its actual compressive strength in order to substantiate the carrying capacity of the masonry built from that stone.

Most stone is not isotropic and for some, particularly sedimentary rocks, the strength parallel to the bedding plane is significantly different from that perpendicular to it. It is therefore essential that test results for compressive strength refer to the direction of loading, relative to the orientation of the bedding plane in the structure.

In traditional through-thickness load-bearing masonry buildings, the compressive strength of the stone was rarely important; for piers and arches the geometric proportions would be more likely to govern the buckling stability, and the requirements for temporary stability during construction led to wall thicknesses that resulted

Table 9.1. *Properties of dimension stone for various uses*

	Properties								
	Compressive strength	*Bending strength*	*Tensile (pullout) strength*	*Elastic modulus*	*Thermal and moisture movement*	*Weathering resistance*	*Abrasion resistance*	*Precision workability and 'polishability'*	*Colour variability and permanence*
Building uses: 1									
Load bearing and self-supporting masonry									
Through-thickness stone walls, piers and arches	●	–	–	–	–	◑	–	○	◑
Outer leaf of external (cavity-) walls	○	–	–	–	○	●	–	○	●
Stone facing bonded to backing brickwork	○	–	–	○	○	●	–	○	●
Self-supporting, brick-backed facade wall to steel frame	○	–	–	○	○	●	–	●	●
Ashlar with rubble- and mortar core	○	–	–	–	–	◑	–	○	●
Random rubble outer skins with concrete core	–	–	–	–	–	◑	–	–	○
Masonry facades to framed buildings									
Stone facing with brickwork backing, supported floor-by-floor on steel frame	–	–	–	–	○	●	–	○	●
Ditto on reinforced concrete frame	–	–	–	–	○	●	–	○	●
Building uses: 2									
Cladding and lining slabs to framed buildings									
Claddings and linings of slabs, individually fixed by metal devices	–	●	●	–	○	◑	–	●	●
Claddings of stone slabs, as permanent formwork for reinforced concrete	–	○	–	○	●	◑	–	○	●
Claddings of stone slabs, 'hedgehog-pinned' to precast concrete panels	–	–	●	–	●	◑	–	○	●
Claddings of stone 'fingers' set in formwork for precast concrete panels	–	–	–	–	○	○	–	–	○
Claddings of stone slabs, bolted to steel trusses, fixed to the frame	–	○	●	○	●	◑	–	○	●
Roofing									
Slates, parapet cappings, gutters, etc.	–	○	○	–	○	○	–	○	–
Miscellaneous									
Floor pavings and stair treads	–	○	–	–	–	◑	●	○	○
'Cantilever' stairs and landings	–	●	–	–	–	–	●	○	○
Lintels, cornices, ornamental bands, quoins, etc. on brick buildings	–	○	–	–	–	◑	–	○	○
Civil engineering uses									
Solid stone arch bridges	●	–	–	○	–	●	–	○	–
Masonry dams, retaining-, dock- and quay walls and bridge abutments	○	–	–	–	–	●	●	–	–
In situ bonded facings to brick- or concrete walls, bridge piers and -abutments	○	–	–	○	○	●	●	–	–
Solid stone masonry bridge piers	●	–	–	–	–	●	●	–	–
In situ facings to intake structures and spillways to dams									
Linings to tunnels through rock	○	–	–	○	–	○	○	–	–
Portals to, otherwise brick-, or concrete-lined, tunnels	○	–	–	–	–	○	○	○	–
Cladding of stones, set in formwork for precast cladding panels	–	–	–	–	○	○	○	○	○
External paving, kerbs, bollards, etc.	–	○	–	–	–	○	○	–	–

– Not important.
○ Of some importance in some cases.
◑ Important for external applications.
● Important.

Table 9.2. *Characteristic masonry strengths in N/mm² (After DoT: BD 21/93)*

	Strength of stones (N/mm²)				
	40	80	120	160	200
Ashlar	7.0	11.0	14.0	16.1	17.5
Squared rubble in 1:2:9 mortar	5.2	8.4	10.5	12.0	13.0
Random rubble in lime mortar	3.5	5.5	6.9	8.0	8.8

Characteristic strength refers to the statistical concept that of an infinite number of samples, 95% would have a strength equal to or greater than that value.

in generally low stresses. Where the stone was used as facing, bonded to backing brickwork, the significantly lower strength of the backing would be the factor governing the load-carrying capacity of the wall as a whole.

Padstones in brick buildings, supporting iron or steel beams, and cappings to piers and abutments, subjected to concentrated loads from bridge bearings were traditional applications of stone, for which the compressive strength was important.

Some modern architectural uses of stone, e.g. in slender, sometimes prestressed, piers, with simultaneous specific demands for colour, etc. require compressive strength, which may be at the upper limits of the stone that may be desired for its other properties, e.g. colour. This calls for extensive testing *before* the choice of stone and the design is finalized.

On a recent project for a prestigious building, a series of tests demonstrated that reinforcement of the bed joints with a steel mesh significantly increased the compressive strength of the masonry. There was also found to be significant variability of the strength of stone even from the same bed in the quarry. Samples from each block were, therefore, tested and the subsequently cut stones were sorted so as to allow the stronger to be used in the more heavily loaded parts of the masonry.

9.5.1.2. Bending and shear strength

Stone elements that have to carry loads perpendicular to their largest dimension, either spanning between isolated supports such as cladding slabs, or distributing concentrated loads onto a larger area of a weaker substrate such as flooring and pavings, have to work in bending and shear. The bending strength of the stone then becomes a critical structural property, the more so because, as for all brittle materials, the bending strength is governed by the inherently weaker tensile strength. Bending strength is normally measured by modulus of rupture or flexural strength tests. Guidance upon the use of the results of these tests in calculations of loading for cladding panels can be found in Lewis (1995).

At low levels of loading, bending causes stresses that increase linearly from the middle plane of the member (the neutral axis) towards the faces. These stresses are compressive on the face that becomes concave as the originally flat member bends, and tensile on the face that becomes convex. As the loading increases, the neutral axis moves towards the concave (compressed) face, the compressive stresses increase at a rate greater than linear, the tensile at a rate less than linear. As this leads to a greater part of the cross-section being in tension, the probability of a local weakness, such as a microcrack or grain boundary, triggering a tensile failure, increases, see Fig. 9.33.

9.5.1.3. Tensile (pull-out) strength

The major force acting on cladding slabs is wind suction. The slabs are restrained against this by various fixing devices, which have one thing in common: they exert local reaction forces at right angles to the plane of the slabs. In the case of through bolts, which are usually countersunk and the hole pelleted to hide the bolt, failure would take the form of a truncated cone pulling out of the back face of the slab. The traditional cramp, located in a hole in the edge of the slab would, at failure, pull out a 'half-cone', see Fig. 9.34. In a similar way, any metal devices fixed to, or into, stone by anchor bolts of one kind or another, or by embedment in a hole, rely for

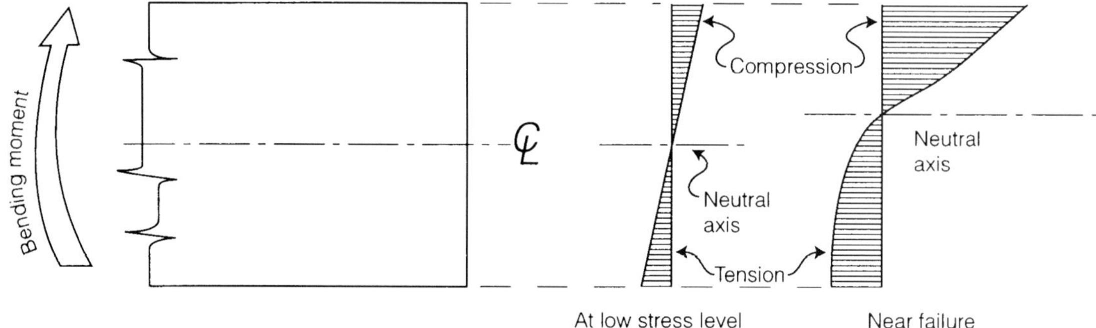

Fig. 9.33. Diagram of stress distribution in a section under bending.

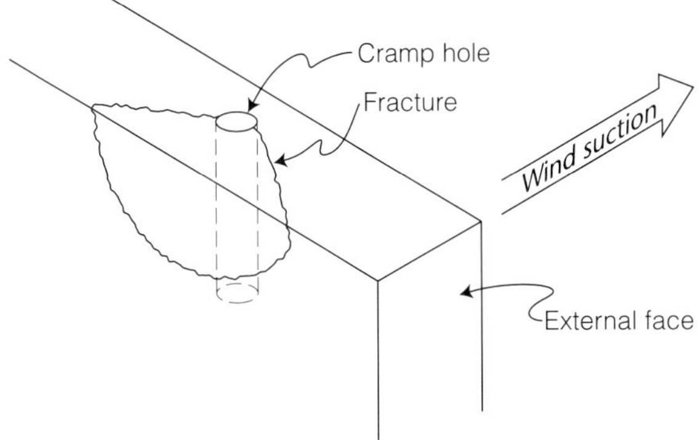

Fig. 9.34. Cladding slab failure due to pull-out of fixing cramp.

their stability and resistance on the tensile strength of the stone, be they handrails on street kerbs or mooring rings on quaysides.

9.5.1.4. Modulus of deformation (elastic modulus)
Elastic modulus, or Young's modulus, strictly speaking refers to linear-elastic materials, that is materials for which stress is linearly proportional to strain. Except for very low stress levels, this is not the case for stone, for which the better term for the relation between stress and strain is modulus of deformation. The amount that a stone wall, or pier, shortens under load is equal to its height times the compressive stress, divided by the modulus of deformation of the masonry. Due to the relative thinness of the mortar joints, compared to the height of the stone courses, the modulus of the masonry is largely determined by the modulus of the stone.

Therefore, under compression the modulus of deformation of the stone may be important where the load has to be shared between a backing masonry of brick or block and a bonded stone facing masonry. If the modulus of the backing units is significantly lower than that of the stone, the backing masonry will tend to shorten more under the same load than the stone masonry. The stiffer masonry will then carry the majority of the load and may become overstressed. If, conversely, the modulus of the stone is too low, overloading of the backing may then occur (this is the less probable case).

9.5.1.5. Thermal and moisture movements
When the temperature of an unrestrained body is increased, it will get longer. The elongation will be proportional to the original length and to the temperature rise. It will, however, not be the same for different materials. The temperature movement of a particular material is characterized by the coefficient of thermal expansion, that is: the increase in length, per degree of temperature rise, divided by the original length. Typical coefficients of thermal expansion for some stones are given in Table 9.3.

When the moisture content of a body increases, it will get longer. The elongation will be proportional to the original length and to the rise of the moisture content. Neither will it be the same for different materials. The moisture movement of a particular material is characterized by the increase in length, per percentage of increase of the moisture content, divided by the original length. Typical values for some stones are given in Table 9.3. The moisture content is usually defined as the mass of water in a given volume of the stone, divided by the oven-dry mass of the same volume. Some sedimentary stones display drying shrinkage between extraction, when the moisture content, fresh from the quarry, may be relatively high, and in the finished work, when the moisture content will have reached equilibrium with the environment.

At first glance, it may seem surprising to find movements due to thermal and moisture variations under the heading of structural properties. However, locally, stresses caused by restraint of movements, due to environmental fluctuations, can be of the same order as those caused by gravity- and/or wind loads. Thick, solid, walls in climates with very high diurnal temperature fluctuations will on their internal face maintain a temperature equal to the 24 hour mean (or if the building is air-conditioned, well below the diurnal mean for the external environment). The external face, if exposed to the sun, may during early afternoon reach temperatures 40–50 degrees centigrade above the diurnal mean, whereas at night the face temperature may drop to about 10 degrees *below* the mean. The consequent expansions and contractions of the external face are restrained by the mass of the masonry that remains at the mean temperature. The internal stresses, resulting from such restraint can in time cause the stone to crumble. This has been observed in India, where carved sandstone on east- and west-facing facades, which are subjected to the most severe temperature fluctuations, is seen to have deteriorated at a faster rate than north-facing similar work. Some stones also display thermal anisotropy, that is, their coefficient of thermal expansion is not the same in all directions; this can also lead to internal stresses in masonry.

Where stone is used as facing to backing masonry, a temperature change that is the same for both materials can cause the one to expand more than the other, if their coefficients of thermal expansion are significantly different. For cladding slabs, the restraint of temperature movements, due to the stiffness of the fixing devices, can lead to high stresses at the holes and rebates in which the fixings hold the slab.

Temperature movements are usually fully reversible. In certain stones, such as some marbles, temperature expansions do, however, not reverse completely on cooling; leaving a residual permanent elongation and a weakening of the stone observed as a loss of flexural strength. There have been examples where marble

Table 9.3. *Physical properties for different stone types (see also Table C2 in Appendix C). (Based on Winkler 1973, Schaffer 1932 and Farmer 1968)*

Rock Type	*Aggregation properties*			*Thermal properties*				*Mechanical properties*			
	Bulk density (tonnes m^{-3})	*Porosity (%)*	*Permeability μ ($-\log d$)*	*Thermal expansion ($10^{-6}/°C$)*	*Thermal conductivity* K *(mcal/cm.S.°C)*	*Diffusivity* k *(10^{-2} $cm^2 s^{-1}$)*	*Moisture expansion (%)*	*Moh's hardness* H	*Young's modulus* E *(Mpa) $\times 10^4$*	*Compressive strength* S *(MPa)*	*Modulus of rupture* R *(MPa)*
Granite	2.5–2.7	0.1–4.0	9–6	5–11	3–10	0.5–3.0		5.0–7.0	2–6	80–330	10–70
Gabbro	2.8–3.1	0.3–3.0	7–5	4–7	4–6	1.2		5.0–6.5	7–11	110–300	10–70
Rhyolite-Andesite	2.2–2.5	4.0–15.0	8–2	5–9	2–9	0.4–3.0		5.0–6.5		60–220	1–70
Basalt	2.7–3.1	0.1–5.0	5–1	4–6	2–5	0.4–1.5		4.0–6.5	6–10	50–290	10–90
Quartzite	2.5–2.7	0.3–3.0	7–4	10–12	8–16	2.8		4.0–7.0		110–360	10–100
Marble	2.4–2.8	0.4–5.0	6–3	5–9	3–7	0.5–1.5		2.0–4.0		40–190	4–30
Slate	2.6–2.9	0.1–5.0	11–8	8–10	3–9	0.5–3.0		3.0–5.0		50–310	5–100
Sandstone	2.0–2.6	1.0–30.0	3–0	8–12	2–12	0.4–5.0	0.032	2.0–7.0	0.3–8	20–250	1–40
Limestone	1.8–2.7	0.3–30.0	9–2	4–12	2–6	0.4–1.5	0.008	2.0–3.0	1–8	20–240	1–50
Shale	2.0–2.5	2.0–30.0	9–5	9–15	1–8	0.3–2.0		2.0–3.0	1–3.5	30–130	2–50
Soapstone	2.5–2.8	0.5–5.0	6–4	8–12	2–7	0.4–1.5		1.0		10–40	1–10
Travertine	2.0–2.7	0.5–5.0	5–2	6–10	2–5	0.4–1.0		2.0–3.0		10–150	2–10
Serpentinite	2.2–2.7	1.0–15.0	7–2	5–12	3–9	0.5–3.0		2.0–5.0		70–190	5–10

cladding panels have distorted and bowed as a result of thermal cycles and this has been attributed to differential expansion and to creep induced by weakening of the panels (Bouineau & Perrier 1995).

9.5.2. Weathering and wear resistance

9.5.2.1. Chemical resistance

The chemical resistance of natural stone is particularly important for stones that are to be exposed to polluted atmospheres where acidic gases are present, for example industrial areas. Other sources of chemical attack include, amongst others, spray from roads treated with de-icing salts, some cleaning agents, particularly those used for stone cleaning. The types of stone that are particularly affected by acidic gases are limestones, calcareous sandstones and metamorphic slates containing significant amounts of calcium carbonate. In addition, a number of weathered igneous rocks can also contain calcium carbonate and, therefore, be susceptible to chemical weathering. Chemical weathering can affect igneous rocks, for example granites, but the timescale over which the weathering takes place is usually much longer than the expected life of a building.

9.5.2.2. Frost resistance

Frost or freeze-thaw resistance is important for stones used in locations where temperatures will drop below freezing for extended periods. The effect of freeze-thaw on a stone will depend on the temperature the stone is exposed to, the porosity and pore size distribution and the amount of water present in the stone at the time of freezing as it is the formation of ice crystals that leads to the disruption of the structure of the stone, see Fig. 9.35. Stone with a low porosity, such as marble, or stones that are dry will have little water within their pore structure and therefore ice will not form when freezing occurs. As usual there are exceptions to this general statement. For example, metamorphic slates with water absorption greater than 0.3% by weight are considered to be susceptible to frost damage. It seems likely that this is because the water absorption is concentrated along the cleavage planes leading to delamination. However, porous stones with high water absorption, for example Portland limestone Whit Bed, can still be very resistant to freeze–thaw cycles because there are few micro-pores in the stones. The disruption of the structure is usually measured by determining the reduction in compressive or flexural strength when the stone is subjected to repeated freezing cycles but can also be determined non-destructively by measuring changes in the natural frequency of the stone.

9.5.2.3. Abrasion resistance

The abrasion and wear of stone occurs in areas subjected to high levels of pedestrian traffic. Wear is defined as the progressive loss of substance from the surface of a body brought about by mechanical action. Abrasion is wear caused by fine solid particles (Harper 1965). Forms of wear other than abrasion include cutting, adhesive or galling, corrosive, and surface fatigue (Burwell 1957). Burwell described abrasion and cutting as the most important forms of wear as far as flooring is concerned. It is generally recognized that wear resulting from feet is most severe in places where changes of direction occur and where people are moving in a confined area.

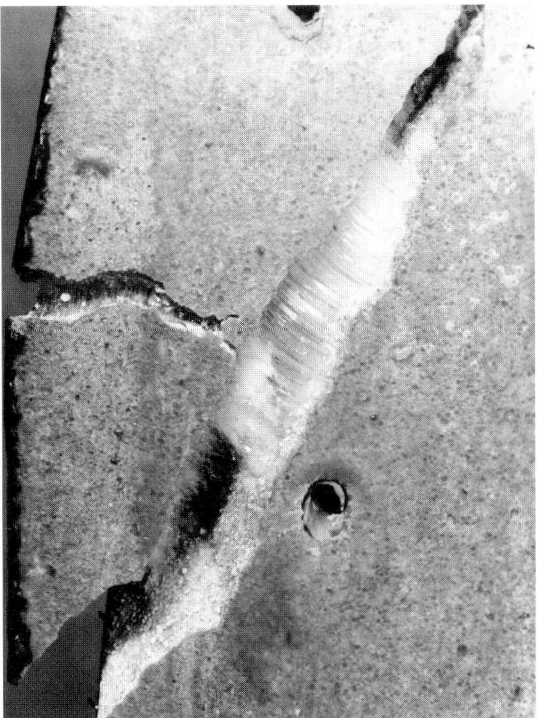

Fig. 9.35. Disruption of natural stone as a result of the formation of ice.

9.5.2.4. Slip resistance

The slip resistance of natural stone paving and flooring is becoming increasingly prominent as safety in use of flooring materials becomes more important. The slipperiness of a surface is related to many factors including the surface texture (e.g. honed or polished), presence of water or oil, and the footwear of users. Many natural stones have very good natural slip resistance but some polished materials can become hazardous in wet conditions. Some stones, consisting of mineral grains with nearly equal hardness, e.g. granites, tend to polish with wear and become slippery, whilst those with hard grains in a softer matrix, e.g. some sandstones, remain 'rough'. There is also some concern over areas where there is a sudden increase in slipperiness, which can result in tripping and where surfaces have a very high slip resistance which can result in stumbling, see also §9.6.2.6 below.

9.6. Testing requirements and regimes for the different uses

Tests that are applicable to building stone can be divided into three groups

(1) Testing for structural properties
(2) Testing for weathering and wear resistance
(3) Testing for workability and appearance

These properties can be determined by direct measurements, where the stone is subjected to the same conditions that it would encounter in use, but also by indirect measurements, where the composition and internal structure of the stone is used to determine a different property. Indirect tests are particularly common in assessments of durability.

It is also essential to ensure that the results from any test can be interpreted to provide practical information. In general, this can only be achieved by comparing test results to a reference point. This reference point can be

- a theoretical value, for example a calculated bending stress, due to wind load
- a safety limit, for example a coefficient of resistance for a slip test
- a direct comparison to a reference sample of known qualities.

Sometimes it may be necessary to compare two or more stones in order to determine which has the better properties. However, this is an unsatisfactory approach unless a reference point is used as it may be that all or none of the stones under consideration are suitable for their intended use.

The tests that are appropriate vary with both the type of stone and its intended use. Tables 9.1 is intended to show which tests are appropriate but it is only designed to give guidance and is not comprehensive. In the next section the purpose of each test is discussed briefly and references to current standards or other accepted methods are given.

However, it must be remembered that the results from some of these tests will not vary significantly within a single quarry bed. Consequently it is not necessary to repeat all of the tests for each new project if the supplier can provide the results of tests recently carried out to an accepted standard and detailed records or the specimens, for example size and shape, are available. However, the reader is also referred to §9.5.1.1, last paragraph.

The importance of interpreting results in the context of the end use and the known performance of the stone is simply summed up by a quotation by R. J. Schaffer taken from an article published by the Stone Federation in 1959 (Schaffer 1959)

> *'In conclusion, it is worth repeating that tests are not an end in themselves. They must be interpreted against the background of experience and practical needs if they are to be of real value.'*

Table 9.4 shows some of the methods available for testing natural stone. The methods listed are a combination of national standards and established methods that appear in the BRE Report on durability tests for materials. It is envisaged that these references will be superseded as the European Standards (EN) come into force, see §9.6.4.

Most of these references are to test methods and few give any guidance on the interpretation of the results. There are separate ASTM Standards covering the 'standard specification' for a range of natural stones. These are:

C 406-89 Specification for Roofing Slate
C 503-89 Specification for Marble Dimension Stone (exterior)
C 568-89 Specification for Limestone Dimension Stone
C 615-89 Specification for Granite Dimension Stone
C 616-95 Specification for Quartz based Dimension Stone
C 629-89 Specification for Slate Dimension Stone

These generally contain a series of limiting values for water absorption, density, compressive strength, flexural strength or modulus of rupture, and abrasion resistance.

9.6.1. Testing for structural properties

The testing of structural properties has traditionally been carried out on specimens of the material in question. However, in recent years there has been an increased demand for the testing of products for example, paving units, and for the testing of units for example, fully sized cladding panels or masonry wall units. This demand for product and unit testing is being reflected in both the new European standards, see below, and in some more recent publications such as Lewis (1995). It is essential that the moisture content and orientation of load are described in accordance with the appropriate standard.

9.6.1.1. Compressive strength

This test is the basic measure of the load that a stone can withstand without being crushed. It is also referred to as uniaxial compressive strength as the load is applied on a single axis. The most common test method is ASTM C170-90 which is carried out on cubes, square prisms or cylinders. It is sometimes stated that measurement should not be undertaken on cubes as they cannot be subjected to a true uniaxial load. Many European countries have standards for this test, for

Table 9.4. *Current standards available for testing natural stone*

	British Standard	*ASTM Standard*	*Other Standard (1)*	*Other Standard (2)*
Petrographic description	BS 812: Part 104 BS 5930		UNI 9724: Part 1	ISRM
Density	BRE Rep. 141	C 97-90		
Water absorption	BRE Rep. 141 BS 680: Part 2	C 97-90	NF B 10-502	
Compressive strength		C 170-90	NF B 10-509	DIN 52.105
Flexural strength		C 880-89 C 99-87 C 120-90		
Tensile strength				
Modulus of elasticity		D 3148-86		
Thermal and moisture movement				
Weathering resistance (Durability)	BRE Rep.141		DIN 52.104	
Abrasion resistance		C 241-90	NF B 10-508	
Slip resistance	BS 8204: Part 4			
Workability and polishabilty				
Colour variability and permanence				

BRE Rep.141, Building Research Establishment Report No.141; ASTM, American Society for Testing and Materials; ISRM, International Society of Rock Mechanics; BS, British Standard; DIN, German National Standard; NF, French National Standard; UNI, Italian National Standard.

example DIN 52.105 in Germany or NF B 10-509 in France. British Standard BS 5628: Parts 1 and 2 refers to the testing of masonry 'units' – that is measuring the strength of a wall. This approach is also found in Eurocode EC6 and it is likely to increase in importance with the advent of European Standards.

Testing can be carried out with the samples wet or dry and with the load applied perpendicular or parallel to the bedding or other anisotropic feature (that is having different physical properties when measurement is made in different directions). These variations allow the conditions of use to be more accurately reproduced. In general, the results of the compressive strength tests can be compared directly to the structural requirement of the application, for example the load to be supported plus an acceptable safety margin.

Masonry testing may allow higher load intensities than BS 5628, see §9.5.1.1.

9.6.1.2. Flexural strength

This test is often referred to as the bending test and can be measured using one or two loading points. It is a measure of the strength of a thin sample when loaded whilst supported at the extremes of the sample. Loading at two points applies an equal bending moment to all places between the two loading points; loading at a single point applies a greater load at the point of loading and can overestimate the strength if failure occurs away from the loading point. A method for carrying out a four-point bending test (that is two loading points) is described in ASTM C 880-89.

A similar test that is frequently specified is the modulus of rupture. This is carried out in a similar manner to a bend test with a single loading point but on samples whose thickness is sufficient to make the sample fail without significant bending. The most common method is that described in ASTM C 99-87.

As with the compressive strength test, all of these flexural strength tests can be carried out with the samples wet or dry and with loading perpendicular or parallel to the bedding or aniostropy. In general the results of flexural strength tests can be compared directly to the structural requirement of the application, for example the bending moment to be supported plus an acceptable safety margin.

ASTM specifies a separate method for testing slates (ASTM C120-90). It is very similar to the flexural strength test but the sample size is, of course, different.

9.6.1.3. Strength around fixings

This type of test is often referred to as a 'dowel push off test' and is usually undertaken by pushing or pulling a dowel (to represent a restraint type fixing) perpendicularly until failure occurs, see Fig. 9.34. A number of standards contain this test, for example the French Standard NF B 10-514.

The area around the fixings on cladding panels can also be subject to microfracturing due to inappropriate methods of forming slots and holes. On polished surfaces the presence of such fractures can be determined using a UV fluorescence dye test.

9.6.1.4. Modulus of elasticity
The modulus of elasticity is usually quoted as Young's Modulus (E) and is based on the relationship between stress and strain. The E-value is the stress-strain relationship expressed as the ratio of the stress to the rate of strain. The limit of elastic deformation is the strength in a brittle material. In general, coarse-grained rocks are less elastic than finer grained ones (Winkler 1973). Test methods for determining Young's Modulus are given in ASTM D 3148-86 and for slates in ASTM C 120-90. It is also possible to determine elasticity non-destructively using the natural resonance of a stone core or prism.

9.6.1.5. Thermal and moisture movement
Thermal and moisture movement are usually determined by measuring changes in dimensions under closely controlled conditions. The commonest method for measuring thermal changes of dimension is to use a dilatometer. Expansion is usually expressed in units equivalent to microns per linear metre per degree C see Table 9.3, for example a 1m long panel of sandstone is expected to expand by 0.4 mm–0.6 mm for a temperature rise of 50°C. Thermal expansion is usually reversible but there is evidence that some marbles retain a residual expansion on cooling (Widhalm *et al.* 1995).

9.6.2. Testing for weathering and wear resistance

9.6.2.1. Petrographic description
Petrographic description can range from the correct petrographic name to a full description based on macroscopic study of the stone and microscopic study of a thin section. There is no British Standard for petrographic descriptions of building stone but there is one for aggregates (BS 812: Part 1: 1975) and for site investigations (BS 5930: 1981: Section 44). There is an Italian standard (UNI 9724 Part 1) and a number of geological organisations produce guidance on how and what to describe, for example the International Society for Rock Mechanics (ISRM 1977). It is a useful test to undertake as it provides the basic information on the stone such as its correct geological description, the origins of the stone and an indication of any minerals present that could cause the stone to fail at a later date. A 'favourable' test result is, however, no guarantee that the stone will have good weathering resistance.

9.6.2.2. Density and porosity
The density of a stone is expressed in mass per unit volume, usually grams per cm^3 or kg per m^3. There is no British Standard but the tests described in BRE Report 141 for porosity and saturation coefficient can be used to calculate density. The ASTM standard C 97-90 contains a method for measuring the bulk specific gravity which is in effect the same as the density. In both tests it is the density of the bulk stone rather than a crushed sample (often referred to as the real density) that is measured. Measurement of the density allows the weight of flooring, walling or cladding panels to be calculated. The porosity can give an indication of durability when considered together with other parameters such as water absorption.

9.6.2.3. Water absorption
Water absorption can be measured by a number of methods. It can be measured by soaking the samples in water at room temperature for a fixed period (ASTM C 97-90, BRE Report 141) or, in the case of natural slates, by placing in boiling water for a similar period (BS 680: Part 2: 1971). The water absorption can also be measured by placing the sample in 2–3 mm of water and measuring the weight change over several days. This method is usually referred to as water absorption by capillarity and details can be found in a number of standards used in European countries, for example the French standard NF B 10-502.

9.6.2.4. Durability
The term durability covers a very wide range of properties and they are probably the most difficult to relate to behaviour in the environment. Durable is defined in the Oxford English Dictionary as

> *'Capable of continuing in existence' and*
> *'Able to withstand change, decay or wear'*

However, in assessing or measuring the durability of natural stone it is not realistic to state that stone must be able to withstand change and decay and continue in existence. The standard definition of durability given in ASTM C 119-90 is more helpful:

> *'the measure of the ability of dimension stone to endure and to maintain its essential and distinctive characteristics of strength, resistance to decay, and appearance. Durability is based on the time that a stone can maintain its innate characteristics in use. This time will depend on the environment and the use of the stone in question (for example, outdoor versus indoor use)'.*

In the UK, durability is usually taken to be the extent to which a stone will weather in a given period of time. It must be remembered that all stones will weather – the important question is 'Is the rate of weathering acceptable?'.

Some aspects of the durability of slates are covered by BS 680: Part 2: 1971 but this contains no requirement to test flexural strength nor any guidance on size and frequency of sampling. The acid immersion test described in BRE Report 141 will allow sandstones that are likely to be susceptible to attack by acid rain to be identified.

Sandstones that are to be subject to salt attack can be tested using the sodium sulphate crystallization test described in BRE Report 141, but this test should not be used to allocate a general durability class. The saturated crystallization test in the same report should only be used to assess performance under the most severe conditions when exceptionally long life is required (for example stone used for sea defence walls, quaysides, etc.). The majority of sandstones are considered to be frost resistant.

The potential durability of limestones can be assessed in a number of ways. Their resistance to salt crystallisation can be determined using the sodium sulphate crystallization test (BRE 1989). The crystallization test can also be used to give an indication of the overall durability of a limestone, particularly if the stone suffers little weight loss, but a stone that gives a poor result may in reality perform better than the result would suggest. The frost resistance of limestones can be measured using the German standard DIN 52.104/1 and /2.

However, at present it seems difficult to measure the resistance of any porous stones to de-icing salts but this is an important property when stone is used for external paving or where it is subject to spray from roads.

Both the crystallization test and the freeze–thaw tests may require reference stones to be used because the tests are comparative rather than absolute. Research is continuing to develop a methodology to determine the tests necessary to measure the durability of the wide range of natural stones currently used in the UK. Further information on the design life of buildings and building materials can be found in BS 7543:1992 (Guide to Durability of buildings and building elements, products and components).

9.6.2.5. Abrasion resistance

The abrasion resistance test estimates how much paving or flooring will wear. It is usually undertaken as a comparative test using reference stones of known behaviour. All of the commonly used methods are based on the abrasion of the sample by a wheel or disc and an abrasive material. The three most commonly used methods are the ASTM system described in C 241-90, the German Bohme test and the French Capon test (NF B 10-508). The results can given a relative value for the rate of wear if a number of different stones are compared but it is difficult to interpret the results in absolute terms, e.g. mm per year per million people.

9.6.2.6. Slip resistance

This test is carried out to assess the slipperiness of flooring or paving when in use. The usual test method is the pendulum developed for road surfaces and ceramic pavers; this is usually termed the Unpolished Skid Resistance Value. It is described in BS 8204 Part 4 and is being developed for inclusion in a number of European standards (see below). The test is usually only carried out on samples that have a polished or honed finish as the rougher finishes (for example riven) are considered to be safe. The results from the pendulum test are a measure of the friction between the slider on the pendulum arm and the stone surface and the greater the value the higher the co-efficient of friction. Values obtained by using this test on new surfaces, that is one that have not undergone any polishing by use, can range from 8 to more than 100. Experience in the UK has shown that values greater than 40 can be considered safe. Values less than 40 may be acceptable if the surface can be kept dry when in use.

Two other values that can be specified are the Polished Paver Value (PPV) and the Polished Stone Value (PSV). The PPV measures the resistance of a product to polishing by vehicles and the PSV provides a control/calibration sample for the PPV using a standard material. These tests are fully described in BS 7932:1998.

9.6.2.7. Impact resistance and surface hardness

These tests can be used to determine the resistance of cladding panels or flooring units to impact damage that may result from cleaning cradles or the dropping of heavy objects. The surface hardness can also be used as a measure of abrasion resistance. A typical test for impact resistance is given in BS 8200: 1985 which also gives some specification details. Surface hardness tests are common in Italy and France where they are included in their standard tests results. The methods used are found in UNI 9724: Part 6 and NF B 10-506 respectively.

9.6.3. Programme of testing

No tests should be commissioned, the outcome of which do not affect the performance in the finished work, e.g. compressive strength of stone for single-storey bungalows.

Testing can be carried out at three distinct stages in the use of natural stone

1. Initial testing

Tests on samples from a quarry to establish the intrinsic qualities of the stone, e.g. the compressive strength of a prism of stone;

2. Prototype testing

Tests on finished or semi-finished products, either as components or as finished units, e.g. the flexural strength of a flame textured cladding panel;

3. Production control

Tests as part of the quality control process, e.g. carrying out some form of testing on a random selection of the stone either prior to fabrication, or as produced, or as finished product or prior to use in construction.

Many stone producers already have the first type of information, gathered from earlier requests for test results but are still required to carry out further similar testing for individual projects at the pre-contract stage and immediately prior to production. The producers may also have some information on the qualities of the stone as a finished product but the range of products may be too great for detailed results to be available for every product. At present there are no guidelines on how to interpret existing results or how to assess when the new results are significantly different from those obtained in earlier tests. The European Standards, see §9.6.4 below, place considerable emphasis on attestation and factory production control but as yet few guidelines have been produced for by committees drafting these standards. Until these standards are available the most straightforward approach would seem to be for the stone producer or importer to collate all data currently available for a particular stone or bed. These results should be expressed so that the range of results is clear. New tests should be carried out at intervals depending on the quantity of stone produced and the recorded variability of that stone or bed. Architects and specifiers should be willing to make use of the existing results and only request further testing of quarry samples if they believe that the new stone may not meet the specification or if the finished form of the stone may have significantly altered the intrinsic qualities of the stone. In addition, any testing specified as part of a quality control procedure must be realistic and pass/fail criteria agreed together with the action to be taken when failure of a test sample does occur.

9.6.4. Future testing –European standards

As part of the preparation for the single European Market, 'harmonized' standards are being developed by the Comité Européen de Normalisation (CEN) through a series of Technical Committees (TC), sub-committees (SC), working groups (WG) and task groups (TG). The European Standards (EN) usually comprise three parts – specifications, test methods and a section on the evaluation of conformity. The specification is a list of requirements for a particular use (for example external cladding). The requirements can include tolerances for products or units and minimum values for classes of use based on test methods. Each standard contains a set of test methods, these may be part of the

Table 9.5. *Test methods being considered for inclusion in European Standards*

Test method	*TC 125 Masonry*	*TC 178 Setts*	*TC 178 Kerbs*	*TC 178 Paving*	*TC 246 Cladding*	*TC 128 SC 6 Slate roofing*
Porosity	×				×	
Density	×			×	×	
Water abs. Capillarity	×	×	×	×	×	
Water abs. (atmospheric)					×	×?
Water vapour permeability	×					
Compressive strength	×	×			×	
Bending strength	×		×	×	×	×
Durability	×	×	×	×	×	×
Abrasion resistance		×		×	×	
Skid/slip resistance		×		×	×	
Petrographic description	×	×	×	×	×	×
Dimensions	×	×	×	×	×	×
Dowel test					×	
Impact resistance					×	
Velocity of sound					×	
Modulus of elasticity					×	
Coeff. of thermal exp.					×	
Hardness					×	
Surface roughness					×	
Thermal shock					×	×

standard or part of a separate standard. The final section, on the evaluation of conformity, describes when and how the product should be tested. It may include recommendations on factory production control and type testing of the material.

The standards are designed to fulfil the Construction Products Directive and as a result will contain some parts that are mandatory and backed by statute. These parts will be clearly identified in each standard.

It is important that all those involved in the production and use of natural stone for building are fully aware of these standards and their implications in order that necessary actions can be taken in advance of the introduction of the new standards from 1999 onwards.

The Technical Committees which include natural building stone within their programmes of work are:

CEN/TC 125–Masonry units
CEN/TC 128–Roof covering products for discontinuous laying (SC8–Slate and stone products for roofing)
CEN/TC 178–Paving units and kerbs (WG2 - Natural stone)
CEN/TC 246–Natural stone

References

Anon 1996. Cheap roofing tiles threaten the diversity of old England. *Times*, Nov 14th.

——1997. Sealants, staining and failing. *Natural Stone Specialist*, January, 23–26.

Ashurst, J. & Dimes, F. G. 1977. *Stone in building – Its use and potential today*. The Architectural Press, London.

American Society for Testing and Materials *Test Methods for Absorption and Bulk Specific Gravity of Dimension Stone*. ASTM C 97-90.

——*Test Method for Modulus of Rupture of Dimension Stone*. ASTM C 99-87.

——*Methods of Flexure Testing of Slate (Modulus of Rupture, Modulus of Elasticity)*. ASTM C 120-90.

——*Test Method for Compressive Strength of Dimension Stone*. ASTM C 170-90.

——*Test Method for Abrasion Resistance of Stone Subjected to Foot Traffic*. ASTM C 241-90.

——*Specification for Roofing Slate*. ASTM C 406-89.

——*Specification for Marble Dimension Stone (Exterior)*. ASTM C 503-89.

——*Specification for Limestone Dimension Stone*. ASTM C 568-89.

——*Specification for Granite Dimension Stone*. ASTM C 615-89.

——*Specification for Slate Dimension Stone*. ASTM C 629-89.

——*Specification for Quartz Based Dimension Stone*. ASTM C 616-95.

——*Flexural Strength of Dimension Stone*. ASTM C 880-89.

——*Test Method for Elastic Moduli of Intact Rock Core Specimens in Uniaxial Compression*. ASTM D 3148-86.

Beckmann, P. 1994. *Structural Aspects of Building Conservation*. McGraw-Hill, London.

Bouineau, A. & Perrier, R. 1995. La decohesion granulaire, maladie des revetments de facade en marbre. Pierre Dimensionnelle, August–September 1995.

Building Research Establishment (BRE) 1989. *Durability Tests for Building Stone, BRE* Report 141.

——1992. *Radon: Guidance on Protective Measures for New Dwellings*. BRE Report 211.

——1993. *Surveying Dwellings with High Indoor Radon Levels: a BRE Guide to Radon Remedial Measures in Existing Dwellings*. BRE Report 250.

——1997. *Selecting Natural Building Stones*. BRE Digest 420.

British Standards Institution 1972. *Code of Basic Data for the Design of Buildings*. BS CP3.

——1975. *Specification for Dressed Natural Stone Kerbs, Channels, Quadrants and Sets*. BS 435.

——1971. *Specification for Roofing Slates Metric Units*. BS 680: Part 2.

——1975. *Methods for Determination of Particle Size and Shape*. BS 812: Part 1.

——1990. *Code of Practice for the Design and Installation of Terrazzo Tile and Slab, Natural Stone and Composition Block Floorings*. BS 5385: Part 5.

——1984. *Code of Practice for Stone Masonry*. BS 5390: 1976.

——1987. *Design (code of practice for slate and tiling)*. (1985) BS 5534: Part 1.

——1987. *Code of Practice for Use of Masonry*. BS 5628: Parts 1 & 2 (also *Structural Use of Unreinforced Masonry*. Part 1 – 1992; *Structural Use of Reinforced and Prestressed Masonry*. Part 2).

——1983. *Specification for Coping of Precast Concrete, Cast Stone, Clayware, Slate and Natural Stone*. BS 5642: Part 2.

——*Guide to the Selection of Constructional Sealants*. BS 6213: 1982.

——1995. *Code of Practice for Wind Loads*. BS 6399: Part 2.

——1988. *Code of Practice for Imposed Roof Loads*. BS 6399: Part 3.

——1986. *Specification for Pavers*. BS 6677: Part 1.

——1992. *Guide to Durability of Buildings and Building Elements, Products and Components*. BS 7543.

——*Workmanship on Site*. BS 8000.

——1985. *Code of Practice for the Design of Non-loadbearing External Vertical Enclosures of Buildings*. BS 8200.

——1994. *Code of Practice for Design and Installation of Natural Stone Cladding and Lining*. BS 8298.

Burwell, J. T. 1957. Wear, 1 119–125.

Corbella, E. 1990. *The Architect's Handbook of Marble, Granite and Stone*. Van Nostrand Reinhold, New York.

CWCT 1997. *Selection and Testing of Stone Panels for External Use*. Centre for Window and Cladding Technology, Bath.

Deutsches Institut fur Normung 1992. *Testing of Natural Stone; Freeze-Thaw Cyclic Test Methods A-Q*. DIN 52. 104.

——*Testing of Natural Stone; Compression Test*. DIN 51. 105.

DoT 1993. BD21/93.

EC6 1988. *Eurocode No 6 Common unified rules for masonry structures*. CEC Report EUR 9888 En.

EC8 *Eurocode No. 8 Structures in seismic zones*.

Harper, F. C. 1965. *Friction and Wear*. Building Research Station Report No. IN 143/65.

Harrison, P. 1997. Facing the problems. *Natural Stone Specialist*, January, 14–17.

HILL, P. R. & DAVID, J. C. E. 1995. *Practical Stone Masonry*. Donhead, London.

INTERNATIONAL SOCIETY FOR ROCK MECHANICS 1977. *Suggested Method for Petrographic Description of Rocks*. Committee on Laboratory Tests, Document No 6, March.

LEWIS, M. D. 1995. *Modern Stone Cladding – Design and Installation of Exterior Dimension Stone Systems*. American Society of Testing and Materials Manual Series: MNL 21, ASTM, Philadelphia.

NORME FRANCAIS. *Quarry Products – Limestones – Measurement of Water Absorption by Capillarity*. NF B10-502.

——*Quarry Products – Limestones – Measurement of Surface Hardness*. NF B10-506.

——*Quarry Products – Limestones – Abrasion Test Using a Metal Disk*. NF B10-508.

——*Quarry Products – Limestones – Compression Test*. NF B10-509.

——*Quarry Products – Limestones – Strength of Fixings*. NF B10-514.

——NF P32-301. *General Characteristics of Slates*.

SCHAFFER, R. J. 1932. *The Weathering of Natural Building Stone*. Department of Scientific and Industrial Research, DSIR Special Report 18. (Facsimile produced by Building Research Establishment 1985).

——1959. *Testing Natural Stone*. Stone Federation Note, London.

SHADMON, A. 1996. *Stone – an Introduction*. Intermediate Technology, London.

TANNO, S. 1997. *Design and Procurement*. Natural Stone Specialist, January 19–22.

ENTE NAZIONALE ITALIANO DI UNIFICAZIONE. *Determination of Knoop Microhardness*. UNI 9724: Part 6.

——*Natural Stones – Petrographic Denomination of Stones*. UNI 972: Part 1.

WARLAND, E. G. 1929. *Modern Practical Masonry*. Pitman Books/Stone Federation, London.

WIDHALM, C., TSCHEGG, E. K. & EPPENSTEINER, W. 1996. Anisotropic thermal expansion causes deformation of marble cladding. *Journal of Performance of Construction Facilities*, **10**(1), 5–10.

WINKLER, E. M. 1973. *Stone: Properties, Durabilty in Man's Environment*. Springer, New York.

——1994. *Stone in Architecture: Properties, Durability*. Springer, Berlin.

10. Stone repair and restoration

10.1. Introduction

The repair and restoration of stone masonry has a history of its own. Stone, being a material which withstands the ravages of time, has been used to construct many important buildings throughout the world. Undoubtedly, because many of these buildings have been of such importance, a great deal of care has been and needs to continue to be taken to ensure their continued life. The architect or person responsible for the building must educate himself to understand both the structure of the building and the materials used.

In the past the most widely used method of repair has been to cut away the defective or weathered stone and replace it with new to match as near as possible the remaining stone.

This process does, however, destroy the existing fabric of the building. In this more 'enlightened age' and in the particular case of historic buildings it is necessary to adopt a different attitude to the repair of stone work and to further consider the archaeological aspects and the interests of other groups concerned with the preservation of the building or structure. Whereas a bronze age sword or even The Mary Rose can be more or less preserved, buildings cannot be conserved unless they are protected from the environment by erecting a large tent over them.

Modern buildings often require different consideration. New materials and construction techniques have put forever greater stresses on any stone employed in them. Weathering may be more critical and problems may arise relatively rapidly. Repair may not be straightforward with complicated fixing systems often requiring individual consideration.

In this chapter the various methods of cleaning and repair of stone will be discussed together with the factors to be considered when deciding upon a programme of works for stone repair and restoration.

10.2. Defects requiring repair or restoration

10.2.1. Need for repair or restoration

If natural materials are exposed to the weather changes will occur and stone, no matter how durable, is no exception. The changes that occur may be of no structural consequence and may be either aesthetically pleasing or distressing. However, where weathering has resulted in a significant loss of material from the surface of the stone this may endanger the structure or permit water to penetrate the building envelope. In these cases some action is clearly necessary.

The causes of the decay of stone-masonry are very complex and have been studied for a long time. Those responsible for the repair and restoration of the buildings in which stone-masonry is decaying need to understand the process of decay and the causes of decay. There are many causes of weathering, deterioration and decay of masonry and these require careful analysis so that the appropriate method of repair or restoration can be effected. The effects and causes can be broadly grouped into two categories as follows:

- The first category can best be described as those attributed to the method of construction, detailing of the design, the use of the building and man-made causes of decay.
- The second category includes the effect of weather, the action of acidic gases in the air, rain and frost action and salt crystallization together with chemical, biochemical and physical attack.

The following sections outline some of the more common manifestations of stone decay and their causes.

10.2.2. Failures caused by construction, detailing and use

Section 9.4 has outlined a design methodology that gives some guidance on the potential problems that must be taken into account when a building or structure is being designed. When stone is used incorrectly or the underlying structure is incompatible with the stone being used then problems occur. The first indication of a problem may be staining, cracking or damp on the stone work. In many cases the stone will be blamed whereas the true problem may lie with the design, construction or use.

10.2.2.1. Construction and design

The following problems and failures may arise owing to faults in construction or design:

- The cracking of stones and joints can be caused by movement of the building through inadequate use of expansion joints, settlement of the building or unbalanced thrusts from arches or roof rafters.
- Load transfer from the backing masonry with a lower modulus of deformation (E-value), being brickwork or rubble and mortar, to the more rigid masonry of the building façade may cause the latter to split or bulge.
- Mortar should be compatible with the stone. Choice of an excessively strong (dense) mortar, can lead to cracking at the arris of stones, see §9.2.1.5. The use of a high proportion of Portland cement in the mortar can lead to alkali induced staining. If porous stone is laid in or pointed with impervious cement based mortar rainwater may be prevented from draining

down and will lodge on the bed joints. Freezing of this retained water may result in damage to the surface of the stone. Similar damage may result from crystallization of salts introduced by the cement. Insufficient bedding may lead to load concentrations resulting in spalling.

- Structural steel frame members which are encased in masonry may be inadequately protected against corrosion caused by the ingress of water. The steel will rust and the consequent expansion will lead to cracking, spalling, splitting or lifting of stonework. The same applies to other embedded ironwork particularly cramps, straps, window and door fixings and ferramenta.
- The corrosion of metal fixings above stonework leads to staining such as the brown colour caused by iron and the greenish blue stain derived from copper, see Fig. 10.1. This is particularly noticeable on light coloured stones.

Fig. 10.1. Staining of Portland stone below a bronze lamp bracket, Royal School of Mines.

- Inaccurate positioning of metal cramps leads to over stressing of the stone and eventual cracking around the cramp. Feather edge detailing may allow the edge of a stone to break easily.

10.2.2.2. Selection of materials
The following failures may arise owing to incorrect selection of materials:

- The use of more than one type of material on the façade of a building can cause staining and decay by salt crystallization. For example, alkaline rainwater running off from brickwork and limestone can react with a sedimentary rock bonded by a siliceous cement. For this reason, in general, limestones should only be placed over sandstones with caution as, in many instances, this has resulted in the accelerated decay of the sandstone.
- Inadequate specification of the stone for the environmental conditions in which the building is located can lead to the rapid deterioration of the façade in exposed conditions, for example, near the sea. It is also important to consider which stone may be suitable for ashlar but not appropriate for copings, cornices and string courses unless protected with a lead covering. Permeable stones should not be used for weatherings as this will promote the formation of efflorescence and penetration of water into the structure.
- Soft seams in an otherwise durable, strong stone may lower the resistance of the masonry to weathering. A stone containing vents may be acceptable for plain walling but not for carved or moulded work. A stone with shakes which may not be aesthetically acceptable.

10.2.2.3. Detailing
The following failures and problems may be attributed to the inappropriate detailing of the stonework:

- Poor detailing of stone, such as providing inadequate area of the bearing for lintels, can cause cracking. Insufficient depth of drips will not allow water to run off properly. Hollow bedding of stones, that is, where the surface of the stone is concave, can lead to an excessive load being carried near the surface with consequent spalling.
- Poor detailing of the plinth and damp proof course may allow water to enter the lower courses causing damage by crystallization and general staining.
- Staining and decay may be due to run-off of water from wall heads, copings, cornices, string courses and other projections and ingress of water into the structure due to open joints.
- Masonry, except overhanging or projecting features such as cornices, is normally built with the stone bedded on its natural bed, that is, the bedding plane of the rock laid in the horizontal plane. Face bedding

Weathering of limestones

Of all building stones limestones are the most likely to exhibit natural features that may give rise to problems. Typically limestones are formed of reef structures, branching corals and large shells which may produce hollows (vents) and areas of poor compaction or sedimentation. Once exposed or brought close to the Earth's surface many limestones will suffer dissolution, the calcite and other carbonate minerals being susceptible to attack by mildly acidic solutions typical of rain. Dissolution principally occurs at joint locations where the passage of moisture may be greater in volume (BRE 1975; BRE 1965). With dissolution, insoluble residues of clays, oxides and organics remains may be left to concentrate. The stone immediately adjacent to these features may be of lower quality although no different from the best stone.

usually accelerates the decay of the stone as each layer of stone peels away. However, sometimes the Designer may choose to face bed certain stones for aesthetic reasons.

The impermeable nature of glass means that run-off below windows can be excessive. Windows also attract dirt which may then wash downwards and concentrate on the stone below. The drier stone below sills often exhibits salt concentrations and excessive damage as these migrate from the sill.

10.2.2.4. Use

Some aspects of the use of a building may also contribute to the decay of stone:

- Inadequate heating and or ventilation can give rise to condensation. Occupants and visitors to a building will increase the relative humidity inside a building and this may cause condensation on the walls. Where there is a cold external wall, moisture from exhaled air may condense on the inner surface and the walls may become wet. Where soluble salts are present these will absorb the water and dissolve before recrystallizing when the relative humidity decreases after the visitors have gone. If the cycle is repeated sufficiently often crystallization damage to the stone can occur.
- Wear of stone floor surfaces is caused by grit in the soles of shoes. Highly polished dark stone may suffer from 'matting up', sometimes within weeks of installation. The dark stone colour is normally caused by the majority of the incident light entering the stone and being absorbed. With wear and tear imperceptible scratches will scatter incident light rather than absorb it. Thus, as wear and tear increases so does the light scattering and the stone appears lighter. Metal heels can cause considerable damage, being able to scratch granites. One feature is starmarking caused by damage where the crystalline structure is disrupted locally at the point of heel contact.
- The effect of rubbing of clothes and oil or grease from hands that have come into regular contact with stone is found around stone windows, door openings, spiral staircases, handrails and stone features. The effect on the stone is the presence of unsightly marks and that the stone becomes polished. It tends to become darker in comparison to the surrounding stonework, in effect, being the opposite of matting up.
- Smoke deposits can be left on the stone by the use of candles and the smoking of cigarettes.
- A fire in a building can effect stone in several ways; first, by blackening through the deposition of carbonaceous or tarry substances, second, by shattering the stone surface due to the creation of thermal gradients by rapid temperature changes during heating or cooling by water and third, by calcination. Calcination can significantly weaken certain stones by converting the calcium carbonate matrix or cement into 'quicklime' which is weak and subsequently hydrates expansively.

10.2.2.5. Maintenance

The neglect of maintenance or use of inappropriate methods (BRE 1965) may result in decay of the stonework as described below:

- Damage may have been caused by previous poor repair or restoration measures such as discoloration, staining and efflorescence associated with inappropriate cleaning methods, or pitting or disking of the stone surface by careless cleaning or use of abrasive or disc pad cleaning.
- Poor maintenance of the structure by the building owner/occupier will accelerate the decay of masonry. Gutters, downpipes and hopper heads that become blocked allow excessive amounts of water to flow over the stone surface. Blocked gutters can also lead to water ingress into rubble core walls with the risk of subsequent frost damage. The building should be kept free of tree growth, climbers and creepers as roots seek sources of moisture and grow into the structure forcing masonry apart. Algae, fungi, lichens and bacteria may grow and spread over the stone surface accelerating the rate of decay. The effects of birds and bees can be seen in the softer stones where they have

worn away the surface or, in the case of masonry bees, bored holes. There are also the detrimental effects of bird droppings and nesting materials.

- The rusting of iron cramps used in the past to hold repairs together may subsequently cause further decay, see Figs 10.2 and 10.3.
- The use of strong Portland cement based grouts and mortars for pointing can cause further deterioration of adjacent masonry.
- Many buildings will undergo some degree of repointing of the mortar. This may be to insufficient depth whereby the mortar will rapidly detach or is incompatible with the remaining mortar. Often the reasons for the original decay of the mortar are not adequately addressed and the same decay will affect the new mortar. Placing stones in the exposed face of the pointing mortar, or galetting, can reduce the exposed mortar surface and likewise the weathering potential.
- Finally a few warnings concerning miscellaneous actions that may contribute to stone decay and should be avoided: (i) materials should not be stacked against stone walls, (ii) common salt should not be used for removing ice off stonework, (iii) cleaning materials that contain salts of sodium, potassium or other alkaline materials including laundry detergents should not be used.

10.2.3. Failures caused by the effects of weather

10.2.3.1. Introduction

The effects of poor design or maintenance, detailed in §10.2.2, are made much worse by the action of weathering processes. Many of the processes involved in the weathering of buildings are similar to those described in §2.4 as part the natural geological weathering. Once any stone has been removed from the quarry it is in a state of disequilibrium with its new environment. The stone can be subjected to a wide range of weathering processes as it tries to reach a new equilibrium. Man-made problems such as acid rain contribute to this weathering and the rate of change can be greatly increased. The key to success in selecting a stone is to ensure that the rate of change is such that no significant alteration occurs within the life of the building or construction. When the stone is unsuitable or the environment becomes harsher e.g. more polluted, or where the planned life of the structure is exceeded then excessive weathering and decay will occur.

Stone geometry plays an important role in weathering. Away from the surface stone fabric is constrained by itself, that is, the mineral interlock that gives the stone its strength. Any adverse forces are dissipated towards the outer surface and damage to the stone fabric will only

Fig. 10.2. Stone that has been broken away by the rusting and expansion of an iron cramp.

Fig. 10.3. Rusting iron cramps causing damage to stone.

occur if the force acting upon a particular location is greater than the constraining force. The flat surfaces of plain walling are only constrained to one side and are thus less able to cope with adverse forces, especially if these forces are close to the surface. Most weathering mechanisms are found to apply forces to the outermost surface. The corner edge of a quoin stone or other similar detail has only one quarter the protection, true corners will only have one eighth the protection, thus the more intricate a feature the more susceptible it will be to potential decay. When considering carving, some features may reduce the constraining protective force even further which is why statues commonly exhibit extreme weathering.

The changes resulting from weathering may take the form of growth or diminution of the mineral grains without any change in composition, for example, by reprecipitation of calcite in a limestone. In other cases the changes involve actual changes to the mineral composition. For example, feldspars will change into clay minerals. The different energy states between the mode of formation and the environment in which the stone is located, be that a building, a sea defence structure or fill for an engineering structure, is so great that it is not normally practical to reverse the reaction. In addition, as a result of weathering and chemical changes some stones expand e.g. Blue Lias and Kentish Ragstone.

Many weathering reactions will take place spontaneously. Others have a high activation energy and will progress infinitely slowly unless energy is put into the system to break the chemical bonds. This energy may be in the form of heat, directly through impact, or via catalysts. That some reactions take place spontaneously does not imply that there is instantaneous change, it merely reflects the fact that external influences are not required. The development of many secondary minerals in igneous rocks falls into this category.

The environment in which the stone is situated influences the rate of reaction. Chemical change in the dry state is slow since diffusion of ions and molecules will be very slow. If moisture is present, the reactions can take place much faster. This is one of the reasons why increased erosion along joints in granite will leave large, apparently unweathered, granite tors. Similarly the 'blue-hearted' blocks of yellow Jurassic limestone are a result of enhanced reaction along discontinuities.

Great care should be taken when stone is flame-textured, finished with a tool which imparts a large number of impacts to the surface or is treated with a chemical which may act as a catalyst to a chemical reaction within the stone. Most degradation produces a large increase in surface area which will tend to increase the ingress of moisture and other reagents which facilitate, or even promote, the chemical reactions. The aim of those involved in restoration and conservation of stonework is to slow down the process of chemical change.

The speed of a reaction can be affected by the presence of moisture or a catalyst. The exclusion of such materials and the reduction of the surface area in contact with them, would have the effect of slowing down the mineral changes. However, it must be borne in mind that, certainly with older buildings, the structure was designed to 'breathe' and any inhibition of this process may well produce effects which result in more damage to the fabric than was being caused by the degradation of the stone. Since it is impracticable to completely prevent water ingress, nothing must be done to impede drying out by evaporation and down drainage.

The manner in which moisture is excluded and the weathered friable stone is held together and protected, can also have side effects on the stone itself. For example, recent research on the effect of coating sandstone with a well know commercial consolidant has shown that, although effectively reducing the degradation of the stone due to weathering, once the consolidated layer was breached there was a rapid and total destruction of the sandstone. The long term result on the stone was considerably worse than if no treatment had been given.

The following sections outline some of the stone decay processes which can result in a desire to clean, repair or conserve stonework.

10.2.3.2. Wind erosion

It has long been believed that wind can erode softer stones so wind erosion is usually associated with the sandstones or limestones rather than the harder igneous or metamorphic rocks. However, it is doubtful if wind erosion itself is a significant agent of weathering of building stones in an historic timescale.

Wind will act by driving rain hard against a stone structure wetting the stones thoroughly and, when the rain stops, the wind will assist in drying out the stones more rapidly. It is these conditions which will assist in salt crystallization attack.

Wind-borne dust and sand would have an abrasive effect on stone be it in the form of a natural stone outcrop or in a building. In these circumstances the wind really does only affect the very outermost surface.

10.2.3.3. Frost

Frost damages those parts of a building that become frozen when the stone is laden with moisture. Saturated stone subjected to freezing can suffer dramatic cracking and large pieces can break away from the stone structure.

Weathering of stone

The weathering of natural stone used in buildings has been the subject of research for more than a hundred years. Many of the early research records relate to the effect of pollution from coal burning, for example the Report of the Committee on the decay of the stone at the New Palace of Westminster produced in 1861 (House of Commons, 1861) or Bonner (1913). Much of the earlier research was reviewed by Schaffer in 1932 in his report on 'The weathering of natural building stones' (Schaffer 1932). This interest has continued until the present day with the publication of the Report of the Building Effect Review Group (BERG 1989) and Cooke & Gibbs (1994). The weathering of sandstones has recently been reviewed by Young & McLean (1992) as part of their research on the cleaning of sandstones for Historic Scotland and a general introduction to the natural weathering of sandstones can be found there. The weathering of limestones has been reviewed by the BERG (1989) and in other volumes such as Amoroso & Fassina (1983) and the North American Programme on Acid Precipitation (NAPAP 1992).

The weathering of igneous rocks seems to be less well studied, probably because they are usually considered to weather on a geological rather than an historic time scale. However, it is important to consider the geological weathering as in many cases this will have considerable impact on the properties of the stone and its behaviour over an historic timescale.

The weathering of some groups of metamorphic rocks has been studied in great depth, particularly the weathering of marbles, which are usually included with limestones, and to a lesser extent slates. Other groups seem to have received little attention.

Wind erosion

Young & McLean (1992) describe alveolar or honeycomb decay which is the main form of decay usually associated with wind erosion. They quote from a number of other research studies that emphasize the importance of salt crystallization in the formation of this effect.

Quayle (1992) discusses the role of wind erosion in alveolar decay. He proposes that the decay is the result of natural weaknesses in the stone, particularly along bedding planes, which are exacerbated by the natural weathering and develop into hollows. The wind passing over these irregularities accelerates to keep pace with the surrounding airflow so producing a fall in air pressure in these specific areas. The reduced air pressure causes a sharp increase in the rate of evaporation and subsequent damage to the stone matrix in these areas. If Quayle is correct, then the damage is not a result of abrasion by particles carried in the wind but wind is still a critical factor. Young & McLean (1992) quote from Lewin (1982) who also believed that the variation in wind speeds was an important factor.

However, research on the Great Sphinx at Giza suggests that erosion is due to the suction effect of air vortices close to the stone surface removing loose particles.

Frost damage

In contrast to many other areas of research, the literature on frost damage to natural stone is considerable. Amoroso & Fassina (1983) state that the vulnerability to damage by frost is determined by a number of factors such as type of stone, its mineralogical properties, porosity and location. They comment that the forms of damage vary widely and include deep cracking, surface scaling and exfoliation. Young & McLean (1992) reviewed the mechanisms that cause frost damage. They suggest three mechanisms as follows:

- Volumetric expansion of water on freezing. Under normal conditions when water freezes it expands approximately 9% by volume. If this growth is restricted then a pressure will develop.
- Ice lensing or wedging. This is the persistent growth of a crystal large enough to disrupt the stone with enough water available to feed further growth. The lens or wedge can grow under pressure but, if the stone is very strong, it will exert enough pressure to inhibit growth.
- Hydraulic pressure theory. As ice grows in a pore or other space, owing to the expansion associated with freezing, unfrozen water will be expelled from the space. At this point three different mechanisms may create internal pressures. The first is the action of the unfrozen water being pushed into smaller spaces and the resistance to this flow increasing the hydrostatic pressure. Second, freezing typically occurs first at the outer surfaces forcing the remaining water inwards creating a 'saturated flow hydraulic pressure'. Pressure is developed due to the resistance of the water flowing rapidly through the capillaries. The third mechanism involves saturated materials whereby an advancing ice front produces a hydrostatic compression that will create a tensile force within the constraining stone.

Experiments carried out in the 1950s by Honeyborne & Harris (1958) showed that expansion was not the only mechanism as their findings showed that liquids that do not expand can still cause damage when frozen. In this latter instance it is possible that the thermal expansion coefficient of the stone is greater than that of the introduced liquid and the stone thus contracts more as the temperature is lowered and attempts to compress the introduced liquid causing a build-up of pressure.

It is clear that water must be present for damage to occur and so a large number of rock types with low porosities, for example granites and schists will not usually be damaged. However, there is evidence that not all porous stones are affected. Amoroso & Fassina (1983) postulated that stones with a saturation coefficient (a measure of the proportion of pore space filled with water at atmospheric pressure) of more than 0.9 are liable to frost cracks whereas those with a coefficient below 0.8 are not. Chatterji & Christensen (1979) predict that there will be a critical degree of saturation below which no damage will occur. Unpublished research by Honeyborne at the Building Research Establishment showed that the situation is more complex and that the relative proportions of macro and micropores (pores of diameter less than 5 μm) is also important.

Certain newly quarried stones containing quarry sap may be buried if they cannot be used before the onset of winter to prevent splitting. Frost damage appears to be most pronounced where stones retain higher proportions of moisture. Therefore, frost damage typically affects those features that are exposed and hold rainwater i.e. copings, cornices, cills and window heads. Other causes can be broken gutters or blocked rainwater pipes causing a continuous excess of water on a stone surface that has not been anticipated by design. Hygroscopic salts may help to attract or trap moisture in specific zones where decay may be accelerated by a combination of freeze-thaw and salt crystallization.

A stone does not need to be saturated by moisture to suffer frost damage. During dry spells changes in temperature may lead to condensation on cold stone surfaces and later freezing (typically through the night) may be sufficient to loosen the stone fabric at the surface making it more susceptible to other weathering processes. Some highly porous stones may be very resistant to freeze–thaw effects, water rapidly draining from them before it freezes or there being enough internal pore space to accommodate the freezing expansion of water.

10.2.3.4. Thermal cycles

The effect of thermal movements by the heating of the stone surface by the sun can lead to surface decay although in countries like Britain it is not a frequent cause. Some stones suffer irreversible temperature expansion but this is almost exclusively those containing calcite that has been preferentially orientated through metamorphic processes, chiefly marbles. Calcite, when subjected to heating, will expand in two directions whilst contracting in the third. Upon cooling it is found that the calcite does not return to its original form, a residual strain remaining.

The random orientation of calcite within a limestone means that all the strains act against each other and on average there is no net strain. Marbles, on the other hand, may exhibit foliations whereby most, if not all the constituent calcite crystals are formed with approximately the same orientation. Heating a marble comprising predominantly calcite with a preferred direction of formation means that the net strain will be greater in one direction relative to the direction of the foliation. Repeated thermal cycling will eventually cause the stone to disintegrate. Furthermore, differences in expansion between the outer and inner surfaces of slabs may result in them bowing or dishing. Cracks observed to form at the edges of marble tend to bifurcate as they travel inwards and slowly turn towards the direction of foliation.

Warping of marble has been known for some considerable time. In 1919, Kessler identified marble slabs used for tombstones that were generally bowing and carried out cyclic heating and cooling tests to demonstrate how this could cause the observed bowing. Similar distortion is known to affect marble panels around fire places. The most spectacular instance of dishing was the Amoco Building in Chicago where 43 000 panels of Carrara marble were replaced when various forms of warping developed.

Granites used in buildings are not usually affected but the heat of the sun may assist in the development of blisters on limestones once a sulphate skin has formed. Work carried out by Scott Russell showed that the thermal expansion of gypsum is five times that of limestone and such a difference is likely to lead to the separation of the sulphate rich layer during a period of heating.

Thin cladding panels will be at risk from fatiguing stresses from thermal cycling because they have a large surface to volume ratio and respond quickly to temperature changes. If the stone is rigidly fixed, for instance, by being bolted to a metal frame, the differential expansion between the stone and the frame will apply a stress to the fixing positions. In extreme circumstances the stone may be torn apart if movement tolerances are inadequate.

10.2.3.5. Biochemical weathering

There are a wide variety of biological agents, both botanical and zoological, which may effect the durability of stone. However, it is the botanical agents e.g. bacteria, lichen, ferns and higher plants, which far outnumber the zoological agents e.g. birds and bees and are mainly responsible for the biodeterioration of stone. Decay resulting from the growth of these organisms is induced by differing means including the dissolution of otherwise insoluble minerals by excreted acids and chelating agents and physical and mechanical disruption by invading roots and thalli. Schaffer (1932) discussed the possibility of the decay of stone being caused by bacteria but concluded that, although nitrogen-fixing and nitrifying bacteria had been identified in weathered stone, there was no proof that they were the cause of the degradation. Recent reports of the presence of bacteria deep within rock formations have added support to the possibility of bacterial activity being a factor in stone weathering. Lichens, an intimate association of fungi and algae, can produce organic acids such as oxalic and citric. These chemicals will certainly react with many rock substrates and there is a general consensus that lichens should be removed from stonework (Honeyborne 1990). Algae, fungi and other bacteria also fall into this category. There are some lichens that are totally benign and will not cause decay but may be removed for aesthetic reasons only.

It has been suggested by Jefferson (1993) that the change of colour from blue to creamy-yellow which occurs in the weathering zone of some of the Jurassic limestones of England, is due to the bacterial oxidation of iron sulphides (blue) which are present in the unweathered stone to iron oxides (yellow/orange). He also suggests that the gypsum found in the weathered surface layers of the stone may be the result, at least in part, of the migration of sulphur from the interior of the stone, rather than from atmospheric pollution. The weathering of some Purbeck Marble columns, which appear to weather from the inside out towards the surface, has been attributed to a similar bacterial process.

The coal and power generation industries have spent considerable time and effort in researching the decay of iron-sulphur compounds (Irdi & Booher 1994). It has been determined that the bacterium, *Thiobacillus ferro-oxidans*, can convert pyrite and other iron-sulphur compounds to ferric ions and sulphuric acid. The ferric ions are then believed to further attack remaining pyrite and a self-sustaining reaction is initiated. It is possible that some slate failures caused by iron-sulphur compound oxidation were initiated by bacteriological action. The worst slate decay is found where oxidizable pyrite is surrounded by calcite because the sulphuric acid formed can attack the calcite to form gypsum, the volumetric expansion leading to spalling, flaking and delamination.

10.2.3.6. Chemical weathering

Research on the effect of chemical weathering on natural stone is dominated by two related fields of work, the effect of air pollution and acidic deposition and the effect of salt crystallization (Kaiser 1929).

In general the pollutants likely to affect buildings or monuments can be either in the gaseous, liquid or solid phase (e.g. gaseous sulphur dioxide from power stations, gaseous oxides of nitrogen from motor vehicles exhausts, aqueous acid in the form of acid rain, solid particulate matter as dust or emission from diesel engines or possibly fertilizers on agricultural land). Any effect of a pollutant will be determined by the reactivity of the stone surface with the pollutant in the appropriate form and its topology, physical properties, chemistry and durability.

Sulphates moving through masonry may preferentially react with the mortars. In extreme circumstances the mortar may be completely altered to minerals such as thaumasite and will have very little if any strength. Such mortar breakdown may allow considerably greater infiltration of other weathering agents.

One special form of decay caused by acidic rain is contour scaling which is the breaking away of a crust that follows the man-made contours of a stone rather than any natural features. The crust is found to be gypsum rich and fatigue occurred just behind the choked layer as a result of thermal changes and the high coefficient of thermal expansion of the gypsum.

10.2.3.7. Rain and water weathering

The dissolution of calcium carbonate by unpolluted rainwater seems to account for much of the surface dissolution-recession of exposed limestone and marble surfaces. It must be remembered that the factors affecting the weathering of the surface of a carved stone monument will be a combination of physical, chemical and meteorological variables of the environment in which the stone is positioned in addition to the physical, geological and chemical properties of the stone itself. The design of a building or monument will affect the direction of water flow which can lead to streaking patterns or dissolution when there is ponding in pools, crevices or indents. Infiltration into the stone may occur when there is a natural porosity or one created by erosion or reaction. Rates of flow of rainwater may affect the form of micro-weathering features on a surface of

Acid rain

One type of material sensitive to attack by pollutants is calcareous building stone. Manifestation of damage includes loss of mass, change in porosity and discoloration. However, in the case of stone it is difficult to dissociate the effects of historical concentrations of pollutants from current ones which in the case of sulphur dioxide are lower.

In the Building Effects Review Group (BERG) report (1989) reviews are made of historic data from the studies carried out during the 1960s and onwards on laboratory samples of stone and of stone on real buildings to ascertain changes in rate of decay caused by pollution and natural weathering. The results indicated that on a real building (St. Paul's Cathedral) the rates of decay of limestone have not reduced proportionally to the reduction in concentration of air pollutants, especially sulphur dioxide. The main conclusion from experimental studies was that in polluted areas the main damage to calcareous stone is by dry deposition of sulphur dioxide; in areas of low pollution it is dissolution by rain water. Acidified precipitation, acid rain, appears to play little part in the process. The same is basically true of nitrogen oxides. Similar conclusions for calcareous stones were reached in the North American study of the National Acid Precipitation Assessment programme (NAPAP 1992).

The formation of calcium sulphate is common in many forms of stone decay. Because it is soluble, more so than the carbonate, it can recrystallize within stone giving rise to disruptive effects. The formation of black gypsum crusts on monuments and buildings, see Fig. 10.4, particularly in urban areas, is well documented (Kaiser 1910). The crust comprises gypsum, soot and other particulate matter derived from combustion processes often dating back to a time before pollution control was introduced.

carved stone. Orientation of the stone will also have a bearing on the rates of dissolution, especially when driving rain is common in certain directions.

Duffy & O'Brien (1995) highlight the different moisture conditions that may be found on a building façade and their effect on salt presence and acidity. The effect of projections such as sills and string courses on these regimes was also demonstrated. Beijer (1977) suggested that the upper 25% of a façade may receive 60% of the driving rain and, therefore, this area has the greatest washing. Salts tend to concentrate downwards or in drier zones protected by projections. Surface acidity increases towards the ground but is low below projections where salts are concentrating.

Blackening of stone where sheltered areas of the building do receive run off, particularly rainwater, is very pronounced. Air pollutants which consist of carbon become cemented on to the stone surface by gypsum formed as a result of chemical attack on the limestone by sulphur-based acids. Because gypsum is slightly soluble

Fig. 10.4. Heavy deposits on the underside of a string course that is so badly damaged it has been cut out for replacement.

in water any dirt that adheres to stone faces that are regularly washed by rainwater is removed. On sheltered surfaces the heavy black deposits accumulate, see Fig. 10.4. With sandstones the effect is different and the pollutants remain firmly in the pores of the sandstone giving an overall black effect, see Fig. 10.5.

10.2.3.8. Salt crystallization

This is traditionally considered to be potentially the most damaging to stone and has been left until last since it brings together many of the areas that have been covered above, particularly the deposition of pollutants and the movement of water. The sequence of events that gives rise to such damage occurring is as follows.

When salts are in contact with water a solution of both is transferred into the pores, fissures or joints of stone. Under circumstances when the stone then dries out and the water evaporates, the salt is deposited on the stone surfaces or within the pores or fissures and joints. A salty growth will appear on the surface (efflorescence). Crystallization that occurs invisibly within the pores of the stone is termed cryptoflorescence.

Salt crystallization is particularly noticeable on many limestones. The behaviour of sandstones is variable but they are not effected to the same degree.

The appearance of the surface of the stone, which can be white and fluffy, can be unsightly but is totally harmless. In contrast, that which occurs (cryptoflorescence) within the stone exerts pressure in the pores, fissures and joints. If the pressure builds up as the result of continuous wetting and drying, powdering of the surface will occur, sometimes leading to fragmentation of the stone surface initially along any lines of weakness in that particular piece of stone. This process is accelerated by salts absorbing water from moisture in the air or through changes in temperature with some salts and damage can re-occur indefinitely, see Fig. 10.6.

Table 10.1 is taken from Ashurst & Dimes (1990) and lists salts known to damage stone masonry and their sources. These salts are listed broadly in order of decreasing aggressiveness, however, salt mixtures may often be more aggressive than the constituents alone.

Decay due to crystallization is produced when tensions generated by local crystal growth in a pore or fissure exceed the tensile strength of the stone. Tensile strength is less at the surfaces, corners and other features than within the main stone body as these features are partly surrounded by space rather than constraining fabric. Hydration reactions from an anhydrous salt to its hydrated phase typically involves a volume increase

Fig. 10.5. Spalling of a ledge on sandstone.

Weathering by rain

The different effects of rainwater can be classified into its action as a medium for reactions, as a transporting agent and as a weathering agent. Rainwater itself is acidic because it is saturated with carbon dioxide and, therefore, has a pH of around 5. The interaction of rainwater with calcareous stone is immensely complicated especially as a series of solution, dissolution and sometimes crystallization stages are involved. Dissolution of calcareous stone (limestone, dolomitic sandstone) can be the prime mechanism of erosion in environments where there is no significant anthropogenic pollution in the atmosphere other than carbon dioxide. The properties of stone also affect the nature and rate of dissolution. Winkler (1975) studied the reaction of Cleopatra's Needle in New York and concluded that the permeability of the stone to rainwater was related to the differing solubilities of the fossil shell content and the matrix of the stone which was in turn related to grain size and packing density.

Schaffer (1932) has pointed out that if in an homogeneous material differences in the external conditions cause water to evaporate from one part of the stone construction more quickly than another, water will flow towards the more rapidly evaporating portions with consequences for salt movement also. He also states that the factors which appear to have the most significant influence on movement of water and soluble salts are evaporation and capillary properties of the materials. Reddy (1988) describes one of the many studies of rainwater run-off from marble specimens where by chemical analysis it was possible to assess rates of surface diminution with time. It should also be noted that the effect of rainwater on stone surfaces can also lead to physical disruption of the surface and grain removal (NAPAP 1992).

It is believed but not proven that wetting and drying plays a considerable part in the deterioration of porous stones (Building Research Digest 177, 1975). The act of wetting many stones can cause a small expansion and consequently contraction upon drying. Between wet and dry zones a shear force may be set up and continual cycling and movement of this shearing force fatigues the stone. There is no known evidence to demonstrate in any incidence of stone weathering that wetting and drying cycling has been solely responsible.

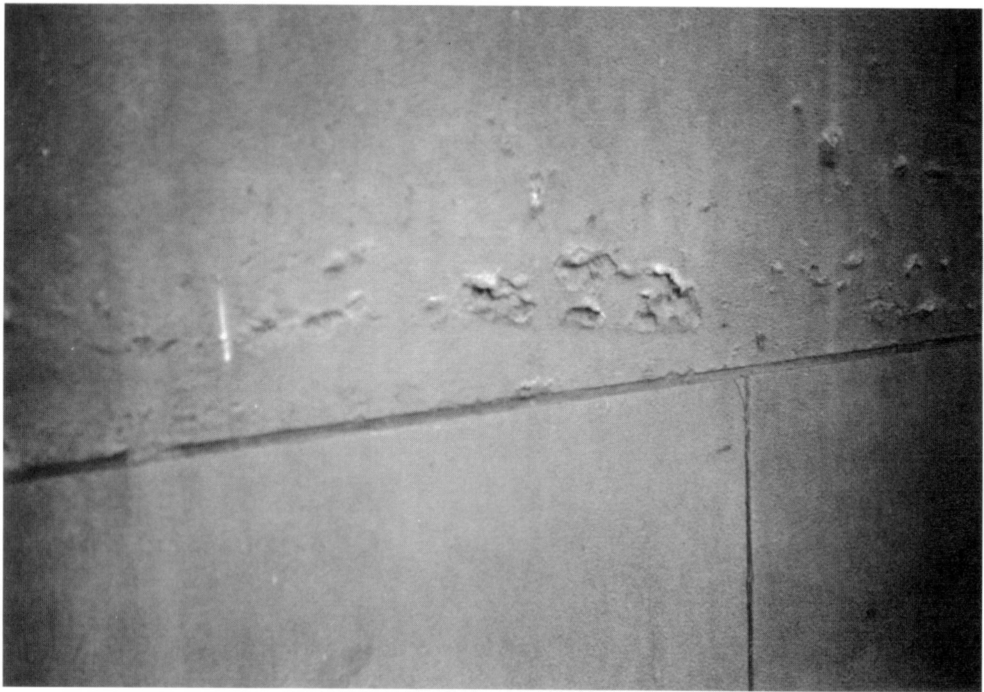

Fig. 10.6. Blistering on a limestone (Bathstone) façade in north London.

Table 10.1. *Salts that have been known to damage stone masonry and their sources (taken from Ashurst and Dimes 1990)*

Type of salt	*Common sources*
Sodium sulphate	Clothes washing powders; soils, some types of fired clay bricks; some processed solid fuels; by action of polluted air on sodium carbonate.
Sodium carbonate (washing soda)	Clothes washing powders; many domestic cleaning aids; some proprietary cleaners for limestone faced buildings; fresh concrete and cement based mortars.
Magnesium sulphate (Epsom salt)	Some fired clay bricks; rain washings from dolomitic limestone affected by polluted air.
Potassium carbonate	Fresh concrete and cement based mortars; fuel ashes and ash mortars.
Potassium sulphate	Some types of fired clay bricks; by action of polluted air on potassium carbonate.
Sodium chloride (common salt)	Seawater; road and pavement de-icing salt; salt used for preserving meat, etc., soil.
Potassium chloride	Soil
Calcium sulphate	Many types of fired clay bricks; limestone and dolomitic limestone affected by polluted air; gypsum based wall plasters.
Sodium nitrate (Chile salt petre)	Soil; preserved meat; fertilisers.
Potassium nitrate (salt petre)	Soil; fertilisers; gun powder.

that leads to a build up of internal pressure on the pore walls and other stone features (Esbert *et al.* 1997). When the pressure exceeds the tensile strength of the stone at a given point then the stone will fail.

The most notable reaction of this nature is that involving sodium sulphate. Sodium sulphate salts contained in a solution that is able to evaporate will leave anhydrous salt deposits which will not damage the stone. Rehydration to a decahydrate phase may involve a 200% expansion which exerts a pressure within the stone pores. Conversion back to the anhydrous phase after drying means that there is now room for new salt laden solutions to enter and increase the mass of salts which increases the potential for damage owing to hydration and expansion. The salt crystallization test, see Appendix B tries to imitate the sodium sulphate reaction and the mechanisms of the test are discussed in great detail by, amongst others, Arnold (1976), Niesel (1978), Price (1979), McMahon *et al.* (1992), Doehne (1994) and Grossi *et al.* (1997).

Sandstones may suffer considerable salt crystallization damage if placed below limestones. Here calcium sulphate formed by acid attack and pollution may be washed from the limestone and into the sandstone to cause damage.

10.3. Masonry condition evaluation

10.3.1. Introduction

Before a decision is made to repair, restore or leave a masonry construction alone a series of evaluations must be undertaken concerning history and historical significance, structural assessment, prevailing environmental conditions and current masonry condition. Most information can be obtained from expert visual inspection ranging from simple visual appraisal to highly detailed mapping of damage to intricate carving.

A range of non-destructive and destructive tests are available for assessing masonry conditions beyond the visible surface. Monitoring over time may also be required to assess decay mechanisms, particularly those associated with structural dislocations.

10.3.2. Building history

Building history is rarely anything other than complex. The older a building the greater the potential for alterations and additions to the structure and the loss of this historical data. The younger a building the more likely a wider variety of construction methods and materials. Thus, the more information that can be obtained prior to later investigations the better.

The main information to be obtained should include the following:

1. Age and time of construction
2. Architect and builder
3. Plans, specifications, bills of sale, invoices
4. Historical usage

For any repair, restoration or alterations the above four items are re-applied.

Documentation may be found from a variety of sources, most notable being local authorities with whom planning applications may have been lodged. The details of ancient structures may require exhaustive research through historical memoirs, libraries and may extend to national museums.

Once the age of a masonry element is known the amount of exposure can be calculated by consulting local weather records. This should include a historical assessment of the effects of local pollution, which may offer clues to decay mechanisms.

Other information required may include local ground conditions such as geology, including soils, which may have structural implications. For example, high water tables may result in capillary water rise in masonry both internally and externally.

10.3.3. Visual assessment

Visual assessment should be used to classify possible decay mechanisms affecting different structural elements and the degree to which such deterioration is occurring. Viles *et al.* (1997) classify three scales of visible deterioration on historic stone monuments demonstrated in Table 10.2. It must be remembered that the three scales all overlap and that deterioration has different manifestations at different scales.

The main aspects to consider when conducting a visual survey of a masonry structure should include the following:

1. Materials present, e.g. stone, brick, mortar, glass, metal.
2. Material geometry – size, shape and position of various materials relative to each other.
3. Visual variation caused by, amongst others
   (a) salt efflorescence
   (b) uneven material loss
   (c) surface encrustations
   (d) discoloration
   (e) cracking/crazing
   (f) loss of detail
   (g) presence of surface treatments including paint
4. Moisture flow over and movement through the masonry, especially the following
   (a) roofing and guttering details
   (b) details breaking wall planarity such as cornicing
   (c) capillary rise from the ground
   (d) internal condensation
   (e) window to masonry area ratio
   (f) areas of possible standing water
5. Major structural factors such as areas of concentrated loads, particularly those in tension or point loading.

At this stage the type(s) of stone employed in the masonry should have at least a basic geological classification such as sandstone, limestone, granite, marble and slate. For many older buildings the stone used may have been won locally and it is a relatively easy task to identify the stone. Correct identification may require more exhaustive techniques described in §10.5. Ultimately the derivation of all the masonry materials will need to be ascertained.

Many younger structures are ascribed finite design lives, often 30 years or less, rarely 60 years or more. Within such short time spans it is not common for stone to exhibit any form of serious structural deterioration. Visually, buildings are not expected to alter in their appearance to any great degree, however, modern constructions may develop aesthetically displeasing discolorations, in the most extreme circumstances occurring before construction completion. Hunt & Miglio (1992, 1994) and Hunt (1996) discuss many occurrences of staining and discoloration, their derivation and how to avoid them. Table 10.3 summarizes the various forms of staining and discoloration and their causes.

From the visual inspection the various probable decay mechanisms can be assigned to different parts of the construction and recommendations for more detailed investigation provided. Such further investigations may be restricted as destruction of the fabric may be required. Thus, there has been research into a variety of non-destructive methods for evaluating stone masonry.

10.3.4. Non-destructive testing

The Schmidt hammer is a well known portable field test. It applies an impact force and the rebound of the hammer applying the force is measured. The test is useful for identifying potential sub-surface delaminations which 'cushion' the blow leading to a lower rebound value. A considerable drawback of the method is that weak stones, including many sandstones and limestones, may suffer an indentation at the point of testing which will affect the result. Carrying out the test on weathering crusts over soft inner zones may also provide ambiguous results.

Surface permeability can be measured in a variety of ways. Nappi & Côte (1997) describe a method where a section of masonry is sprayed with water and at the same time some pressure is created to simulate the effect of wind. The water that is not absorbed is utilized again while the amount of water lost is measured. In this way the permeability of a wall can be measured *in situ*.

The initial surface absorption test given in BS 1881 was developed for assessing concretes but is equally

Table 10.2. *Classification of scales of deterioration (after Viles et al.* 1997)

Term	*Scale*	*Major science involved*	*Examples of measurements of deterioration*
Degradation	Microscale (cm or less)	Chemistry, physics, microbiology, petrology	Mass loss, dimension change, porosity change
Distress	Mesoscale (cm to m)	Geosciences, materials science, ecology	% surface damaged, presence of a range of deterioration features
Decay	Macroscale (whole façades or buildings)	Structural engineering	Structural stability, lifetime left, aesthetic appearance

Table 10.3. *Staining and discoloration of natural stone. Aesthetic reasons often dominate the choice of a given stone material but there are many factors which can upset the final appearance, as illustrated in this outline. Inferior stone and associated materials can affect aesthetics at any stage in the life of a stone*

	Erratic Spotting	Overall Discoloration	Patchy Discoloration	Related to Stone Features	Related to Construction Features
Quarrying and Finishing Processes	cutting residues - iron shot		oil, ink and other spillages	weathered materials entering stone	uneven finishing
		acid cleaning	acid cleaning		
During Construction	welding/grinding spatter	general dirt and dust	decay of packaging		reaction with protective sheeting
		fire damage; introduced contaminants from shipping/transport	moisture darkening; introduced contaminants from shipping/transport	moisture darkening; dirt concentration in high porosity areas	dirt in joints etc.
Post-Construction	alteration of flame-textured constituents, then decay, heel impact damage	abrasion, surface attack, pollution	efflorescences, general usage, spillages	growth of organics	rusting of fixings etc., uneven loss of polish, growth of organics
Inferior Stone Materials	trace mineral decay	ageing, bleaching		deleterious minerals in veins and other discontinuities	
	reaction with cleaning materials - maintenance	reaction with cleaning materials - maintenance	reaction with cleaning materials - maintenance; decay in moisture -affected zone		
Associated Materials		organic growth, wax discoloration	migration of materials by moisture flow	incorrect impregnation	joint mastic/silicone decay, ageing of epoxy resins

applicable to stones. A measured area of surface is kept wet via a constant head of water. After different times of exposure a second inlet is opened to a graduated capillary of known dimensions. The loss of water in the capillary over time is measured and provides an accurate determination of surface absorption at the different times of exposure chosen. Working in a similar way is the German Karsten tube test (Knofel *et al.* 1995).

Ground penetrating radar is another technique favoured by engineers and becoming more popular in the assessment of historical buildings. Radar pulses can either be picked up in reflection at the point of propagation or by transmission located at a different point such as the opposing side of a wall. The technique is obviously useful in looking at the heart of a structure and locating voids, different fill materials or layers and even cracks. Closer to the surface the technology may be used to locate ties and other fixing items.

Moisture profiles deep within masonry may be investigated using monofrequency electomagnetic waves which have been developed by the Laboratoire Central des Ponts et Chaussées, Centre de Nantes, France. The method relies upon the mean value of the wave attenuation across the whole thickness of the structure under investigation. These methods are still the subject of considerable research.

Pulse velocity testing can be related to elastic properties and sometimes also compressive strength. A known frequency pulse is transmitted at a given location and received at one or more points. Discontinuities such as cracks and voids may alter the signal and be shown up on sonic tomographies that can be calculated from a large set of data (Esbert *et al.* 1997). The method appears useful in assessing the effectiveness of injected materials that should fill voids and improve mechanical properties. Higher frequency pulses are more sensitive to detecting small cracks but will also be subject to greater signal attenuation. This can be a problem for masonry where the mortar joints introduce a strong attenuation.

The Open University employed three non-destructive techniques to characterize granite columns of Roman age found around the Mediterranean and Europe. Magnetic susceptibility, gamma ray and portable x-ray fluorescence demonstrated that the granite columns were derived from locations in Turkey and Egypt. Each method had a variety of drawbacks but used together provided powerful correlations.

Infra-red thermography was used by Paljak (1971) in the testing of external walls whereby heatflow across a medium can be measured. Moisture and insulation may be evaluated as these will affect thermal properties. One major application is the location of metal ties and other fixings which increase heat flow.

One of the most useful non-destructive techniques in the assessment of material condition is dye testing. Originally developed for the aerospace industry for the identification of fatigue cracking in aircraft it has been adapted for stone assessment. A dye penetrant is painted onto the surface under investigation and, after a period of time, the excess is either wiped or washed from the surface leaving only the dye that has penetrated. Cracks show up against a background haze of minor features such as partings along crystal grain boundaries and cleavages. The methods has proven successful in the assessment of blast affected stone cladding (Hunt 1994) and has numerous potential applications including determining moisture flow regimes.

10.3.5. Semi-destructive testing

One of the most useful invasive techniques in the use of optical probes, either borescopes or endoscopes. These normally require the drilling of holes 10 mm to 15 mm in diameter into which the probes are inserted. Careful location selection in deteriorated zones or at mortar bed/joint junctions can reduce the visual impact of the damage. Sometimes wooden frameworks can be removed or drilled through rather than the masonry fabric. In ashlar type construction optical probes are most useful in assessing fixing decay.

The *in situ* stress can be calculated via the use of a flat jack (Rossi 1985). This essentially comprises two metal sheets with an internal cavity into which hydraulic fluid can be pumped. The distance between two points in a vertical line is measured. A thin horizontal slot is cut between the two points into which the flat jack can be inserted. The flat jack is pressured until the original distance between points A and B is restored. At this point the flat jack pressure corresponds to the *in situ* stress. The main draw back with the method is an uneven contact surface for which a correction must be made. By using two jacks in parallel alignment the elastic modulus can be calculated.

10.3.6. Destructive testing

By taking samples of stone a full range of tests such as those described in Chapter 9 can be undertaken. The quantity of material potentially required to carry out the tests could have serious consequences upon the appearance of the structure. This problem can be resolved to some degree by taking samples from hidden faces, the material being invisibly replaceable.

Certain types of testing require destruction of visible fabric to obtain essential data. The main tests include:

1. Petrographic examination to assess surface decay mechanisms and extent of this decay.
2. Chemical analyses of components and products of decomposition, including salt profiling.
3. Other analytical techniques including x-ray diffraction, scanning electron microscopy and micro-analysis, infra-red spectrometry and laser ionisation mass spectrometry.

Petrographic analyses of masonry structures must be carefully planned to obtain the optimum information. Undisturbed samples that may include mortar joints can be carefully cut or cored, preferably in areas of low visual impact. In certain circumstances, consolidation with resin prior to sampling may be required to reduce possible damage. Large format thin-sections of at least 100 mm by 70 mm should provide enough material in a location to provide information from the weathered through to the fresh zones. Slices may also be taken in both horizontal and vertical directions.

Impregnation of slices ready for thin-sectioning can include a fluorescent dye which will allow later investigation of pore structures and crack networks. Gypsum and other sulphates may form part of the weathering products and cutting, grinding or finishing the thin-section using water is not recommended as the salts may be removed.

Petrographic examination of mortar can determine general quality, types of cement/lime used, aggregate details including constituent proportions and damage mechanisms. It is important that thin-sections are prepared without the assistance of water that may dissolve certain of the weathering products.

Chemical analysis can be used to quantify the amount of salts and other possible weathering products affecting masonry. By taking incremental drill samples salt profiles can be determined. The reliability of the results may be reduced for a variety of reasons and often chemical analysis should be used in conjunction with petrographic analyses and the other analytical techniques available. Some of the major problems include the following:

1. Presence of shell and other carbonate bearing materials in mortar aggregate will lead to over-estimation of lime proportions.
2. Small samples may have large errors related to the inhomogeneity expected from the materials under investigation.
3. Mineralogical assemblages may be misinterpreted.

The main salts that are known to damage stone masonry and their sources are given in Table 10.1 taken from Ashurst & Dimes (1990).

The advantage of techniques such as x-ray diffraction and scanning electron micro-analysis is that they can utilise very small samples. Whilst initial costs may appear large, the rapid acquisition of information can quickly compensate for the lower accuracy of the data than that obtained from chemical analyses.

10.3.7. Monitoring structural movements

From the start of construction masonry is subject to change resulting from movements between the different structural elements and failure of materials. These faults may develop through the life of the structure either continually or in bursts. Of paramount importance is preventing structural collapse and monitoring of cracks and movements is required. Once structural problems have been alleviated only then should repair and restoration work to the fabric be undertaken.

The main forms of failure leading to cracking and movement include the following:

1. Foundation failure
2. Superstructural failure
3. Compression failure
4. Arch failure
5. Material defects

Prior to any monitoring of these possible defects care should be taken to ensure that apparent cracks are not in fact natural features of the stone such as veins and vents which can weather differently from the surrounding material.

The foundations of older structures are often considered inadequate by today's standards. However, if there is no evidence of any distress the utmost care must be taken in any remedial works not to upset the status quo.

Evidence of foundation failures may be indicated by an uneven plinth line or misalignment at wall junctions. Desiccation or hydration of clay-rich soils may lead to either shrinkage or heave in response to changes in the surrounding vegetation or episodes of drought or prolonged rains.

Superstructural failure will depend on whether the compressive and shear strength of the masonry units are greater than the applied load. The areas most prone to failure are lintels and other spanning features not built as arches. Other risk factors include the slenderness ratio whereby a long unit will support a lower compressive load than a short unit of the same cross-sectional dimensions. Where a façade is tied back to an inner wall differential movements may fatique the fixing locations. Where forces are not applied uniformly through a structural member such eccentric loading may increase stress in one part to the point where failure occurs either by crushing or buckling.

Compression failure typically occurs from point loading of unevenly dressed surfaces not separated by mortar. Similarly, inadequate bedding with well compacted mortar in the outermost zone (0–25 mm from the surface) may also cause point loading. The effects of such loading typically manifest as spalling and may be difficult to tell apart.

Arches transfer the vertical load that would normally act through the space underneath into both vertical and lateral forces to the sides of the arch. The horizontal force may easily lead to movement unless adequate restraint is provided and may become serious if the mortar is deteriorating.

Material failures will include the deterioration of stone by any of the mechanisms described earlier in this chapter. Other failures of materials include the oxidation/expansion of metal fixings. The use of strong cements may lead to spalling similar to that caused by compressive point loading.

With so many different reasons for crack propogation and movements, careful monitoring must be undertaken of structures that are statutorily listed and for which approval for works to be carried out may be refused if it is considered that the structure could be damaged.

Differential movements can be measured by employing strain gauges across cracks or planes of weakness. One of the most effective and unobstrusive methods is the Demec mechanical demountable strain gauge developed by the British Concrete Association. The method employs an Invar Bar to allow a correction for temperature variation. The method allows movements to be measured in increments down to 0.025 mm.

10.3.8. Preparing for remediation

Once the stone decay mechanisms have been assessed a programme of works can be prepared.

Research needs to be carried out to establish if there is record of drawings that were used at the time when the building was constructed. If these are unavailable then a detailed set needs to be made that also includes all necessary measurements. Once this set of drawings has been either found from the archives or prepared, then a set of elevation drawings should be marked up identifying the defects of the stone. Detailed drawings of complete elevations should be made on which the positions and nature of defects are marked. Defects should be classified according to their nature and be quantified as proportions of the total elevation. This may include badly weathered stones, weathered open joints, blistering of the face, cracked stones, broken stones etc. Record drawings after completion of the repairs will also be required.

Inadequate weatherings, drip mouldings, or missing lead flashings should also be highlighted. In the case of structurally induced defects if these are still active the ordinary stone repairs would be a waste of time and money until the structural cause has been adequately remedied. The masonry repair may have to incorporate some structural reinforcement that will minimize the effect of further structural movement. These items need to be considered together with the environment of the building. The building may be in an exposed location adjacent to the sea, on an exposed inland hill or protected in a large town or city by closely surrounding higher structures.

10.3.9. Final decisions, repair, restore or leave alone

With the documentation to hand the next steps have to be carefully considered by the architect and the building owner. The first decision is whether to do anything or whether to leave the stonework alone. If remedial work is deemed necessary the extent of repair and the methods have to be decided.

There are a number of factors that need to be considered within the overall approach to the work. Generally the purpose of the work is to hand on to the next generation the building or monument in a good state of repair.

If a cleaning, restoration or conservation technique is to be acceptable, it is important that it does not introduce problems which were not already present in the stone. In the case of conservation techniques, these should be reversible.

An architect may, for example, only consider replacing stone if it has weathered back a substantial distance or is so soft that a knife can be easily inserted. The decision may be that if the stone is firm and is only weathered to a relatively shallow depth that it stays where it is. Every stone is different and every stone weathers differently. This same stone may well weather in a different manner depending upon its position on the building, for example depending upon the elevation in which it is situated. Some limestones may weather to show black crusts and little erosion on one side of the building and no crust but extensive erosion on another side.

10.3.10. Factors and financial influences on nature and extent of remedial works

Factors which may well be considered when deciding upon a suitable course of action include:

- The historic value of the building and the desire to retain as much as possible of the original stonework.
- The necessity to replace stone with exactly the same type and the length of time that the repairs need to last. For example, if the remaining stonework will only last another 10–15 years it may be possible to replace damaged stones with another less durable and less expensive stone.
- Ease of future inspections. For example, the stonework may be at ground level and, therefore, always accessible for repair. On the other hand, owing to the cost of scaffolding to gain access to the top of the spire the repair may need to last at least 50–60 years.
- The rate of decay of the stone.
- The funds that are presently available to carry out the works.

All these various factors need to be taken into account together sometimes with the views of the conservation offices of the local planning authority, English Heritage and the Council for the Care of Churches and other such bodies that may have an interest in the building or property.

10.4. Stone cleaning

10.4.1. Introduction

For many years the smoke emissions from the burning of coal were seen as the primary cause for the soiling of buildings. In England the Clean Air Acts of 1956 and 1968 in part removed this cause. However, today vehicle exhaust emissions and acid rain are now seen as largely responsible for the rapid resoiling. Studies have shown that buildings may require cleaning now every 10–15 years to remove dirt, see Figs 10.5 and 10.6.

Building cleaning is now undertaken for mainly aesthetic reasons. Many companies who own stone buildings as their headquarters or office wish to project a good image of the company and this they are unable to do with a dirty building façade.

Cleaning techniques have improved during the last 15 years and there is less opposition now to cleaning in the United Kingdom. However, there have been problems in Scotland during recent years which have halted some projects north of the border but there are generally very good sound practical reasons for cleaning or removing dirt from heavily soiled buildings. For example, decay takes place around cracked stone, open joints and encrustations that are obscured by the dirt and heavy soiling. Buildings may be cleaned if other external repairs are being carried out and access becomes available because scaffolding is being erected to the façade.

Ideally the cleaning of a historic/listed building should be undertaken with the same amount of care and attention to detail as that which is given to the cleaning of sculptures. It is, therefore, essential that cleaning should be carried out by fully trained operatives. Building façades can be so easily damaged by an inappropriate cleaning method or an incompetent operative working to a competitive price for the work.

If it is decided to clean the façade, for whatever the reason, aesthetic or maintenance, then the risks involved must be considered and a number of basic questions need to be answered

The desirability of cleaning a façade will depend upon whether the dirty soiled appearance of the building is worse than that of the cleaned façade. It may be that a cleaned façade will reveal an untidy patchwork of repairs after cleaning.

The type of dirt or soiling that is adhering to the building needs to be considered. Calcium carbonate and calcium sulphate deposits on sandstone and brickwork are damaging. Ground level soiling may be viewed as a contribution to the general staining of the surface only and similarly other types of soiling may present no particular problems.

Finally, the selection of a suitable method of cleaning for removing the dirt deposits from the surfaces without causing any damage to the stone surface must be considered and the matter of whether the work can be executed with the necessary skill and expertise. Cleaning methods are described in §10.4.3 but the reader is warned that the use of inappropriate methods may cause more harm than good to stonework. The authors accept no responsibility for any such damage. Owners of buildings must obtain expert advice upon the most appropriate method of cleaning as indicated in the text box.

10.4.2. Cleaning trials

Cleaning trials are a fact finding and extremely important exercise. The sample clean is an important part of the study and part of the survey to determine the correct cleaning method for the contract. The sample clean should also establish an acceptable reference panel for the future project. The cleaning of the sample trial area must be carefully supervised and recorded, see Figs 10.7 and 10.8.

The trial area or areas should cover all of the differing material types on the façade and varying amounts of soiling. The trials may employ any one of the following methods that are detailed later in the chapter.

The cleaning trial should determine the following:

- Whether cleaning will produce an aesthetically desirable result.
- The correct cleaning method or methods to be employed.
- The appropriate techniques and equipment to be employed for cleaning and to be specified by the architect.

Advice on cleaning of stone

There is an increasing number of books that give guidance on the cleaning of buildings. These include two volumes by Ashurst (1994) which cover the cleaning of historic buildings – both the investigation of the substrate and soiling and cleaning materials and processes. Historic Scotland has produced a practioner's guide to stone cleaning (Andrews 1994) which covers techniques and the effects of differing methods. Further information can be found in Ashurst & Dimes (1990), BRE Digest 280 (BRE 1983b), Moncrieff & Weaver, (1983) and Spry (1982).

The Stone Federation of Great Britain has formed a stone cleaning section who can advise on appropriate cleaning methods and companies that can carry out the work.

Fig. 10.7. Cleaning trials in progress on a Portland stone building.

(**a**) (**b**)

Fig. 10.8. Trial cleaning. (**a**) Masked cleaning trial area before cleaning using Joss system. (**b**) Trial area after cleaning.

- Provide information to identify the stone of the building if not already known.
- Give an indication of the amount of surface repair that may be necessary.
- The form of protection to windows, openings or any painted or other treated surfaces.

The attainment of all these objectives will allow the correct specification for the cleaning work to be issued so that the work can be carried out in the correct manner. It is essential that a contractor with experience of all cleaning systems is selected for the cleaning trials.

10.4.3. Cleaning methods

10.4.3.1. Water washing
This is principally used for cleaning masonry of limestone, marble and polished granite. The dirt which tends to form on these surfaces is usually soluble in water. Therefore, washing by water, which is a very simple process in principle, requires putting sufficient water in contact with the dirt/soil deposits to wash them away or to soften them to allow them to be brushed away. Water can be used in several differing ways.

Water spraying. Water is sprayed onto the stone surface by a single spray or a series of jets on booms that can be moved up and down the façade of the building as required, see Fig. 10.9. Water can be applied by differing types of jets or nozzles and the type required will depend upon the type of surface to be cleaned and the amount of dirt to be removed. The spraying of a single jet or spacing of several jets on a boom should be controlled to give an even wetting of the surface or controlled to give an application to a particular area which may require more thorough cleaning. While a flat surface may be cleaned in a matter of a few hours, two or more days may be required for a carved cornice with encrusted dirt deposits.

Hot water can be effective where the deposits are greasy. As the solubility of gypsum increases with temperature hot water will be more effective in its removal. Where the outer surface of limestone has actually changed from limestone to gypsum, washing with water, especially hot water, will remove a layer of stone from the fabric. Whereas this may not matter on walling, any carved feature will actually lose its outer surface.

Intermittent nebulous or pulse washing. This was developed from the water spraying techniques. It is one of the most effective ways of cleaning without many of the problems associated with using large quantities of water. This system of washing stone makes use of atomized sprays of water playing intermittently on the masonry surface at a low pressure. Special fine nozzles are used and are directed onto the masonry structure where the area of soiling is to be softened so that sufficient water is applied to moisten and soften the deposits but not so as to cascade down the building. The water is controlled electronically by means of sensor heads or a preset clock. Sensors are pinned to the masonry and activate the controls at preset limits. The more usual method however, is to use a clock control. As a starting point the clock should be set for spraying times of eight seconds interspersed by four minute shut down periods. By using this method timely commencement of scrubbing can begin once it is noticed that the soiling is sufficiently softened and responsive and the times can be adjusted to suit particular projects. This method of working requires the purchase of quantities of special fine nozzles, fixed and flexible bars to position the nozzles, time clocks and water metering devices in addition to other equipment.

Fig. 10.9. Cleaning stone with low pressure water sprays.

Pressure washing/water lance. Using both high and low pressure water washing, water is directed at the masonry face through a lance held by an operative. Water supplied at 500 psi is normally called low pressure, 700–1000 psi is termed medium pressure and that exceeding 1000 psi is high pressure. These figures are based on a fan tip spray nozzle of 30°, a water flow rate of 4 litres per minute and distance from the masonry surface of 250 mm.

The cutting action of the pressure of the water lance can be useful in removing stubborn areas of dirt. However, with this method it is very easy to cause loss of masonry from the surface or jointing/pointing material. The correct nozzle shape and size must be selected and the operative must observe the action of water on the stone surface very carefully to prevent potential damage. Soft stones or stones having soft sand or clay beds should not be cleaned with this method. For each stone type surface there will be maximum pressure which should not be exceeded.

Steam Cleaning. Steam generated by equipment is directed against the masonry through a low pressure nozzle. The steam and the resultant condensed water soften and swell the dirty deposits on the façade which are removed from the surface by the force of the steam jet.

The use of steam on dirty masonry structures, particularly limestone and carved features, was extensive before the last war but it has fallen into disrepute partly due to the fact that caustic soda (or soda ash), which was added to the boiled water to avoid furring, was then deposited on the cleaned surface. Considerable damage was done at Southwell Minster where the stone contained clay minerals. It is still used for removing chewing gum, greasy or tarry deposits and wax crayon.

Considerations. The problems associated with water washing relate to the excessive quantities of water applied to the structure leading to saturation of the masonry and water penetrating the fabric of the building. The general principle should be to apply only as much water as is necessary, for a minimum length of time and only to the area to be cleaned in such a way that the water run off does not saturate adjacent masonry unnecessarily. For example, on taller buildings horizontal catchments should be provided at regular intervals to collect the water run off and take it away from the building façade in plastic guttering and downpipes.

The use of brushes of differing sizes and design, manufactured from natural bristle and fine phosphor bronze wire (never steel wire brushes) to remove the softened soiling reduces the wetting period and quantity of water needed.

Water penetration of the fabric can have the most serious consequences. Water will penetrate through the mortar joints where defective, through cracks or fractures in the stone and contact iron fixings, plaster, timber beams or battens, timber panelling or electrical wirings and furnishings. The water penetration can result in either a water stain on paintwork or woodwork or the rusting of iron cramps or result in future damage by way of dry rot in timber.

Saturation of the masonry structure can also encourage efflorescence to appear where salts migrate to the surface when the structure is drying out. It can also lead to light brown or orange staining. One of the causes is believed to be the high iron content of the water that has been used and the latent iron content of the stones in the structure. The brown staining can appear as a mottled pattern. However, in time and after several rainwater washings the staining can be reduced if not eliminated.

When considering water cleaning careful attention needs to be paid to protection of the structure before work commences, particularly around any gaps to window and door frames and to any obvious cracks in the masonry structure that may need to be temporarily sealed prior to cleaning. Similarly, the scaffolding will need to be sheeted in, to prevent nuisance to third parties such as passers-by on the pavement. In addition, where there has been heavy soiling, particularly under projections, and there is a substantial thickness or build-up of black encrustations this may need to be removed by hand held scrapers, small scale abrasive techniques or alike beforehand. Unless such areas are first attended to the remainder of the façade can suffer from the excessive quantities of water that the more heavily soiled area will require.

Finally, water washing is to be avoided in winter months to prevent any damage by water freezing in the masonry. Many of the problems associated with masonry cleaning by water can be overcome by proper preparation, careful planning, constant and conscientious supervision and use of the additional techniques of brushing and removal of heavy encrustations.

10.4.3.2. Mechanical and air abrasive cleaning

Mechanical and air abrasive cleaning methods remove dirt by mechanical force by either hand held implements or mechanized equipment. The dirt or soiling is removed by abrasion of the stone surface. The simplest form is the use of a brush and may be called the dry brushing technique. Whatever form of mechanical method is used they all operate by removing the soiling and the particles or layer of stone to which the soiling or dirt is attached. How much of the stone or masonry structure is removed depends on the severity of the mechanical process and the type of stone involved (Grimmer 1979). Although mechanical cleaning methods in the past have been the most damaging to the stone surface, a variety of new methods have been developed and these will be dealt with later. As a general rule, if damage is being done to the stone surface stop and consult the Architect.

(1) Dry brushing, surface scraping and spinning off. As previously stated the simplest form is dry brushing of the stone surface. The use of stiff bronze bristle brushes will remove any loosely bound dirt and organic growth such as moss and some lichens. A more severe method is the

use of a carborundum block on flat surfaces or the use of a masons drag. Abrasive discs (hard or flexible) are used where they are attached to an electric power tool and the surface of the stone is spun-off. The pads can use a fine or coarse type of sand paper and the surface dirt and the stone surface is removed. Accurate spinning-off, even by the most experienced of operatives, is very difficult and can lead to surfaces that are scalloped in appearance, uneven arises and moulded profiles and wavy lines. Good work usually has to be finished by hand and be re-dressed to bring back the original appearance. The use of spinning-off is suited to small areas of masonry repair rather than a large scale cleaning method.

However, in recent years cleaning of flat stone floor areas has been achieved using a grinding machine with heads of carborundum using blocks of a coarse grade then following by finer blocks to ultimately 'polish' the floor.

Compressed air abrasives. There has been a significant development in recent years in this field. Due mainly to cost constraints, differing methods have been developed and promoted to try to bring down the cost of cleaning and at the same time reduce the amount of damage to the stone surface.

The significant factors that relate to the air abrasive methods are air pressure from the compressor, type and size of nozzle, type of abrasive, volume of air, and or water, the pressure, the skill of the operatives using the equipment and the supervision of the work. Each factor must be selected from the results of trials upon the particular application.

For the various different types of system the basic equipment is a compressor, a 'pot' for the air and abrasive material to mix, the delivery lines or hoses and the nozzle through which the material is directed to the solid stone surface. Some of the systems introduce a water hose running in tandem with the delivery line or hose and both discharge at the same nozzle or adjacent nozzles but both directed at the soiled stone surface.

Materials for use as abrasives vary greatly and may include shot, glass beads, sand, blasting grit, non-siliceous grits (copper and iron slag, carborundum, aluminium oxide powders), olivine, dolomite, crushed egg or nut shells. There continues to be development in this area.

Nozzles need to be chosen carefully depending on what background is to be cleaned. Long venturi nozzles give an even spread over a large impact area and are most suitable for large flat areas. Long and short straight nozzles are better suited to more detailed or carved areas of masonry, see Fig. 10.10.

Air pressures for cleaning will be determined when the sample areas of cleaning are carried out.

Typical nozzle pressures are 20–100 psi. However, the lower the pressure the less damage will be done to the stone work. Detailed trials need to be undertaken to find

Fig. 10.10. Air abrasive cleaning in progress.

the most suitable pressure for the degree of soiling and the hardness of the stone façade.

Most of the various abrasive methods may be used either wet or dry. The advantages of the dry system are:

- no water penetration of building.
- no water staining of façade.
- simple and fast to use.
- versatile and wide range of abrasives.
- no problems caused by chemicals.
- dry cleaning is non-seasonal.
- cleaned surface is immediately visible.

The disadvantages are:

- requires greater control by operative.
- large quantities of dust.
- surface of stone is quickly damaged.
- residue of dust on the stone surface.

The wet process is often adopted due to the elimination of dust either for general protection of the public in the street or for the operatives using the system in confined areas. Also, owing to the dust cloud, it can be difficult for operatives to see what they are doing when dry cleaning. The added benefits of using the wet method are its ability to soften the dirt, rinsing down and final cleaning of the façade and that it is not quite so harsh a clean as the dry blast. The wet abrasive method is preferred to the water clean as less water is required and, therefore, the façade does not become saturated, see Figs 10.11, 10.12 and 10.13.

Microblasting. Microblasting has been developed from the abrasive methods described above. These methods have assisted in cleaning highly carved pieces of stone and to help conservationists clean pieces of sculpture. They are effective on a much smaller and potentially less damaging scale. Fine abrasive powders (50–100 μm) are used to achieve a milder mechanical cleaning action and the nozzle is similar in size to a pencil, see Fig. 10.10. Due to the fine powders which are used the system must have an efficient moisture removal system so that the abrasive material can flow properly. On site, therefore, dust is a problem.

Considerations. The range of mechanical abrasive techniques have been developed to overcome the water penetration and saturation problems described in §10.4.3.1. The operatives carrying out the work must be fully experienced and aware of the changes taking place to the stone surface while they are cleaning to avoid any future 'gun shading' appearing. Whether wet or dry systems are used the façade should always be finished with a water wash to remove all dust and abrasive dust. Abrasive systems have improved and have become increasingly flexible and should be used in conjunction with other cleaning methods. When any trial area is carried out the operative should always start with the lowest pressure and least abrasive grit and work

(a)

(b)

Fig. 10.11. Wet abrasive cleaning. (**a**) Cleaning carved masonry with very fine nozzles. (**b**) Another view of the wet abrasive cleaning process.

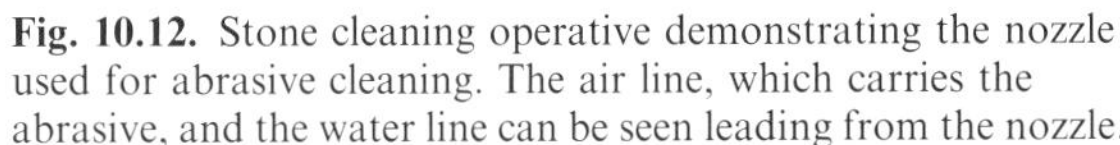

Fig. 10.12. Stone cleaning operative demonstrating the nozzle used for abrasive cleaning. The air line, which carries the abrasive, and the water line can be seen leading from the nozzle.

up to a higher pressure and more abrasive grit. Figures 10.14 and 10.15 show examples of successful cleaning using the wet abrasive method.

10.4.3.3. Chemical cleaning

The cleaning of masonry by chemicals involves the use of a wide range of chemicals usually based on alkalis or acids combined into proprietary formulations. Alkaline materials clean by breaking down the greasy constituent of the soiling while hydrofluoric acid based agents operate by dissolving part of the substrate thereby releasing the soiling. Most chemicals either contain soluble salts or react with the stone to form soluble salts and this means that the chemicals that are applied must be completely washed out of the masonry when the cleaning is completed. The only chemical cleaner that leaves no soluble salts in masonry is hydrofluoric acid but, because this chemical is extremely dangerous in inexperienced hands, its use should be left to firms employing appropriately trained operatives.

Fig. 10.13. Two views of masonry comparing cleaned and uncleaned areas.

It has been said generally that chemical cleaning is the least understood category of the various cleaning methods. There have been a number of recent examples of poor quality work resulting from the lack of understanding of the stone and the particular chemical used. Chemicals have been applied by poorly or inadequately

(a)

(b)

Fig. 10.14. (**a**) North elevation of St Luke's Church, Chelsea before cleaning. (**b**) North elevation eight years after cleaning.

(a)

(b)

Fig. 10.15. (**a**) South elevation of St. Luke's Church, Chelsea after cleaning in 1991. (**b**) South elevation five years after cleaning.

Table 10.4. *Observations on cleaned masonry surfaces after ten or fifteen years*

Surface	*System*	*Observations*	*Appearance and condition (typical after cleaning)*	
			Appearance	Condition
Limestone	Washing	Satisfactory to good, tarry stains fade, slow re-soiling	good	good
Limestone	Sand-blasting	Satisfactory – soiled areas 'blotchy', pitting noticeable on carved/moulded work, fast re-soiling	fair to poor	fair
Sandstone	Sand-blasting	Generally unsatisfactory, badly pitted surfaces, medium-fast re-soiling	fair to poor	poor
Limestone	Chemical (alkali)	Some efflorescence and patchy staining	poor	poor
Sandstone	Chemical (acid)	Some iron staining, slight streaks of silica deposit	good	good

trained and inexperienced operatives which has given this particular cleaning method a bad reputation, particularly in Scotland.

This section details the materials, processes and protective measures needed for successful chemical cleaning. The procedures for cleaning a masonry façade are detailed below.

1. All operatives must wear personal protective equipment including full face and head protection, heavy duty gauntlets, waterproof clothing and boots.
2. Operatives must be fully trained in the use of the chemicals and be aware of the first aid procedures and address/telephone number of the local hospital should an accident occur.
3. The building and the access scaffolding must be fully protected and sheeted to protect both the public and operatives from spillage or spray drift. Glass should be protected either with latex masking paint or polythene sheeting taped securely in place. Precautions should be taken to prevent chemical solutions accumulating in pools.
4. Chemicals can enter the body in three ways (i) inhalation through normal breathing (ii) ingestion via eating, drinking and smoking and (iii) absorption through the skin. Operatives need to be aware of these hazards. The Health and Safety Regulations, particularly the Control of Substances Hazardous to Health Regulations (1988) (COSHH) set out the obligations of every employer and operatives. Assessment of work practices need to be carried out to eliminate risks to health.
5. The chemicals to be used for cleaning must be kept on site in a secure store with notices clearly indicating the chemicals. Where chemicals are to be diluted prior to use this procedure must be carried out in controlled areas specifically defined for this purpose.
6. Areas to be cleaned must generally be pre-wetted with clean water applied by the use of a low volume, high pressure water lance. The objective of this is to provide an even damp surface upon which the chemical will easily spread. If the surface is dry it will be absorbed into the masonry and, in particular, the joints. There is a fine balance between pre-wetting a masonry wall and over saturating it. This must be determined by experience and on a case-by-case basis.
7. The acid or alkali can now be applied by either brush or spray and the applicator must ensure that the application is even over the contact area. Coverage rates and contact period will vary dependent upon the acid, the stone type, type and amount of soiling and on weather conditions. Cleaning materials must never be allowed to dry on the surface and repeated applications may be necessary in some instances to remove all the soiling.
8. The acid should be thoroughly washed off at the correct time again using a low volume, high pressure water lance. Care should be taken not to damage the surface with the water lance and, therefore, the water pressure and distance of the lance from the surface should be carefully controlled. When washing it is essential that rinsing water does not accumulate in pools or traps. When the water evaporates the acid concentration is increased and those deposits that may be left behind sometimes form white streaks down the face of the building. There are proprietary materials containing agents that identify the presence of any residual acid.
9. Scaffolding must be thoroughly washed after applications of acid and scaffold tubes checked for corrosion.
10. Subsequent applications of other chemicals must follow the same procedures.

There is an ever increasingly wide range of chemical cleaners with new products coming onto the market. The main chemical cleaning agents fall into two categories.

1. Acidic cleaners.
2. Alkaline cleaners.

Acidic cleaners

The most common types of acidic cleaners are:

Hydrofluoric acid (HF)
Ammonium bifluoride (NH_4HF_2)
Phosphoric acid (H_3PO_4)
Hydrochloric acid (HCL)
Sulphuric acid (H_2SO_4)
Acetic acid (CH_3COOH)

There is no single acid that can be used in all cleaning circumstances and each has to be considered on its own merit as each acid operates in a different manner.

Hydrofluoric acid is the most commonly used acid as a cleaning agent; usually on sandstone, brick, terracotta and unpolished granite. Hydrofluoric acid cleans sandstones by reacting with the silica (which is the main constituent of the stone), and weakening the bond between the dirt and the surface until the dirt can be washed away. However, if there is a delay before washing-off, some of the dissolved silica may be redeposited and it will show as a white bloom or streaks which are even more difficult to remove. Sandstones that contain iron compounds will be attacked by the acid and brown stains may form. This risk can be reduced by adding phosphoric acid to the hydrofluoric acid. Sandstones particularly susceptible to decay in polluted environments are calcareous sandstones and dolomitic sandstones. Both, however, are attacked by hydrofluoric acid and there will be a greater loss from the stone surface than sandstones having a siliceous matrix.

The other commonly used acid is phosphoric acid used together with hydrofluoric acid to prevent the hydrofluoric acid attacking the iron. Ammonium bifluoride is used as an alternative to hydrofluoric acid because it is less dangerous and corrosive to quartz and other minerals. In addition it tends to emulsify grease and oils. Hydrochloric acid is available for removing excess pointing mortars, cementations paints and limewash. However, it is not recommended for wide spread use.

Alkaline cleaners

The most common type of alkaline cleaners are:

Sodium hydroxide (NaOH)
Potassium hydroxide (KOH)
Ammonium hydroxide (NH_4OH)
Sodium carbonate ($NaCO_3$)
Sodium bicarbonate ($NaHCO_3$)

All these cleaners have the risk of depositing soluble salts in the masonry. This can largely be overcome if the products are used correctly and on the appropriate surfaces.

The most commonly used is sodium hydroxide (caustic soda) and somewhat less frequently potassium hydroxide (caustic potash). Some of the chemicals contain surfactants and detergents to degrease particularly soiled surfaces before cleaning with hydrofluoric acid in which case there is unlikely to be a problem with any salt residues. Caustic alkali cleaners should not be used on porous brick or stone as even with pre-wetting more of the chemical may be absorbed than can be washed off and soluble salts will be left behind. Caustic alkali cleaning of limestone should only be considered as a last resort when other methods have proved impossible. Reduced concentrations of alkaline cleaners have been used successfully on porous surfaces using short dwell times accompanied by adequate and proper water washing. One of the main advantages of alkaline cleaners is the reduced quantity of water required.

Ammonium hydroxide is available as a paste and is used as a degreasing agent and to dissolve gypsum bound dirt on calcareous stones.

However, there are a few products that contain organic solvents. The reader is referred to the text boxes for details of chemical cleaning agents.

The cleaning action involves chemical reaction with the stone and/or the contaminant so there are dangers of over-reaction with certain types of stone containing certain minerals. For example, hydrochloric acid will not react with silica sandstones with a silica cement. It will, however, react violently with silica sandstone with a carbonate cement. Similarly, caustic soda may react only slowly with coarsely crystalline quartz, but potentially much more rapidly with cryptocrystalline silica or with certain silicates such as feldspathoids. Chemicals should not be used on any stone containing clay minerals due to the possibility of disruption of the layered crystal structure of clay minerals.

Chemical cleaning, as with other cleaning methods, has to be carried out with fully trained and experienced operatives having carefully carried out cleaning of sample areas to ensure its suitability. Product manufacturers of the chemicals contained in many of the proprietary cleaning products produce full product data. They will also have trained staff who will visit sites and advise on the suitability of the product. Data will be given on the chemical product dealing with all associated hazards, protective clothing, handling, storage and waste disposal. Chemical cleaning of buildings at its best gives excellent results. But, if carried out in a hastily and ill considered manner using the an inappropriate chemical or unsuitable concentrations of reagent not properly cleaned off, it can produce very disappointing results or induce even more staining. Table 10.4 compares observations upon masonry cleaned by several methods between 10 and 15 years ago.

10.4.3.4. Special cleaning methods

There are available special cleaning systems that have been developed and 'tailored' for specific problems and situations. Some were used during the 1980s for sculptures or for museum and conservation work. In the 1990s these methods are being developed for use on large façades as commercially viable techniques, for example, the Lime Method.

The Lime Method. Developed by Professor Robert Baker in the 1950s, this involves cleaning with a hot lime poultice. The lime was originally slaked against the surface of the stone. Hot lime is applied to the surface by gloved hand and trowel pressing the putty well into the pre-wetted surface of the stone. Once the 'plaster' has been applied it is covered with scrim and wet sacking and secured. This is then covered with polythene and over a period of approximately 2–3 weeks the polythene is removed periodically and the scrim sacking is sprayed with water to ensure the putty is kept moist. It is essential that no drying out of the putty is allowed. At the end of the period the covering layers are removed and the lime putty carefully lifted off in small areas taking with it some of the dirt from the stone surface. The remaining dirt, which has been softened by the poultice, can be carefully removed with the use of hand sprays or low pressure wash, dental picks, soft bristle, phosphor bronze brushes, small toothbrushes or small abrasive tools. It is the wet pack that is in contact with the dirt for the long period which softens the dirt so that it is easily removed by varying methods without damaging the stone surface. It is not now generally used as it is very expensive.

Other poultices and packs. Various other poultices and packs have been developed for use in differing circumstances. Poultices are generally absorbent materials such as clay. Other materials that are used are diatomaceous earth, talc and chalk. The procedure is to mix the absorbent solid with a solution to form a paste which is applied to the pre-wetted surface of the stone. The poultice is covered with hessian or similar material to hold it in position and left for a period of time. When the poultice dries it is removed and the surface can be brush cleaned or washed with water.

Packs are generally pastes of cleaning agents that are kept moist while in contact with the stone. The paste containing a cleaning agent is applied to the pre-wetted masonry and covered with a plastic or polythene sheet to retain all moisture. After a period of time the pack is removed and the stone surface rinsed thoroughly.

Mora poultice. This is a system developed by Italian conservators for cleaning limestone and marble using a chelating agent. The chelating agent in ethylene diamine tetra acetic acid (EDTA). The poultice, in the form of a clear jelly, is applied to the pre-wetted surface by spatula or brush and covered with polythene to prevent drying. After a contact period of 24 hours the poultice is lifted and removed from the surface. If necessary, reapplication of the poultice may be carried out and finally the surface is washed with clean water.

The Hempel Biological Pack. This pack was developed by Professor Ken Hempel while at the Victoria and Albert Museum and it was primarily used to clean sculpture and small areas of fine detail on limestone. Clays such as attapulgite and sepiolite are used with a blend of 25 g urea, 10 ml glycerol in 500 ml of water to form a thixotropic pack. The structure of the clays is such that it enables them to contain considerable amounts of water and to produce a suction effect as they dry out. Again, the pack is applied to the pre-wetted surface and covered with polythene to retain the moisture. The poultice may be effective within a few days or it may need to stay in place for several weeks. Only periodic checking, by lifting the edge and checking the dirty stone surfaces, can determine the length of time needed. The covering and the poultice are removed and the surface finally cleaned as previously described.

Special poultices and packs. These are used to achieve a high quality of cleaning of extremely delicate historically valuable surfaces. A proprietary pack for commercially cleaning limestone has been available in the USA for sometime. The pack is applied to a thickness of 6mm by plasterers using a trowel. The pack is covered with polythene and left for a period of 24 hours. The polythene is then removed and the pack scraped from the surface. The residue is washed from the surface using low to medium pressure water wash. Similarly an alkaline pack has been used for sandstone surfaces. The method is similar to that for limestone except that when the pack is removed the cleaned surface needs immediate neutralisation by acetic acid or hydrofluoric acid based cleaning agent.

Soaps and detergents. Oil, grease and tar will clean off extremely well with the use of a scrubbing brush, warm water and a suitable soap. Powdered detergents which contain a considerable proportion of soluble salts should not be used. Marble and limestones respond particularly well to cleaning with a soap solution as do polished granites. However, sandstones and slates may be less responsive.

Suitable soaps include Vulpex, Synperonic N and Lissapol. The soaps may be diluted in water or white spirit. It is important that only neutral solutions are applied to marbles and other calcareous stones. The diluted soap solution is applied by brush to the masonry surface and agitated with a soft natural bristle brush. It is then allowed to remain in contact with the masonry for a short while and rinsed from the surface by low pressure water (spray).

Ultrasonic cleaning. This method principally remains a museum technique. It is suitable for objects that can be fitted into a bath that has been filled with the cleaning fluid through which high frequency sound waves are transmitted. Soiling is dislodged by ultrasonic vibration and possibly cavitation.

Laser cleaning. Since 1972 laser radiation has been employed as a means of stone cleaning specifically in the museum environment. The attraction of this method is the ease with which the soiling is removed from the sculpture. This method is now being employed on statues and carved works outside of museums.

10.4.3.5. Removal of algae, lichen and moss

There are many circumstances in which small plants, lichen, algae and mosses will grow on masonry, many of them without any harmful effect on the stone structure. However, for reasons of appearance or maintenance these may need to be removed.

Unsightly algal slime on paving should be removed because it becomes very slippery when wet.

The cleaning process usually begins with removal of the excess growth or thick mosses by hand by using dry bristle, soft brushes or phosphor bronze brushes when the surfaces are dry. When wet the growths on plain surfaces may be removed with low pressure water lance or the application of water with brushes.

Any living organic growth will normally be treated with a biocide chemical sprayed onto the surface according to the recommendations of the particular manufactures. This will kill the growth and, after a period of approximately two weeks when the growth has died or withered, the remains can be brushed or washed off. When this has been done a second application is usually made and allowed to soak into the stone as a further growth inhibitor.

As most products available are water soluble, most are gradually rinsed from the building by rainwater and, therefore, periodic renewal is necessary to prevent further growth reappearing.

Regrowth of organic soiling is dictated by moisture levels, pH and sunlight. Reduction of these factors will delay the resoiling of the stone. In the longer term growth may be inhibited by the installation of thin gauge copper strips. However, this may lead to copper staining on light coloured masonry appearing.

10.4.4. Stains and their removal

In addition to the general cleaning methods outlined above, certain stains can only be removed from porous masonry by specific treatments. The causes of these particular stains include items that are fixed to the masonry structure such as metal gutters, roofing fixings and metal ornaments, birds and the actions of people. Specific methods have been developed to deal with stains caused by iron, copper, bronze, smoke and soot, oil, tar, grease, bird droppings, anti-pigeon gel, graffiti and paints.

Also, in the past, acids or alkalis used for cleaning may have reacted with substances on the stone surface, such as coloured paints on statues, causing unsightly staining.

10.4.4.1. Metallic stains

Stains caused by iron and copper are most frequently found and those by bronze to a lesser extent, see Fig. 10.1. These stains are caused by metal fixings or features fixed to the masonry structure which are corroded by rainwater run off leaving a deposit on the façade of the building. The most common are iron fixings for rainwater disposal systems, external ornamental metalwork for example light fittings, iron railings, copper lightning conductors or copper roofs and flashings.

Formulations for the removal of stains, principally from limestone and marble, are as follows:

Copper stain removal
70 g ammonium chloride is dissolved in 570 ml of concentrated ammonia solution. Add water to make 1 litre. To this litre add 37 g of EDTA, add attapulgite clay to form a paste.
Pre-wet the surface, apply paste and leave until dry.
Remove paste and clean with water.
Repeat the process as required to remove as much of the stain as possible.
Copper stains can also be removed with a 10% solution of sulphuric acid in a poultice. However, long standing stains are almost impossible to remove.

Iron stain removal
7 parts of glycerine and 1 part of sodium citrate are added to 6 parts warm water.
Attapulgite clay is added to form a paste which is applied to the surface and left until dry.
The paste is removed and the process repeated as many times as required to remove as much of the stain as desired.
Particularly stubborn stains may be removed by wetting the surface with a mixture of 1 part sodium citrate and 6 parts water, followed by an application of an attapulgite wet pack containing sodium hyposulphite which is later removed and the surface cleaned with water.

10.4.4.2. Smoke and soot
These have a greasy content which responds to scrubbing with non-ionic soap and warm water or various alkaline cleaners. The more resistant areas can be cleaned using a poultice based on methyl chloroform (trichloromethane) or trisodium phosphate (Calgon) and bleaching powder.

10.4.4.3. Tar, asphalt, bitumen
Bitumen is soluble in organic solvents such as paraffin or petrol. However, there is a high risk of this just spreading the stain to a larger area. Where no surface damage is likely to occur the tar can be removed by use of a scraper or chisel after the surface has been frozen with ice or dry ice. The surface is then scrubbed with water and an emulsifying detergent followed by rinsing off or the application of a paraffin poultice.

10.4.4.4. Oil and grease
This can be removed successfully with the use of non-ionic detergents, hydrocarbon solvents and alkaline cleaning agents. Non-ionic soaps are applied with warm water and agitated with a brush, left for approximately five minutes and rinsed off with water. The use of Vulpex soap, followed by steam cleaning, is an alternative method that has proved very successful.

Hydrocarbon solvents are highly flammable and noxious if inhaled and their use with a poultice has proved to be the best method.

For removing stains from marble the poultice comprises a cloth soaked in acetone and 1 part amyl acetate which is applied to the stained area and then covered by polythene and left for approximately three days. The covering is removed and the surface rinsed with clean water.

10.4.4.5. Timber stains
Stains due to water spreading tannin or resin from the timber can be removed by scrubbing with a 1:40 solution of oxalic acid in warm water.

10.4.4.6. Cement and mortar deposits
Removal of the heavier deposits with scrapers is followed by the application of hydrochloric acid. The surface must be pre-wetted and thoroughly washed afterwards.

10.4.4.7. Bird fouling and anti-pigeon gel
The removal of bird fouling, particularly that of pigeons, usually forms the first part of a general masonry building clean. Accumulations of fouling on ledges, cornices and projecting surfaces can be thick and unsightly. Removal of the main part with scrapers followed by the softening of underlayers with water can assist removal. Removal of pigeon fouling is essential as the fouling contains soluble salts that will damage the masonry. The operatives removing pigeon fouling must wear personal protective clothing and equipment as it is a potential health risk. At the same time it may also be necessary to remove pigeon gel, a failed means of pigeon control, which was applied to ledges where the birds roosted but gradually collected dirt and became ineffective. In addition, any metal fixings, wires or netting previously used to prevent pigeon fouling must be removed. Gels can be removed with hard scrappers followed by the application of a methylene chloride or organic solvent which is then washed off the surface with water.

10.4.4.8. Paint
Masonry structures in the past have been coated in paint for aesthetic reasons. The removal of paint must be fully considered beforehand and advice sought. It is not unusual on historic buildings to find paint 6mm thick that has been applied over many years. In many cases paint was applied as an integral part of the original finish. However, paint was also applied to hide staining, soiling or deterioration of the masonry surface. In historic buildings a wide range of paints and coatings will be found together with modern synthetic coatings. It is, therefore, essential that a careful analysis of the various paint coatings is undertaken so that the correct method for its removal is established.

Some of the coatings that may be found include whiting, limewash, distemper, gloss paints, varnish, polishes, modern synthetic paints and masonry paints. The list is endless and each paint system will have its own method of removal.

10.4.4.9. Graffiti

Most paints used for graffiti can be removed from the masonry surface (McLaughlin 1989). However, it is very difficult to remove the traces of pigment that have been carried into the pores of the stones. In many cases materials used to remove the paint carry the colour pigment more deeply. The ease with which graffiti is removed will depend on the type of product used and the condition of the stone to which it is applied. A wide range of cleaning procedures are available and once again the graffiti must be fully analysed to establish which is the most effective and least damaging removal method (Butlin *et al.* 1992). Chemical methods are now most commonly used and product manufacturers will give advice and clean sample areas before the major cleaning work commences.

It is now quite common for anti-graffiti coatings to be applied to masonry structures to facilitate the removal of graffiti which may be applied in the future. The protective coatings may be either of a permanent or temporary nature. Permanent coatings may be either film forming or pore blocking. Temporary coatings may be either wax or polysaccharide. Once again there are a number of product manufacturers who will give advice and test samples in advance of the work being carried out. It is essential before coating masonry that professional advice is sought as certain coatings can either damage the stone or be aesthetically unacceptable. To the purist these coatings are never justified.

10.5. Methods of repairing stone buildings and surface treatments

10.5.1. Introduction

A stone building of any age and condition requires an experienced person to assess its current state and issue instructions for its necessary repair. As stated earlier in the chapter a detailed survey will have been carried out and this will need checking once the façade has been cleaned as described in §10.4. Once this survey has been completed and updated and areas requiring attention that have been revealed by the cleaning process have been marked, repair works may then begin.

As discussed in §10.3, evaluation of the type of repair has been completed within the total project and details are given here of the specific repair methods. It must be remembered that when carrying out repairs on historic buildings that there may have been incorrect or unnecessary repairs in the past. These may include:

- Unnecessary mass concrete inserted into masonry walls.
- Cement grouting or pointing.
- Epoxy or polyester repairs.
- Widening of joint widths with cutting disks or chisels to facilitate unnecessary repointing.
- Damage by air abrasive or chemical cleaning methods.
- Damage by spinning-off of the surface.
- Use of inappropriate water repellants, anti-graffiti coatings or other modern coatings.
- Replacement stones of the wrong profiles and inappropriate petrology.

In some cases the works previously carried out may not be reversible and/or of good masonry practice. The repair may not always be in harmony with the aims of a stone conservator. The architect responsible, the stonemason and building owner may be in agreement on the replacement of all the heavily weathered or damaged stones and the approach may be in best masonry practice. Indeed, the owner of the building may want a complete pristine building. However, the conservator and conservation techniques desire the minimum replacement and little restoration.

Following the survey that has examined the condition of the masonry structure as a whole, the conditions of individual stones and the pointing of the joints, the alternatives to be considered where stones are badly decayed or damaged are as follows:

- Provide protection against further decay in the form of lead flashings, weatherings, coverings or similar to shed water from the stone surface.
- Surface treatments for the stone.
- Stitch and fill of fractured or cracked stones.
- 'Piece-in' replacement of decayed portion of a larger stone.
- Replacement of whole stones.
- Mortar repairs.

Alternatives to cutting out or replacing the stone should be considered as an initial measure wherever the building has historic or intrinsic value. Whether the stone is part of the work of a Norman mason or a relatively common piece of 18th century façade will make the approach very different.

Further information on the repair and conservation of stonework can be found in Ashurst & Dimes (1990) and in Ashurst & Ashurst (1988).

10.5.2. Replacement

When decisions have been taken to replace stone, these will need to be identified on record drawings, or photographs. The stone must also be clearly marked on site. It must then be decided how the stone is to be cut out and what necessary temporary supports are required for executing the work. These may take the form of simple wooden struts or props or, in the case of arches or vaults, may involve timber centres, see Fig. 10.16.

(a)

(b)

(c)

Fig. 10.16. Repair of stonework by replacement. (**a**) Removing the damaged stone. (**b**) Stone completely removed and the recess cleaned ready to receive the new stone. (**c**) New stone in place and grouted in position.

(a)

(b)

Fig. 10.17. Repair of a damaged balustrade of Englefield House by replacement. (**a**) Damaged and weathered balustrade. (**b**) Repaired balustrade containing new stones and some replacement copings and plinth.

Fig. 10.18. Newly carved stone statue for replacement of the weathered original in the background.

The method of cutting out of the decayed or damaged stone will vary according to the situation. However, the greatest of care must be taken to avoid damage to any adjacent stones. The masonry saw or diamond disc may be used to cut the perimeter joints and form vertical saw cuts in the stone to facilitate removal. Tungsten tipped chisels will then be employed to hammer out the decayed stone to the required depth which is usually 4 inches (100 mm) or greater if required in the case of bonder stones. The architect will need to agree if the new stone is to be replaced on existing joint lines or new joint lines, see Fig. 10.16b.

The replacement stone should match the original as closely as possible, see Figs 10.17 and 10.18. The architect or person responsible would naturally prefer to use the stone from the same quarry and even from the same bed in the quarry as the stone originally used so that both the colour and weathering characteristics are the same. With the help of a geologist familiar with building stones and an experienced stone-mason it will be possible to identify the type of stone but it will probably be far more difficult to identify the particular quarry (if there is more than one for that particular stone such as Portland) or even the bed. Even if the quarry is established the working face or bed of stone will inevitably have retreated so far that the exposed stone is slightly different from that used in the building.

Often in the case of old but large buildings such as medieval churches or castles the stone will have been obtained from a number of small quarries and outcrops. In these cases there will be a variety of stone in the fabric and it would, therefore, be appropriate to replace with local stone of a similar type.

The architect is then faced with selecting the stone which is the closest match to the original in terms of colour, texture of surface, durability and other properties appropriate to the circumstances. To provide a good match the stone must appear similar to the neighbouring stones both when wet and dry and its appearance must also merge well with the weathered surfaces of the adjacent stones. Many stones change colour owing to weathering and, therefore, the Architect should make due allowance in his choice of replacement stone. In all cases the proposed substitute stone should be petrographically similar to the stone it is required to match.

Organisations such as the British Geological Survey, the Building Research Establishment and the Stone Federation of Great Britain will be able to help locate appropriate quarries. There are a number of collections of building stones held at the Building Research Establishment, The British Museum and the Sedgwick Museum in Cambridge. The Stone Federation of Great Britain has several publications which may assist the Architect. Although a number of quarries have closed or have been worked out, there has been in more recent years a move to open many old quarries as the demand for stone has increased through the 1980's and into this decade. The Technical Department of the Stone Federation is able to advise researchers. A geologist specialising in stone would also be able to assist by assessing the validity of data supplied by these organisations and advise the architect accordingly.

After a suitable stone has been chosen to match the existing, consideration must be given to the life expectancy of the new stone in its fixed position on the building. The existing stone may have failed due to its poor durability so the architect may need to consider an alternative suitable replacement which is more durable. Determination of durability of stone with any certainty is not easy, if not impossible. There are testing houses in the UK, Europe and USA that will carry out tests that will give an indication of the stones durability but the results are not conclusive. Tables have been published for example in Elaine Leary's book 'The Building Limestones of the British Isles' 1983 giving indications of the durability of stones and where on a building they are suitable for use. The durability of the replacement stone should be compared with the existing by way of the various tests (BRE 1983*a*).

It must be emphasized that the greatest care must be taken in selecting a suitable stone and all possible investigations made in terms of seeking publications on the known stone, review of buildings where the stone has been used, the results from testing houses and the knowledge of experienced stone-masons and contractors that use the stone. Only when all this information has been collated can a decision be made.

Stones must be carefully cut to the original size and profile assuming that the original profile is identifiable on the weathered building. Examples may survive on a sheltered area of the building or advice may be sought from an experienced archaeologist. The stone profile may be drawn onto a plastic or zinc template and, together with face measurements and elevation details, form the pattern to which the mason will work to produce the replacement stone. The drawings and templates are recorded and marked to identify their location on the building. The stone will be produced in the masons yard and finished off in the banker masons workshop where it is marked with its identification to correspond with the drawings. It is usual practice now to place the finished piece of stone onto a wooden pallet, to separate adjacent stones and protect from external damage with polystyrene sheet, secure with banding and the cover the whole with shrink wrap to keep out the weather.

The pallets will be loaded onto a lorry either by the use of a fork lift truck or a crane (static or lorry mounted) and the stone delivered to site. On arrival the pallets of stone should be stored in a secure, safe and dry compound.

Stones for fixing will be selected from the compound with the appropriate cleaned finished face to match the existing and raised into position either by hand, hoist, block and tackle or other suitable lifting appliances depending upon their weight and location in the building. The opening to receive the new stone should be carefully cleaned out and a mortar bed evenly spread onto the prewetted area. The new stone surfaces must also be wetted to avoid the risk of dewatering the mortar and the new stone should be laid in position on the mortar bed. Very heavy stones may require the additional temporary support of slate or plastic packers or timber wedges. The surrounding joints are then pointed leaving grout holes as necessary. Grout is then allowed to run into the various joints. When complete the grouting cups are removed and the pointing of joints completed and the stone surface cleaned off, see Fig. 10.16(c).

In fixing new stone it must be remembered that the mortar joints must match in width and type of mortar to the existing. Thus, it may be necessary to carry out trial areas of repointing so that the right proportions of cement, lime, crushed stone and aggregate are achieved.

10.5.3. Indentation

Indentation or 'piecing repairs' as it is sometimes called is the term applied when only a small section of a complete stone is to be cut out and renewed rather than the whole stone, see Figs 10.20 and 10.21. The procedure for replacement is similar to that for a complete stone. There are differences, however, due to the small size of the replacement stone and a suitable procedure to be adopted is given below:

1. Determine the size of the piece to be renewed.
2. Select suitable stone as described in §10.5.2.
3. Cut out the decayed or damaged stone.
4. Measure and cut the proposed new replacement stone.
5. Offer the prepared piece and scribe the exact size of the opening.
6. Prepare the opening so that the new stone exactly matches the opening size.
7. Prepare stainless steel dowels or pins and drill holes in the new stone and existing stone to correct size, and make sure the holes are free from dust.
8. Fill the drill holes in the new stone with epoxy anchor grout and drop in the pins/dowels.
9. When the resin has cured slurry the surfaces of the opening and the new stone with a fine paste of masons putty, fill the holes in the existing stone with epoxy anchor grout and offer up the new stone into position, locating the dowels into the dowel holes.
10. Slurry the joints with the masons putty and finally sponge off the slurry from the stone face.
11. After a suitable curing time the mason can finally surface dress and finish off the stone so that it matches the surrounding area.

Fig. 10.19. Repairs to a buttress of All Saints Church, Fulham by replacement of stones.

Provided that indentation or piecing is carried out carefully it can greatly save on the cost of replacing whole stones and is not unsightly to the eye, but see Figs 10.21 and 10.22.

Epoxy anchor grout, epoxy adhesive or mortars together with stainless steel dowels or pins may be used to secure new stone as well as repairing old or decayed stone. For example, dowels or pins can be used in conjunction with adhesives for fixing stones together.

Lime mortar or mortar with small quantities of cement may be used where some degree of flexibility is required in the repair.

10.5.4. Dressing back

Dressing back the surface of the stone wall, or 'redressing' as it is sometimes called, is a practice to be considered on some occasions. The removal of the original face of a wall is a drastic operation but it may be considered necessary when the original stone face has badly blistered, split or spalled.

Successful dressing back requires a high degree of skill of the mason to know how far to go and when to stop. There is no technical reason why redressing should not take place except that many masons believe the removal of the already weathered surface greatly reduces the weather resistance of the remaining stone. A coating of limewater will improve its initial weathering resistance. However, the new surface exposed by redressing will inevitably, over a period of time, take on a weathered appearance.

10.5.5. Mortars and pointing

The composition of mortar and the style of pointing is of considerable aesthetic and structural importance. The mortar has to be of the correct strength, neither too strong nor too weak. The mortar should resemble the existing as far as possible. The aggregates or stone dust

Fig. 10.20. Indentation or 'piecing' repairs to a buttress, King's College Chapel, Cambridge.

should match in terms of type, size and colour and it is usually possible to match the existing with grit, sands, crushed brick or stone. Typical mixes are approximately 1:2:9 or 1:2:6 for cement, lime putty and aggregate, see Table 10.5. It is common practice to mix the lime and aggregate with water to form a lime putty mortar and, when required for use, add one part cement. Colours of mortar may be adjusted by experiment with differing mixtures and components. 'Weathering' the mortar by brushing after the initial set has taken place is usual so that it exposes the aggregate and gives a natural weathered appearance.

The use of additives in the mix to colour the mortar is not recommended. Every attempt to obtain the correct colour match by natural means should be made and it will be necessary to carry out several trial pointing areas before the final mix is selected. The sample areas should be allowed to dry out thoroughly before examination.

Fig. 10.21. Indentation repairs poorly carried out so that the repairs do not match the original.

Fig. 10.22. The façade of this building in Knightsbridge is clad in Portland stone which has been repaired by replacement of some panels. However, they have not weathered to match the original.

Table 10.5. *Suggested mortar mixes*

Masonry type	*Sheltered conditions*	*Exposed conditions*
Weak, Soft and Decaying Material		
1. Limestone	1 part lime: 4 parts sand 1 part lime: 3 parts sand	1 part lime: 22 parts sand 1 part lime: 2 parts sand
2. Sandstone	1 part lime: 4 parts sand: 2 part brick dust 1 part lime: 3 parts sand: 2 part brick dust	1 part lime: 3 parts sand: 1/10th part PFA 1 part lime: 22 parts sand: 3 HTI
Moderately Durable Material		
3. Limestone	Any of the above or: 1 part lime: 22 parts brick dust 1 part hydraulic lime: 4 parts sand	Any of the above or: 1 part hydraulic lime: 3 parts sand 1 part hydraulic lime: 22 parts sand 1 part OP cement: 3 parts lime: 12 parts sand
4. Sandstone	As 2 above or: 1 part hydraulic lime: 4 parts sand	1 part hydraulic lime: 22 parts sand
Durable Material		
5. Limestone and Sandstone	Any of the above	1 part hydraulic lime: 22 parts sand 1 part OP cement: 3 parts lime: 12 parts sand 1 part OP cement: 2 parts lime: 10 parts sand 1 part OP cement: 2 parts lime: 8 parts sand

When the mix has been decided, test cubes should be sent away to laboratories so that the crushing strength of the mix can be determined and advice on its suitability sought from a qualified engineer.

10.5.6. Repair with mortar (plastic repair)

The repair of decayed or damaged stone with mortar, or 'plastic repair' as it is sometimes known, is useful as an alternative to cutting out stone and piecing in with new stone. However, the reputation of these plastic repairs has suffered through poor workmanship or specification in the past. Plastic repair is also thought of as a cheap option compared to that of repairing with natural stone. Properly carried out plastic repair is not necessarily cheap but its use may compliment stone replacement by reducing the amount of existing stone to be cut away and yet still retaining many historic stones. Its use may avoid any possible damage to adjacent stonework or the structure or fabric of the building.

Conservators particularly favour the use of plastic repairs to stone as it reduces the amount of original stone that is being cut away or destroyed and it causes much less disturbance to the building. When considering whether to carry out a repair in stone or a plastic repair the following may be taken into consideration:

- Whether the use of mortar will enable more of the existing fragile or historic stones to be retained.
- Whether structural elements will be retained.
- Whether mortar repairs will perform satisfactorily.
- Whether the areas to be repaired are of the appropriate size.
- Whether the mortar repair will be visually acceptable.

When it has been considered appropriate that a plastic repair will be carried out the following procedure should be adopted as illustrated in Figs 10.23, 10.24 and 10.25:

- Prepare a drawing detailing the repairs to be carried out together with photographs of the existing stonework.
- Prepare samples of mortar repair for colour, mix, texture and testing for approval and final selection.
- Cut out appropriate areas of stone as detailed on the record drawings and wash out any dust.
- Prewet the area and apply the repair mortar in layers of thickness 10 mm one at a time. Allow each layer to dry out before prewetting and applying a further layer.
- Where the void exceeds 50 mm in depth or 50 mm^2 in surface area, non-ferrous or stainless steel reinforcement is required. The reinforcement is fixed to the stone by drilling holes and fixing the reinforcement with the use of epoxy adhesive or anchor grout

(a)

(b)

Fig. 10.23. Mortar (plastic) repairs to stone. (**a**) Cracks in masonry. (**b**) Filling the cracks with mortar.

or similar. Depending on the size of the repair the reinforcement may be simply pins or a more complex reinforcement cage. There should be at least 25 mm of mortar cover over the reinforcement.

- The repair is finished to the required profile using a wood float or profiler. Experienced operatives will be able to gauge how quickly the mortar is setting in the ambient weather conditions and will work the mortar to the required profile with various purpose-made profilers or scrapers.
- Careful attention must be paid to preventing the repair from drying out too quickly and avoiding shrinkage cracks. Hessian or sacking material that is wetted may be employed to keep repaired areas damp and moist and allow them to dry out slowly.

There are a wide variety of mortar mixes employed for plastic repairs. Generally repair mortars contain a lime binder. However, when repairing sandstone a cement binder and plasticizer or masonry cement is better used. This is due to the fact that sandstone may deteriorate further in the presence of lime washing adjacent to the plastic repairs. A high proportion of aggregate to binder in the cement aggregate mixes is an added advantage when matching coloured sandstones.

When lime is used it is always better to mix the aggregate and the lime as far as possible in advance of the work, storing the mix (coarse stuff) in a plastic dustbin or under polythene and adding the cement only when required to carry out the repair. This mix will be strong enough for repairs in sheltered areas.

On more exposed areas a higher strength mortar may be required using hydraulic additives. These additives should be added to the coarse stuff and mixed with the lime and aggregates immediately before use. Such additives, which increase the strength of the plastic repair, include, finely powdered brick dust, high temperature insulation (HTI) powder, hydraulic lime, some pulverized fuel ash (PFA), white cement, ordinary Portland cement and masonry cement.

Fig. 10.24. Mortar or plastic repairs to carved masonry. (**a**) Damaged freize. (**b**) Applying and moulding the mortar. (**c**) Completed repair.

(a)

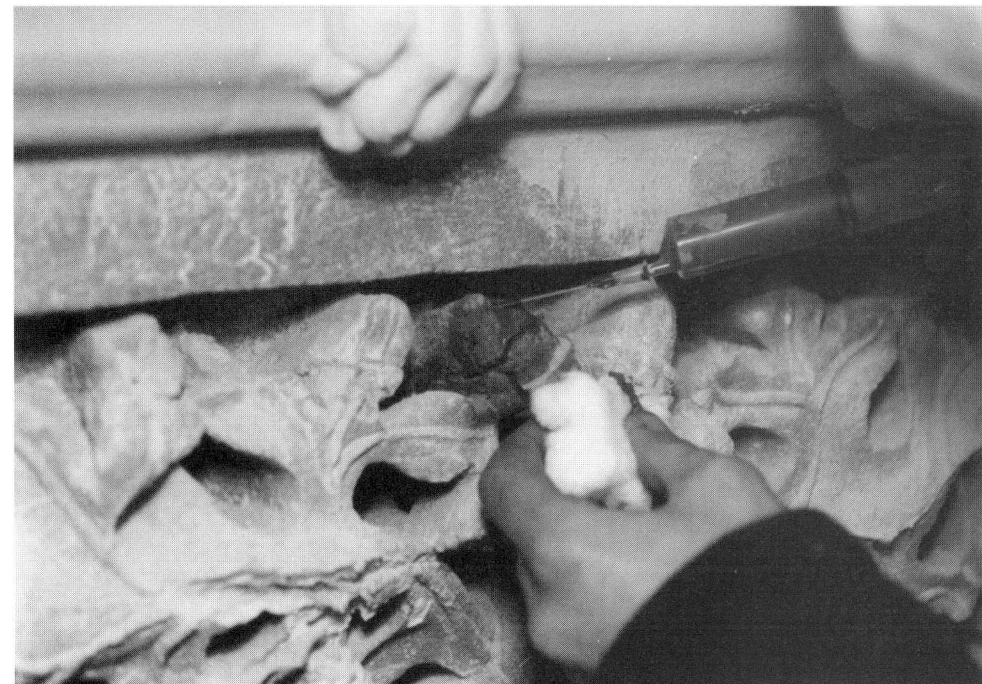

(b)

Fig. 10. 25. (**a**) Plastic repair using resin bound mortar. (**b**) Plastic repairs showing reinforcement of stone by resin injection and wire supports.

Examples of repair mixes by volume:

Sandstone
1 part hydraulic lime.
2 parts sharp sand.
1 part soft sand.
Limestone
1 part white cement.
2 parts lime putty.
10 parts aggregate.

There are a number of proprietary mixes available on the market today from various companies. Before considering their use a thorough investigation should be made into the constituents of the mix.

When carrying out plastic repairs it should always be remembered that the plastic repair should always be weaker and fail in advance of the surrounding stone. There are many cases where strong cement mixes have been used in the past and this had led to accelerated decay of the surrounding stonework. Furthermore, where plastic repairs are used on areas of extreme exposure, such as cornices, then a lead flashing over may be employed to give added protection.

10.5.7. Grouting

Historic stone walls that are constructed of a double skin of stone filled in between with rubble core often fail due to the percolation of water through the structure over a considerable number of years. Water first enters the wall through washed out open joints and, due to the poor quality of the filling or core, percolates down the wall. The wall or structure deteriorates by bulging or cracking and displacement of the stones of the outer skin or core filling washing down to the base of the wall.

In most situations it will be necessary to make detailed investigations to determine the causes of failure. These may take the form of removing selected stones and drilling into the core of the wall in various locations or probing for voids. Sounding with a hammer can be useful to test for hollows. In more special cases a detailed specialist investigation using gamma radiography or ultrasonic measurements can be made.

The method of grouting to fill hollows or voids in masonry walls in order to stabilise and strengthen them and prevent further decay has been employed for a considerable time. The first recorded use in the UK was in 1876 but it had been employed in Europe before this date. In the 1920's hand or machine grouting was employed for consolidating the fabric of historic monuments.

There are three basic methods employed for grouting:

- Gravity systems.
- Hand or pumped systems.
- Vacuum systems.

The particular choice of system is dictated by the type and condition of the masonry structure. Gravity grouting is suitable where the masonry is susceptible to movement under pressure, pumped systems are universally employed and vacuum systems are useful where there are fine fractures and small voids.

10.5.7.1. Gravity systems

The grouting apparatus required for filling large voids consists of large containers with outlets in the bottom. A pipe is then fitted to the outlet. At the other end of the pipe is a nozzle with a stopcock.

Holes are drilled in the walls where the voids are located or anticipated at intervals of 1m horizontally or 500 mm vertically. When the holes have been drilled they should be washed out with water.

Grouting the wall commences at the bottom. When the grout level in the wall rises and grout flows out of the holes above these are plugged and the apparatus moved up the wall and the process repeated. A pressure of 0.6–1.0 bar is obtained with the grout container 5m above the inlet.

10.5.7.2. Hand/pumped systems

For small cracks and fissures a small grouting cup may be used and grout hand fed to the area in question. Hand or power operated pumps, delivery hoses and nozzles fitted with stopcocks are required for larger repairs.

This system is similar to the gravity system except that the grout is pumped into the wall under greater pressure. Again, work starts at the base of the wall and moves upwards as the grout is seen to flow out of the holes previously drilled. A pressure of 0.6–2.6 bar is usually obtained.

The possible danger of disturbing the face and integrity of the wall must be assessed before works starts and monitored during the process.

10.5.7.3. Vacuum

The area to be grouted is enclosed in an airtight, transparent, flexible shroud such as a polythene tent or capsule. Air is evacuated from the enclosed area by means of an air line and powerful vacuum pump and a tap opened to allow the grout from the grout pan to be sucked in. Its use for masonry structures is very limited and it is rarely employed today.

Mixtures for grouting vary greatly. Until recently a mixture of cement and water was commonly used. These cement grouts have proved unsuccessful for a variety of reasons, however, and should not be employed on historic buildings or monuments.

In more recent times PFA (pulverized fuel ash) has been used increasingly with either cement or lime or other additives to aid the grouting process.

PFA and lime combined can produce a very mobile low/medium strength grout suitable for rubble cored walls. Bentonite is another additive commonly used.

It is recommended that experienced grouting firms are employed to carry out the work and it is usual for them to purchase pre-bagged grout mixtures with a good consistency from specialist suppliers.

For historic structures a pre-bagged lime: PFA: Bentonite mix of 2 : 2 : 1 is suitable. Higher strength grouts may be employed where required. However, specialist advice needs to be sought.

Grouting should only proceed with extreme caution as the process is largely irreversible and should problems occur again a very different approach may be required.

10.5.8. Surface treatments

As stated earlier in this chapter all masonry materials undergo an ageing and deterioration process over a period of time. Some stone weathers slowly and others, after a period of slow change, then deteriorate more quickly and dramatically. There is always the solution to replace the decayed stone with new or repair with plastic stone as detailed earlier.

However, there is a further course of action; to apply a surface treatment to extend the life of the stone and retain as much as possible of the decayed surface for a future generation. The objective in applying a surface treatment must be to enhance the durability of the stone. The surface treatment should be a last resort when all other remedial or protective work (e.g. lead weatherings) have been carried out and still an unacceptable rate of decay continues. This situation and condition may be the subject of some controversy.

The earliest forms of treatment included boiled oil, paraffin wax and preservatives which react with the calcium carbonate producing insoluble compounds such as sodium silicate, fluorosilicic acid and its salts. These earlier forms of surface treatment have been superseded by modern methods.

10.5.8.1. Water repellants

Several types of water repellants have been tried to prevent water or reduce the amount of water entering stonework. The most commonly used are waxes and silicones as applied in solutions in organic solvents and applied to the stone when thoroughly dry. However, wax solutions tend to discolour the stonework, and silicones tend to be more successful on sandstones than limestones. From experiments carried out by Clarke & Ashurst (1972) it would appear that many water repellants are not worth the great expense as a stone preservative.

10.5.8.2. Consolidants

The use of consolidants should only be considered when:

- The stone is deteriorating quickly.
- The causes of decay are known.
- When there are no other protective measures that can be taken.
- When the properties of the proposed consolidant are known.
- When full details have been taken of the stone before treatment, during treatment and allowance made for regular inspections after treatment.

The most common forms of consolidants used during the last century include egg albumen, lime-casein, lime-tallow, limewater, baryta water, Shellac, linseed oil, beeswax, paraffin wax, zinc or magnesium silicafluorides and potassium and sodium silicates.

This century has added significantly to the list of consolidants. The most useful new materials are:

(1) alkoxoysilanes – ethyl silicates, triethoxoymethylsilane and trimethoxymethylsilane,
(2) acrylic polymers – methylmethacrylate – acrylics and siliconesters
(3) epoxies
(4) polyurethanes and
(5) microcrystalline waxes.

These materials, together with the limewater treatment, are likely to remain in use for the consolidation of sculpture and carved detail on buildings.

Consolidants will not perform miracles. They are to be used as part of a conservation treatment and never used where there is a high degree of moisture movement.

10.5.8.3. Brethane

Many consolidants have been imported from abroad. However, Brethane has been developed by the Building Research Establishment at Garston, Watford. It is a silane and it must be applied by licensed operators and is very expensive.

10.5.8.4. Treatments based on lime

Lime water and lime wash has been used with great success in the conservation of limestones on many projects. The stone figures on the West front of Wells Cathedral have been successfully conserved using lime.

Lime water is a solution of slaked lime in water and the carbon dioxide gas in the air will react with the calcium hydroxide (slaked lime) to form calcium carbonate (limestone).

A sheltercoat is a lime wash of a slurry of slaked lime, fine sand and stone dust in water to which casein has been added. It is applied to masonry and its purpose is to fill small crevices and depressions caused by the decaying process. Then, by coating the rest of the surface, it acts as a barrier or sacrificial layer against further attack.

10.6. Case studies of repair and restoration

10.6.1. St Margaret's Church, Westminster

The Speaker's appeal raised the much needed funds to carry out the repair works to the MP's Church opposite the Houses of Parliament during the period 1987–1991.

The lead roof required renewal, the external stone façade needed cleaning and repairing, the external rendered surface of the North Aisle walls facing Parliament Square would be improved by replacement with Portland stone and the interior required redecorating with limewash.

The masonry work to the North and South clerestorys was cleaned using a low pressure abrasive wash. Sample cleans were carried out. However, it was decided to use a low pressure abrasive method to minimize the amount of water (not wanting to saturate the stonework with buried metal cramps below the surface of the stone), to avoid damage to the stonework and to prevent dust in the vicinity of public areas, see Fig. 10.26.

The type of abrasive material specified was to contain less than 1% free silica 'olivine sand'. The pressure at the cleaning nozzle was maintained below 25 psi. Thick deposits of dirt were to be removed by masons with their tools before cleaning commenced and delicate mouldings and ornamentation were to be cleaned with suitable small nozzles. Lead light windows and openings were protected before work commenced.

The cleaning and masonry repairs were carried out in sections as the general repair programme was executed.

The North and South clerestorys were cleaned first, followed by the East End, South Aisle and Vestries, then the Tower and finally the new Portland stone wall to the North Aisle.

The general method of cleaning described was adapted for all areas. However, the philosophy adopted was not to clean the buildings and make it totally white. It was decided that where areas of dirt deposits were particularly stubborn, rather than risk damaging the stone, the small deposits of dirt would remain. Thus, the building was clean but not sparkling bright.

There were two areas where an alternative cleaning method was adopted, these being the small east entrance porch and the west porch. Due to the number of carvings it was decided to use a soap wash. However, this proved unsuccessful and it was resolved to use a water wash and bronze bristle brushes to assist dirt removal.

The Portland stone was generally in a good state of repair considering the age of the building. However, many weathering stones showed considerable deterioration, for example, detail on pinnacles that were particularly exposed to the weather had weathered away and pieces were missing. The ashlar had also suffered where the original iron cramps were close to the surface and had blown or cracked the Portland stone through rusting.

Weathered copings were replaced with new, together with window sills, hoods moulds and string courses. New stones were carved for replacements of the pinnacles over the East and West ends and on the tower.

The wall at the west end of the South Aisle showed the most damage due to rusting iron cramps, particularly between the window sills and heads. A survey of the walls was made and a number of measures were undertaken to carry out the repairs and to conceal them. Masonry was cut out in the areas of the cramps and the rusting cramps were removed and replaced by stainless steel fixings. New stone was cut to the rectangular shape and fixed. Fake masonry joints and careful choice of the sizes of the new stones were used to conceal as much of the repairs as possible.

The final area of restoration was the North Aisle. The windows had been constructed of Portland stone. However, the walls had a rendered finish. A new foundation was constructed to take the new 100 mm thick Portland stone wall. The render and part of the wall was taken down to allow the building of the new wall facing Parliament Square so completing the masonry restoration of the Church.

10.6.2. All Hallows staining and crypt of Lambe's chapel

Earliest mention of the church and tower, which is situated opposite Fenchurch Street Station in London, dates back to 1177. It is maintained by the Cloth workers Company and in the 1980's it was decided to carry out a repair programme. In July 1991 work commenced on site and was completed within ten months, see Fig. 10.27. The following programme of works was carried out.

1. Erection of an independent scaffold, survey of the building and instructions issued to the contractor for the works.
2. Removal of encrusted carbon deposits by brush or scraper. All the loose sulphate skin on the Kentish Ragstone masonry and flintwork was removed using bronze and nylon brushes and wooden scrapers.
3. Five sample areas of cleaning were carried out to determine the most appropriate method to remove the dirt deposits.
4. The tower was cleaned with a light abrasive water wash commencing at the parapet and working down the tower. Bronze bristle and nylon brushes were again used to assist in the removal of the dirt deposits.
5. Defective areas of masonry were marked up and recorded on drawings for replacement. The weathered and defective stones were cut out and the walls prepared to receive replacements. New Kentish Ragstone was supplied by the Offham Quarry, West Malling in Kent, Portland stone from the Isle of Portland and Ketton, Clipsham and Weldon stones resourced by Rattee and Kett of Cambridge, the main contractors.
6. Some repairs were carried out in 'plastic stone'. Defective patches were cut out and prepared and successive thin coats of repair mortar applied

(a)

(a)

(c)

Fig. 10.26. St Margaret's Church, Westminster. (**a**) Before cleaning in 1987, (**b**) after cleaning in 1990 and (**c**) in December 1995.

(a)

(b)

Fig. 10.27. All Hallows Tower. (**a**) Before cleaning and masonry repairs (**b**) After repairs and cleaning.

incorporating stainless steel pins and wire fixings as appropriate. Work was brought forward proud of adjacent surfaces and then worked back flush to match adjacent areas.

7. All hard mortar pointing was cut away and joints raked back to a minimum depth of 25 mm. The joints were then repointed with mortar forced well into the joint.
8. Projections of masonry were covered in Code 7 lead.
9. Sheltercoats were applied at low level and at various positions to consolidate the masonry. Loose dust was removed by nylon brush and the surface sprayed with clean, fresh water to leave the stone surface damp but not wet. Whilst still damp the surface was sprayed with limewater which was allowed to soak into the surface. Before the surface was dry further applications were made for a total of 30 applications.

References

AMOROSO, G. G. & FASSINA, V. 1983. *Stone Decay and Conservation*, Materials Science Monograph II, Elsevier, Amsterdam.

ANDREWS, C. 1994. *Stone cleaning-a guide for practioners*, Historic Scotland & RGU.

ARNOLD, A. 1976. Behaviour of some soluble salts in stone monuments, *In*: *2nd International Symposium on the deterioration of building stones, Athens*, 27–36.

—— & ZEHNDER, K. 1989 Salt weathering on monuments. *In*: *The conservation of monuments in the Mediterranean Basin*, Bari, Italy, 31–58.

ASHURST, J. & ASHURST, N. 1988. *Practical Building Conservation*: English Heritage Technical Handbook Volume 1 Gower Technical Press, Aldershot.

—— & CLARKE, B. L. 1972. *Stone preservation experiments*, BRE Report, Gartson.

—— & DIMES, F. G. (eds) 1990. *Conservation of Building and Decorative Stone*. Volume 2 Butterworth/Heinemann, London.

ASHURST, N. 1994. *Cleaning Historic Buildings*, Volumes 1 & 2, Donhead, London.

BEIJER, O. 1977. Concrete walls and weathering, in Symposium on the *Evaluation of the Performance of External Vertical Surfaces of Buildings*. RILEM/ASTM/CIB, Otanieme, Espoo, Finland, 28 August-2 September, Vol 1.

BONNER, R. C. 1913. *The Effect of Smoke on Building Materials*. Mellon Institute, Smoke Investigation Bulletin 6 Pittsburg.

BUILDING EFFECTS REVIEW GROUP (BERG) 1989. *The Effect of Acid Deposition on Buildings and Building Materials*, HMSO, London.

BUILDING RESEARCH ESTABLISHMENT (BRE) 1965. *The Weathering, Preservation and Maintenance of Natural Building Stone, Part 1*, Building Research Station Digest, 20, Pt. 3 HMSO, London.

——1975. *The Decay and Conservation of Stone Masonry*, Building Research Digest, 177, Pt. 2 HMSO, London.

——1983*a*. *The Selection of Natural Building Stone*, Building Research Establishment Digest No. 269, HMSO, London.

——1983*b*. *Cleaning External Surfaces of Buildings*, Building Research Station Digest 280. Garston: HMSO, London, 6.

BUTLIN, R., RUSSEL, C. & MCCAIG, I. 1992. The Removal of Graffiti, Stone Cleaning and the Nature, Soiling and Decay Mechanisms of Stone. *In*: *Proceedings of the International Conference* held in Edinburgh, UK, 14–16 April 1992, Donhead, London. p. 2 (full article issued at the conference).

CHATTERJI, S., CHRISTENSEN, P. & OVEGAARD, G. 1979. Mechanisms of breakdown of natural stones caused by sodium salts. *In*: *3rd International Congress on the deterioration and preservation of stones*, Venice, 131–134.

COOKE, R. U. & GIBBS, G. B. 1994 *Crumbling Heritage*, studies of stone weathering in polluted atmospheres, National power/Power Gen, Reading.

DOEHNE, E. 1994. *In situ* dynamics of sodium sulphate hydration and dehydration in stone pores: observation at high magnification using the environmental scanning electron microscope. *In*: *3rd International symposium on the conservation of monuments in the Mediterranean basin*, Venice, 143–150.

DUFFY, A. P. & O'BRIEN, P. F. 1996. A basis for evaluating the durability of new building stone. *In*: SMITH, B. J. & WARKE, P. A. (eds) *Processes of Urban Stone Decay*, Donhead, London, 253–260.

ESBERT, R. M., ORDAZ, J., ALONSO, F. J., MONTOTO, M., GONZALEZ LIMON, T. & ALVAREZ DE BUERGO BALLESTER, M. 1997. *Manual de diagnosisi y tratamiento de materiales petreos y ceramicos*, Collegi d'Apaelladors I Arquitectes Tenics de Barcelona, Barcelona, 139.

EVANS, I. S. 1970. Salt crystallization and rock weathering: a review. *Revue de geomorphologie dinamique*, XIX Annee, No. 4 153–177.

GRIMMER, A. E. 1979. *Dangers of Abrasive Cleaning to Historic Buildings: Preservation Briefs 6*, Technical Preservation Services Division, Heritage Conservation and Recreation Service. Washington: US Government Printing Office, p. 6.

GROSSI, C. M., ESBERT, R. M., SUAREZ DEL RIO, M., MONTOTO, M. & LAURENZI-TABASSO, M. 1997. Acoustic emission monitoring to study sodium sulphate crystallization in monumental porous carbonate stones. *Studies in Conservation*, **42**, 115–125.

HONEYBORNE, D. B. 1990. Weathering and decay of masonry. *In*: ASHURST, J. & DIMES, F. G. (eds) *Conservation of Building Stone*, Volume 1, Butterworth-Heinemann.

—— & HARRIS, P. B. 1958. The structure of porous building stone and its relation to weathering behaviour. *In*: *Proceedings of the 10th Symposium, Colston Research Society, Bristol, March 1958*. Butterworths, London.

HOUSE OF COMMONS 1861. *Report of the Committee on the decay of the stone of the New Palace at Westminster*, London.

HUNT, B. J. 1993/4. The use of fluorescent dyes in highlighting some construction problems, *Structural Survey*, **12**, 6, 4–7.

——1996. Discolouration, designing out the problem. *Natural Stone Specialist*, **31**, 9, 12–18.

—— & MIGLIO, B. F. 1992. Deterioration of stone floors, *Stone Industries*, **27**, 6, 21–28.

IRDI, G. A. & BOOHER, H. B. 1994. Light microscopical evaluation of pyrite oxidation of heap leached samples from a Pittsburgh seam coal, *Journal of Microscopy*, **176**, October, 34–44.

JEFFERSON, D. 1993. Building stone: the geological dimension. *Quarterly Journal of Engineering Geology*, **26**, 305–319

KAISER, E. 1910. Skin Formation on Limestone, *Der Steinbuch*, **5**, 254.

——1929. A Fundamental Factor in the Weathering of Rocks and a Comparison of the Chemical Weathering of Stone in Buildings and in Nature, *Chemie der Erde*, **4**, 342.

KESSLER, D. W. 1919. *Physical and Chemical Tests on the Commercial Marbles of the United States*, Technical Paper 123, U.S. Bureau of, Washington.

KNOFEL, D., HENKEL, S. & ASCHHOFF, A. 1995. Ist die Messung der Wasseraufnahme mit dem Karstenschen Prufrohr zuvertassig, *Anwendung & Forschung*, 36–40.

LEWIN, S. Z. 1981. The mechanism of masonry decay through crystallisation. *In*: *Conservation of Historic Stone Buildings and Monuments*. National Academy of Sciences, Washington, 120–144.

MCLAUGHLIN, D. 1989. Paint removal from Bath Stone, *ASCHB Transactions*, **14**, 50.

MCMAHON, D. J., SANDBERG, P., FOLIARD, K. & METHA, P. K. 1992. Deterioration mechanisms of sodium sulphate. *In*: *7th International Congress on Deterioration and Conservation of Stone*, Lisbon, 705–714.

MIGLIO, B. F. & HUNT, B. J. 1993. The staining and discoloration of stone, *Structural Survey*, **11**, 3, 234–243.

MONCRIEFF, A. & WEAVER, G. 1983. *Science for Conservators, Book 2 Cleaning*. Crafts Council Conservation Science Teaching Series, Crafts Council, London, 94.

NAPAP 1992. *Effects of Acidic Deposition on Material*. SOS/T Report 19, Washington.

NAPPI, A. & COTE, P. 1997. Nondestructive test methods applicable to historic stone structures. *In*: BAER, N. S. & SNETHLAGE, R. (eds) *Saving our Architectural Heritage, the Conservation of Historic Stone Structures*, Wiley, Chichester, 95–112.

PALJAK, I. 1971. Infrared thermography applied to testing external walls. *Mat. Const.*, **4**, 247–251.

PRICE, C. A. 1978. The use of the sodium sulphate crystallization test for determining the weathering resistance of untreated stone. *In*: *International Symposium on Deterioration and Protection of Stone*, Paris, 3. 6, 10.

QUAYLE, N. J. T. 1992. Alveolar decay in stone -its possible origins. *In*: DELGADO RODRIGUES, J., HENRIQUES, H. & TELMO JEREMIAS, F. (eds) *Proceedings of the 7th International Congress on deterioration and conservation of stone*, Lisbon, June, 109–118

REDDY, M. M. 1988. Acid rain damage to carbonate stones: A quantitative assessment based on the aqueous geochemistry of rainfall runoff from stone. *Earth Surface Processes and Landforms*, **13**, 335–354.

ROSSI, P. 1985. Flat jack test for the analysis of mechanical behaviour of brick masonry structures. *In*: MCNEILLY, T. & SCRIVENER, J. C. (eds) *Proceedings of the 7th International Brick Masonry Conference*, Melbourne, Frank Daniels Pty Ltd., Melbourne, 137–148.

SCHAFFER, R. J. 1932. *The Weathering of Natural Building Stones*, Department of Scientific and Industrial Research Spec. Rep. **18**, 28–29, HMSO, London, (available from the Building Research Establishment, Watford WD2 7JR, England).

SPERLING, C. H. B. & COOKE, R. U. 1980. *Salt Weathering in Arid Environments, 1 Theoretical Considerations*, Papers in Geography, No. 8.

SPRY, A. H. 1982. *Principles of Cleaning Masonry Buildings*, Australian Council of National Trusts and National Trust of Australia (VICTORIA), p. 25. Reproduced with permission of the Australian Council of National Trusts, Melbourne.

VERHOEF, L. G. W. (ed.) 1988. *Soiling and Cleaning of Building Façade*. Report of Technical Committee 62 SCF RILEM, Chapman & Hall, London, 131.

VILES, H. A., CAMUFFO, D., FITZ, S., FITZNER, B., LINDQVIST, Q., LIVINGSTON, R. A., MARAVELAKI, P., SABBIONI, C. & WARSCHEID, T. 1997. Group Report, What is the state of our knowledge of the mechanisms of deterioration and how good are our estimates of rates of deterioration? *In*: BAER, N. S. & SNETHLAGE, R. (eds) *Saving our architectural heritage, the conservation of historic stone structures*, Wiley, Chichester, 95–112.

WINKLER, E. M. 1973. *Stone: Properties, Durability in Man's Environment*, Springer, New York.

YOUNG, M. E. & MCLEAN, C. 1992. *Stone Cleaning in Scotland – A literature review*. Research Commission Investigating the Effects of Cleaning Sandstone, Robert Gordon University, 38–39.

Useful addresses:

British Geological Survey, Keyworth, Nottingham, NG12 5GG, England.

Building Research Establishment, Garston, Watford, Herts WD2 7JR, England.

The Sedgwick Museum of Geology, Downing Street, Cambridge, England.

Appendix A: Glossary

To save space, definitions given in this glossary have been simplified and abbreviated as far as possible whilst still providing sufficient explanation for the purpose of understanding the text. The inexperienced reader should be aware that through common usage in the stone industry the meanings of several terms have become established although not technically correct. Granite and marble are perhaps the best examples. For further information and definitions the reader is referred to technical dictionaries including; *Penguin Dictionary of Geology* (1988), *Penguin Dictionary of Building* (1982) and *Penguin Dictionary of Civil Engineering* (1991), Penguin Books Ltd., Harmondsworth, Middlesex, *Concise Oxford Dictionary of Earth Sciences*, Oxford University Press, 1990 and *A dictionary of quarrying terms*, Sheppard, R. P., Institute of Quarrying, Nottingham, 1992. There are also published glossaries of building terms such as BS 6100; 1984, *Glossary of building and civil engineering terms*, and the *Natural Stone Glossary*, Stone Federation, London together with articles in trade journals, for example, Glossary of stone terms, *Stone World,* vol 12, 1996 and *Natural Stone Directory 1994-95*, Stone Industries, Herald House, Worthing. A glossary of mason's terms is included in *Modern Practical Masonry*, Warland, E.G., Pitman, London, 1929 reprinted by the Stone Federation, London in 1953 and architectural terms are the subject of new paperback version of *Encyclopedia of Architectural Terms*, Curl, J., Donhead, 1997. European standards are being prepared by CEN/TC 246 'Natural Stone'. A draft of EN12440, 'Denomination of natural stone' has been circulated and others are under discussion including 'Terminology of natural stone' and 'Petrographic examination'.

abutment	Supporting structure for a bridge or for an arch
accessory mineral	A minor mineral component of a rock.
acid	A description of an igneous rock rich in silica
adit	A near horizontal tunnel providing access to a mine
age	A relatively short unit of geological time.
aggregates	Natural sands and gravels and crushed rocks used in construction.
air-blast	Sound energy released by an explosion and transmitted through air at a low frequency that cannot be heard.
alabaster	Originally a form of travertine (calcium carbonate) but now used to describe a massive form of gypsum or anhydrite (calcium sulphate).
amygdaloidal	Description of volcanic rock containing 'almond shaped' cavities (amygdales) produced by gas bubbles which are often then filled with crystals.
amphibole	A rock forming silicate mineral; best known example being hornblende.
ANFO	Ammonium nitrate and fuel oil mixture forming an explosive.
angle of dip	Angle between the horizontal and line of maximum inclination of a stratum or discontinuity.
anorthosite	A plutonic igneous rock containing in excess of 90% plagioclase feldspar especially the calcium feldspar, anorthite.
anticline	Arched or upward (convex) folding of rocks so that older rocks occupy the core of the structure.
AONB	An officially designated 'Area of Outstanding Natural Beauty'.
aperture	The width of a discontinuity.
aquifer	A permeable geological formation which is capable of storing and yielding water.
aragonite	Calcium carbonate crystallised in the orthorhombic system.
arch	A structure, curved in the vertical plane, which carries its vertical load across an opening, mainly by axial compression, due to its end supports being prevented from moving apart.
architrave	The beam or lowest member of an entablature resting on the capitals and supporting the frieze.
arcuate	Curved as in 'arc'.
area of influence	The plan area of a deposit to which the assay of a sample taken from that deposit e.g. drill core, is assigned.
arenaceous	Sandy, sediment formed from sand, (sandstone = arenite).
argillaceous	Containing or comprising muds and clays, (mudstone = argillite).
arkose	(i) A sandstone containing clastic grains of feldspar (ii) a refinement is a sandstone containing more than 25% feldspar.

armourstone	Pieces of natural rock used to protect shorelines, riverbanks and structures from damage by water and wave action.
arris	The line or edge formed by the meeting of two surfaces at an angle to each other.
ashlar	(i) Square-hewn stone as opposed to rubble and (ii) Masonry constructed with stones that are precisely dressed with plane smooth surfaces at right angles to each other, usually with thin (3–5 mm) mortar joints.
assay	Chemical analysis of an ore or rock, especially with respect to the valuable mineral or element.
augite	A rock forming silicate mineral of the pyroxene group.
azimuth (of dip)	Compass direction of line of maximum dip.
baluster	Miniature pillar or column supporting a rail to form balustrades.
bankable document	A report of a feasiblity study and economic evaluation conducted to justify capital loans.
barchans	Crescent shaped, wind blown dunes of sand that move progressively in the direction of the wind.
basalt	Fine grained, basic, igneous rock usually extrusive (lava) or intrusive sill or dyke.
base charge	Explosive charge at the bottom of a blasthole, usually more powerful than the column charge above.
base course	Lowest course of a masonry wall.
basic	A description of an igneous rock containing little or no free silica.
batholith	Deep intrusion of igneous rock underlaying a large area or region
batter	An artificial slope formed by either excavation or deposition which has uniform slope angle. Batter may also be used as a measure of the uniform angle e.g. a batter of 1 (vertical) in 3 (horizontal).
beam	A structural element, usually horizontal, that carries vertical load across an opening by bending.
bed joint	The horizontal surface of a stone or stones in masonry, normally with a bed of mortar placed on it, upon which the stone(s) above are laid.
bedding	The arrangement of distinct sedimentary rock layers or beds one upon another.
~plane	Planar surface that separates successive beds.
current ~	A feature of sediments deposited by flowing water, see cross-bedding.
graded~	A gradation of the size of particles of the sediments throughout the bed.
bench	A working level in a quarry.
bench height	The height of the rock face between two benches in a quarry.
bentonite	A impure form of montmorillonite clay that hydrates and wells in water to produce a viscous fluid or gel. A common constituent of grouts.
berm	The width of the horizontal rock surface or bench at a given level. Berms are also usually left between the final vertical faces to catch falling rocks.
biostatigraphy	See stratigraphy.
biotite	A dark coloured mica containing iron.
black powder	Gun powder used for blasting.
blasting	Fragmentation of rock by the use of explosives.
smooth~	The practice of presplitting especially with respect to producing a smooth wall to a tunnel.
trim~	A technique using explosives and closely spaced blastholes to remove irregularities from the surfaces of rock, especially tunnels and underground chambers.
blast specification	Documentary record of the design of and works required for a blast.
blast vibration	Energy released by an explosion and transmitted through the ground.
block	A large, roughly equidimensional piece of rock.
block size distribution	The frequency distribution of the volumes of blocks defined by natural discontinuities that make up a rock mass.
boasting	A surface finishing process for stone which employs a broad chisel to create an irregular chiselled surface.
bollard	A piece of street furniture made from stone or metal with the purpose of preventing vehicles passing.

bond	(i) A pattern of stones in a wall in which the stones in one course overlap the butt joints in the courses above and below. (ii) Sometimes used to mean adhesion.
boss	An igneous intrusion that is roughly circular in plan and extends to considerable depth.
braided river	A river system comprising many interlaced convergent and divergent streams.
Brazil test	Indirect tensile strength test for stone (see Appendix C).
breccia	A rock formed by the induration of coarsely sized, angular fragments of eroded rocks.
Brethane	A consolidant for weathered stone surfaces developed by Building Research Establishment.
broach	(i) A type of chisel. (ii) To cut out the material between closely spaced drill holes using such a chisel.
bulk density	Total mass per unit volume of stone, (see Appendix C).
bund	An extended mound of soils or overburden erected as a barrier to sight, sound or water.
burden	The distance between a free rock face and a blasthole.
butt joint	Vertical joint, usually mortar filled, between two stones or bricks in the same course of masonry.
buttress	A masonry support to a masonry wall usually constructed perpendicular to the line of the wall in order to (i) prevent the wall from toppling and (ii) to resist sideways thrusts created by vaulting supported by the wall.
cable bolt	A means to reinforce a rock mass using lengths of cable, (see rock bolt).
CAD	Computer aided design.
caisson	A hollow, watertight box, chamber or cell used to construct dams, harbours, sea-walls etc. and as a floating platform.
calcite	Calcium carbonate crystallised in the hexagonal system.
calcrete	Rock formed by cementation of grains with calcite deposited by evaporation of groundwater.
calibration	The milling of sawn tiles to a consistent thickness prior to polishing.
cantilever stairs	Staircase where the stone steps are built into a wall and supported at one end only.
capital	The culminating stone at the top of a column or pilaster, often richly carved.
carbonation	reaction of a substance, typically lime in mortars, with carbon dioxide in the atmosphere to form a carbonate, often calcium carbonate.
Carborundum	Trade name for silicon carbide used as an abrasive.
Cardox	A patented non-explosive process to fragment rock using liquid carbon dioxide.
cavity wall	A wall constructed of two leaves, separated by a continouous void, which forms the protection against the weather.
cement	Natural or synthetic material that binds rock particles together. In sedimentary rocks this may be silica, carbonate, clay or iron oxide.
chamosite	An iron silicate mineral which may act as a cement.
channelling	The cutting of rock by creation of a slot using chisels.
chert	A rock comprising a microcrystalline form of silica.
chlorite	A cleavable, layer silicate mineral, usually green or brown in colour, often formed by alteration and weathering or iron-magnesium minerals such as olivine.
chloritoid	Minerals simlar to chlorite but not actually of the same structure.
chron	A unit of geological time.
chrono-stratigraphy	See stratigraphy.
circular saw	A rotating disc having abrasives fixed around the perimeter and used to cut rock.
cladding	Non-load bearing 'clothing' of walls and roof of a building which forms the protection against the weather and provides an architectural feature.
classified tip	A tip exceeding certain criteria of height, area and volume that must be registered with the Mines and Quarry Inspectorate in the UK.
clay	(i) A specific group of layered silicate minerals. (ii) Particles of size less than 2 micrometres forming rock.
cleavage	The property of a rock or mineral having a propensity to break preferentially along certain plane(s). The principal plane in slates.
cobblestone	Naturally rounded stone large enough to be used in paving but commonly used to describe setts.

coefficient of thermal expansion	Increase in length per unit length per unit rise in temperature.
column	Vertical building element, usually circular or polygonal in cross-section and load bearing.
compressive strength	Stress required to fracture stone in unconfined compression test.
concordant	A description of intrusions of igneous rocks than do not cut across the bedding planes of the intruded rocks.
cone and quatering	See quartering
cone sheet	An igneous dyke which has the form of part of an inverted conical surface, dipping inwards towards the apex and surrounding a major intrusion.
conglomerate	A rock formed by the induration of coarsely sized particles, usually partially rounded pebbles and gravels, derived by erosion of other rocks, see breccia.
consolidation	The expulsion by loading of free water from the voids within a weak rock or soil.
coping	One or more layers of stone (brick or concrete) placed on top of a wall or a parapet to protect it against ingress of water.
coquina	A loosely cemented rock comprising shells and shell fragments, principally that found in Florida.
corbel	(i) A stone projecting from a wall to support a load, (ii) A short bracket, projecting from the wall face, usually for supporting the end of a beam (iii) A metal plate, set in the backing structure, which supports a cladding stone slab.
core	(i) The inner part of a thick wall or pillar, which is constructed of material that is cheaper than that used for the visible surfaces; for example, a medieval wall may have ashlar facings and a rubble and mortar core. (ii) The centre of a dam which provides a water proof barrier. (iii) Centre of an embankment.
cornice	A continuous, horizontal projecting course or moulding, usually at the top of a wall.
course	A horizontal layer of stones of the same height, including the mortar joint on which it is bedded.
coursed rubble	Masonry of squared rubble which is laid in courses.
crag and tail	A structure remaining after the erosion of a protruding rock mass by a glacier.
cramp	Metal device for securing one stone to another or for securing stone facing to backing brickwork.
cross bedding	Feature exhibited by sedimentary rocks laid down by wind or water confused with true bedding planes.
cross-cut	A tunnel within a mine driven from a gallery or level.
crust	The outer portion of the Earth above the Mohorovic discontinuity. It is composed of two layers; the lower sima and the upper sial.
oceanic~	The lower continuous layer comprising rocks containing silica and magnesia which underlies the deep oceans and the continents.
continental~	The upper discontinuous sial comprising rocks containing silica and alumina which appears to be restricted to the major land masses or continents.
cryptoflorescence	Crystallisation of salts within the pores of a rock.
cut-water	The end of a bridge pier, shaped like the bow of a ship, in order to minimise disruption of the flow of water and build up of debris.
D_{50}	Median block size; the nominal sieve aperture that will pass 50% by weight of the blocks.
deciBel	The unit of measurement of sound intensity denoted dB.
decking	The vertical separation of the explosive charge in a blasthole into two or more parts by void space or stemming.
decoupled	The situation where the explosive is not in contact with the wall of the blast hole.
delay (detonator)	An interval of time (milliseconds) between the detonation of individual explosive charges that make up a blast usually effected by using detonators with in-built delay mechanisms.
dentils	Small, rectangular blocks under a cornice used to decorate a classical entablature.
derrick	A crane used to lift and move blocks.
detonator	A device which initiates the detonation of (fires) an explosive charge.

detonating cord	A cord containing small amounts of explosive which can be used to connect and initiate explosive charges.
detritus	Loose rock and mineral fragments produced by erosion and weathering of rock.
diabase	(i) Altered form of dolerite (ii) American term for dolerite.
diagenesis	Those processes affecting a sediment while at or near the surface of the Earth, that is at relatively low temperature and pressure.
diatreme	A volcanic vent through sedimentary rocks.
dilatant	A powder or mass of particulate material is described as dilatant if the volume occcupied by the material increases when the material is disturbed or agitated.
dimension stone	A natural stone product that has been cut or fashioned to a particular size and shape.
diorite	A plutonic, igneous rock of intermediate composition commonly containing hornblende and plagioclase feldspars.
dip direction	see azimuth.
direction of strike	Direction perpendicular to the line of maximum dip of a stratum.
discontinuity	A natural fracture of planar feature in a rock mass which has no tensile strength.
dogs	Hooks used to lift blocks.
dolerite	A basic igneous rock of fine to medium grain size found in dykes and sills.
dolomite	(i) A mixed carbonate mineral containing equal quantities of calcium and magnesium carbonates (ii) a rock containing more than 15% magnesium carbonate.
Dolos unit	Trade name for a cast concrete unit used in sea-defences. The unit has four short, projecting legs or bosses arranged in tetrahedral coordination.
down-the-hole	A method of drilling in which the drill motor is within the hole.
dressed	Stones that are sawn or otherwise cut to precise dimensions with fairly flat surfaces.
dressing back	The restoration of stone by removal of the weathered surface.
drill and broach	A method of splitting rock in which the intervening material between drill holes is broken out using a tool, the broach.
drip	Recess cut under a sill to prevent water from running back and down the face of a wall.
dripstone	A stone or course of stones having a drip placed above a door, window or arch.
drop-ball	a method of breaking oversize rocks by dropping a heavy steel ball or weight upon the block.
drum	A cylindrical stone used to form part of a column.
drumlins	Smooth hills or mounds of oval plan formed by deposition of till by a glacier around a rocky protrusion.
dunite	An ultrabasic, igneous rock composed almost entirely of the mineral olivine.
dry	See dry-jointed.
dry-jointed	Masonry built without mortar.
DTH	Down-the-hole
duricrust	A superficial rock formed in arid climates by the evaporation of water which deposits a cement (often calcite or salt) within the rock mass.
dyke	Igneous rock infilling a vertical or sub-vertical fracture that cuts across bedding planes. Dykes are generally narrow but may extend for kilometres along strike.
dynamite	An explosive comprising nitroglycerine absorbed into an inert, porous substrate.

efflorescence	A deposit appearing on the surface of stone or masonry formed by the crystallisation of soluble salts carried to the surface by moisture movement.
elastic modulus	The modulus of deformation when it is a constant; also called Young's modulus.
engineering geology	The science devoted to the investigation, study and solution of the engineering and environmnetal problems which may arise as the result of the interaction between geology and the works and activities of man as well as the prediction of and the development of measures for the prevention or remediation of geological hazards.
entablature	In classical architecture, the upper part of a stone ornament above the columns comprising architrave, frieze and cornice.
eon	A unit of geological time.
epoch	A relatively short unit of geological time.
era	The longest unit of geological time.

erosion	The mechanical process by which rock is worn away by the action of debris transported by a fluid i.e. water, ice or wind.
~hollow	A depression in rock created by erosion.
esker	A long, narrow, sinuous deposit of sands and gravels deposited by a stream flowing within a melting glacier.
extrados	The upper surface of an arch or vault.
extrusive	A description applied to igneous rocks which are extruded onto the surface in the molten state e.g. lava, rhyolite, basalt.
façade	The front elevation of a building.
facies	Features of a rock, usually sedimentary, that characterise the depositional environment in which the sediment was laid down.
facing	Stone masonry forming the visible surface of a wall or pillar, otherwise constructed of less expensive material e.g. brickwork.
feldspathoids	Rock forming minerals which are silicates of sodium and potassium but unsaturated with respect to silica. They are never found in igneous rocks together with quartz.
feldspars	The most abundant group of rock forming silicate minerals.
felsite	A light coloured, fine grained extrusive or hypabyssal rock composed mainly of feldspars and quartz with distinctive texture.
ferramenta	Ironwork fixed to stone.
fixings	The metal components which connect stone cladding to the backing structure.
flagstone	A thin slab or flag of stone that may be used for paving.
flame jet	A tool to cut rock which uses a fuel -air or fuel-oxygen flame to fracture the rock by spalling.
flame textured	A finishing technique producing a rippled rock surface by playing a flame across the surface to spall the rock.
flashing	Sheeting, usually of lead, used to seal masonry and prevent water ingress.
flexural strength	Stress required to fracture stone in bending test using quarter-point loading (see Appendix C).
flint	Chert when found in chalk.
flow-banding	Texture of an igneous rock produced by the orientation and distribution of minerals created by flow while the rock was molten.
fly-rock	Rock projected into the air by blasting.
fold	A flexure in rocks; that is a change in the amount of dip of a bed.
fold axis	A line parallel to the hinge of a fold, that is the line along which the change of dip takes place.
foliation	Parallel orientation of platy minerals or mineral banding in a rock.
footwall	The rock below that being extracted in a mine.
frame saw	A saw having one or more linear, tensioned blades within a reciprocating frame.
freestone	A stone that may be easily worked by a mason in any direction i.e. not exhibiting preferential cleavage in any plane nor brittle.
frieze	The central member of the entablature usually comprising a vertical panel of decoration, often of carved relief.
gabbro	A coarse grained, plutonic, basic igneous rock comprising plagioclase, pyroxene and sometimes olivine.
gabion	A stone filled rectangular box fabricated from wire mesh.
gallery	A horizontal tunnel in a mine driven to provide access to the ore.
gangsaw	See frame saw.
gelignite	Gelatinous explosive made by mixing nitroglycerine and nitrocellulose.
geomorphology	The classification, description, nature, origin and development of landforms, their relation to underlying geology and the history of geological changes recorded by these surface features.
geophysics	Exploration techniques based upon detecting the physical properties of rocks e.g. density, magnetism, electrical conductivity.
geostatistics	Mathematical methods of estimating assay values and rock properties from sampling data based upon the theory of 'regionalised variables' or spatial correlation of values.

geotextile	A textile usually woven from synthetic polymers which is used together with rock and soils in construction to confer strength and stability and/or to control groundwater.
gloss (value)	Polish (degree of polish)
gneiss	A foliated rock produced by regional metamorphism having bands or lenses of granular minerals alternating with bands or lenticles of flaky minerals.
graded	A term used with qualification, poorly~ or well~, to describe the size distribution of particles in a sediment.
poorly~	In engineering terms, a narrow range of particle sizes is present. In geological terms, a wide range of sizes is present.
well~	In engineering terms a wide range of particle sizes is present. In geological terms, a narrow range of particle sizes is present.
grading	Description of the size distribution of particles within sediments and rocks.
grading curve	A graphical plot of particle size on the abscissa, sometimes on a logarithmic scale, against percent weight, usually expressed as passing a given sieve or less than a given size, on the ordinate.
grain	(i) a description of the cleavage of rock, usually igneous and granite. (ii) an individual mineral component of the rock.
granite	(i) acidic, plutonic igneous rock comprising feldspars, micas and quartz. (ii) Also misused to describe any igneous rock that can be polished e.g. 'black granite' may be dolerite or gabbro.
granulite	A metamorphic rock having a granular texture.
gravel	Commonly defined as particles of size greater than 2 mm contained in unconsolidated rocks.
greywacke	A sedimentary rock comprising mineral and rock fragments, typically quartz and feldspar, cemented by clays which may have been altered to chlorite.
grizzly	A rugged screen comprising a number of parallel, heavy steel bars.
grout	A fluid cementious mix used to fill voids and retain fixings.
groyne	A fixed, linear structure projecting perpendicularly from a beach into the sea the purpose of which is to prevent long-shore drift of beach materials.
gun-shading	The creation of areas of uncleaned stone in the shadow of stone of higher relief which prevents the jet of cleaning agent from impingeing upon the surface.
gypsum	The dihydrate of calcium sulphate, $CaSO_4.2H_2O$.
hanging wall	The rock above that being extracted in a mine.
hem	Cleavage in an igneous rock i.e. granite.
hemispherical-projection	A graphical method of presenting the dips and azimuths of discontinuities.
hewn stone	Stone dressed by hammer and chisel.
honed	A very smooth, but non-reflective, finish typically imparted to surfaces of slate and sandstones.
hopper head	Part of the rain water system on a building into which collects the flow from one or more down pipes.
hornblende	The most common amphibole mineral.
hornfels	A metamorphic rock produced by contact with an igneous intrusion.
hydration	Alteration of mineral by reaction with water to produce hydrated compounds.
hydraulic	A description applied to cements and lime that set under water as a result of the reaction between lime and siliceous material in the mix as opposed to those, such as lime itself, that harden by reaction with carbon dioxide in the atmosphere.
~conductivity	Specifically a measure of the resistance to the flow of *water* presented by a porous medium or packed bed of particles. Units are m/s and the parameter is the velocity of water flowing through the bed under an unit hydraulic gradient (mH_2O/m). Often and incorrectly called permeability
hydrothermal alteration	Modification of the existing minerals in a rock by heated or superheated aqueous fluids usually generated by igneous activity.
hypabyssal	Rock formed at very great depth.
igneous rock	A rock that has solidified from the molten or near molten state.
ignimbrite	A rock produced by accumulation of volcanic ash (tuff) and lava spray.

incline	An inclined adit.
indentation	A method of repair of weathered stone in which only a part of a block is cut out and replaced.
index mineral	A mineral indicative of the zone of metamorphism in a rock and, thereby, the grade of metamorhism.
induration	Transformation of soft, weak sediments into hard, strong rocks. See also diagenesis.
infill masonry	Masonry supported floor by floor on a framed structure.
instantaneous charge weight	The weight of explosive initiated instantaneously by detonators on the same delay.
intrados	The visible underside of an arch or vault.
isograd	A contour line connecting points of equal value of assay or other property.
isopachytes	Contour lines of equal thickness of a named stratigraphic unit.
isotropic	A description of a homogenous material in which properties are independent of direction.
jad	The space created above a block in a mine to permit the block to be raised and moved.
Jenny Lind	A polishing machine comprising a single rotating polishing disc that is moved by hand across the surface to be polished.
joggle	An identation cut in the joint surfaces of a stone.
joint	(i) A discontinuity where no relative movement has taken place between the rock faces either side. (ii) The space between two stones (in masonry) or two stone slabs (in cladding); it may be filled with mortar, or in the case of movement joints, filled with sealant or left open.
joint set	A set of discontinuities having approximately the same dip and azimuth i.e. produced by the same tectonic events.
kame	A deposit of sands and gravels on the margin of a melting glacier.
kerf	The void space created by a saw blade while cutting rock.
keystone	Last trapezoidal stone placed in the crown of an arch and regarded as binding the arch.
knives	A local (north Wales) name given to joints in slate.
krigeing	A technique within geostatistics for estimating an assay value at an unsampled point from sampling data and the spatial correlation (named after D. Krige).
laccoliths	A dome or mushroom shaped intrusion of igneous rock between strata.
lag	Distance between sample positions, (see geostatistics).
landfill	Disposal of waste into excavations.
larvikite	A coarse grained syenite rock found near Larvik, Norway having a characteristic blue-green irridescence when polished.
leucite	A feldspathoid containing potassium, $KAlSiO_4$
level	A horizontal tunnel driven at a certain elevation or level in a mine to provide access to the ore from a shaft or incline.
lichens	Associations of algae and fungi capable of living in hostile environments.
lime	Hydrated 'quick lime', chemically calcium hydroxide, a white powder commonly used to make mortars and lime-wash.
limestone	A sedimentary rock composed mainly of calcium carbonate.
limonite	A mineral comprising the hydrated form of iron oxide.
line drilling	Drilling of overlapping drill holes as a means to cut or split rock
lining	Stone cladding a door or window opening.
load bearing masonry	Masonry that supports loads in addition to that of its own weight.
loess	Accumulation of wind born, usually siliceous, dust derived from a desert area or ice sheet.
lopoliths	Large, basin-like intrusions of igneous rock that do not cut across bedding planes (concordant).
magma	Molten rock from which igneous rocks are formed.
marble	(i) Petrologically a metamorphic rock comprising recrystallised calcium and magneiusm carbonates (ii) historically and in the stone industry, any rock that can be polished to a shining or bright finish, especially limestones.

masonry	Building construction of stone blocks and/or lumps of stone.
mason's drag	An implement for smoothing the surface of a stone.
metamoprhic rock	A rock that has been affected by heat or pressure resulting in some recrystallisation of minerals.
metamorphism	
contact∼	Alteration of rock by contact with igneous intrusion.
thermal∼	Metamorhism by heat e.g. by deep burial or contact with molten rocks
dynamic∼	Metamorphism caused by movements in the Earth's crust which can generate both high pressures and temperatures.
regional∼	Metamorphism affecting a large area.
grade of∼	A scale, low to high, indicating the intensity of metamorphism through heat and pressure.
metasomatic	Replacement of substance, such as elements within a mineral, without change of form e.g. dolomitisation of limestones.
mica	The group of layered lattice silicate minerals exhibiting strong cleavage, including biotite and muscovite.
micrite	Microcrystalline calcite in a carbonate rock.
mid-ocean ridge	The boundary between plates of oceanic crust which are moving apart where submarine volcanism creates new oceanic crust.
migmatite	A composite rock formed by reconstruction of igneous or metamorphic rocks caused by injection of magma or partial melting.
mill	A machine having a rotating cutting head used principally to produce curved shapes in stone.
mineral	A naturally formed chemical compound or element having a characteristic crystal form and approximately fixed composition.
mineralogy	Study of minerals, composition, formation, association, identification, etc..
modulus of deformation	Stress divided by strain.
modulus of elasticity	Modulus of deformation when this has a constant value, that is the material is elastic. Also called Young's modulus (see Appendix C).
modulus of rupture	See transverse strength.
Mohs' scale	A non-linear, comparative scale of mineral hardness employing ten standards: talc 1; gypsum 2; calcite 3; fluorite 4; apatite 5; orthoclase 6; quartz 7; topaz 8; corundum 9 and diamond 10.
moraine	A mound or ridge of unsorted glacial till deposited at the melting face of a glacier.
mould	A template having the desired section of the finished stone.
moving average	See rolling mean.
mucking out	Removal of blasted rock from the quarry, mine or tunnel face.
mullion	A vertical component of a window tracery or frame.
Namurian	An European name for the base of the Upper Carboniferous.
natural repose, angle of	The steepest angle at which the surface of a heap of soil or other granular material will stand naturally without restraint.
nepheline	A feldspathoid containing sodium, $NaAlSiO_4$.
New Red Sandstone	A name given to the red sandstone of Permian-Triassic age.
obsidian	Natural acid volcanic glass.
odeometer	A laboratory apparatus for determining the consolidation characteristics of small samples of weak rock and soil under static loading.
ogee	A curved surface or moulding comprising two reversed curves, essentially 'S' shaped.
Old Red Sandstone	A name given to the red sandstone of Devonian age.
oolith, ooidal	Spherical or ovoid accretions of calcium carbonate, usually, around a nucleus of a sand grain or shell fragment. An accumulation of ooliths, typically sized from 0.25 to 2 mm, resembles 'fish roe' and forms oolitic limestone.
olivine	A mineral of iron and magnesium silicate having a green or brown colour.
onyx	(i) Strictly a banded, translucent and often coloured form of cryptocrystalline silica similar to agate. (ii) A banded, often green, brown and white, form of calcite deposited like travertine.

ophiolite	An assemblage of ultra basic and basic rocks, frequently layered, with an upward transition from plutonic to hypabyssal and volcanic. These represent sections of the ocean crust upthrust into sedimentary sequences.
ophitic	The desription of the texture of ophiolite.
orbicular	A description of an igneous rock, usually porphoyritic granite, containing large, spherical or sub-spherical crystals (phenocrysts) comprising concentric shells of feldspars of differing composition.
orogeny	Event in geological time during which mountains were created by folding and upthrust of rocks.
orthoclase	A potassium silicate of the feldspar group.
overburden	Rock, which is of little or no value, overlying the valuable stone.
overpressure	See air-blast.
oxidation	Reaction with oxygen usually accompanied by an increase in volume and even heat generation. In the case of metals an oxide e.g. rust, is formed. In the case of non-metals, a soluble salt may be formed e.g. sulphur to sulphate.
padstone	A stone included in masonry to bear and distribute the localised load imposed by a beam to prevent crushing of masonry units.
palaeontology	The study of fossils; especially use for dating and correlating sedimentary strata.
palffia	A local (north Wales) name given to circular imperfections in slate.
parapet	A low wall, guarding the edge of a roof, balcony or bridge.
parquetry	Inlay of stone floors.
patina	The supeficial layer of crystallised salts and deposits that may accumulate upon weathered stone surfaces.
peak particle velocity	The maximum velocity of a particle caused by passage of a vibration. A measure of the energy contained in blasting vibration.
pegmatite	Very coarse grained, lenticular and pipe-shaped bodies created by injection of fluid matter from cooling granites into surrounding rocks; especially rich in sodium and potassium feldspars and micas.
pell-mell	See rip-rap.
penetrating pulley	A device used to introduce a wire saw into a rock mass.
period	A unit of geological time.
permeability	A fundamental measure of the resistance of fluid flow presented by a porous medium or packed bed of particles. Units are m/s^2 and the parameter is independent of the properties of the fluid but dependent upon particle size and shape and porosity of the bed.
perpends	The vertical faces of stones, forming butt-joints; also used loosely for butt-joint.
persistence	A measure of the lateral extent of a discontinuity.
petrography	The description of rocks in terms of mineralogy and texture.
petrology	The study of rocks.
pfa	Pulverised fuel ash, a weakly cementitious material.
phenocryst	A relatively large crystal set in a finer grained or glassy ground mass.
phonolite	An igneous rock containing nepheline as the principal mineral.
photogrammetry	The use of photographs to make precise measurements of length, area and volume.
phyllite	A low grade, foliated, metamorphic rock which may exhibit imperfect, undulating cleavage surfaces produced from silts and mudstones.
physical geology	Those aspects of geology that are concerned with the physical geological processes; their actions and results.
piecing repair	See indentation.
pier	(i) Vertical load bearing masonry element between wide openings or intermediate support for multiple span bridge. (ii) buttress protruding a short distance beyond the face of a wall and bonded to it.
pilaster	A shallow square pillar that projects from a pier or wall.
pillar	(i) Vertical, slender, load bearing masonry structure usually of square or rectangular cross-section used in support. (ii) Rock deliberately left in place in an underground mine to support the roof.

pillaring plane	The second cleavage direction in slate.
piping	Within a structure made of unbound materials, piping is the movement of smaller particles through the interstices between the larger particles usually under the influence of flowing water. The structure is usually degraded.
plagioclase	The group of sodium and calcium silicate minerals forming part of the feldspar group.
plane failure	See sliding block failure.
plaster shooting	A method in quarrying of breaking large (oversize) blocks by packing an explosive charge on the surface of the block.
plastic repair	Repair of stone using mortar applied to the stone to replace material lost or damaged by weathering.
plate tectonics	An explanation of the geological history of the Earth based upon the concept of the Earth's crust being made of large plates moving relative to one another.
plinth	(i) Lower square base of a column or pedestal, (ii) Lowest projecting course of a wall often made from different stones either for decoration or to resist the particular weathering conditions.
plug and feathers	A method of splitting blocks by driving a wedge, the plug, between two tapered steel bars, the feathers, inserted into a drill hole.
plutonic	Description of an igneous rock which solidified at depth and, therefore, generally contains large crystals e.g. granite, gabbro.
point load test	Indirect tensile strength test for rock (see Appendix C).
polygonal method	A method of estimating reserves by assigning sample assay values to a polygonal area of influence. Polygons are drawn by bisecting the distances between surrounding samples.
popping	A method of breaking oversize by drilling a blast hole into the block and charging this with explosive.
porosity	Percentage volume of pores in stone.
porphyry	An igneous rock, usually granite, containing large crystals (phenocrysts), usually of feldspar, in a finer grained groundmass.
poultice	In stone cleaning, the name given to a pack or mix of chemicals applied to the surface of a stone and retained by sacking or polythene sheeting in a moist state.
pozzolana	A naturally occuring siliceous material which when mixed with lime forms a hydraulic cement. It also raects with the lime released by the setting of Portland cement and is used as an inexpensive diluent. Named after Pozzouli, Italy where volcanic ash from Mt. Vesuvius has created pozzolana.
presplitting	The creation of a fracture surface by firing lightly charged holes drilled in a line in a rock mass prior to the use of blasting to fragment the rock in front of the presplit. A technique employed to promote slope or face stabilty or produce a smooth surface.
prospect(ing)	An area believed to have potential for mineral extraction; exploring for prospects.
pyrite	A cubic mineral form of iron sulphide.
pyroclastic	Formed of volcanic ash and fragments of cooled lava.
pyroxene	A group of rock forming silicate minerals.
Q rating	A parameter calculated from descriptions of a rock mass that predicts the stability of an excavation in that rock mass. A similar system to RMR which is now less popular.
QA	Quality Assurance, a management system that assures that the product is of adequate quality for the design purpose.
quartering	A method of dividing a sample into smaller lots representative of the original sample. The sample is mixed by forming a conical heap which is then flattened into a disc and divided into quarters.
quartz	A mineral form of silica, SiO_2.
quartzite	A metamorphic rock produced from a sandstone or chert comprising essentially quartz.
quick lime	The product of calination of limestone, calcium oxide, CaO.
quoin	A corner between two walls, especially if emphasised by being built of large dressed stones(quoin stones), set slightly proud of the general surfaces of walls meeting at an external corner.

raise	A shaft driven upwards from the bottom.
random rubble	Masonry of rubble, squared or otherwise, which is laid without the bed joints forming a continuous horizontal surface.
Rapakivi	A term used to describe the texture of some Scandinavian granites in which large oval crystals of orthoclase have a mantle of plagioclase.
ravelling	The progressive loss of blocks from a rock slope.
razzer	Long, thin hand saw.
reduction	Removel of oxygen or the reduction of the state of oxidation of an element, e.g. sulphate to sulphur or hydrogen sulphide.
reed	A description of a cleavage plane in granite.
regionalised variables	Theory of spatial correlation of variables e.g. sample assays, see geostatistics.
relative density	Mass of solids in stone divided by the mass of an equal volume of water.
reserve	A defined volume or quantity of mineral that may be legitimately and economically extracted.
resource	A defined volume or quantity of mineral.
respirable dust	Dust particles of a certain size that can accumulate in the lungs.
restoration blasting	A technique using explosives to create rock faces and scree slopes having a natural appearance after quarrying.
retaining wall	A wall holding back soil with a vertical face or at an angle steeper than the angle of natural repose.
return	Right-angle turn of a moulding.
reveal	Depth of stone between the exterior surface of a wall and the door or window unit set into the wall.
revetment	Cladding of stone to protect a slope or shoreline.
rhyolite	A fine grained, extrusive (lava) rock of granitic (acid) composition.
rift	A description of cleavage in igneous rock.
rip-rap	Smaller rocks used in the same way as armour stone to prevent erosion by flowing water.
riven	The natural state of the surface of cleaved stone.
RMR	A parameter calculated from descriptions of a rock mass that predicts the stability of an excavation in that rock mass. A similar system to Q rating which is now more popular.
roadstone	Crushed rock or gravel suitable for use in roadmaking. Usually applied to the aggregate used for unbound and bituminous bound pavement construction.
rock	Massive, indurated, naturally occurring mineral material.
rock bolt	Long steel rods inserted and anchored into holes drilled into a rock mass in order to reinforce the rock mass by preventing the movement of blocks.
rock dowel	A steel pin which when inserted into a preformed hole stabilises a loose rock block by improving the shear resistance across a discontinuity between the block and the underlying material.
rockfill	Fragmented, loosely sized rock deposited and usually compacted as part of construction projects.
rolling mean	A method of producing an estimate of a value at a point in time by averaging values obtained earlier.
room and pillar	An underground mining method in which rock is excavated from rooms while pillars are left to support the roof.
router	A machine having a rotating conical cutting head that is useful to create bas-relief.
royalty	A payment made to the owner of the mineral being extracted.
RQD	Rock Quality Designation, a parameter calculated from the spacing of the discontinuities along a scan line on a rock mass.
rubble	Stones that are only roughly shaped with hammer and chisel if shaped at all.
rubble wall	A form of construction with rubble and mortar packed between two external leaves of masonry.
sand	(i) Commonly used to refer to sand-sized sediments of silica (SiO_2) which is the principal mineral component of most natural sands. (ii) A definition of particle size of sediments between 2mm and 0.06 mm.

sarsen stone	A residual block of well cemented sandstone thought to be produced by the incomplete erosion of a bed of sandstone, probably a silcrete, overlying the chalk of southern England.
scaled distance	A parameter used in the prediction of blasting vibration; distance divided by the square root of the charge weight.
scant	A slab of rock produced by primary saws.
scarp	Escarpment, cliff usually produced by a relatively erosion resistant stratum.
schist	Metamorphic rock characterised by a parallel arrangement of the bulk of the constituent minerals.
schistosity	A description of cleavage exhibited by schist.
sealant	Adhesive compound, usually organic, applied in paste form, which cures to an elastic material, used to seal joints, so as to prevent ingress of water.
sedimentary rock	A rock resulting from the consolidation of loose sediment that has accumulated in layers, or a chemical rock formed by precipitation or an organic rock consisting largely of remains of plants and animals.
self supporting	Masonry that supports its own weight the whole height of the wall.
semi-variogram	A graphical and mathematical expression of the correlation between regionalised variables, (see geostatistics).
sett	A rectangular prism of rock used for paving of roads sometimes, incorrectly, called 'cobble'.
shakes	A local name given by quarrymen to defects in blocks of stone where a feature crosses a bedding plane.
shale	A fine grained, sedimentary rock composed of clays and other finely sized mineral particles.
sheltercoat	A protecive or sacrificial coating such as limewash applied to weathered stone.
shield area	A large area of exposed, ancient, often PreCambrian, rocks forming the platforms, or basements of the continents upon which later sedimentary rocks were deposited.
shotcreting	The application of concrete to a rock surface by pump and spray nozzle.
siderite	An iron carbonate mineral.
silcrete	A duricrust cemented with silica.
silicates	The most important group of rock forming minerals which are classified according to their crystal structure and the interlinking of the basic, tetrahedral SiO_4 unit.
siliciclastic	Rock derived from detritus generated by erosion of other siliceous rocks.
sill	(i) A horizontal feature at the base of a window for the purpose of throwing rainwater clear of the wall below. (ii) A horizontal or inclined, concordant igneous intrusion.
silt	A definition of particle size of sediments between 0.06 mm and 0.002 mm.
slab	A cut block or slice of rock having one dimension, thickness, significantly less than the other two.
slabbing saw	A machine mounting at least two circular saws working at right angles that can divide a trimmed block directly into slab.
slate	(i) A rock produced by low grade regional metamorphism of a mudstone which has developed pronounced cleavage. Little recrystallisation has occured so that the rock is still very fine grained. (ii) A term used loosely and incorrectly to describe any fissile rock that cleaves to produce roofing tiles. Such rocks include phyllites, and sedimentary limestones and sandstones that cleave along bedding planes.
sliding block failure	Instability of a rock slope caused by blocks sliding upon the surface of a single discontinuity that outcrops on the slope.
slip	Movement on the plane of a fault.
dip~	Movement on a fault parallel to the dip of the fault.
strike~	Movement on a fault parallel to the strike of the fault.
oblique~	Movement on a fault along any other direction.
smooth and trim blasting	The use of small charges of explosive to remove unstable parts of a rock face to enhance stability or achieve the required slope profile or improve the aethetics of a slope.
soffit	Exposed underside of a lintel, arch or portico.

sorted	A description of the size distribution of particles in a sediment related to the sorting action of flowing water.
well~	A narrow range of particle sizes is present.
poorly~	A wide range of particles sizes is present.
spacing	The distance between blastholes or discontinuities.
spandrel walls	The walls standing on the edges of the space between the extrados of the arch and the top of the road carried by the bridge. They usually retain the fill under the road. Also , in church architecture, the walls extending from the internal arches below to the windows above.
sparite	Coarsely crystalline calcium carbonate forming the matrix of a rock.
sparry	Containing spar or coarse crystals.
specific gravity	See relative density.
spherical model	One mathematical model of the semi-variogram, see geostatistics.
spillway	Channel to convey water past the crest of a dam.
spinning-off	The use of rotary discs of abrasive to clean a stone surface.
squared rubble	Rubble stones that have been shaped to have rectangular faces at right angles to each other.
SSSI	Site of Special Scientific Interest as designated by English Nature.
stemming	Material, usually comprising chippings of crushed rock, used to contain the explosion within the blasthole.
step-featuring	A topographical feature created by several parallel faults.
stereoplot	See hemispherical projection.
stitch drilling	See line drilling.
stock	A pipe-like vertical feeder through which magma flows from deep within the Earth to volcanos and intrusive bodies.
stone	(i) Rock used for building construction. (ii) Small block of stone used in masonry construction.
stone slates	An incorrect term for stone tiles.
stone tiles	Thin slabs of stone used for roof cladding.
stope	The site of mineral extraction in an underground mine.
strain	Change in length per unit length. It can be caused by stress, temperature change or change of moisture content.
stratigraphy	The study of bedded, stratified rocks (sediments and volcanics) with respect to geological time, petrology and correlation between beds in different localities.
bio~	Division, identification and correlation of beds by fossil content.
chrono~	Division, identification and correlation of beds by geological age.
litho~	Division, identification and correlation of beds by rock type and petrology.
stratigraphic column	The sequence of stratified rocks determined according to one of the above systems.
stress	Force per unit area.
string course	A continuous, horizontal course of plain or moulded projecting stones in a wall.
structural geology	Geology concerned with the relationship between rock masses such as folding, faulting, unconformities and intrusions.
stuff	A mix for mortar which does not contain the cementitious part.
subduction zone	The zone where a drifting continental plate overides the ocean crust forcing it deep into the interior of the Earth.
suction	Stress free negative pore water pressure of water in porous stone.
swallow hole	A vertical hole connecting to sub-terranean caverns produced by dissolution of the rock, usually limestone, down which flows a river or stream.
syncline	Upwards (concave) folding of rocks(cf.anticline) so that younger rocks occupy the core of the structure.

tectonism	The name given by structural geologists to major movements within the Earth's crust such as continental drift and orogenesis, see plate tectonics.
tensile strength	Stress required to fracture stone in tension.
terrazzo	Concrete made with fragments of stone such as marble that is cut and polished after hardening.

terrigenous	Sediments deposited on land rather than in the sea (marine).
texture	The relationship between the constituent minerals of a rock in terms of associations, zoning, grain size etc.
thiobacillus	A strain of bacterium including ferro-oxidans which oxidise iron and sulphur compounds and minerals.
tholeiite	A type of basalt comprising crystals of plagioclase and pyroxene in a matrix of glass or quartz-feldspar intergrowths.
till	Unstratified, unsorted material deposited directly by a glacier without reworking by water. A heterogeneous mixture of clay, sand, gravel and boulders. Includes 'boulder clay'.
toes	Irregularities and uneveness of the floor in the quarry created by poor blasting practice.
toppling	Falling forward of blocks from the face or rock slope into the quarry.
transform fault	A plate boundary along which two plates slide passed each other, see plate tectonics.
transom	A horizontal bar in a window.
transverse strength	Stress required to fracture stone in bending test using half-point loading (see Appendix C).
travertine	A typically layered and porous limestone produced by precipitation of calcium carbonate from solution in warm/hot water e.g. hot springs, spa water.
trench	(i) A linear excavation. (ii) The deepest parts of the oceans usually between the mid-ocean ridges and continental shelves.
trend surface	A technique for presenting spatial sampling imformation in which a polynomial describing a surface is fitted to point data. It provides methods of extrapolating from and interpolating between assay values determined at fixed sampling points.
tuff	A rock comprising compacted, often stratified deposit of pyroclastic material e.g. volcanic ash.
type section	A locality chosen to be a standard for comparison of a stratigraphic unit
unconformity	An interruption in a geological sequence representing an interval of time during which no sediments or other rocks were deposited. The underlying, older rocks may have been deeply eroded, tilted, folded or metamorphosed resulting in a marked difference between the geological structure above and below the unconformity.
vents	Natural flaws (cracks and voids) in dimension stone.
vesicular	Containing vesicles or voids created, for example, by gas trapped in igneous rocks as they solidify on cooling. When filled with mineral these vesicles become amydales.
vibrograph	An instrument to measure vibration e.g. blasting vibration.
vibrometer	See vibrograph.
volcanoclastic	See pyroclastic.
voussoirs	Stones that are dressed to have a tapering vertical thickness so as to allow the construction of an arch with mortar joints of constant thickness.
water absorption	Percentage mass of water in saturated stone (see Appendix C).
way	A description of cleavage, especially in granites.
weathering	(i) Process by which rocks are decomposed or altered by the action of wind, rain, temperature change etc. (ii) The same process causing deterioration of masonry.
wedge failure	Instabilty of a rock slope caused by the intersection of the planes of two different discontinuities.
Whinstone	A local term used to describe dolerite forming the Whin Sill of northern England and other dykes some of which are actually basalt.
wire saw (diamond wire)	A device for cutting rock that employs a travelling wire and a separate abrasive or diamonds attached to the wire.
wrist block	The first block to be removed from a new face thus permitting access for rock cutting devices

xenolith — An inclusion of a fragment of an older rock in an igneous rock.

Young's modulus — See modulus of elasticity.

zeolite — Silicate minerals containing water of crystallisation and, thereby, often porous and chemically active. Often found in amygdales and hydrothermal veins.

Appendix B: Details of test methods

B1. Introduction

B1.1. General

This Appendix outlines the tests and procedures used to describe or evaluate the physical, mechanical and chemical characteristics of natural stone and rock used in construction. The different characteristics required by the uses of stone and rock covered in this book have resulted in a wide range of tests being developed to describe the material and to assess its potential value. Most assess some physical or mechanical attribute and are performed on the material at the exploration, quarrying or primary production stage. The testing of finished products is restricted to materials that undergo little or no processing, for example rockfill materials. However, there is now a trend towards the performance testing of paving and cladding materials and it seems likely that this trend will continue.

The literature is extensive so the Appendix does not include a full description of each test but aims to provide sufficient information to allow the basis of the test to be described. In addition, a full reference is given that will allow further details of the method and any related requirements to be found. The Appendix also contains a brief section on the collection of samples and on repeatability and reproducibility of tests.

Some of the material is drawn from the Chapters but is included again here in order to give an overview of the subject. Some results of the tests described in this Appendix are given in Appendix C.

Tables B1 to B4 summarize the tests found in each Chapter.

B1.2. Exploration and assessment

A key part of exploration and assessment is the testing of samples obtained from surface collections, coring or other site investigations. The test results will not only determine if the material is suitable for its intended purpose, but also provide information on which the planning of the extraction can be undertaken. For example, if the variation within a bed results in some parts being suitable for blockstone which can then be sawn, whereas other parts are only suitable for breaking into walling stone for houses or field boundaries, then adequate test results must be available to ensure that the quarry is designed for both types of stone.

The precise testing that is carried out will depend on the proposed end use of the stone – rockfill, armour or buildings – and guidance on appropriate tests are given in Chapters 7, 8 and 9 respectively.

B1.3. Rockfill

Rock fragments with a dimension as large as 1 m or more have sometimes been used in rock fills and the large size of these rock fragments causes obvious difficulties in determining the engineering properties of rock fill in laboratory tests. It is clearly impractical and uneconomic to design equipment that could test such material. The non-availability of large-scale testing equipment means that some scaling down of the field particle size distribution has to be adopted in laboratory tests and the simplest approach is to remove all the oversize material and test what is left. It has been suggested that it is preferable to test a material with a

Table B1. *These tests are referred to in Chapter 3*

Physical tests			
Density	3.7.2	No method given	
Water absorption (Slate)	3.7.3	BS 680: Part 2: 1971	Ref to Chapter 7
Saturation and porosity	3.7.6	No method given	
Petrography/Petrographic thin section	3.7.1	No method given	Cox *et al.* 1988
Mechanical tests			
Strength			
Strength (Compressive)	3.7.4	ASTM C 170-90	
Strength (Modulus of rupture)	3.7.4	ASTM C 99-87	
Strength (Flexural)	3.7.4	ASTM C 880–89	
Coring	3.7.4	ASTM D 2938-71a	
Durability			
Salt resistance	3.7.6	Crystallization test	
Acidic pollution resistance		Acid immersion	
Acidic pollution and frost resistance		BS 680: Part 2: 1971	For slate
Frost resistance		DIN 52.104/1 and /2	Freeze/Thaw test
Abrasion resistance	3.7.5	No method given	Ref to Chapter 7
Slip resistance	3.7.5	No method given	Ref to Chapter 7

Table B2. *These tests are referred to in Chapter 7*

Physical tests			
Particle size distribution	7.3.2 (b)	No method given	
Durability	7.3.2 (a)	Slake durability test	Franklin & Chandra 1972
Water absorption/saturation coefficient (As a measuring of weathering potential)	7.3.2 (a)	No method given	
Moisture content	7.3.2 (c)	BS 1377: 1990: Part 2	
Compactness	7.3.2 (d)	No methods given	Includes voids ratio, porosity, dry density, dry unit weight, air voids, density index
Mechanical tests			
Strength			
Particle strength	7.3.2 (a)	Uniaxial compressive strength	
Strength	7.3.2 (a)	Aggregate crushing test	Perry & Parsons 1986
		Point load strength	Broch & Franklin1972
			Sowers *et al.* 1965
			Fumagalli 1969
			Marsal 1973
			Penman & Charles 1976
Shear strength tests	7.3.3	No method given	
Compressibility	7.3.4	No method given	Kjaernsli Sande 1963
Durability			
Shale Durability	7.5.2	ASTM D 4644	
Compaction test	7.5.2 (a)	'Rammer compaction test'	BS 1990a

Table B3. *These tests are referred to in Chapter 8*

Physical tests			
Shape and size	8.5.2	BS 812	
		NEN 5181	
		BS 812	Flakiness index
		NEN 5182	Size of larger particles
Density and water absorption	8.5.3	BS 812	
Petrography	8.5.1	ASTM C 295	
Clay content	8.5.1		Stewart & McCulogh (1985)
			Hills & Pettifer (1985)
		ASTM C 837	
		ASTM C 127-84	
Mechanical properties			
Strength			
Strength	8.5.4	No method	Block integrity test
		ISRM (1988)	Fracture toughness
		BS 812	Impact resistance
		BS 812	Crushing resistance
		ISRM (1988)	Point load strength
Durability			
Abrasion resistance	8.5.4	Deval test	LCPC (1989)
		Sandblast test	Verhoef (1987)
Sonic velocity	8.5.4	No method	Dearman *et al.* (1987)
Sulphate soundness	8.5.6	ASTM C 88	Sulphate soundness
		BS 812: Part 121	Sulphate soundness

grading parallel to that of the field grading. However, this latter approach requires far more work in sample preparation and has the disadvantage that the tested sample may have an excessive quantity of fines.

Most, although not all, of the types of tests appropriate for rock fill are described in BS 1377: 1990 'Methods of test for soils for civil engineering purposes', Brown (1981) 'Rock characterisation, testing and monitoring' and BS 812 'Testing aggregates'. However, the BS test specifications were written for soils or small size aggregate not rockfills. Therefore, in most cases, there will need to be some adjustment to allow for the testing

Table B4. *These tests are referred to in Chapter 9*

Physical tests			
Density	9.4.2	BRE Rep. 141 ASTM C 97-90	BRE 1989
Water absorption	9.4.2	BRE Rep. 141 BS 680: Part 2 ASTM C 97-90 NF B 10-502	BRE 1989
Petrographic description	9.4.2	BS 812: Part 104 BS 5930 UNI 9724 Part 1	
	9.4.2	ISRM	
Mechanical tests			
Strength			
Compressive strength	9.4.2	ASTM C 170-90 NF B 10-509 DIN 52.105 BS 5628: Part 2	
Young's modulus (E)	9.4.2	ASTM D 3148-86 ASTM C 120-90	
Flexural strength	9.4.2	ASTM C 880-89 ASTM C 120-90	
Modulus of rupture	9.4.2	ASTM C 99-87	
Durability			
Salt resistance	9.4.2	BRE Rep. 141	Crystallization test BRE 1989
		DIN 52.104	Freeze/thaw
		BS 680: Part 2	For slate roofing tiles
	9.5.1.6	BS 5642	For slate sills and copings
Slip resistance	9.4.2	BS 6677: Part 1	
Abrasion resistance	9.4.2	ASTM C 241-90 NF B 10-508	

of rock fragments larger than the maximum particle sizes specified in the BS test procedures.

B1.4. Armourstone

Testing for armourstone is dominated by the need to establish the likely durability of stone in aggressive marine environments. Testing includes both direct tests, for example frost tests, indirect tests such as water absorption and petrographical and mineralogical methods such as the methylene blue test. There is also a wide range of impact and abrasion tests which are also aimed at establishing the longevity of the rocks to be used.

B1.5. Stone for buildings and civil engineering

The testing of structural properties has traditionally been carried out on specimens of the material in question. However, in recent years there has been an increased demand for the testing of products (for example paving units) and for the testing of units (for example full sized cladding panels or masonry wall units). This demand for product and unit testing is being reflected in both the new European standards (see below) and in some more recent publications such as Lewis (1995).

B2. Sampling

In order to provide an acceptable estimate of the overall properties of a stone to be used in various projects, whether the stone is still a deposit or as extracted material prior to construction, samples for testing must be representative of the rock or stone. Consequently sampling is as important as testing and proper and careful sampling and sample handling is a prerequisite for an analysis that will give reliable results and avoid biased sampling.

Three main factors affect the accuracy of sampling: the size of the particles within the sample, the mass of the sample and the number of samples taken. All of these are interelated and are also linked to the expected variation within the deposit, both vertically through the bed or beds and horizontally along the beds.

Sampling of natural stone can have a number of different purposes:

- Sampling as part of preliminary investigations of deposits is generally performed in order to decide the character and general quality of the deposit.
- Sampling at the quarry extraction stage or raw block production stage is generally performed in order to decide the quality and quality variations within a quarry or within certain parts of the quarry.
- Sampling in processing plants are generally performed as part of a company's quality control system and may include aesthetic, dimensional and technical properties.
- Sampling of products from deliveries or at final destination as part of a conformity assessment or contractual agreement.
- Sampling of 'finished' products as part of a production control procedure.

Each of these situations may require a different sampling method, sampling frequency, sample type and sample mass.

Practical experience suggests that many sampling schemes underestimate, often considerably, the quantity of sample which is required for both accurate assessment and for production control. Many schemes are based on conventional statistics, as if rock or stone were made up of random spheres, whereas in reality there are always relationships between different parts of a deposit. In a sedimentary rock these will relate to the depositional environment, whereas in an igneous rock the parent magma and the mode of emplacement will result in mineralogical relationships within the resulting rock mass. Later diagenetic and structural changes will superimpose other patterns upon those related to the original formation but spatial relationships will always exist. Therefore, wherever possible, sampling schemes should be based on analytical methods which take these spatial relationships into account.

Probably the greatest danger in sampling is not taking a representative sample. The calculation of sample size for particulate materials is relatively easy. However, when sampling stone for use as armourstone or dimension stone, the problem is made more difficult by the size of the blocks produced. What is required is an estimate of the variation within the beds from which the blocks are taken and an estimate of the variation within the blocks themselves.

B3. Repeatability and reproducibility

Important considerations in any test programme, whatever its aims, are the notions of repeatability and reproducibility. A number of quite different factors can contribute to a spread in test values and to allow for this in comparing results obtained by the same or by different operators in different laboratories, some estimate of the distribution of values is necessary. The determination of repeatability and reproducibility is well established in the quality control of manufactured products. It is also becoming established in some extractive inducstries and is discussed at some length in the Engineering Group Working Party Report on aggregates (Smith & Collis 1993). However, the limited testing traditionally carried out on blocks of natural stone means that there is rarely sufficient data to establish values for repeatability, reproducibility or variability within a natural stone quarry.

B3.1. Repeatability (r)

This is the quantitative expression of the random error associated with a single test operator obtaining successive results on identical material, with the same equipment and constant operating conditions. It is the difference between two single results which would be expected to be exceeded in only one case in twenty, assuming normal and correct operation of the test. This is expressed by

$$r = 1.96\sqrt{2\sigma_1^2}$$

where σ_1 is the single operator standard deviation within a laboratory.

B3.2. Reproducibility (R)

This is an expression of the random error associated with test operators working in different laboratories, each obtaining single results on identical test materials when applying the same method. As with r, it is the difference between two single and independent results which would be expected in only one case in twenty. This is expressed by

$$R = 1.96\sqrt{2}\sqrt{\sigma_1^2 + \sigma_2^2}$$

where σ_2 is the standard deviation applicable to all causes of variability other than repeatability, when the results from different laboratories are compared.

B4. Physical tests

B4.1. Particle size and shape

The determination of the particle size distribution is important for material to be used for rockfill and armourstone. It is generally determined by sieving of a representative sample and will be a major task where the fill contains large rock fragments. In some instances the shape of the rock fragments may also be important; in these cases the shape can be determined using methods outlined in BS 812 and in NEN 5181. In addition, the draft European Standard for Armourstone contains details of a method to be used to determine the content of stones with a specified length to thickness ratio.

B4.2. Density

The density of a stone is expressed in mass per unit volume, usually grams per cm^3 or kg per m^3. There is no British Standard but the tests described in BRE Report 141 (BRE 1989) for porosity and saturation coefficient can be used to calculate density. The ASTM standard C 97-90 contains a method for measuring the bulk specific gravity which is in effect the same as the density. In both tests it is the density of the bulk stone rather than a crushed sample (often referred to as the real density) that is measured. British Standard BS 812 Part 107 gives density tests for aggregate that can be used for building stone, etc. All of these methods are based on long-established techniques using dry weight, wet weight in air, and wet weight in water.

Measurement of the density allows the weight of flooring, walling or cladding panels to be calculated.

The density index (I_D) is a useful way of relating the in-situ dry density of a granular fill (e_d) to the limiting conditions of maximum dry density (e_{dmax}) and minimum dry density (e_{dmin}) and is given by the expression:

$$I_D = \frac{(e_d - e_{dmin})e_{dmax}}{(e_{dmax} - e_{dmin})e_d} \times 100(\%)$$

Test specifications for the determination of the maximum and minimum densities of gravely soils are given in BS 1377: 1990: Part 4. Test methods for the determination of *in situ* density are given in BS 1377: 1990: Part 9. However, for a rockfill containing large rock fragments, there will be great difficulties in measuring the three dry densities needed to compute I_D, namely the *in situ* field density and the maximum and minimum densities.

Dry density and water absorption are considered as vital parameters for designing armourstone projects. They will give information on the stability of the construction along with reference values for volume filling and weight relations for the execution-induced properties of the armour layer. The CIRIA/CUR Manual (1991) also advocates the use of density as a quality control measure, particularly as an indicator of changes in a quarry, for example to more weathered zones.

B4.3. Water absorption

Water absorption can be measured by a number of methods. It can measured by soaking the samples in water at room temperature for a fixed period (ASTM C 97-90, BRE Report 141) or, in the case of natural slates, by placing in boiling water for a similar period (BS 680: Part 2: 1971). The water absorption can also be measured by placing the sample in 2–3 mm of water and measuring the weight change over several days. This method is usually referred to as water absorption by capillarity and details can be found in a number of standards used in European countries, for example the French standard NF B 10-502. In these countries, the test is used as an indicator of weathering resistance, either on its own or in combination with a frost test. Each country has developed a classification system that is used to assess the suitability of stones for different regions and also for different locations on a buildings. British Standard BS 812: Part 107 also gives a method of measuring water absorption of aggregates that can be used for stone. It is important to establish which method was used and whether the results are expressed as weight or volume percentages.

BS 1377: 1990: Part 2 describes the definitive method of ‘moisture content’ determination by oven drying at 105°C to 110°C. As rock fills usually have a very wide range of particle sizes, the moisture may be very non-uniformly distributed throughout the fill.

For armourstone, water absorption is often used as a simple indicator of resistance to weathering with stones usually being classed as <2% or <6%.

B4.4. Petrographic description

This can range from the correct petrographic name to a full description based on macroscopic study of the stone and microscopic study of a thin section. There is no British Standard for petrographic descriptions of building or construction stone but there is one for aggregates (BS 812: Part 104) and for site investigations (BS 5930: 1981: Section 44). There is an Italian standard (UNI 9724 Part 1) and a number of geological organizations produce guidance on how and what to describe, for example the International Society for Rock Mechanics (ISRM). It is a useful test to undertake as it provides the basic information on the stone (such as its correct geological description), the origins of the stone, and an indication of any minerals present that could cause the stone to fail at a later date.

When stone is to be used for armourstone a petrographic description is considered to be a vital early stage in the evaluation of rock sources. In this case the description can include both a mineralogical description, an estimate of the degree of weathering, and a physical description (for example likely density and water absorption).

It seems that there is little guidance on the actual interpretation of the observations and that any assessment relies heavily on the experience of the petrographer.

B5. Mechanical tests

B5.1. Strength

B5.1.1. Introduction

There is a wide range of methods for determining the ‘strength’ of natural stone. The choice of method will depend on the end-use and it should be noted that the result will vary with the test, type, sample size and application.

B5.1.2. Particle strength

The uniaxial compressive strength (q_u) of cylindrical specimens of rock can be measured but considerable time and effort is required to prepare the cylindrical sample of rock for this standard test.

In the point load strength test (Broch & Franklin 1972) cylindrical specimens or irregular lumps of rock are loaded to failure between the conical platens of a portable tester. Point load strength correlates reasonably well with q_u provided diametrical loading is used for cores.

B5.1.3. Aggregate crushing test

The aggregate crushing value (ACV) is determined by crushing a sample of aggregate of specified size in an open ended 150 mm diameter steel cylinder under a gradually applied compressive load and measuring the fines which are produced. The associated ten per cent fines test, in which the load required to produce ten per cent fines (TFV) is determined, is used for softer rocks but the equipment is identical. These tests are described by Smith & Collis (1993), Chapter 7 and BS 812, Parts 110 and 111.

B5.1.4. Compressibility tests

Rockfill compressibility is most commonly measured under conditions of one dimensional compression in a large oedometer. An oedometer, 1.0 m internal diameter and 0.5 m high, is available at the Building Research Establishment. The rockfill is compacted in layers with an electric vibrating hammer to the field density. The one-dimensional compression behaviour of most rockfills on first loading is non-linear and so it is important to determine the compressibility over a range of stress that is applicable to the field situation. Poorly compacted unsaturated rock fill is likely to be susceptible to collapse compression when first inundated and the effect of inundation on an unsaturated rock fill can be examined in an oedometer test by flooding the sample at an appropriate stress level.

B5.1.5. Compressive strength

This test is the basic measure of the load that a stone can withstand without being crushed. It is also referred to as uniaxial compressive strength as the load is applied on a single axis. The most common test method is ASTM C 170-90 which is carried out on cubes, square prisms or cylinders. It is sometimes stated that measurement should not be undertaken on cubes as they cannot be subjected to a true uniaxial load. Many European countries have standards for this test, for example DIN 52.105 in Germany or NF B 10-509 in France. British Standard BS 5628: Parts 1 and 2 refers to the testing of masonry 'units' which when combined with the mortar mix proportions can be used to derive the tabulated design strengths of masonry, i.e. the measuring the strength of a wall. The approach in Eurocode EC6 and in the drafts of CEN/TC 125 (Masonry) involves 'wall panels' constructed of the proposed masonry units (e.g. bricks, blocks or cut stone) and mortar which are tested as units. It is likely that this approach will increase in importance with the advent of European Standards.

Testing can be carried out with the samples wet or dry and with the load applied perpendicular or parallel to the bedding or other anisotropic feature (that is having different physical properties when measurement is made in different directions). These variations allow the conditions of use to be more accurately reproduced. In general, the results of the compressive strength tests can be compared directly to the structural requirement of the application; for example the load to be supported plus an acceptable safety margin.

B5.1.6. Shear strength testing

Shear strength testing of rock fills is usually carried out under axisymmetric conditions in triaxial testing equipment. Drained compression tests are often simplest to perform and most closely resemble field conditions, but in some situations undrained testing may be required. The axial compressive strain rate should not greatly affect the measured strength. End restraint can increase the apparent strength of cohesionless samples, but the effect decreases with increasing height to diameter ratio and is of little significance with the usual height to diameter ratio of 2:1. The largest triaxial testing equipment in the world can only accommodate samples of up to about 1 m in diameter and is thus only suitable for testing rockfill with a maximum particle size of 150–200 mm. Even this size of equipment is not widely available and a single test at this scale is extremely expensive.

The direct shear test is carried out in a shear box and is appropriate for testing free draining granular soils. However the failure plane is very closely defined in the test and an unrepresentatively high value of shear strength may be measured for a rockfill due to the failure plane being constrained to pass through an artificially large number of rock particles.

As the shear strength of rockfill is a function of both density and stress level, it is essential that test samples are compacted to an appropriate density and sheared under an appropriate confining pressure if strength parameters measured in the laboratory are to be applicable to the field situation. When triaxial tests are carried out to derive shear strength parameters for a limit equilibrium slope stability analysis, values of cell pressure should be used such that the stresses in the triaxial test correspond to the range of stress which will be encountered on potential critical failure surfaces in the embankment slopes.

Effective stress triaxial tests are specified in BS 1377: 1990: Part 8.

B5.1.7. Flexural strength

This test is often referred to as the bending test and can be measured using one or two loading points. It is a measure of the strength of a thin narrow rectangular sample, supported at its ends and loaded at right-angles to its plane. Loading at two points applies an equal building moment to all places between the two loading points; loading at a single point applies a greater load at the point of loading and can over estimate the strength if failure occurs away from the loading point. A method for carrying out a four-point bending test (that is two loading points) is described in ASTM C 880-89.

A similar test that is frequently specified is the modulus of rupture. This is carried out in a similar manner to a bend test with a single loading point but on samples whose thickness is sufficient to make the sample fail without significant deflection. The most common method is that described in ASTM C 99-87.

As with the compressive strength test, all of these flexural strength tests can be carried out with the samples wet or dry and with loading perpendicular or parallel to the bedding or aniostropy. In general the results of flexural strength tests can be expressed as an ultimate bending stress that can be compared with the bending stress induced by the lateral loads on the proposed element, e.g. a cladding panel plus an acceptable safety margin.

ASTM specifies a separate method for testing slates (ASTM C 120-90). It is very similar to the flexural strength test but the sample size is, of course, different.

B5.1.8. Strength around fixings

This type of test is often referred to as a 'dowel push off test' and is usually undertaken by pushing or pulling a dowel (to represent a restraint type fixing) perpendicularly until failure occurs (see Fig. 9.34). A number of standards contain this test, for example the French Standard NF B 10-514.

The area around the fixings on cladding panels can also be subject to microfracturing. On polished surfaces the presence of fractures can be determined using a UV fluorescence dye test.

B5.1.9. Modulus of elasticity

The modulus of elasticity is usually quoted as Young's Modulus (E) and is based on the relationship between stress and strain. The E-value is the linear stress–strain relationship expressed as the ratio of the stress to the strain. The limit of elastic deformation is the strength in a brittle material. In general, coarse-grained rocks are less elastic than finer grained ones (Winkler 1973). Test methods for determining Young's Modulus are given in ASTM D 3148-86 and for slates in ASTM C 120-90. It is also possible to determine elasticity non-destructively using the natural resonance of a stone core or prism.

B5.2. Durability

The term durability covers a very wide range of properties and they are probably the most difficult to relate to behaviour in the environment. Durable is defined in the Oxford English Dictionary as

> *'Capable of continuing in existence' and*
> *'Able to withstand change, decay or wear'*

However, in assessing or measuring the durability of natural stone it is not realistic to state that stone must be able to withstand change and decay and continue in existence. The standard definition of durability given in ASTM C 119-90 is more helpful:

> *'the measure of the ability of dimension stone to endure and to maintain its essential and distinctive characteristics of strength, resistance to decay, and appearance. Durability is based on the time that a stone can maintain its innate characteristics in use. This time will depend on the environment and the use of the stone in question (for example, outdoor versus indoor use)'.*

In the UK, durability is usually taken to be the extent to which a stone will weather in a given period of time. It must be remembered that all stones will weather – the important question is 'Is the degree of weathering acceptable?'

The durability of slates is currently covered by BS 680: Part 2: 1971 but this is likely to be superceded in the near future by a more comprehensive set of tests related to the required performance of the slate. The current slate tests and the acid immersion test described in BRE Report 141 (BRE 1989) will allow sandstones that are likely to be susceptible to attack by erosion by acid rain to be identified.

Sandstones that are to be subject to salt attack can be tested using the sodium sulphate crystallization test described in BRE Report 141 (BRE 1989), but this test should not be used to allocate a general durability class. The saturated crystallization test in the same Report should only be used to assess performance in the severest locations when exceptionally long life is required (for example stone used for sea defence walls, quaysides, etc.). The majority of sandstones are considered to be frost resistant.

The potential durability of limestones can be assessed in number of ways. Their resistance to salt crystallization can be determined using the sodium sulphate crystallization test (BRE Report 141). The crystallization test can also be used to give an indication of the overall durability of a limestone, particularly if the stone suffers little weight loss, but a stone that gives a poor result may in reality perform better than the result would suggest. The frost resistance of limestones can be measured using the German standard DIN 52.104.

However, at present it seems difficult to measure the resistance of any porous stones to de-icing salts but this is an important property when stone is used for external paving or where it is subject to spray from roads.

Both the crystallization test and the freeze–thaw tests may require reference stones to be used because the tests are comparative rather than absolute. Research is continuing to develop a methodology to determine the tests necessary to measure the durability of the wide range of natural stones currently used in the UK. Further information on the design life of buildings and building materials can be found in BS 7543: 1992 (Guide to Durability of buildings and building elements, products and components).

B5.2.1. Slake durability test
In the slake durability test (Franklin & Chandra 1972) the resistance of a rock to wetting and drying cycles is assessed by immersing samples in water and noting the rate of disintegration. The test is useful for relatively weak rocks which are sensitive to the test and is often applied to rock to be used for fill.

B5.2.2. Abrasion resistance
The abrasion resistance test estimates how much paving or flooring will wear. It is usually undertaken as a comparative test using reference stones of known behaviour. All of the commonly used methods are based on the abrasion of the sample by a wheel or disc and an abrasive material. The three most commonly used methods are the ASTM system described in C 241-90, the German Bohme test and the French Capon test (NF B 10-508). The results can given a relative value for the rate of wear if a number of different stones are compared but it is difficult to interpret the results in absolute terms, e.g. mm per year per million people.

B5.2.3. Slip resistance
This test is carried out to assess the slipperiness of flooring or paving when in use. The usual test method is the portable skid-resistance tester (pendulum) for road surfaces and ceramic pavers; this is usually termed the Unpolished Skid Resistance Value. It is described in BS 6677: Part 1: 1986 and is being developed for inclusion in a number of European standards (see below). The test is usually only carried out on samples that have a polished or honed finish as the rougher finishes (for example riven) are considered to be safe. The results from the pendulum test are a measure of the friction between the slider on the pendulum arm and the stone surface and the greater the value the higher the co-efficient of friction. The skid-resistance value (SRV) is sometimes specified for pedestrian walkways and is measured with the pendulum on the actual surface to be used.

Two other values that can be specified are the Polished Paver Value (PPV) and the Polished Stone Value (PSV). The PPV measures the resistance of a product to polishing by vehicles and the PSV provides a control/calibration sample for the PPV using a standard material. These tests are fully described in BS 7932 : 1998.

B5.2.4. Thermal and moisture movement
Thermal and mositure movement are usually determined by measuring changes in dimensions under closely controlled conditions. The commonest method of measuring thermal changes is to use a dilatometer. Expansion is usually expressed in units equivalent to microns per linear metre per degree C (see Table 9.3), for example a 1 m long panel of sandstone is expected to expand by 0.4 mm–0.6 mm for a temperature rise of 50°C. Thermal epansion is usually reversible but there is evidence that some marbles retain a residual expansion on cooling (Widhalm *et al.* 1995).

B5.2.5. Impact resistance and surface hardness
These tests can be used to determine the resistance of cladding panels or flooring units to impact damage that may result from cleaning cradles or the dropping of heavy objects though it should be noted that many panels will failed in bending before significant impact damage occurred. The surface hardness can also be used as a measure of abrasion resistance. A typical test for impact resistance is given in BS 8200: 1985 which also gives some specification details. Surface hardness tests are common in Italy and France where they are included in their standard tests results. The methods used are found in UNI 9724: Part 6 and NF B 10-506 respectively.

References

ASTM C 88-63 Standard Test Method for Soundness of Aggregates by the use of Sodium Sulphate or Magnesium Sulphate.
ASTM C 97-90 Test Methods for Absorption and Bulk Specific Gravity of Dimension Stone.
ASTM C 99-87 Test Method for Modulus of Rupture of Dimension Stone.
ASTM C 119-90 Standard Terminology Relating to Dimension Stone.
ASTM C 120-90 Methods of Flexure Testing of Slate (Modulus of Rupture, Modulus of Elasticity).
ASTM C 127-84 Standard Test Method for Specific Gravity and Absorption of Fine Aggregates.
ASTM C 170-90 Test Method for Compressive Strength of Dimension Stone.
ASTM C 241-90 Test Method for Abrasion Resistance of Stone Subjected to Foot Traffic.
ASTM C 295-85 Standard Practice for Petrographic Examination of Aggregates for Concrete.
ASTM C 837-88 Methylene Blue Index for Clay Test.
ASTM C 880-89 Flexural Strength of Dimension Stone.
ASTM D 2938-71a Standard Method of Test for Unconfined Compressive Strength of Intact Rock Core Specimens.
ASTM D 3148-86 Test Method for Elastic Moduli of Intact Rock Core Specimens in Uniaxial Compression.

ASTM D 4644-87 Standard Test Method for Slake Durabilty of Shales and Weak Rocks.

BUILDING RESEARCH ESTABLISHMENT (BRE) (1989). Durability tests for building stone, BRE Report 141.

BS 680: Part 2: 1971 Specification for Roofing Slates Metric Units.

BS 812 Testing Aggregates; Part 104 – Method for qualitative and quantitative petrographic examination of aggregates; Part 107 – Methods for determination of density; Part 110 – Methods for determination of aggregate crushing value (ACV); Part 111 – Methods of determination of ten percent fines value (TPF).

BS 1377 Methods of test for soils for engineering purpopes; Part 2 – Classification tests; Part 4 – Compaction-related tests; Part 8 – Shear strength tests (effective stress); Part 9 – *In situ* tests.

BS 5628: Parts 1 & 2: Code of practice for use of masonry 1987.

BS 5642: Part 2: 1983 Specification for coping of precast concrete, cast stone, clayware, slate and natural stone.

BS 5930 Code of practice for site investigations.

BS 6677: Part 1:1986 Specification for pavers.

BS 7543: 1992 Guide to durability of buildings and building elements, products and components.

B 8200: 1985 Code of practice for the design of non-loadbearing external vertical enclosures of buildings.

BSDD 155: 1986 Method for determination of polished paver value for pavers.

BROCH, E. & FRANKLIN, J. A. 1972. The point-load strength test. *International Journal of Rock Mechanics and Mining Science*, **9**(6), 669.

BROWN, E. T. 1981. *Rock characterisation, testing and monitoring*, ISRM suggested methods, Pergamon, Oxford.

CIRIA/CUR 1991. *Manual on the use of rock in coastal and shoreline engineering*. CIRIA Special Publication 83, CUR Report 154.

COX, K. G., PRICE, N. B. & HARTE, B. 1988. *The practical study of crystals, minerals and rocks*. Revised first edition, McGraw-Hill, London.

DEARMAN, W. F., TURK, N., IRFAN, Y. & ROWSHANEI, H. 1987. Detection of Material Variation by Sonic Velocity Zoning. *Bulletin of the International Association of Engineering Geologists*, **35**, 1–8

DIN 51.105 Testing of natural stone; compression test.

DIN 52.104. 1982. Parts 1 and 2. Testing of natural stone; freeze-thaw cyclic test Methods A-Q.

EC6. 1988. Eurocode No 6 Common unified rules for masonry structures. CEC Report EUR 9888 En.

FRANKLIN, J. A. & CHANDRA, R. 1972. The slake-durability test. *International Journal of Rock Mechanics and Mining Science*, **9**, 325.

FUMAGALLI, E. 1969. Tests on cohesionless materials for rockfill dams. *ASCE Journal of Soil Mechanics and Foundations Division*, **95**, 37–55.

HILLS, J. F. & PETTIFER, G. S. 1985. The clay mineral content of various rock types compared with the methylene blue value. *J. Chem. Tech. and Biotech.*, **35A**, 4, 168–180

ISRM 1988. Commission on texting methods. Suggested method for determining the fracture toughness of rock, *International Journal of Rock Mechanics and Mining Science*, **15**(2), 71–96.

KJAERNSLI, B. & SANDE, A. 1963. Compressibility of some coarse grained materials. *Proceedings of European Conference on Soil Mechanics and Foundation Engineering*, Wiesbaden, 245–251.

LCPC 1989. (Laboratoire Central des Ponts and Chausses) Les Encochments. Rapport de la Ministere de L'equipment du Logement des Transports et de la Mer.

LEWIS, M. D. 1995. Modern Stone Cladding – Design and installation of exterior dimension *stone systems*. American Society of Testing and Materials Manual Series: MNL 21, ASTM, Philadelphia.

MARSAL, R. J. 1973. *Mechanical Properties of Rockfill*. Embankment Dam Engineering – Casgrande Volume (ed. Hirschfeld, R. C. & Poulos, S. J.), 109–200. Wiley, New York

NEN 5181 1988. Determination of particle size distribution, Dutch draft standard, March.

NF B 10-502 Quarry Products – Limestones – Measurement of Water Absorption by Capillarity.

NF B 10-506 Quarry Products – Limestones – Measurement of surface hardness.

NF B 10-508 Quarry Products – Limestones – Abrasion Test Using a Metal Disc.

NF B 10-509 Quarry Products – Limestones – Compression Test.

NF B 10-514 Quarry Products – Limestones – Strength of fixings.

PENMAN, A. D. M. & CHARLES, J. A. 1976. The quality and suitability of rockfill used in dam construction. *Transactions of 12th International Congress on Large Dams, Mexico*, **1**, 533–556.

PERRY, J. & PARSONS, A. W. 1986. Assessing the quality of rock fill: a review of current practice for highways. Department of Transport, TRL Report RR60. Transport Research Laboratory, Crowthorne.

SMITH, M. R. & COLLIS, L. 1993. *Aggregates, Sand, gravel and crushed rock aggregates for construction purposes*. 2nd Edition. The Geological Society of London.

SOWERS, G. F., WILLIAMS, R. C. & WALLACE, T. S. 1965. Compressibility of broken rock and the settlement of rockfills. *Proceedings of the 6th International Conference on Soil Mechanics and Foundation Engineering, Montreal*, **2**, 561–565.

STEWART, E. T. & MCCULLOUGH, L. M. 1985. The use of the methylene blue test to indicate the soundness of road aggregates. *J. Chem. Tech. and Biotech.*, **35A**, 4, 161–167.

UNI 9724: Part 1: Natural Stones – Petrographic Denomination of Stones.

UNI 9724: Part 6 : Determination of Knoop microhardness.

VERHOEF 1987. Sandblast testing of rock, *International Journal of Rock Mechanics and Mining Science and Geomechanics, Abstract*, **24**, 3, 185–192.

WIDHALM, C., TSCHEGG, E. K. & EPPENSTEINER, W. 1996. Anisotropic thermal expansion causes deformation of marble cladding. *Journal of Performance of Construction Facilities*, **10**(1), 5–10.

WINKLER, E. M. 1973. *Stone: Properties, Durabilty in Man's Environment*. Springer, New York.

Appendix C: Stone and rock properties

In this Appendix some information on stone and rock properties is given. Firstly, the properties of some currently produced natural building stones from the British Isles and secondly, more generalized data on the properties of some types of rock that are used as building stones. It is *strongly emphasised* that all the information given in this Appendix must be regarded as providing only a general appreciation of stone and rock properties, and should not be relied upon for specific test values for particular stones and rocks or sources of them.

C1. Properties of some British building stones

The reported properties of some 183 natural building stones from the British Isles are given in Table C1. The data for these are reproduced from the *Natural Stone Directory*, No. 9 1994–1995 (Tel: 01903 821082) by permission of the publisher. The number beneath the stone name in the first column of Table C1 is the *Natural Stone Directory* reference number of the quarry owner or quarry operator. All stones from the *Directory* having at least one result for the physical or strength tests listed below have been included in Table C1.

The stones in Table C1 have been grouped by country, in the order England, Scotland, Wales, Northern Ireland and Eire. For England, the stones are then grouped by county, arranged in alphabetical order (e.g. Avon, Cambridgeshire, Cheshire, etc). Finally, the rock types are listed alphabetically (e.g. for Cumbria: granite, limestone, sandstone, slate).

In some cases in compiling Table C1, where the geological information on a particular stone was lacking it has been made good, and occasionally where an item of data was clearly incorrect it has been omitted. Where a piece of information was not available the entry NA is given in the Table. None of the data has been confirmed independently. It should be noted that some individual quarries produce more than one variety of stone (e.g. the various Ancaster stones in Lincolnshire). Conversely, one variety of stone can be produced by several different quarries (e.g. the Purbeck stone in Dorset).

Because stone properties are liable to vary, the test results in Table C1 should not be taken as an indication of present production for particular quarries; instead prospective users should seek up-to-date information from the suppliers. In particular, the data in the Table should not be used for contractual or other such purposes. Also, it should be remembered that stone properties are likely to vary within a quarry, both laterally and with depth, and with the degree of alteration or weathering, and may show anisotropy, so that the single value given in the Table can only be a pointer to what in reality is a range of values. The following quantitative physical and strength properties are tabulated in Table C1.

Bulk density. A piece of stone consists of solids, water and air (Fig. C1). The bulk density is the total mass of the solids and water, divided by the total volume of the solids, water and air. The units are, therefore, mass per unit volume, which in the *Systeme International d'Unites* (SI) is Mg/m^3. Bulk density is simply called 'weight' in the stone industry, and is quoted for stone in its 'normal' condition as supplied to the user. For porous stones, this 'normal' condition is very variable because it depends on the amount of water in the stone. This variability must be borne in mind when consulting the values of bulk density listed in Table C1.

Relative density. (Formerly called specific gravity.) The mass of the solids, divided by the mass of an equal volume of water. Relative density is dimensionless. However, because the volume of 1 Mg of water is 1 m^3, the relative density can be thought of as having units of Mg/m^3, which is useful when comparing it with bulk density.

Porosity. The volume of pore space (Fig. C1) in the stone divided by the total volume of the solids and pores. Porosity is dimensionless and usually expressed as a percentage.

Water absorption. The mass of water required to saturate the stone divided by the mass of the solids. Water absorption is dimensionless and usually expressed as a percentage.

Compressive strength. The compressive load required to cause failure of an unconfined cylindrical or cubical specimen of the stone, divided by the cross-sectional area of the specimen perpendicular to the axis of loading (Fig. C2). The units are, therefore, force per unit area, which in the SI system is MN/m^2. Compressive strength is simply called 'strength' in the stone industry. Sometimes the compressive strength has been given for stone tested both dry and wet, and this is so indicated in Table C1. Also, for some rocks the compressive strength has been given for stone tested both perpendicular to the cleavage and parallel to the cleavage (cleavage is called 'grain' in the stone industry), and this is indicated in Table C1 by 'perp' and 'para' respectively.

Table C1. *Reported properties of some natural building stones from the British Isles*

Stone name and NSD number	*Quarry*	*Location*	*Rock description and colour*	*Geology*	*Bulk density (Mg/m^3)*	*Relative density*	*Porosity (%)*	*Water absorption (%)*	*Compressive strength (MN/m^2)*	*Flexural strength (MN/m^2)*
England										
Stoke Ground No. 1001	Stoke Hill	Limpley Stoke Avon	Oolitic limestone Light buff	Great Oolite Jurassic	2.65		19.0		21	
Cambridgeshire Clunch No. 1958	Barrington	Cambridge Cambridgeshire	Limestone White/cream	Lower Chalk Cretaceous	1.91		33.1			
Kerridge Bridge No. 1008	Bridge	Kerridge Cheshire	Sandstone Grey/brown/fawn	Lower Coal Measures Carboniferous	2.45				62	
Kerridge Marksend No. 1186	Marksend	Rainow Cheshire	Sandstone Grey/fawn	Lower Coal Measures Carboniferous	2.69				62	
Kerridge Sycamore No. 1186	Sycamore	Kerridge Cheshire	Sandstone Fawn/grey	Lower Coal Measures Carboniferous	2.69				62	
Macclesfield No. 1186	Ralph Henshall	Kerridge Cheshire	Sandstone Fawn/grey	Millstone Grit Series Carboniferous	2.45			0.9	62	
Caradon No. 1190	Caradon Hill	Liskeard Cornwall	Granite Silver grey/brown	Muscovite biotite granite Igneous	1.79				206	
De Lank No. 1218	De Lank	Bodmin Cornwall	Granite Silver grey	Muscovite biotite granite Igneous	2.64				126	
Hantergantick No. 2063	Hantergantick	Bodmin Cornwall	Granite Silver grey	Muscovite biotite granite Igneous	2.64				165	
Trenoweth No. 1195	Trenoweth	Penryn Cornwall	Granite Silver grey	Granite Igneous	2.45					
Delabole No. 1199	Delabole	Delabole Cornwall	Slate Blue/grey	Devonian Slate Metamorphic	2.80		0.3		103	
Lantoom Rustic No. 1200	Dobwalls	Liskeard Cornwall	Slate Rust/brown/grey	Devonian Slate Metamorphic	1.59					
Shap Pink No. 1218	Shap Granite	Penrith Cumbria	Granite Grey/pink/brown	Porphyritic biotite granite Igneous	2.64				206	
Orton Scar No. 1856	Orton Scar	Orton Cumbria	Limestone Light grey/fawn	Carboniferous Limestone Carboniferous	2.64				81 to 108	
Salterwath No. 1856	Crosby Ravens- worth Fell	Penrith Cumbria	Limestone Grey/brown	Carboniferous Limestone Carboniferous	2.67				70 to 135	
Ulverston Marble No. 2053	Baycliff	Ulverston Cumbria	Limestone Oatmeal/brown	Carboniferous Limestone Carboniferous	2.50					
Lamb Hill No. 1856	Lamb Hill	Whitehaven Cumbria	Sandstone Buff/grey	Hensingham Gritstone NA	2.24			4.3	34	

Plumpton Red Lazonby No. 1856	Lazonby Fell	Penrith Cumbria	Sandstone Pink/red/buff	Penrith Sandstone Permian	2.24		11.5	5.0	
Red St Bees Birkhams No. 1856	Birkhams	St Bees Cumbria	Sandstone Red	Bunter Sandstone Triassic	2.24		17.2 to 20.9	5.0	
Red St Bees Bank End No. 1511	Bank End	Near A595 Cumbria	Sandstone Red	Bunter Sandstone Triassic	2.16			5.1	34
Stoneraise Red Lazonby No. 1235	Stoneraise	Penrith Cumbria	Sandstone Pinkish red	Penrith Sandstone Permian	2.35		9.5	4.7	84
Talkin Fell No. 1511	Talkin Fell	Brampton Cumbria	Sandstone/Limestone Grey/Cream	NA NA	2.36			2.1	75
Brandy Crag No. 2011	Brandy Crag	Coniston Cumbria	Slate Silver/grey	Borrowdale Volcanic Series Metamorphic	2.86			0.3	87 para 215 perp
Broughton Moor No. 2011	Broughton Moor	Coniston Cumbria	Slate Green/olive	Borrowdale Volcanic Series Metamorphic	2.86			0.3	87 para 215 perp
Burlington Blue/Grey No. 2011	Burlington	Kirkby-in- Furness, Cumbria	Slate Blue/grey	Upper Silurian Metamorphic	2.86			0.3	87 para 215 perp
Cumbria Green/ Millom No. 1222	Ghyll Scaur	Millom Cumbria	Slate Mottled green	Borrowdale Volcanic Series Metamorphic					283
Elterwater No. 2011	Langdale Valley	Langdale Valley Cumbria	Slate Pale green	Borrowdale Volcanic Series Metamorphic	2.86			0.3	87 para 215 perp
Kirkstone No. 1225	Petts	Ambleside Cumbria	Slate Light green	Borrowdale Volcanic Series Metamorphic		2.79		0.1	161 para 151 perp
Moss Rigg No. 2011	NA	NA Cumbria	Slate NA	Borrowdale Volcanic Series Metamorphic	2.86			0.3	87 para 215 perp
Sheldon No. 1229	Once-a-Week	Sheldon Derbyshire	Limestone Blue-grey/light-grey	Carboniferous Limestone Carboniferous	2.69				82
Birchover Gritstone No. 1218	Ann Twyfords	Birchover Derbyshire	Sandstone Light pink/buff	Millstone Grit Series Carboniferous	2.37		5.2		53
Chatsworth Grit No. 1231	Hayfield	Hayfield Derbyshire	Sandstone Buff/grey/blue	Millstone Grit Series Carboniferous	2.50				
Chinley Moor No. 1232	Chinley Moor	Hayfield Derbyshire	Sandstone Fawn/heather/brown	Milstone Grit Series Carboniferous	1.46				
Delph Sandstone No. 1235	Wingerworth	Chesterfield Derbyshire	Sandstone Green/grey	Coal Measures Carboniferous	2.56				
Duke's Gritstone No. 1235	Duke's	Whatstandwell Derbyshire	Sandstone Purple/yellow/buff	Millstone Grit Series Carboniferous	2.25		13.4	4.9	38
Hall Dale No. 1243	Darley Dale	Matlock Derbyshire	Sandstone Pink/buff	Millstone Grit Series Carboniferous	2.40				70

Table C1. *(continued)*

Stone name and NSD number	*Quarry*	*Location*	*Rock description and colour*	*Geology*	*Bulk density (Mg/m^3)*	*Relative density*	*Porosity (%)*	*Water absorption (%)*	*Compressive strength (MN/m^2)*	*Flexural strength (MN/m^2)*
England *(continued)*										
Millstone Edge No. 1238	Hathersage	Hathersage Derbyshire	Sandstone Pink/lilac/mauve	Millstone Grit Series Carboniferous	2.56					
Pilough No. 1511	Dale View South	Stanton in Peak Derbyshire	Sandstone Pale buff	Millstone Grit Series Carboniferous	2.39			3.6	70	
Ridgeway No. 1239	Ridgeway	Ridgeway Derbyshire	Sandstone Pink/biege	Millstone Grit Series Carboniferous	2.11					
Stancliffe Darley Dale No. 1235	Darley Dale	Matlock Derbyshire	Sandstone Pale buff	Millstone Grit Series Carboniferous	2.31		13.2	4.4	93	
Stanton Buff Dale No. 1218	Palmers Pilough	Stanton in Peak Derbyshire	Sandstone Buff	Millstone Grit Seris Carboniferous	2.30		5.2		71	
Stanton Moor – Lees Cross No. 1218	Stanton Moor	Matlock Derbyshire	Sandstone Pink/buff	Millstone Grit Series Carboniferous	2.37		5.2		53	
Stanton Moor – Pilough No. 1235	Pilough	Stanton Moor Derbyshire	Sandstone Buff/pink/brown	Millstone Grit Series Carboniferous	2.25		16.8	4.8	60	
Stoke Hall No. 1238	Grindleford	Grindleford Derbyshire	Sandstone Fawn/buff	Millstone Grit Series Carboniferous	2.64					
Watts Cliff No. 1235	Watts Cliff	Elton Derbyshire	Sandstone Lilac/white	Millstone Grit Series Carboniferous	2.23		17.2	4.0	56	
Merrivale Devon Grey No. 1511	Merrivale	Princetown Devon	Granite Light grey	Biotite granite Igneous	2.64			0.0	187	
Beer No. 1258	Beer	Beer Devon	Chalk Cream/yellow/white	Chalk Cretaceous	2.40		17.0		17	
Marnhull No. 2034	Marnhull	Marnhull Dorset	Limestone Cream	Corallian Series Jurassic	2.30					
Portland Roach Stone No. 1257	Admiralty	Portland Dorset	Oolitic limestone Grey/creamy white	Portland Beds Jurassic	2.35		19.0		47	
Portland Basebed Stone No. 1257	Bowers	Portland Dorset	Oolitic limestone Creamy white	Portland Beds Jurassic	2.25		16.5		41	
Portland Stone Whitbed No. 1257	Bowers	Portland Dorset	Oolitic limestone Creamy white	Portland Beds Jurassic	2.19		19.4		56	
Portland Whitbed Stone No. 1257	Independant	Portland Dorset	Oolitic limestone Creamy white	Portland Beds Jurassic	2.19		19.4		56	
Portland Basebed Stone No. 1257	Independant	Portland Dorset	Oolitic limestone Creamy white	Portland Beds Jurassic	2.27		17.0		38	

Portland Roach No. 1257	Various	Portland Dorset	Oolitic limestone Grey-white/cream	Portland Beds Jurassic	2.08	16.0		37
Portland Stone No. 1258	Various	Portland Dorset	Oolitic limestone Creamy white	Portland Beds Jurassic	2.30	19.5		43
Purbeck No. 1265	Downs	Langton Matravers Dorset	Limestone Grey/white	Purbeck Beds Jurassic	2.56			
Purbeck No. 1268	Langton	Langton Matravers Dorset	Limestone Various shades	Purbeck Beds Jurassic	2.24			
Purbeck No. 1273	California	Swanage Dorset	Limestone Various shades	Purbeck Beds Jurassic	2.24	1.8 to 2.3		
Purbeck No. 1273	Swanage	Swanage Dorset	Limestone Blue-grey/cream/brown	Purbeck Beds Jurassic	2.24	1.8 to 2.3		
Purbeck No. 2030	French Grass	Worth Matravers Dorset	Limestone Brown/grey/blue	Purbeck Beds Jurassic	2.24	2.3		
Cat Castle No. 1276	Cat Castle	Barnard Castle Durham	Sandstone Cream-buff/brown-grey	Coal Measures Carboniferous	2.76	4.4		65
Dunhouse No. 1276	Winston	Darlington Durham	Sandstone Crreamy buff	Coal Measures Carboniferous	2.27			65
Stanton No. 1511	Stainton	Barnard Castle Durham	Sandstone Pale buff	Coal Measures Carboniferous	2.24		47	48
Cotswold No. 1286	Kineton Thoms	Naunton Gloucestershire	Oolitic limestone Grey/brown/yellow	NA Jurassic	1.85		3.7	138
Cotswold Hill No. 1281	Cotswold Hill	Ford Gloucestershire	Oolitic limestone Fawn/cream/yellow	Inferior Oolite Series Jurassic	1.29			
Daglingwroth No. 1288	Daglingworth	Cirencester Gloucestershire	Oolitic limestone Cream	Great Oolite Series Jurassic		5.0	0.8	135
Farmington No. 1284	Farmington	Northleach Gloucestershire	Oolitic limestone Cream/grey	Great Oolite Series Jurassic	2.10			
Cotswold Stone No. 1940	Soundborough	Soundborough Gloucestershire	Oolitic limestone Cream/grey	Great Oolite Series Jurassic	2.30			
Swell Wold No. 1281	Swell Wold	Stow-on-the-Wold Gloucestershire	Oolitic limestone Fawn/cream	NA Jurassic	1.30			
Guiting No. 1288	Coscombe	Temple Guiting Gloucestershire	Oolitic limestone Cream/buff-orange	Inferior Oolite Series Jurassic	1.97			16
Upper Bathonian No. 1941	Veizey's	Tetbury Gloucestershire	Oolite Cream/honey-gold	Upper Bathonian Jurassic		18.0		21
Forest of Dean No. 1289	Barnhill	Coleford Gloucestershire	Sandstone Grey	Coal Measures Carboniferous	2.38			45

Table C1. *(continued)*

Stone name and NSD number	*Quarry*	*Location*	*Rock description and colour*	*Geology*	*Bulk density (Mg/m^3)*	*Relative density*	*Porosity (%)*	*Water absorption (%)*	*Compressive strength (MN/m^2)*	*Flexural strength (MN/m^2)*
England *(continued)*										
Forest of Dean No. 1289	Bixhead	Coleford Gloucestershire	Sandstone Blue	Coal Measures Carboniferous	2.45				57	
Forest of Dean No. 1291	Coleford	Coleford Gloucestershire	Sandstone Grey/green	Coal Measures Carboniferous	2.38				45	
Red Wilderness No. 1292	Wilderness	Mitcheldean Gloucestershire	Micaceous sandstone Red	NA Devonian	2.61	2.67	2.3	0.9		
Dearnley Knoll Flag Rock No. 1297	Ford	Burnley Lancashire	Sandstone Grey-buff	Coal Measures Carboniferous	2.34			0.3	37	
Galgate No. 1298	Ellel	Galgate Lancashire	Sandstone Cream/fawn/brown	Millstone Grit Series Carboniferous	2.31		14.7			
Revidge Grit No. 1301	Little	Chorley Lancashire	Sandstone Brown/grey/blue	Millstone Grit Series Carboniferous		2.31				
Scout Moor No. 1529	Scout Moor	Ramsbottom Lancashire	Sandstone Blue/green	Millstone Grit Series Carboniferous	2.82		1.0		104	
Waddington Fell No. 1303	Waddington	Waddington Lancashire	Sandstone Buff/mauve/grey	Millstone Grit Series Carboniferous	2.12					
Clipsham No. 1478	Big Pits and Longdales	Clipsham Leicestershire	Oolitic limestone Buff	Inferior Oolite Series Jurassic	1.83			4.7	32	
Ancaster Freestone Ancaster Hardwhite Ancaster Weatherbed No. 1480	Wilsford Glebe	Ancaster Lincolnshire	Oolitic limestone Yelllow/white Creamy white Blue/brown	Inferior Oolite Series Jurassic					20 – 59	
Ancaster (freestone) Ancaster (hardwhite) Ancaster (weatherbed) No. 1235	Ancaster	Ancaster Lincolnshire	Oolitic limestone Biege/white Biege/blue/grey	Inferior Oolite Series Jurassic	2.11 2.34 2.41		– 15.6 8.3	5.0 4.9 3.0		
Ketton No. 1479	Ketton	Stamford Lincolnshire	Oolitic limestone Cream	Inferior Oolite Series Jurassic	2.08			9.8	34	
Stamford Freestone No. 1958	Little Casterton Road	Stamford Lincolnshire	Oolitic limestone Buff/brown	Inferior Oolite Series Jurassic					14	
Weldon No. 1488	Weldon	Weldon Northamptonshire	Oolitic limestone Cream/silver-grey	Inferior Oolite Series Jurassic	2.16					
Black Pasture No. 1564	Chollerford	Chollerford Northumberland	Sandstone Light buff	Carboniferous Limestone Carboniferous	2.33			14.0	73	

Bearl No. 1275	Bearl	Bywell Northumberland	Sandstone Grey	NA NA	2.19		6.1	50
Blaxter No. 1275	Blaxter	Elsden Northumberland	Sandstone Yellow-grey	Carboniferous Sandstone Carboniferous	2.19		12.2	57
Blaxters High Nick No. 1511	High Nick	Otterburn Northumberland	Sandstone Pale buff	Carboniferous Limestone Carboniferous	2.19		6.1	50
Darney No. 1511	Darney	West Woodburn Northumberland	Sandstone White/pale buff	Carboniferous Limestone Carboniferous	2.19		5.9	57
Doddington No. 1511	Doddington	Wooler Northumberland	Sandstone Pink	Carboniferous Limestone Carboniferous	2.20		5.2	28
Ladycross No. 1493	Slaley	Hexham Northumberland	Sandstone Brown/grey	Coal Measures Carboniferous		11.7		81
Copley Lane No. 1514	Copley Lane	Sherburn-in-Elmet North Yorkshire	Limestone Cream/buff	Magnesian Limestone Permian		9.0		50
Hovingham No. 1218	Hovingham	Hovingham North Yorkshire	Oolitic limestone White/blue	Corallian Series Jurassic	2.29	5.5		25
Swale Dale Fossil No. 1218	Barton	Barton North Yorkshire	Limestone Light fawn/honey	NA Carboniferous	2.67	2.7		94
Tadcaster No. 1518	Highmoor	Tadcaster North Yorkshire	Dolomitic limestone Light cream/yellow	Magnesian Limestone Permian	2.40			61 to 77
Wath No. 1518	Wath	Hovingham North Yorkshire	Oolitic limestone Whitish	Corallian Series Jurassic	1.55			
Linby No. 1859	Abbey	Linby Nottinghamshire	Dolomitic limestone NA	Magnesian Limestone Permian	2.22	4.7		42
White Mansfield No. 1480	Nottingham Road	Mansfield Nottinghamshire	Dolomitic sandstone White	NA Permian	2.22		1.1	64
Hornton No. 1495	Edgehill	Banbury Oxfordshire	Ferruginous limestone Blue/grey/brown	Lias Jurassic	2.16	20.0		69
Wroxton No. 1496	Hornton Grounds	Wroxton Heath Oxfordshire	Ferruginous limestone Brown/blue	Lias Jurassic				37 blue 28 brown
Grinshill No. 1497	Grinshill Stone	Clive Shropshire	Sandstone Cream/yellow/white	Keuper Sandstone Triassic	1.93	18.5		26
Myddle No. 1497	Webscott	Myddle Shropshire	Sandstone Dark red	Bunter Sandstone Triassic	1.93	18.5		24
Blue Lias Marble No. 1498	Tout	Charlton Adam Somerset	Limestone Grey/blue	Lower Lias Jurassic	2.59	1.0		93 to 101
Doulting No. 1258	Doulting	Shepton Mallet Somerset	Detrital limestone Creamy brown	Inferior Oolite Series Jurassic	2.40	13.0		21

Table C1. (*continued*)

Stone name and NSD number	*Quarry*	*Location*	*Rock description and colour*	*Geology*	*Bulk density (Mg/m^3)*	*Relative density*	*Porosity (%)*	*Water absorption (%)*	*Compressive strength (MN/m^2)*	*Flexural strength (MN/m^2)*
England (*continued*)										
Ham Hill No. 1501	Ham Hill	Stoke-sub-Hamdon Somerset	Shelly limestone Honey brown/grey	Lias Jurassic			16.0		188	
Ham Hill No. 1502	Norton	Stoke-sub-Hamdon Somerset	Shelly limestone Honey brown	Upper Lias Jurassic		2.09				
Nightingale Farm No. 2029	Nightingale Farm	Higher Halstock Leigh Somerset	Shelley limestone Blue/grey	Forest Marble Jurassic	2.68		0.8		75	
Somerset Marble No. 1499	Gurney Slade	Gurney slade Somerset	Limestone Pink/fawn	NA Carboniferous	2.65		1.0		100	
Cadeby No. 1516	Cadeby	Doncaster South Yorkshire	Dolomitic limestone White/cream	Magnesian Limestone Permian	2.56					
Permian Magnesian No. 2069	Dolomite	Warmsworth South Yorkshire	Dolomitic limestone Pale cream/buff	Magnesian Limestone Permian	2.50					
Hollington No. 1504	Red Hole	Hollington Staffordshire	Sandstone Dull red/mottled	Keuper Sandstone Triassic					31	
Hollington No. 1713	Tearne and Great Gate	Hollington Staffordshire	Sandstone Red/mottled	Keuper Sandstone Triassic			9.0		41	
Hurtwood No. 1507	Pitch Hill	Ewhurst Surrey	Glauconitic sandstone Honey/buff	Lower Greensand Cretaceous	1.79					
Springwell No. 1511	Springwell	Gateshead Tyne and Wear	Sandstone Buff	Coal Measures Carboniferous	2.17			4.9	58	
Sussex Sandstone No. 1509	Bognor Common	Little Bognor West Sussex	Sandstone Dark green/brown	Lower Greensand Cretaceous	1.20					
Wealden No. 1510	Philpots	West Hoathley West Sussex	Sandstone Honey	Wealden Series Cretaceous					31 to 52 dry 13 to 51 wet	
Bolton Woods No. 2024	Bolton Woods	Bradford West Yorkshire	Sandstone Light brown	Coal Measures Carboniferous	2.80				67	
Bolton Woods No. 1543	Bolton Woods	Bradford West Yorkshire	Sandstone Grey to buff	Coal Measures Carboniferous	2.75		3.9		72	
Brackenhill No. 1544	Brackenhill	Ackworth West Yorkshire	Sandstone Light brown	Coal Measures Carboniferous	2.30					
Bramley Fall No. 1528	Blackhill	Bramhope West Yorkshire	Sandstone Golden brown/fawn	Millstone Grit Series Carboniferous	2.22		16.4		43	
Buck Park Grippon No. 1532	Buck Park	Cullingworth West Yorkshire	Sandstone Blue/grey	Millstone Grit Series Carboniferous	2.40			2.6	117	

Chellow Grange Noi 1545	Haworth Road	Bradford West Yorkshire	Sandstone Light brown	Coal Measures Carboniferous	2.75			
Clock Face No. 1529	Clock Face	Scammonden West Yorkshire	Sandstone Buff/grey	Millstone Grit Series Carboniferous	2.57	2.4		76
Cromwell No. 1529	Cromwell	Southowram West Yorkshire	Sandstone Buff/cream/grey	Coal Measures Carboniferous	2.99	2.1		90
Crosland Hill No. 1530	Wellfield and others	Huddersfield West Yorkshire	Sandstone Light brown	Millstone Grit Series Carboniferous	2.56		2.6	124 dry 76 wet
Elland Edge Rock Yorkshire Delph No. 1559	Deep Lane	Bradford West Yorkshire	Sandstone Mixed/brown	Coal Measures Carboniferous	3.25		0.3	69
Fagley No. 1548	Fagley	Bradford West Yorkshire	Sandstone Buff/blue-grey	Coal Measures Carboniferous	3.25		0.2	69
Greenmoor Blue No. 1549	Sovereign	Shepley West Yorkshire	Sandstone Blue/brown	Coal Measures Carboniferous	2.99			
Greenmoor Rock No. 1529	Appleton	Shepley West Yorkshire	Sandstone Blue/brown	Coal Measures Carboniferous	2.75		2.4	72
Genoside No. 1529	Appleton	Shepley West Yorkshire	Sandstone Dark brown	Coal Measures Carboniferous				69
Hillhouse Edge No. 1535	Holmfirth	Holmfirth West Yorkshire	Sandstone Buff/brown	NA Carboniferous	2.40	2.5		63
Honley Wood No. 1530	Honley Wood	Honley West Yorkshire	Sandstone Light brown	Millstone Grit Series Carboniferous	2.56		2.6	124 dry 76 wet
Moor Top No. 1541	Moor Top	Guiseley West Yorkshire	Sandstone Light buff	NA NA	2.34	10.0		50
Mount Tabor No. 1538	Mount Tabor	Halifax West Yorkshire	Sandstone Fawn/brown/grey/blue	Millstone Grit Series Carboniferous	3.20	0.3		72
Northowram Hills No. 1552	Northowram Hills	Northowram West Yorkshire	Sandstone Light brown/fawn/grey	Coal Measures Carboniferous	2.40	2.5		76
Rawdon No. 1553	Rawdon	Rawdon West Yorkshire	Sandstone Light brown	Millstone Grit Series Carboniferous	2.75			
Ringby No. 1553	Swales Moor	Halifax West Yorkshire	Sandstone Light brown	Coal Measures Carboniferous	2.79		1.5	
Rockingstone No. 1530	Rockingstone	Huddersfield West Yorkshire	Sandstone Buff/red/brown	Millstone Grit Series Carboniferous	2.49		2.9	114 dry 73 wet
Thornhill Rock No. 1529	Howley Park	Leeds West Yorkshire	Sandstone Blue/brown	Coal Measures Carboniferous	2.37	4.7		58
Woodkirk Brown No. 1558	Britannia	Leeds West Yorkshire	Sandstone Fawn/brown	Coal Measures Carboniferous	2.40	4.4		60

Table C1. *(continued)*

Stone name and NSD number	*Quarry*	*Location*	*Rock description and colour*	*Geology*	*Bulk density (Mg/m^3)*	*Relative density*	*Porosity (%)*	*Water absorption (%)*	*Compressive strength (MN/m^2)*	*Flexural strength (MN/m^2)*
England (*continued*)										
Chilmark No. 1513	Chicksgrove	Tisbury Wiltshire	Glauconitic limestone Honey cream	Portland Beds Jurassic	2.40				48	
Chilmark No. 1512	Teffont	Chilmark Wiltshire	Glauconitic limestone Cream	Portland Beds Jurassic	2.20		19.0		28	
Monks Park No. 1258	Corsham	Corsham Wiltshire	Oolitic limestone Light cream	Great Oolite Series Jurassic	2.25		22.5		24	
Westwood Ground No. 1258	Westwood	Bradford-on-Avon Wiltshire	Oolitic limestone Pale cream	Great Oolite Series Jurassic	2.41		19.5		22	
Green Sandstone No. 1512	Old Hurdcott	Barford St Martin Wiltshire	Sandstone Green	Upper Greensand Cretaceous	1.94		10.7		20	
Broadway No. 1285	Fish Hill	Broadway Worcestershire	Oolitic limestone Light/dark cream	Great Oolite Series Jurassic	2.16		19.0			
Scotland										
Correnni Pink No. 1568	Tillyfourie	Alford Grampian	Biotite granite deep pink	Granite Igneous		2.61		0.2	224	12
Cresta Red Fife Redstone No. 1570	Lucklawhill	Balmullo Fife	Felsite Pink/light brick-red	Felsite Igneous				1.9		
Hillend Black No. 1218	Hillend	Caldercruix Strathclyde	Quartz dolerite Black/dark grey	Quartz dolerite Igneous	2.90				314	
Kemnay No. 1568	Kemnay	Kemnay Grampian	Granite Light silver grey	Biotite muscovite granite Igneous		2.62		24.0	160	2
Ross of Mull No. 1564	Isle of Mull	Isle of Mull Strathclyde	Granite Warm pink/red	Muscovite biotite granite Igneous	2.82				200	
Ledmore No. 2084	Ledmore	Ledmore Highland	Serpentine marble Red/brown	Serpentine marble NA	2.74		0.4			
Caithness Flagstone No. 1560	Spittal	Watten Caithness	Sandstone Blue/black	Old Red Sandstone Devonian	2.71		1.0		35	
Clashach No. 1561	Hopeman	Hopeman Grampian	Sandstone Golden/pale brown	NA Permo-Triassic	2.08		13.8		50	
Copp Crag No. 1492	Copp Crag	Byness Lothian	Sandstone Buff/light brown	Carboniferous Limestone Carboniferous	2.19		18.8		50	
Corncockle No. 1276	Corncockle	Lockerbie Dumfries	Sandstone Red	NA Permian					41	

Corsehill No. 1276	Eaglesfield Road	Annan Dumfries	Sandstone Red	NA Triassic	2.28	6.3		68	
Dunmore No. 1564	Shotts	Cowie Central	Sandstone Grey/creamy brown	Old Red Sandstone Devonian	2.17			71	
Gatelawbridge No. 1564	Thornhill	Thornhill Dumfries	Sandstone Warm red	New Red Sandstone Permian	2.22			45	
Locharbriggs No. 1565	Locharbriggs	Locharbriggs Dumfries	Sandstone Red/pink	NA Permian	2.47			43	
Newbigging No. 1564	Burntisland	Burntisland Fife	Sandstone White/cream/buff	Calciferous Sandstone Series Carboniferous	2.65			33	
Caithness Stone No. 1953	Spittal Mains	Wick Caithness	Slate Blue-grey	NA NA					93 tran
Wales									
Nanhoron No. 1590	Nanhoron Granite	Nanhoron Gwynedd	Granite Grey/brown	Microgranite Igneous	2.60			138	
Halkyn No. 1218	Halkyn	Pentre Halkyn Clywd	Limestone Light grey	NA Carboniferous	2.70				180 tran
Moelfre No. 1572	Anglesey	Moelfre Gwynedd	Limestone Light grey	Carboniferous Limestone Carboniferous	2.66				
Blue Pennant No. 1577	Gelligaer Common	Treharris Mid Glamorgan	Sandstone Blue-grey/brown	Coal Measure Carboniferous	2.85			161	
Aberllefenni No. 1578	Aberllefenni	Machynlleth Powys	Slate Blue	Ordovician Metamorphic			0.3	146	64 tran
Penrhyn No. 1221	Penrhyn	Bangor Gwynedd	Slate Blue/heather	Cambrian Slate Metamorphic	2.77			216	
Northern Ireland									
Mourne Glen Pink No. 1618	Newcastle	Newcastle Co. Down	Granite Pink	Granite Igneous	2.69			118	
Eire									
Ballyedmonduff No. 1611	Ballyedmonduff	Sandyford Co. Dublin	Granite Grey	Coarse-grain biotite granite Igneous	2.35				
Ballyknockan No. 1613	Ballyknockan	Blessington Co. Wicklow	Granite Glue-grey/brown	Coarse-grain biotite granite Igneous	2.88				
Ballyknockan No. 1763	Ballyknockan	Blessington Co. Wicklow	Granite Grey/white/pink	Biotite granite Igneous			0.2	93	
Wicklow White No. 1619	Badgers Rock	Granabeg Co. Wicklow	Granite White	Medium-grain biotite granite Igneous	2.61	0.2		93	

Table C1. *(continued)*

Stone name and NSD number	*Quarry*	*Location*	*Rock description and colour*	*Geology*	*Bulk density (Mg/m^3)*	*Relative density*	*Porosity (%)*	*Water absorption (%)*	*Compressive strength (MN/m^2)*	*Flexural strength (MN/m^2)*
Eire *(continued)*										
Ballinasloe No. 1763	Top	Ballinasloe Co. Galway	Limestone Dark grey/black	Carboniferous Limestone Carboniferous	2.67			0.9	82	
Carlow No. 1763	James Walsh & Sons	Bannagagole Co. Carlow	Limestone Dark grey/blue/black	Carboniferous Limestone Carboniferous	2.87		0.9			
Holdensrath No. 1592	Holdensrath	Kilkenny Co. Kilkenny	Limestone Blue/grey/black	Carboniferous Limestone Carboniferous	2.90		0.1			
Kilkenny Black Fossil Kilkenny Blue Grey No. 1594	Threecastles & Ballyfoyle	Threecastles Ballyfoyle Co. Laois	Limestone Blue/grey/black	Carboniferous Limestone Carboniferous	2.69			0.1	102	
Kilkenny No. 2068	Kellymount	Paulstown Co. Kilkenny	Limestone Blue/grey/black	Carboniferous Limestone Carboniferous	2.96					
Lecarrow No. 1614	Lecarrow	Lecarrow Co. Roscommon	Limestone Grey	NA NA	3.25					
Clonaslee No. 1598	Clonaslee	Clonaslee Co. Loais	Sandstone Brown/white	NA NA	2.80					
Liscannor No. 1599	Doolin etc	Doolin Co. Clare	Sandstone Blue/grey/buff	Millstone Grit Series Carboniferous	2.61			2.1	196	

N.B. The data in this table should not be used for contractual or other such purposes.

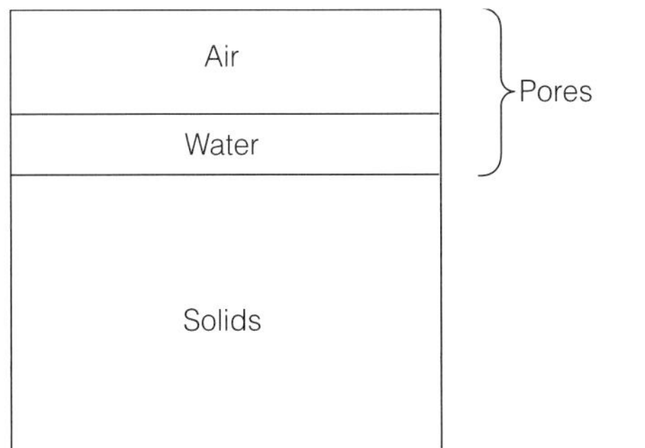

Fig. C1. Constituents of stone.

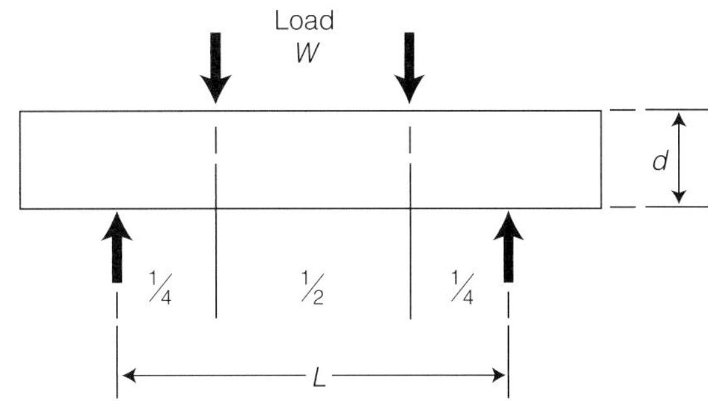

Fig. C3. Measurement of flexural strength.

Flexural strength. The load required to cause failure in a beam-shaped specimen of stone using quarter-point loading (Fig. C3). The test is usually done with the load applied perpendicular to the bedding where this is applicable. The flexural strength is given by:

$$\frac{3WL}{4bd^2}$$

where W is the maximum load, L is the span, b is the breadth, and d is the depth of the specimen; b is made $1.5d$ and L is made $10d$. The units are, therefore, force per unit area, which, in the SI system, is MN/m^2. An earlier version of the test using half-point loading (Fig. C4) is called *transverse strength* and is given by:

$$\frac{3WL}{2bd^2}$$

and these results are indicated in Table C1 by 'tran'. If the specimen in the transverse strength test fails at its centre, the transverse strength is equal to the flexural strength. Sometimes the transverse strength is referred to as the 'modulus of rupture'.

Details of how to carry out these tests are given at the appropriate places in the main chapters of the book, particularly Chapter 9 or in Appendix B.

Discussion. It will be noticed in Table C1 that for some stone types the same test results are quoted for a number of different quarries (e.g. the slates from Cumbria). It is extremely unlikely that these are independent determinations. What seems to be more likely is that a single set of test results has been quoted by several quarries. The reader should be aware of this possibility when using Table C1.

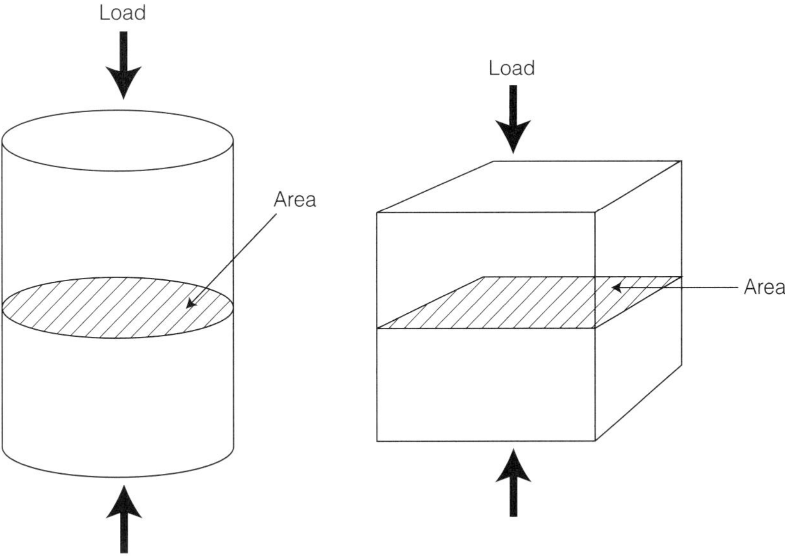

Fig. C2. Measurement of compressive strength.

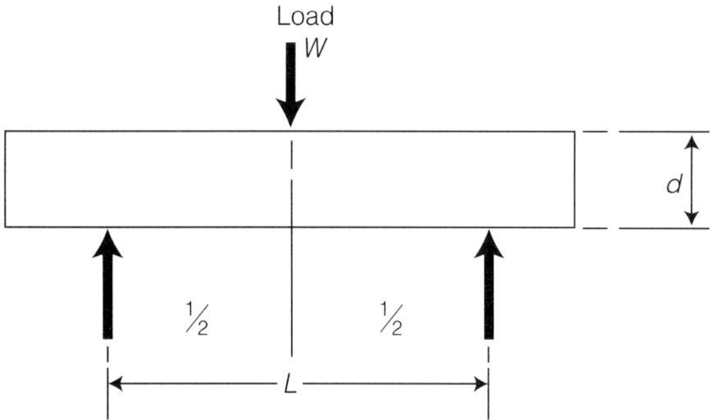

Fig. C4. Measurement of transverse strength.

The most commonly reported property of building stones in Table C1 is the bulk density. The reason for this is not technical but commercial. Stone is sold by the tonne (1 Mg = 1 tonne); each lorry laden with stone is weighed on a weighbridge as it leaves the quarry and the mass of stone is determined by subtracting the mass of the unladen lorry from the gross mass. However, the customer is usually not interested in the mass but needs to know the volume of stone that is being supplied. This can be simply obtained by dividing the mass of the stone by the bulk density.

In the aggregates industry, quantitative physical and strength properties are of paramount importance. Without them there would be difficulty in marketing an aggregate because of the necessity of demonstrating that the aggregate complied with national and local specifications (Smith & Collis 1993). By contrast, in the stone industry, quantitative physical and strength properties are much less importance. Indeed, many of the quarries listed in the *Natural Stone Directory* do not give quantitative data for their stones. Table C1 shows that, with the exception of bulk density, physical and strength properties of building stones are sparsely reported.

After, bulk density, the property most commonly listed is compressive strength, probably because it is seen

Fig. C5. Use of stone requiring compressive strength. Ta'Pinu Basilica, Gozo, Malta GC.

Fig. C6. Use of stone requiring flexural strength. Ta'Pinu Basilica, Gozo, Malta GC.

to be of direct relevance to the load-bearing use of stone in masonry construction (see example, Fig. C5). For the porous stones for which compressive strengths are given both wet and dry, it will be seen that the dry strength is greater than the wet strength. One reason for this is that when a porous stone is dried there is a contribution to the strength from suction, over and above the intrinsic mineral strength of the rock (West 1994). As might be expected, flexural or transverse strength is listed only for those stones for which this property is relevant to their use, such as cladding and paving, and cantilever stairs (see example, Fig. C6).

The range of compressive strength of the building stones listed in Table C1 is from 14 MN/m^2 for the Stamford Freestone, an oolitic limestone, to 314 MN/m^2 for the Hillend Black, a quartz dolerite; a factor of over 20.

The compressive strength of a building stone can be of crucial importance in the selection of a stone for structural purposes in a large, complex building. For example, Fig. C7 shows the front elevation of a masonry building, the front of which, at ground level, is supported on widely spaced free-standing pillars so as to provide a walkway behind, giving access to set-back shop fronts. The pillars not only have to support their own weight, but have to support the weight of all the masonry above, together with some of the floor loading. Therefore, the compressive strength of the stone selected for the pillars must be greater than the total compressive stress induced in them by their own weight plus the much greater weight of the superincumbent load. Further discussion of the importance of compressive strength is given in Chapter 9.

By contrast, for small, simple buildings, the compressive strength of even the weakest building stones can be more than adequate for masonry construction purposes, as the following example shows. The strength of the Beer stone, a chalk, is 17 MN/m^2 and its bulk density is 2.4 Mg/m^3. A one-metre cubical block of this stone exerts a pressure on the base of 0.0235 MN/m^2. Theoretically, therefore, it would be possible to build an unmortared, monolithic structure from such blocks up to 723 m high before the compressive stress in the base course exceeded the compressive strength of the stone.

Table C1 also shows that natural building stones in the British Isles are derived from formations of a wide range of geological age, ranging from Cambrian slate to Cretaceous chalk (see geological column, Chapter 2). However, certain geological systems are more important sources of building stone than others; particularly noteworthy are the Carboniferous for its sandstones and limestones, and the Jurassic for its oolitic limestones.

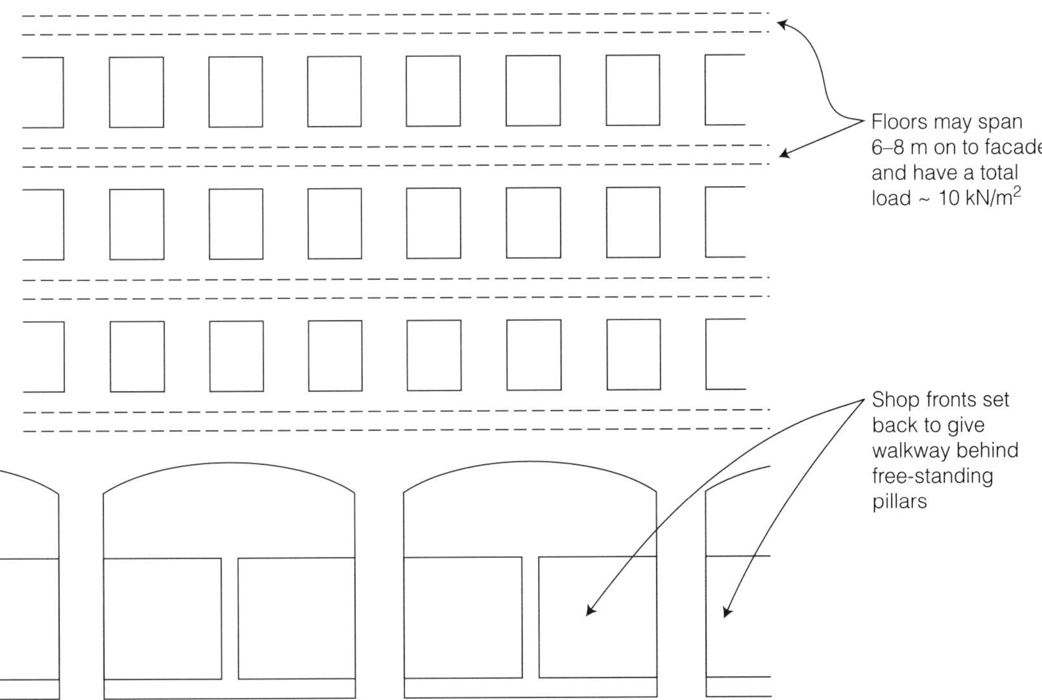

Fig. C7. Front elevation of masonry building with front supported on pillars.

Table C2. *Generalized properties of rocks used as building stones*

Rock type	*Bulk density (Mg/m^3)*	*Apparent relative density*	*Porosity (%)*	*Compressive strength (MN/m^2)*	*Flexural strength (MN/m^2)*	*Transverse strength (MN/m^2)*	*Coefficient of thermal expansion (10^{-6}/°Ψ⊃*	*Modulus of elasticity (GN/m^2)*	*Tensile strength (MN/m^2)*
Igneous									
Granites	2.60–2.80	2.54–2.66	0.4–2.4	96–310		9–38	3.7–6.0	20–60	7–25
Syenites		2.72–2.97	0.9–1.9	186–434	10–20	16–22	3.7	60–80	
Gabbros		2.81–3.03	0.3–2.7	124–303	10–20	14–55	2.0–3.0	70–110	15–30
Diorites	2.70–3.00							70–100	15–30
Dolerites	2.75–2.95	2.87–2.97	1.0–2.0	151–185	8–14			53–77	15–35
Basalts	2.85–3.05			110–338		14–55	2.2–3.5	60–100	10–30
Porphyries	2.50–2.80				10–20				
Sedimentary									
Limestones	2.65–2.85	1.79–2.92	0.3–3.6	14–255		3–36	1.7–6.8	10–80	5–25
Sandstones				34–248		5–16	3.7–6.3	3–80	4–25
Greywackes	2.60–2.75				4–15				
Metamorphic									
Gneisses	2.65–3.10	2.64–3.36	0.5–0.8	152–248	10–20	8–21	1.3–4.4		5–20
Quartzites		2.75	0.3	207–627		8–31	6.0		10–30
Marbles		2.37–3.20	0.6–2.3	69–241		4–27	2.7–5.1		7–20
Slates		2.71–2.90	0.1–4.3	138–206		34–110	4.5–4.9		7–20

C2. Generalized properties of building stones

The generalized properties of different rock types used as building stones are given in Table C2. This has been compiled from ranges of values given by Winkler (1973), supplemented by some data from other sources. Again, the information given is for a general appreciation only and should not be used for contractual or other such purposes. The headings in Table C2 are the same as those in Table C1, except for the following additions.

Coefficient of thermal expansion. The increase in length per unit length per degree Celsius rise in temperature.

Modulus of elasticity. For rocks that behave elastically, the modulus of elasticity is the stress divided by the strain, usually measured axially during unconfined compression (see above). Because strain is dimensionless, the modulus of elasticity has the same dimensions as stress which in the SI system is GN/m^2. The modulus of elasticity is sometimes referred to as 'Young's modulus'.

Tensile strength. The tensile load required to cause failure of an unconfined cylindrical specimen of the stone, divided by the cross-sectional area of the specimen perpendicular to the axis of loading (Fig. C8). The units are, therefore, force per unit area, which in the SI system is MN/m^2. Sometimes called the direct tensile strength to distinguish it from the indirect tensile strength (see below). The tensile load is applied by means of metal caps that are cemented to the ends of the specimen using a cement which is stronger than the tensile strength of the stone. Because of difficulties with the direct tensile test, the indirect tensile strength test is often carried out instead. The values for the range of tensile strength for various rock types given in Table C2 are from Farmer (1968).

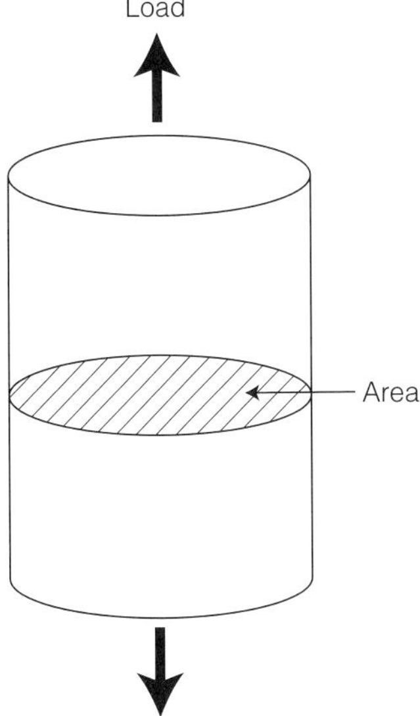

Fig. C8. Measurement of direct tensile strength.

Indirect tensile strength. A disc-shaped specimen of stone is compressively loaded at diametrically opposed surfaces over a small arc of contact (Fig. C9a). Although the loading is compressive, the specimen fails in tension (Fig. C9b) because it has been found that most rocks in biaxial stress fields fail in tension at their uniaxial tensile strength when one principal stress field is tensile and the other compressive. This test is also called the Brazil test. The tensile strength is given by:

$$0.636P/Dt \ (MN/m^2)$$

where P is the compressive load at failure (N), D is the diameter of the test specimen (mm), and t is the thickness of the test specimen (mm) (Brown 1981). Direct and indirect tensile tests on the same rock give closely similar results.

The tensile strength of stone may also be determined by carrying out the *point load strength* test (International Society for Rock Mechanics 1985), which is an index test, and then empirically correlating the point load strength index obtained with the tensile strength. An advantage of the point load strength test is that it can be carried out on pieces of core or irregular lumps of rock rather than on prepared specimens.

Discussion. The coefficient of thermal expansion and the modulus of elasticity of building stone can be important in the following circumstances. Ideally, if two or more types of stone are to be used in juxtaposition in the same large structure (see example, Fig. C10), then to prevent differences in displacement occurring due to temperature change and due to loading, the coefficients of thermal expansion and the moduli of elasticity of the different stones should be chosen to be of similar magnitude. Where this is not possible, the consequences of the differences must be allowed for in the design of the structure. These considerations also apply to the use of stone and concrete together, and to the use of stone cladding on a different substrate. These matters are dealt with further in Chapter 9. Flexural strength of stone is clearly of importance in assessing the suitability of a particular stone for cladding and in deciding on panel thickness. Use of the indirect tensile strength test in testing the condition of masonry construction has been described by Beckmann (1994).

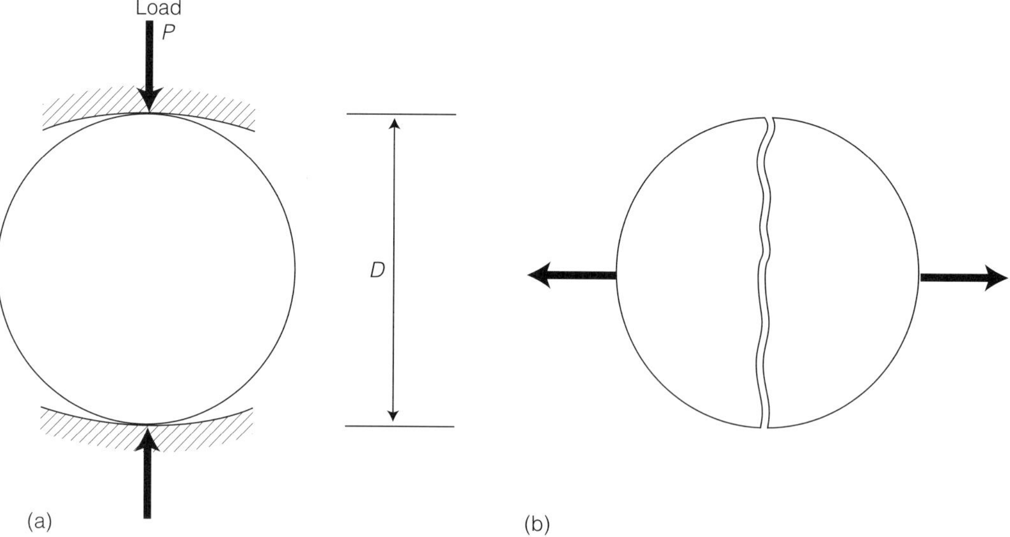

Fig. C9. Measurement of indirect tensile strength.

Table C2 shows that the compressive strength of rocks is about ten times the tensile strength. This difference provides an explanation of the traditional practice of using stone in masonry construction so that it carries compressive rather than tensile loads. This is discussed further in Chapter 9.

The tallest self-supporting, masonry structure in the world is the Washington Monument (Figs C11 & C12),

Fig. C10. Use of two different stones together. Douai Abbey, Woolhampton, Berkshire, UK. (The individual blocks shown are 230 mm square.)

Table C3. *Effect of weathering on some physical properties of granite*

Description	*Rock mass weathering grade*	*Sample*	*Compressive strength (MN/m^2)*	*Saturated bulk density (Mg/m^3)*	*Water absorption (%)*
Fresh granite	I	Fresh	262	2.61	0.11
Partially stained granite	II	Stained rim of block	232	2.62	0.35
Partially stained granite	II	Whole sample II 90% stained	163	2.58	1.09
Completely stained granite	II	Completely stained II block	105	2.56	1.52
Weakened granite	III–IV	Rock core of III block	46	2.55	1.97
Weakened granite	III–IV	Rock core of IV block	26	2.44	4.13

built by Robert Mills in 1885, in Washington DC, USA; it is 169 m high and has the form of a obelisk. It has been estimated that the stone at the base of the monument sustains a maximum vertical compressive stress of 2.17 MN/m^2 (Allen Howe 1910). Even assuming a factor of safety of 20, it can be seen from the ranges of compressive strength listed in Table C2 that all the rock types for which there are data could provide

Fig. C11. The Washington Monument, 169 m high, is the tallest self-supporting masonry structure in the world (see text). It was designed by the architect Robert Mills and largely constructed by the US Army Engineers. Construction commenced in 1848 and was completed in 1885, but there was a hiatus in construction from 1854 to 1879. (*Photo: D. Newill.*)

Fig. C12. Close-up view of the Monument. The exterior is of white marble from Maryland and Massachusetts with an interior of granite. Within the obelisk there is a shaft containing eight wrought-iron columns supporting a stairway and elevator. The slight change in colour of the marble about a quarter of the way up marks the level where construction was interrupted. (*Photo: D. Newill.*)

Table C4. *Descriptive terms for rock strength*

Descriptive term	*Unconfined compressive strength (MN/m^2)*
Extremely strong rock	>200
Very strong rock	100–200
Strong rock	50–100
Moderately strong rock	12.5–50
Moderately weak rock	5.0–12.5
Weak rock	1.25–5.0
Very weak rock	0.60–1.25

examples of stone more than adequately strong for the base of such a monument.

C3. Effect of weathering

Generally speaking, quarry operators working building-stone quarries will extract unweathered rock. How-ever, in some instances partly weathered rocks will be worked for their attractive colours, or for other reasons. In general, the physical properties of rock will decrease in quality as the degree of weathering increases. This is shown, for example, by studies of granite from a quarry on Dartmoor in southwest England reported by Fookes (1980), and summarized in Table C3. It can be seen that the compressive strength of the rock decreases from 262 MN/m^2 to 26 MN/m^2, a factor of 10, as the rock mass weathering grade increases from I to IV. (The rock mass weathering grade scale runs from I: fresh unweathered rock, to V: completely weathered rock.) The bulk density and water absorption show similar trends of reduction in quality with increase in weathering. The weathering of rock is discussed in Chapter 2.

C4. Scale of rock strength

If the compressive strength of a rock has been determined, a descriptive term for the rock, in terms of its strength, can be derived from Table C4. This classification comes from the Geological Society Engineering Group Working Party (1977), and was devised for engineering geology purposes, but there is no reason why it should not be used to describe the stength of building stones.

References

ALLEN HOWE, J. 1910. *The Geology of Building Stones*. Edward Arnold, London, p. 366.

BECKMANN, P. 1994. *Structural Aspects of Building Conservation*. McGraw-Hill, London, 82–83.

BROWN, E. T. 1981. *Rock characterization testing and monitoring: ISRM suggested methods*. Pergamon Press, Oxford, 119–121.

FARMER, I W. 1968. *Engineering Properties of Rocks*. E & FN Spon Ltd, London, p. 57.

FOOKES, P G. 1980. An introduction to the influence of natural aggregates on the performance and durability of concrete. *Quarterly Journal of Engineering Geology*, **13**, 207–209.

GEOLOGICAL SOCIETY ENGINEERING GROUP WORKING PARTY 1977. The description of rock masses for engineering purposes. *Quarterly Journal of Engineering Geology*, **10**, 355–388.

INTERNATIONAL SOCIETY FOR ROCK MECHANICS 1985. Suggested method for determining point load strength. *International Journal of Rock Mechanics and Mining Science*, **22**, 51–60.

SMITH, M. R. & COLLIS, L. (eds) 1993. *Aggregates: sand, gravel and crushed rock aggregates for construction purposes (second edition)*. Geological Society, London, Engineering Geology Special Publications, **9**.

STONE INDUSTRIES 1994. *Natural Stone Directory*, No 9 1994–1995. Herald House, Worthing.

WEST, G. 1994. Effect of suction on the strength of rock. *Quarterly Journal of Engineering Geology*, **27**, 51–56.

WINKLER, E M. 1973. *Stone: Properties, Durability in Man's Environment*. Springer, Vienna, 43 & 46–47.

Index

Page numbers in **bold** are principal sources; terms in *italics* refer to glossary items